Medical-Legal Aspects of Pain and Suffering

Patricia Iyer, MSN, RN, LNCC

Contributing Authors
Stephen Appelbaum, CEP, EPIC
Carol Anne Bales, RN, MSN, AOCN, CCRP
Thomas C. Broderick, Esq.
I. Larry Cohen MD, FCCP, FCCM
Yvonne D'Arcy MS, CRNP, CNS
Michael D'Lugo, Esq.
Thomas Duffy, Esq.
Richard Ford, Esq.
Suzanne Frederick, MSN, RN
Guy Fried, MD
Karen Mandzak Fried, MSN, RN, CRRN, CCM
Reneé Holleran, PhD, RN, CEN, CCRN, CFRN
Diane Hudson-Barr, PhD, RN
Kelly A. Jaszarowski MSN, RN, CNS, ANP, CWOCN
Sally Lambert, PhD, RN
Nancy E. Mooney, MA, RN, ONC
Dorene A. O'Hara, MD, MSE
John Parisi, Esq.
Michael A. Pollack, MD
Lisa Stepp, PhD, MS, RN, APN, AOCN, CRNH
Randall Thomas, PhD, CRC, NCC
Leta Truett, PhD, RN
Tom Vesper, Esq.
J. Michael West, Esq.

This publication is designed to provide accurate and authoritative information in regard to the subject matter covered. It is sold with the understanding that the publisher is not engaged in rendering legal, accounting, or other professional service. If legal advice or other expert assistance is required, the services of a competent professional person should be sought.

—From a *Declaration of Principles* jointly adopted by
a committee of the American Bar Association
and a committee of Publishers and Associations.

The publisher, editors and authors must disclaim any liability, in whole or in part, arising from the information in this volume. The reader is urged to verify the reference material prior to any detrimental reliance thereupon. Since this material deals with legal, medical and engineering information, the reader is urged to consult with an appropriate licensed professional prior to taking any action that might involve any interpretation or application of information within the realm of a licensed professional practice. Opinions of the authors are not necessarily those of the editor. Please note that medical facts and statistics, and standards of care can change with time and new research.

An effort has been made to substitute fictitious names for actual ones in many sample pleadings and cases in this book. We believe that using such fictitious names would be preferred by the actual defendant and plaintiff in each such case. Obviously, in referring to actual reported cases there is no alternative to using the names of the actual parties. The use of such names is not meant or intended to cause grief or hurt to anyone.

P.O. Box 30040 • Tucson, AZ 85751-0040
(800) 209-7109 • FAX (800) 330-8795
e-mail: sales@lawyersandjudges.com

Library of Congress Cataloging-in-Publication Data

Medical-legal aspects of pain and suffering / edited by Patricia Iyer;
contributors, Stephen Appelbaum ... [et al.].
p. cm.
Includes bibliographical references and index.
ISBN 1-930056-39-7
1. Pain. 2. Suffering. 3. Medical jurisprudence. 4. Malingering.
I. Iyer, Patricia W. II. Appelbaum, Stephen.
RB127.M424 2003
614.1--dc21

2003001620

ISBN 1-930056-39-7
Printed in the United States of America
10 9 8 7 6 5 4 3 2 1

Contents

Illustrations

Figures

Tables

Preface

When Steve Weintraub first approached me about editing this new text, I saw this as a unique opportunity to blend the two worlds of law and medicine. As the editor, I developed the framework of chapters, recruited the authors, and established the format for the text. It was my responsibility to be the bridge between medicine/nursing and the law. The authors of this book represent a unique blend of perspectives. Clinicians (doctors, nurses, and a vocational expert), expert witnesses, and attorneys shared their knowledge about the often complex issues associated with pain and suffering. The clinicians were the ideal professionals to explain pain and suffering in various populations. The attorneys were the ideal people to explain how the legal world views pain and suffering.

Pain and suffering is a term that has varying meanings to attorneys, is used to define damages, but is not often understood. Suffering can occur independently of pain, but pain is invariably accompanied by suffering. Pain management has become a hot topic in healthcare, as it is belatedly clear that many patients unnecessarily suffer from unrelieved pain. While improvements are being made in the assessment and management of pain, there is still a need for education and more appropriate relief of pain. There are several audiences for this text. Healthcare professionals, claims adjusters, trial attorneys, and legal nurse consultants will benefit from understanding the content of this text.

Understanding pain and suffering

The text begins with a broad overview of pain and suffering. The often frustrating and difficult organization and analysis of medical records is made easier with the information provided in the first chapter. Key concepts associated with pain assessment are shared in the second chapter. Commonly used pain assessment tools illustrate the chapter. A pain management specialist, Dr. O'Hara, shares a detailed explanation of common types of pain and their treatment. Her pain management chapter is strengthened by highlighting potential and actual legal cases involving pain management. Dr. Stepp expands the concepts of pain and suffering by identifying several types of psychological pain, including post traumatic stress disorder. Dr. Truett and I complete this section with a detailed analysis of the components of suffering, with our chapter supplemented with legal cases.

Client populations and healthcare settings

It became clear in developing this text that clinicians were needed to explain the pain and suffering associated with high risk populations. The groups most likely to experience pain and suffering were identified, and then expert clinicians recruited to share their expertise. Children are often unable to communicate their pain and suffering and thus are at risk for unrelieved pain. Dr. Barr and Dr. Lambert provide a comprehensive overview of how pain and suffering affects the developmental needs of children. Dr. Pollack, a pediatric neurologist, details pain and suffering associated with common neurological conditions likely to be the focus of a lawsuit. His chapter includes the perspectives of two experienced trial lawyers.

Dr. Holleran takes us inside an emergency department to explain the common procedures that cause pain and suffering when the unexpected happens and the healthcare professionals must intervene. Dr. Fried and his nurse and wife Karen skillfully combine their knowledge to explain one of the most devastating types of injuries: spinal cord trauma and paralysis. Orthopaedic injuries are commonly components of personal injury and medical malpractice suits. A skilled clinician, Nancy Mooney shares her knowledge of the types and implications of fractures. Carol Bales, an oncology nurse, provides a view of cancer pain, blending theory and stories of patients grappling with this frightening diagnosis. Wounds and burns, among the most disfiguring injuries, are well explained by Kelly Jaszarowski. The trauma associated with loss of the ability to urinate and defecate in the normal way is the subject of the ostomy and incontinence chapter. Dr. Cohen's chapter takes us inside the intensive care unit for a thorough explanation of what it is like to live on the edge of death. Suzanne Frederick completes this section with an overview of geriatric pain and suffering and helps us understand the vulnerability of this population.

Presenting pain and suffering

The final section of the book is primarily designed for attorneys. Application of the clinical information provided in the first two sections should assist the attorney in evaluating and presenting a claim involving pain and suffering. The life care plan components addressing pain and suffering are presented by Dr. Thomas, an experienced life care planner. The use of an expert fact witness to explain medical records is described in Chapter 17. This role is a cost effective and efficient way to provide the jury with an understanding of the details of medical care. The use of trial exhibits is presented in two chapters, with the first concentrating on the legal and strategic uses, and the second on the practicality of preparing and using exhibits. The second trial exhibits chapter concludes with a framework for selecting the right method to present exhibits.

The valuation of pain and suffering in the moments before death is thoroughly explained by Tom Vesper. Two skilled defense attorneys teamed up to address the issue of malingering and minimizing pain and suffering in the defense attorney's perspective chapter. A successful plaintiffs' trial attorney concludes the book with many practical considerations for evaluating and presenting pain and suffering from the plaintiff's perspective.

Acknowledgments

I appreciate the assistance of everyone who helped me find the authors for this text. Networking, personal acquaintances, recommendations, and the internet were all useful in recruiting the authors for this project. Each chapter was reviewed by an attorney to help ensure that the material was understandable and valuable. Those reviewers were:

Delores Austin, RD, JD
Medical legal consultant
Kingston, WA

Drew Britcher, Esq.
Britcher, Leone and Roth
Glen Rock, NJ

Abbott Brown, Esq.
Bendit Weinstock
West Orange, NJ

Don Cofskey, Esq.
Cofsky & Zeideman, LLC
Haddonfield, NJ

Marjorie Eskay-Auerbach, MD, JD
Medical Consulting Resources, Ltd.
Tucson, AZ

Ray Fleming, Esq.
Sachs Maitlin Fleming, Geene, Wilson and Marrotte
West Orange, NJ

Roy Konray, Esq.
Tobin Koster Oleckna et al.
Rahway, NJ

Ruben Krisztal, Esq.
Shawnee Mission, KS

Bill Lawson, Esq.
Philadelphia, PA

Marvin Pincus, Esq.
West Orange, NJ

Jennie Shatynski, Esq.
Benedict P. Morelli & Associates
New York, NY

John Shea, Esq.
Marks and Harrison
Richmond, VA

Terrence Smith, Esq
Davis Saperstein and Salomon
Teaneck, NJ

Bob Strodel, Esq.
Peoria, IL

Helen Weisgal, Esq,
Sokol Behot and Fiorenzo
Hackensack, NJ

Michael Zerres, Esq.
Blume Goldfaden Berkowitz Donnelly
Chatham, NJ

Brian Zorn, Esq.
Faraci and Lange, LLP
Rochester, NY

The authors patiently worked through the drafts and made changes based on the comments of the reviewers. I am indebted to the authors for sharing their expertise and assisting me in bringing this unique work to your hands. Finally, without Steve Weintraub recognizing the need for this book, it would still remain an intangible dream.

Patricia W. Iyer, MSN, RN, LNCC

Chapter 1

Organization and Analysis of Medical Records

Patricia Iyer, MSN, RN, LNCC

Synopsis

1.1 Introduction

The assessment of pain and suffering sustained as a result of negligence is important in the initial evaluation of a potential new case. Attorneys need to understand the plaintiff's injuries in order to evaluate the worth of the case. Medical records generated both before and after the injury may be analyzed to determine if the results of the alleged negligence produced a demonstrable change in the patient's life. Medical records can also be used to determine if a patient experienced pain and suffering during treatment. Careful analysis of medical documentation can establish whether an individual had a level of awareness of pain or "conscious pain and suffering" prior to death.

1.2 Documenting Pain and Suffering

The creation and contents of medical records are dictated by professional standards and those of accrediting bodies. The standards of the Joint Commission on Accreditation of Healthcare Organizations govern documentation in most hospitals. Increasing emphasis is being placed on appropriate pain management and documentation. The following section summarizes the 2001 Joint Commission on Accreditation of Healthcare Organizations pain standards for hospitals.[1] There is periodic rewording of these standards so the attorney is advised to refer to standards in place at the time the patient was receiving care.

Standard RI 1.2.7: The healthcare organization addresses care at the end of life.

Intent of this standard: The healthcare organization's framework for addressing issues related to care at the end of life provide for appropriate treatment of any primary and secondary symptoms, according to the wishes of the patient or the surrogate decision maker, and manage pain aggressively and effectively.

Standard RI 1.2.8: Patients have the right to appropriate assessment and management of pain.

Intent of this standard: Unrelieved pain has adverse physical and psychological effects. The patient's right to pain management is respected and supported. There is appropriate initial assessment and regular reassessment of pain, education of all relevant providers in pain assessment and management, and education of patients and families when appropriate, regarding their roles in managing pain as well as the potential limitations and side effects of pain treatments.

Standard PE 1.4: Pain is assessed in all patients.

Intent of this standard: In the initial assessment, the organization identifies patients with pain. When pain is identified, the patient can be treated within the organization or referred for treatment. A more comprehensive assessment is performed when warranted by the patient's condition. This assessment and a measure of pain intensity and quality (pain character, frequency, location, and duration) appropriate to the patient's age, are recorded in a way that facilitates regular reassessment and follow-up according to criteria developed by the organization.

Standard T.X. 3.3: Policies and procedures support safe medication prescription or ordering.

Intent of this standard: Supporting safe medication prescription or ordering addresses a number of variables, including as needed and scheduled prescriptions or orders and times of dose administration, appropriate use of patient controlled analgesia (PCA), spinal/epidural or intravenous administration of medications, and other pain management techniques.

Standard T.X. 5.4: The patient is monitored during the post-procedure period.

Intent of this standard: The patient's pain intensity and quality (character, frequency, location, and duration of pain) and responses to treatments are monitored.

Standard PF 3.4: Patients are educated about pain and managing pain as part of treatment, as appropriate.

Intent of this standard: When appropriate, patients and families are instructed about understanding pain, the risk for pain, the importance of effective pain management, the pain assessment process, and methods for pain management, when identified as part of treatment.

1.3 Liability Associated with Failure to Treat Pain Effectively

Throughout the text, the authors emphasize the professional need to alleviate pain and suffering. The undertreatment of pain has become a growing concern in healthcare organizations. Undertreatment affects many groups of patients.

1. Wolfe[2] estimated that 40%–50% of postoperative patients receive ineffective pain management.
2. Approximately 50%–80% of patients with advanced cancer experience pain during the course of their disease. The majority of these patients will not obtain satisfactory relief. This fact constitutes a major problem because unrelieved pain can significantly diminish the patient's quality of life.[3]
3. Often, in the face of life-threatening illness or injury, pain and its treatment are forgotten, or at least under-appreciated by the healthcare team. While a plethora of research exists regarding cancer pain and chronic pain, little attention has been paid to the evaluation and management of pain in critically ill patients. Assessment of pain may be hampered by age-related limitations of communication and cognition, level of consciousness, presence of endotracheal tubes, and the confusion of the ICU environment. It has been shown that caretakers commonly underestimate pain severity and thus may undertreat it.[4]
4. Physicians infer more pain in unattractive patients and those who express pain (e.g., facial expression).[5]
5. Men in pain are more likely to receive an extensive pain workup and treatment than females.[5]
6. The misconception that infants do not feel pain is long-standing. An analysis of forty publications revealed that 77% of newborns undergoing surgical ligation of patent ductus arteriosus (heart surgery) received no anesthesia, only muscle relaxants or intermittent nitrous oxide.[5] Several studies have shown that children receive inadequate amounts of pain medication.[6]
7. Non-Hispanic whites were twice as likely to receive pain relievers after a long bone fracture than were Hispanics visiting emergency departments.[7]
8. Sickle cell crisis is a common problem encountered by patients with sickle cell disease. It is difficult to treat, and there are no objective findings. This results in healthcare workers becoming skeptical regarding true pain versus drug-seeking behavior. There has been much information reported in the medical literature regarding the undertreatment and lack of standardization in the

care of the patient with pain from a sickle cell crisis.[6]

Patients contributed to the undertreatment of pain for a number of reasons. They may be fearful that the pain is an indication of a worsening health problem, and therefore if it is not reported, and ignored, it will go away. They may be concerned about distracting healthcare providers from other issues ("You're so busy, I hate to bother you . . ."). Pain may not be reported because it will signal the discomfort or expense of testing and treating the problem causing the pain. Reporting of pain may result in administration of narcotics/opioids, and cause a fear of addiction, side effects or increased expense. The patient may not report pain because of a fear of being labeled as a complainer. Some patients are fatalistic and believe they are meant to endure pain. Others may infer that the healthcare provider should know that the condition is painful and would provide relief if it were available.[8]

The identification of pain as the fifth vital sign (after temperature, pulse, respirations and blood pressure) was first proposed by the American Pain Society in 1995. Vital signs are monitored in order to detect changes or trends that signal a need for further assessment, diagnosis, and interventions. Making pain a vital sign would ensure that pain is monitored on a regular basis.[9]

Tip

Much effort has been exerted in the last five years to help healthcare professionals better understand myths, misconceptions, and attitudes that interfere with appropriate pain management. Much work still needs to be done.

Furrow[10] argues that failure to assess, treat, and manage pain is professional negligence. Specific theories of liability include failure to refer to a pain specialist, infliction of emotional distress, and failure to provide informed consent by not discussing alternatives to treatments for pain. In all cases, an analysis of medical records, physician orders, medication administration records, and nurses' and other professionals' documentation will be needed to analyze liability and to determine the damages.

1.4 Obtaining Medical Records

The first step in the analysis of personal/bodily injuries is obtaining complete medical records. Complete records are defined as full, certified copies of medical records from institutions (hospitals, rehabilitation facilities, and nursing homes) and complete physician office records. Attorneys and their staff often encounter resistance or delays in obtaining records. A strategy that many find helpful is to send a records request in the form of a letter that contains the state's statutory language regarding providing medical records. This language typically describes the time frame within which the entity must respond to the records request, and the state regulated fee (if any) per page for copying and retrieval. Once the records request has been sent, a reliable method of tracking responses and following up on the requests is needed.

Tip

Production of the nursing home chart is regulated by the federal government. Under 42 CFR 483.10, the nursing home is required to produce a medical record within two working days of a request.

The plaintiff's attorney may contact the governmental agency at the state level responsible for surveying facilities to initiate an investigation if a nursing home chart is not produced within two working days. The rationale behind the two-day time limit is to prevent the nursing home from having time to alter the medical record. The medical records authorization form used to request records should contain the following language:

> If you are a Medicare or Medicaid-certified nursing home or long-term care facility, pleased be advised that this request is made pursuant to 42 CFR 483.10, which states in pertinent part: "The resident or his or her legal representative has the right (1) upon an oral or written request, to access all records pertaining to himself or herself, including the clinical records, within 24 hours (excluding weekends and holidays); and (2) after receipt of his or her records for inspection, to purchase at a cost not to exceed the community standard, photocopies of the records or any portion of them upon request

and two working days advance notice to the facility."

1.5 Assuring Completeness of Institutional Records

When the medical records arrive in the office, some attorneys prefer to make a copy of the records without changing the order of the pages and then store this copy in a safe place. The copy of this original is then used to make subsequent organized sets of records. It is recommended that the law firm keep the envelope in which the records came. If a question of tampering with medical records is raised, it is helpful to be able to verify the date on which the set of records was mailed. This set may be compared with subsequent sets obtained during litigation.

Tip

Some firms make the first set of copies on a copier that has been set for 95%. This setting creates margins that allow for hole punching without the risk of loss of data. It is recommended that the records be organized before analysis of the information occurs. Once pages get shuffled out of order, the complexity of the task of compiling the organized record is unnecessarily increased.

The next step is assuring that the record is complete. Although a copy of a certified medical record is supposed to be compared by the medical records custodian with the original, it is common for pages to be missing. This often happens because of inattention during the process of copying the record, a task that is frequently subcontracted out to a records duplication service.

Determination of the completeness of the record is best accomplished by using a standardized method of organizing the medical record. Medical records may be organized by a legal nurse consultant employed by a law firm as an employee or independent consultant or by a paralegal or attorney. A routine method helps to immediately pinpoint missing sections of the record. Use of preprinted hospital and nursing home indexes is an efficient use of the law firm's resources. Pages in the medical record are often assembled in reverse chronological order when they are copied (i.e., the last physician's orders are on the top of the stack of orders). These should be reorganized so that the first order written (date of admission) is at the top of the stack. This principle applies to other sections of the medical record also.

The author recommends using blank colored sheets to separate subsections of the record and to draw attention to missing information. Colored sheets are helpful to separate

- the many components of nursing documentation;
- each 24 hours' worth of documentation on multipage critical care flowsheets;
- physician progress notes from consultations;
- different types of therapy (physical, occupational, and so on) into sections; and
- operative records if the patient has more than one surgery during an admission.

Colored sheets are also useful to mark a section of the chart with missing information.

Example:
During the organization of the medical record, the legal nurse consultant notes that four days' worth of physician progress notes from a hospital admission are missing. Since physicians have to see the patient every day, it is likely that these were not copied or may be out of order. A colored sheet would be placed after the last note before the gap.

The colored sheet is useful if the missing notes are found later, as it marks where to insert the notes. The sheet can then be removed once the missing pages are located.

Do not discard any blank sheets in the medical record if they are stamped with the patient's name plate. The fact that they were not filled in may be significant. Sometimes the copy service inadvertently makes more than one copy of a page. It is usually all right to discard exact duplicates of records. They must match in all details. The addition of initials or signature to a form does not mean two copies of a form are exact matches. After organizing the medical record, notify the appropriate person if it becomes evident that sections are missing. The missing records may be significant.

Tip

Some firms prefer to Bates stamp, hand number or use clear labels with numbers to identify each page. It is strongly recommended that the numbering of the pages not be performed until the medical record is organized and noted to be complete.

Sending a numbered unorganized copy of a medical record to an expert who is likely to reorganize it into logical categories (nurses' notes, physician orders and so on) is not an efficient use of the law firm's time. Numbering pages of an incomplete medical record makes it difficult to add the missing pages later on.

Providing an expert witness with medical records that have been scanned and saved on a CD is an efficient way to reduce shipping costs. To make the most effective package, be sure that the records are organized and numbered prior to being scanned. The scanned copies should result in clear, easy-to-read material. Attempting to locate information in a disorganized CD or paper set of medical records will increase the expert's frustration and time spent on the file, thus increasing costs to the attorney. The expert's computer must be current and powerful enough to load the images created by the scanned documents.

1.6 Organizing and Analyzing Hospital Records

The following section presents a standardized way to organize and analyze hospital records. There are several acceptable variations of these approaches; however, the use of one uniform way of organizing medical records will increase efficiency within the law firm as time spent trying to locate critical documents will be reduced.

A. Discharge summary

The thoroughness of the discharge summary can range from scanty to complete. It is often the responsibility of a resident or intern to complete discharge summaries in a teaching hospital. If accurate and complete, the discharge summary is usually a good place to begin to understand the major problems the plaintiff experienced during the admission.

Tip

The discharge summary must be completed within 30 days of the discharge of the patient.

B. Emergency room records

Emergency department records are often rich sources of detail regarding the condition of the patient on arrival to the hospital.

Assemble the records in a consistent order. One method of organizing these records is:

- transfer/transport records (rescue squad, mobile intensive care unit);
- face sheet/ER admission sheet (contains demographic data about the patient);
- triage/trauma notes (by nurses);
- M.D. exam/orders by M.D.;
- handwritten or typed physician history and physical notes;
- laboratory studies (blood work, cultures, and tests of other bodily fluids);
- diagnostic tests (x-rays, CT scans, EKGs);
- consent to treatment and/or payment; and
- discharge instructions.

Transfer/transport records should be analyzed to determine

- level of consciousness at the scene of the accident,
- first aid rendered at the scene and while en route,
- evidence of injuries, and
- complaints by the patient at the scene and en route.

Emergency department records should be analyzed to determine

- level of consciousness of the patient on entry to the emergency department and throughout the stay in the department;
- symptoms such as shortness of breath, pain, vomiting, and so on;
- reactions to treatment;
- diagnostic tests and treatment rendered in the emergency department and ancillary departments such as radiology;

- pain medication administered; and
- use of paralyzing medications associated with being placed on a ventilator.

C. Physician orders

Physician orders may paradoxically include orders for diagnostic tests and treatments which inflict pain, and for medications that relieve pain and suffering. Diagnostic tests which are particularly painful include arterial blood gases taken directly from a vein, insertion of arterial lines, spinal taps, bone marrow biopsies, and liver biopsies, to name a few. Painful treatments include debridements, wet to dry dressings, suctioning, insertion of chest tubes, and so on. Medications are ordered to relieve pain and disturbing symptoms, such as itching, hiccoughing, nausea and vomiting, diarrhea, insomnia, and so on. Chapter 3, Pain Management, provides further details.

D. Physician progress notes and consultations

Physician progress notes are generated by the wide variety of physicians who may have interacted with the patient during the hospital admission. From the medical student to the most senior consultant, documentation about the patient's problems can be found in the physician's progress notes. Critically ill patients are often visited by several physicians each day, each of whom is involved in documenting symptoms, examinations, diagnoses, and treatment plans. In teaching hospitals, the end of the intern's or resident's rotation may lead to a comprehensive note summarizing the patient's condition at that point of time. These notes provide a quick overview of the status of the patient. Consultations are also useful to review for a more complete picture of the patient's status than is documented by the physicians involved in the day-to-day care.

Physician progress notes may include terms that describe the patient's pain. Figure 1.1 contains pain terms that may appear in the physician progress notes.

E. Nurses' documentation

Nursing documentation typically consists of several sections. They are described below.

1. The nursing admission assessment consists of information collected by the nurse on admission to the hospital. It is usually a systematic history and examination of body systems and identification of complaints. This is also called the nursing database or the multidisciplinary admission assessment. With healthcare's increased emphasis on comprehensive and systematic pain assessment, many hospitals are revising admission assessments to include questions about the presence of pain and how the patient typically attempts to relieve it. The patient may be asked to rate the intensity of pain, the location, quality, onset, duration, and the alleviating and aggravating factors. Information may also be asked about the pain management history which includes a description of what medications and other interventions are effective, how the pain affects the patient's daily life, and the patient's pain goal.

2. The nursing care plan is generated from the admission assessment and contains the primary problems, the desired outcomes of care and the interventions designed to alleviate the problem. This should be evaluated to see which problems the nurses identified as needing intervention. The problems of a patient who has been injured as a result of an accident often revolve around pain and anxiety.

3. Nurses' notes may be combined with or separated from flowsheets. There are several charting systems in use, ranging from simple narrative notes that tell the story of what has occurred, to Charting by Exception, which contains flow sheets filled out with check marks, arrows, and asterisks. See Iyer and Camp[11] for more information. The nurses' notes are often rich sources of information about the problems the patient experienced during this admission. Poignant quotes are often found here. Nurses' notes will typically contain documentation of the patient's quantification of pain. The most common scale in use is the numeric pain intensity scale. Using this scale, nurses' notes and physician progress notes will often state the patient's pain score in terms of a point between 0 and 10. For example, the record may have an entry such as "patient reports pain is a 6 out of 10." A number of studies have shown that a pain rating at 4 or more on a 0 to 10 pain rating scale

interferes significantly with daily function. A pain rating this high indicates the need to revise pain treatment with higher doses of analgesics, different medications, or other comfort measures.[5] Flowsheets may be used to record pain levels.

4. Pain assessment flowsheets may be in use. There will be space to record data about each site of pain.

5. Critical care flowsheets are multipage forms that are generated on a daily basis. They typically document the patient's vital signs, weight, intake and output, laboratory values, medications, settings of various pieces of equipment (ventilators, intravenous pumps), and observations about the patient. It is common that each page is not dated, making it difficult at times to locate all the pages of a set if they have been shuffled out of order. It is also common for pages to be missed in the duplication process. To detect missing pages, first study the pages that are complete for a 24-hour period to determine the normal order of pages. Sometimes careful review of signatures and handwriting is needed to assemble a complete set of pages for a 24-hour period. At times, it is impor-

air hunger. Gasping for breath.
allodynia. Pain provoked by an innocuous mechanical or thermal stimulus.
breakthrough pain. Pain that increases above the level of pain relieved by the ongoing analgesics.
central pain. Pain that is started or caused by a primary lesion of dysfunction in the central nervous system.
crescendo pain. A period of rapid pain escalation often associated with increasing distress and functional impairment.
dysesthias. Burning, tingling pain.
dyspnea. Difficulty breathing.
hyperalgesia. A lowered threshold to a normally painful stimulus and enhanced pain perception.
hyperpathia. An increased pain threshold, but once exceeded, pain reaches maximum intensity too rapidly
intractable. Symptom that cannot be relieved.
lancinating. Knifelike or stabbing pain.
neuralgia. Pain in the distribution of a nerve, such as sciatica, often felt as an electrical, shock-like pain.
neuropathic. Pain generated when nerve roots or central pain pathways are damaged.
nociceptive pain. Pain resulting from the ongoing stimulation of nerves by noxious stimuli.
noxious stimulus. A stimulus that is damaging or potentially damaging to normal tissue, such as pinching a shoulder.
opioids. Pain relievers, narcotics.
paresthesia. Includes sensations of numbness, prickling, tingling and heightened sensitivity.
paroxysmal. Sudden, periodic attacks or recurrences.
projectile. Vomiting that is so forceful that it travels several inches out of the mouth.
psychogenic. Pain presumed to exist when no neuropathic mechanism can be identified, term that has a negative connotation.
somatic. Pain of the musculoskeletal system.
supratentorial pain. A derogatory term to suggest that no physical cause exists for the pain or that the patient is lying about the pain (literally, it is all in the head).
tabetic pain. Sharp, lighting-type pain, also called lancinating pain.
visceral pain. Pain in the body's internal organs.

Figure 1.1 *Pain terms (McCaffery, M and Pasero, C.* Pain Clinical Manual, *Mosby, St. Louis, Second Edition, 1999 Schwartzman, R. and Maleki, J, Postinjury neuropathic pain syndromes,* Medical Clinics of North America, *Vol. 83, No. 3, May 1999.*

tant to ask the facility to duplicate the critical care flowsheets again if there are questions about the completeness of the flowsheets. Critical care flowsheets are detailed sources of data about the patient's symptoms, such as fever, nausea, vomiting, diarrhea, pain, anxiety, agitation, difficulty breathing, and so on.

6. Patient education forms are filled out by nurses and others who provide teaching about various aspects of treatment and needed self-care. The responses of the patient to the teaching will be documented here. The patient's difficulty in learning how to care for a new problem may be recorded, with comments such as "I don't think I will be able to learn how to change this colostomy bag." Education about pain management should be documented.

7. Routine, one-time only, and prn (*pro re nata*, or as needed) medications and intravenous therapy flow sheets are kept on medication administration records. This documentation should be evaluated to determine which medications were given to address the patient's symptoms, such as pain, fever, nausea, constipation, diarrhea, heartburn, itching, and so on. Medications may also be documented on critical care flowsheets instead of, or in addition to, the medication administration records. Information about medications is also kept by post anesthesia care units (recovery rooms) and endoscopy units (the location of feeding tube insertions, colonoscopies, esophageal examinations, and so on).

8. Some facilities require the nurse to complete a discharge instructions form when the patient is discharged. This typically contains the list of prescriptions given to the patient, the self-care instructions, any equipment needed at home, and specifies when to make an appointment with the physician.

9. When a patient is sent to a nursing home, transfer forms are completed. The status of the patient on discharge, medications that the patient was on at the time of discharge, and other care instructions are provided on this form. This gives an overview of the unresolved problems the patient was experiencing at the time of transfer.

F. Operative records

Operative records should be assembled in the same order for each surgery:

- preoperative checklist
- surgical and anesthesia consent
- anesthesiologist's preoperative evaluation
- dictated report of operation
- anesthesia record
- operating room nurses notes
- count sheets and implant logs
- post anesthesia care unit records/recovery room records
- surgical pathology report

The anesthesiologist's preoperative evaluation is a good source for a current weight and for documentation of the patient's status before surgery. The dictated operative report may describe complications that occurred during surgery, which affect pain and suffering. The anesthesia record is useful for determining the length of surgery, which is important when long, involved surgery has taken place. Review the post anesthesia care unit records for evidence of complaints of pain and pain medication administration and other medications administered for symptoms.

It is common to place these records along with operative records:

- colonoscopy
- endoscopy
- bronchoscopy
- PEG (feeding) tube insertion
- cardiac catheterization
- record of delivery (obstetrics)

G. X-rays

Hospital records contain many diagnostic test results. It is common to group these into two categories: radiology/scans and laboratory tests. While some preprinted medical record indexes have specific tabs for EKG,

EEG, and so on, it is more common to find one tab called "x-ray" and to use this tab for miscellaneous diagnostic tests. These records typically go in the "X-Ray Reports" tab:

- x-rays
- MRI Scans
- CT Scans
- bone scans
- ventilation perfusion tests (VQ scans for blood clots in the lungs)
- Doppler studies of blood vessels
- ultrasound
- EKG (electrocardiogram)
- EMG (electromyelography)
- echocardiograms
- cardiac monitor strips
- 24-hour telemetry report
- pulmonary function tests

Analyze the radiology section for frequency of testing and whether the tests were done at the patient's bedside or in the radiology department. Portable x-rays are completed when the patient is too ill to be moved to the department for the study. The completion of those tests that are essential for a critically ill patient but cannot be done at the bedside, such as a CT scan or MRI scan, may require the presence of a critical care nurse and a portable cardiac monitor.

A variety of specimens are collected from the patient's body. These can include blood, sputum, stool, urine, wound drainage, and spinal fluid. The laboratory test results section often includes documentation indicating that blood transfusions have been administered. These slips are filled out by the nurses or other personnel who verify correct identification of the patient at the beginning of the transfusion and record the initial vital signs before the transfusion.

H. Laboratory

Analyze the laboratory section for the frequency of testing. Pain accompanies the process of piercing the skin in order to obtain blood or cerebral spinal fluid specimens. When a critically ill patient needs frequent testing, blood may be withdrawn from intravenous catheters inserted for this purpose.

Tip

Laboratory results may be printed out at the end of the admission (discharge report). It is rarely possible to sort laboratory results in precise chronological order.

I. Therapies

Separate "therapies" with typed coversheets or colored sheets and place in alphabetical order in the "Miscellaneous" tab:

- dietary
- occupational therapy
- physical therapy
- respiratory therapy
- social services
- speech therapy

The notes of therapists will include documentation of the status of the patient and capabilities at the time that the therapy ends. Complaints of pain and other limitations may be noted by the therapists. Dietary notes are often a good source for tracking weight loss and other evidence of malnutrition, such as low albumin levels.

Consents may be stored in the miscellaneous tab. Examine the handwriting of the patient. Shaky, difficult to read signatures may be noted when the patient is under extreme stress. These make effective pieces of demonstrative evidence when enlarged for the jury.

See Figure 1.2 for a checklist to use in organizing hospital records. The use of this type of checklist helps staff members who are unfamiliar with where to place components of the medical record. The checklist can be modified based on the type of preprinted medical records index tabs purchased by the law firm. The author recommends seeking companies who sell tabs to the hospital industry in order to obtain the most variety of choices.

1.7 Organizing and Analyzing Rehabilitation Facility Records

Extensive personal injury may result in admission to a rehabilitation facility for subacute therapy prior to discharge to home. Rehabilitation records differ from hospital records in a few significant ways. First, there are typically several types of therapy provided: physical, occupational, cognitive, speech, and so on. Each of the therapy departments performs an initial assessment, documents progress notes, and completes an evaluation of the patient's progress at the time of discharge. Interim progress evaluations may be performed by the multidisciplinary team, resulting in typed or handwritten progress notes after evaluations. Preparations for discharge may include a day or weekend pass, determination of the type of equipment needed at discharge, and referral to a home healthcare agency.

Rehabilitation records may be organized using long-term care or nursing home tabs. These typically include tabs for the variety of therapies involved in providing care in this setting. The analysis of rehabilitation records should include evaluation of the patient's complaints and limitations upon arrival and discharge from the facility. Evidence of progress should be documented by the nurses, therapists, and physicians involved in the patient's care. Medications administered to treat symptoms will be documented on the medication administration records. Physician progress notes and nursing notes will often comment on ongoing pain and suffering.

1.8 Organizing and Analyzing Nursing Home Records

Many of the sections found in hospital records are also found in nursing home records. The nursing home chart differs from the hospital chart in specific ways. The patient in the nursing home is referred to as a resident, because the nursing home is the patient's residence.

A. Admission assessment

Each facility has its own form to use within a day after admission to determine the resident's immediate needs. A more elaborate assessment, the Minimum Data Set, is completed within 14 days. This assessment is a standardized form developed by the government. This multipage form is used to establish reimbursement for care. The form is filled out by various disciplines and is updated quarterly or when there is a significant change in the resident's condition.

B. Resident Assessment Protocols

The Minimum Data Set completion results in the identification of problems documented in the form of Resident Assessment Protocols. The facility is to review this identification of needs, make a judgment as to which problems should be addressed, and prepare a nursing care plan with specific approaches. The analysis of this information is important in determining the needs of the resident on admission to the facility and to document changes in the resident's condition.

C. Progress notes

Multidisciplinary care conferences are held periodically in the nursing home. These conferences culminate in progress notes which describe the status of the resident and track the evolution of the resident's care needs. Some issues resolve with time, while others stabilize or worsen. Physicians visit, at a minimum, on a monthly basis. While notes of physicians may be sketchy, the entries of physician's assistants or nurse practitioners are often easier to read and more comprehensive.

D. Nursing notes

Nurses' notes have been used in nursing home negligence cases to establish that substandard care was delivered to the resident. Note that some nursing home chains have asked their facilities to discard the activities of daily living sheets. This is tampering with the medical record.[12]

Tip

Nursing notes are documented with much less frequency than in the hospital setting. Days may go by without nursing documentation except for completion of activities of daily living flowsheet, which consist of documentation of baths, food intake, activities, and elimination.

---

continued on page 13

Hospital Admission Record Organization

Patient Name: ____________________ **Admission Date(s):** ________________

	Present/ Absent	N/A	Need
(Before first section):			
attorney's letter requesting record			
certification letter			
Face Sheet/Front Index Sheet			
dictated discharge summary			
discharge instructions by M.D./R.N.			
death certificate/autopsy records			
transfer form to hospital			
rescue squad/helicopter transport sheet			
ER records:			
triage/trauma records, nurses notes, M.D. exam, M.D. typed H&P			
Physician's Orders:			
handwritten, computer-generated or standing (preprinted) orders in date order			
TPN orders (nutritional IV supplement)			
Graphic Chart:			
temperature, blood pressure, respirations			
frequent vital signs			
intake/output			
Nurses' Notes:			
nursing admission assessment/database			
nursing care plan			
nursing Kardex (computerized)			
nurses progress notes/narrative notes			
critical care/ICU notes (may be five pages)			
code cheets (if any)			
pressure sore assessment/flowsheet			
neurological assessment/flowsheet			
neurovascular assessment/flowsheet			
dialysis flowsheet			
restraint sheets/flowsheet			
medications (insulin and PRN)			
IV care, IV fluids			
patient education/teaching documentation			
discharge instructions by nurse			
death checklist done by nurse			

Figure 1.2 *Checklist useful for organizing hospital records* *(continued on next page)*

Laboratory Reports:	Present/ Absent	N/A	Need
blood tests, cultures (pathology reports—except operative), urine tests, other body fluids tests			
blood transfusion slips			
ABG (arterial blood gases)			
X-ray Reports:			
radiology			
MRI			
CT scan			
EEG—brain wave test			
EKG—cardiac tests			
EKG monitor strips			
ultrasound			
GI studies/barium enema			
Report of Operation:			
OR consent			
pre-op checklist done by nurse			
pre-anesthesia assessment			
report of operation (typed)			
OR nurses' notes (care plan, instrument and sponge counts, assessment)			
anesthesia record (graphic sheet)			
PACU notes/recovery room notes			
pathology report (surgical specimen report)			
History & Physical:			
handwritten or dictated admission exam notes			
history and physical exam notes (form)			
Progress Notes:			
physician (or integrated) progress notes			
consultations in date order			
Miscellaneous Records:			
permission (admission consent)			
special consents (photograph, experimental drugs, release of restraints, invasive (non-surgical) procedures)			
organ donor forms			
blood transfusion consent			
advanced directives/DNR forms			
dietary/nutrition notes			
occupational therapy			

Figure 1.2 *(continued)*

	Present/ Absent	N/A	Need
physical therapy			
respiratory therapy (including ventilator sheets)			
social services			
social services—discharge plan/home care			
speech therapy			
clothing list, valuables			
billing information			

Figure 1.2 *(continued)*

Nursing home charts may include flowsheets which document the decline or improvement of the resident. Examples include monthly weights, pressure sore flowsheets, and activities of daily living flowsheets.

E. Therapies

Physical, occupational, recreational, speech/language, respiratory, and other types of therapy may be provided in the nursing home. Analysis of the documentation of these professionals will provide information about the progression or lack of improvement in the resident. Of note is how much assistance the resident needed. Terms and abbreviations commonly used include I (independent), S (supervision), and CG (contact guard, or standing within arm's reach).

See Figure 1.3 for a flowsheet useful for organizing nursing home records.

1.9 Organizing and Analyzing Physician Office Records

Physician office records for the period before and after the events which precipitated the lawsuit should be obtained. It can be difficult to obtain the records of defendant physicians in medical malpractice suits. Persistence and knowledge of the requirements of physicians to supply records is essential. Complete physician records are important for evaluating pain and suffering following an acute or long-term injury.

Figure 1.4 shows typical components of physician office records. The correspondence section of defendant physicians should be compared with the correspondence section of other treating or consulting physicians to ensure that complete records have been obtained.

Physician office records should be analyzed to determine

- complaints or symptoms at each office visit,
- complaints or symptoms reported over the phone,
- failure of the patient to keep office appointments,
- frequency of painful diagnostic tests,
- details of reports to other physicians summarizing treatment and the patient's complaints,
- progress or lack thereof in a course of physical therapy, and
- progress or lack thereof while under the care of home health nurses.

1.10 Summary

Obtaining, organizing, and evaluating medical records is an essential component of handling a personal injury claim. Medical records provide a view of the pain and suffering endured by the patient during treatment. They are vital components in building an understanding of medical treatment and pain and suffering management.

continued on page 17

Nursing Home Record Organization

Patient Name: ____________________ **Admission Date(s):** __________________

	Present/ absent	N/A	Need
(Before first section):			
certification letter			
face sheet			
Admission Records:			
discharge summary			
admitting record			
admission notice			
patient transfer form			
History and Physical:			
history and physical record			
Physician's Orders:			
physician's handwritten or typed order form			
telephone orders			
Progress Notes:			
physicians annual care and discharge plan			
special review, multidisciplinary care/discharge plan			
multidisciplinary care plan, interim problems			
physician's progress notes			
multidisciplinary progress notes			
multidisciplinary team conference attendance record			
consultations (i.e., podiatrist, pharmacist, dental, others)			
Nurses' Notes:			
agency-specific admission form			
Minimum Data Set			
state-specific admission form			
RAPS (resident assessment protocols)			
nursing care plan			
health care plan			
graphic chart			
vital sign sheet			
narrative notes			
at risk for pressure sore form			

Figure 1.3 *Checklist useful for organizing nursing home medical records* *(continued on next page)*

Medication and Treatment:	**Present/ absent**	**N/A**	**Need**
medication charts			
treatment charts			
other flowsheets (weights)			
Lab and Special Report:			
lab work			
blood transfusion			
portable x-ray			
Rehab and Therapy:			
activities assessment and records			
physical therapy assessment and records			
occupational therapy assessment and records			
speech and language assessment and records			
Dietary:			
nutritional assessment			
progress notes			
Social Services:			
social services assessment			
patient's/resident's social history			
advanced directives			
discharge planning			
Miscellaneous Records:			
DNR documentation			
certification and re-certification			
abnormal involuntary movement scale (AIMS)			
acknowledgment form			
designated representative form			
advanced directives form			
self-administration of medication			
restraints consents/releases			
billing information			

Comments:

Figure 1.3 *(continued)*

Patient name:
Office records of Dr.:
Dates of treatment:

Content	Present/absent	N/A	Need
Office notes			
initial office appointment patient questionnaire			
typed or handwritten office notes for each visit			
Correspondence			
Diagnostic tests			
laboratory testing			
mammograms			
scans (CT, MRI)			
ultrasounds			
x-rays			
Hospital records			
consultations			
discharge summary			
history and physical			
operative reports			
Miscellaneous			
billing records			
phone messages			
prescriptions			
return-to-work forms			
visiting nurses forms			

Figure 1.4 *Checklist useful for organizing physician's office medical records*

Endnotes

1. "Joint Commission on Accreditation of Healthcare Organizations Pain Standards for 2001." www.jcaho.org/standard/pm.html accessed 3/30/02.

2. Wolfe, M., Lein, D., Lenkoski, K., and Smithline, H., "Analgesic Administration to Patients with an Acute Abdomen: A Survey of Emergency Medicine Physicians." *American Journal of Emergency Medicine*, 2000, 18: 250–253.

3. Buhle, E., "Introduction to Pain." OncoLink, University of Pennsylvania Cancer Center, http://msc8a.upenn.edu/specialty/pain/intro.html.

4. Hamill-Ruth, R. and Marohn, M., "Evaluation of Pain in the Critically Ill Patient." *Critical Care Clinics,* 15 (1), January 1999, 35.

5. McCaffery, M. and Pasero, C., *Pain Clinical Manual*, Second Edition. St. Louis: Mosby, 1999.

6. Martin, J. and Moore, G. "Pearls, Pitfalls, and Updates for Pain Management." *Emergency Medicine Clinics of North America,* 15 (2), May 1997, 399.

7. Todd, K., Lee, T., Hoffman, J., et al., "Ethnicity as a Risk Factor for Inadequate Emergency Department Analgesia." *Journal of the American Medical Association*, 269:1537–1539, 1993.

8. Lynch, M., "Pain as the Fifth Vital Sign." *Journal of Intravenous Nursing*, March/April 2001, 24 (2), 85.

9. Mayer, D., Torma, L, Byock, I., and Norris, K., "Speaking the Language of Pain." *American Journal of Nursing,* February 2001, 101 (2), 44.

10. Furrow, B., "Failure to Treat Pain: No More Excuses." *Trial,* October 2002, 32.

11. Iyer, P., and Camp, N., *Nursing Documentation: A Nursing Process Approach*, Third Edition. St. Louis: Mosby, 1999,

12. Ruben Krisztal, personal communication, October 2001.

Additional Reading

Brownfield E. "Pain Management." In Shojania, K., Duncan, B., McDonald, K., and Wachter, R., *Making Health Care Safer: A Critical Analysis of Patient Safety Practices.* Rockville, MD: Agency for Healthcare Research and Quality, 2001.

Vaillancourt P., and Langevin, H, "Painful Peripheral Neuropathies." *Medical Clinics of North America*, Vol. 83, No. 3, May 1999.

Additional References by Author

Iyer, P., editor, *Nursing Malpractice*, Second Edition. Tucson: Lawyers & Judges Publishing Co., 2001.

Iyer, P., editor, *Nursing Home Litigation: Investigation and Case Preparation*. Tucson: Lawyers & Judges Publishing Co., 1999.

Iyer, P., editor, *Principles and Practices of Legal Nurse Consulting*, Second Edition. Boca Raton: CRC Press, 2003.

Internet Resources

Agency for Healthcare Research and Quality
www.ahrq.gov

The American Academy of Pain Management
www.aapainmange.org

The American Academy of Pain Medicine
www.painmed.org

The American Chronic Pain Association
www.theacpa.org

The American Pain Society
www.ampainsoc.org

The American Society of Pain Management Nurses
www.aspmn.org

International Association for the Study of Pain
www.halycon.com/iasp

Joint Commission on Accreditation of Healthcare Organizations
www.jcaho.org

National Headache Foundation
www.headaches.org

National Hospice Organization
www.nho.org

Oncology Nursing Society
www.ons.org

Reflex Sympathetic Dystrophy Association
www.cyboard.com/rsds

Chapter 2

Pain Assessment

Yvonne D'Arcy, MS, CRNP, CNS

Synopsis

2.1 Introduction

This chapter provides information on the elements of pain assessment, describes various pain instruments commonly used to assess pain, and discusses issues with pain assessment in specialty populations such as elderly, pediatric or patients with substance abuse histories. Patient scenarios will be provided to illustrate the assessment process.

The Joint Commission on the Accreditation of Healthcare Organizations (JCAHO), which accredits a variety of healthcare organizations, has developed pain management standards which state that all patients should have their pain assessed and managed. With the implementation of these national guidelines, a new emphasis has been placed on the role of pain assessment and the resultant pain management. Since the inception of the JCAHO standards, the assessment of pain has become a priority, while health care consumers have become better advocates for their own pain management needs.

Section RI.1.2.7 of the JCAHO pain management standards states that patients have the right to appropriate assessment and management of pain. The elements included under this section are: initial assessment and regular reassessment of pain, education of all relevant providers in pain assessment, and education of patients and families when appropriate.[1] Since the healthcare spectrum includes patients of many different cultures and backgrounds, it is important that these patients have the same access to pain assessment and management as all other patients without these barriers.

Tip

Pain which is not properly assessed and relieved contributes to the misery of the patient. While this concept may seem self-evident, it is one that is receiving increased attention in light of JCAHO standards.

Assessment instruments and techniques have been developed to assist healthcare providers in complying with the national standards. These techniques include the use of screening scores, screening tools, and algorithms to drive pain assessment and reassessment.

Screening pain scores (a pain intensity rating at the time of patient visit or admission) can be used to get a baseline indication of pain level upon hospital admission or with each ambulatory care visit. Each patient should be assessed for the presence of pain, pain intensity, and barriers to pain assessment. To make the process easier, simple screening questions may be added to admission forms that ask if pain is present and if so at what intensity, if the patient has any prior problems with pain management, or if the patient has had severe pain for longer than 24 hours. If the patient indicates pain, or responds positively to these questions, a more detailed and comprehensive pain assessment should be carried out. The use of screening scores for pain assessment has been cited by JCAHO as one method of identifying patients with pain.[1]

Tip

Each institution should have a pain assessment policy or assessment process for assessing pain. These documents can be obtained through discovery.

These pain scores or forms with pain assessments should be entered into the patient's permanent chart. If the patient has a pain rating of 3 or above on a 0–10 scale, there should be a documentation of further assessment questions. Appropriate questions might be; what caused the pain, where is it located, how long has it been present, what has the patient been using for pain relief, how many days of work have been lost? There should also be some written indication of what the cause of the pain might be. Tests such as x-rays, CT or MRI scans are ordered if the cause is unclear. The medical plan should include interventions or actions for pain relief. These actions could include pain medications, physical therapy evaluation, or a pain specialist consultation.

Tip

The attorney or her legal nurse consultant should examine the medical record to determine what alternate medication intervention or action was taken to relieve the patient's pain if the initial effort was unsuccessful

---

Court cases involving complaints of pain that were not properly addressed have led to settlements for the plaintiff. Examples of these types of settlement are found in *Medical Malpractice Verdicts, Settlements and Experts*. One case involved a failure to treat unstable angina[2] and another involved a failure to treat ischemia following lumbar laminectomy.[3] Although the pain complaint is usually not the major source of settlement, the failure to address the cause of the pain complaint can lead to significant complications. In some cases, death ensued for the co-morbid condition.

In a much-discussed 1990 case, *Estate of Henry James v. Hillhaven Corporation*, a North Carolina jury awarded $15 million to the estate of the plaintiff for compensatory and punitive damages.[4] The plaintiff was a seventy-five-year-old oncology patient with prostate cancer and metastatic disease to the spine and femur. His pain was well-controlled on oral morphine while he was hospitalized. Upon admission to a second facility the admitting nurse documented in the medical record that the patient was addicted to the morphine used for pain control and her intent to substitute a mild tranquilizer. As a result of the nursing assessment and change in medications the patient was in severe pain until his death seven months later. In addition to the monetary award to the plaintiff, the North Carolina Department of Human Resources fined the second facility for patient endangerment and found the nurse liable.[5]

More recently, in 2001, a California jury awarded $1.5 million to a plaintiff's family and found the physician liable for not prescribing enough pain medication to an eighty-five-year-old cancer patient, citing recklessness and abuse.[6,7] The case was based on the California Elder Abuse and Dependent Adult Civil Protection Act. More pertinent to pain assessment was the fact that nurses caring for the patient had consistently recorded pain ratings of 7 to 10 on the 0 to 10 pain intensity rating scale putting the pain in the severe category. Although in the suit the physician was the primary defendant, the nurses and hospital were not named because of a prior settlement with the plaintiff's family.[5]

Barriers to adequate assessment that should be explored by healthcare providers in a primary pain assessment are language and physical limitations. Patients who speak a foreign language as their first language should be given a pain assessment tool in their own language, or an interpreter can be used for assistance with assessment. Family members are not considered as appropriate translators for pain assessments since their own personal bias towards pain intensity or choices of treatment may color the translations that they provide. Several sources are available for translating and can be found in reference materials or on the Internet.[8,9]

For patients with significant hearing or vision problems, pain assessment can be difficult. Especially with elderly patients, it is important to make sure that hearing aids and glasses are in place before conducting a pain assessment. This applies to both healthcare providers and attorneys who are attempting to communicate with the patients. For patients who use hearing aids or glasses, to answer questions without having the devices in place calls the accuracy of the responses into question. By providing the optimal setting for assessment, even hearing or visually impaired elderly patients may be able to participate in a pain assessment using a standard pain scale.[10]

Tip

A common misconception among healthcare providers is that all pain is the same. However, it has long been recognized by pain management practitioners that acute pain and chronic pain are very different. The assessment techniques used to assess pain should be adjusted so that the pain is adequately assessed no matter what type of pain is being addressed.

Acute pain is a pain that is sudden in onset and has the potential to increase vital signs such as pulse and blood pressure.[11] The patient expects that the pain will not be long-term. Very often the patient is anxious, and if the pain is severe a "fight or flight" response may be evoked. With acute pain, the use of a simple 0 to 10 pain intensity scale, where 0 is "no pain" and 10 is "worst possible pain" is usually adequate to assess and reassess pain intensity and response to pain management modalities. Location, duration, radiation, quality, and aggravating and alleviating factors add important information about the pain.

Chronic pain is pain that lasts longer than six months or beyond the normal period of recovery.[1] The chronic pain patient experiences pain on a daily basis and expects that this problem will be long-term and possibly without resolution. Vital sign changes are not a good indicator of chronic pain since the patient's body may physiologically adjust to the continued painful assault. Since chronic pain is an ongoing condition, depression is a common feature of this type of pain. To assess chronic pain, a more detailed pain history is needed, and a multidimensional pain assessment instrument such as the McGill Pain Questionnaire (MPQ) or the Brief Pain Inventory (BPI) is used.

Tip

Chronic pain may exist just as the patient says it does without x-ray confirmation of damage. Soft tissue damage is difficult to determine with normal scans but is painful nonetheless.

2.2 Elements of Pain Assessment

Pain is an individual response, and each patient must have his pain considered only in reference to his own pain experience. It is impossible for a caregiver or healthcare provider to determine the level of pain in a patient.[12–14] Self-report is considered to be the gold standard for determining pain intensity in patients.[8,11] "Pain is what the patient says it is,"[8,11] and neither behavior nor vital signs can substitute for a self-report.[15] Assessment is a comprehensive evaluation of pain using a valid and reliable tool and a holistic focus. It is meant to measure the level of pain a patient is experiencing and the effect that the pain has on the person as a whole. It is considered to be a social contract between the patient and the healthcare provider. Once the patient tells the healthcare provider what his or her pain intensity is and describes the pain, the patient has the right to have this report believed and respected.[1] It is the patient's expectation that the pain report will be respected and generate an action that is consistent with the pain report.

Tip

Remember that pain is what the patient says it is, occurring when the patient says it does.[8] Attorneys need to carefully examine charts to ensure that this is how pain is being assessed and treated.

Since the assessment of pain is essential to providing adequate treatment for pain, it is important that healthcare practitioners and attorneys understand the elements of the pain assessment. The basic elements for a pain assessment are described in more detail below. They are location, intensity, duration, description, alleviating or aggravating factors, and functional impairment including sleep and activity. Since pain is a dynamic entity, it is necessary to assess the pain not only at rest but with activity. If pain is controlled at rest but the patient does not have adequate pain control to cough, breathe deeply or to ambulate, a higher level of pain relief may be needed. Maintaining this functionality is key to the assessment and management of pain.

For chronic pain patients, a more detailed pain assessment will also show an effect on the quality of life on many different levels such as spiritual, psychologic, physiologic, and social, and include any cognitive attempts that the patient is making to manage the pain.[16] It is helpful for the healthcare provider to include a significant other or family member in the pain assessment so that the full effect of the chronic pain on the family dynamics is ascertained. Many times the person experiencing the chronic pain is not aware of the full scope of how the pain is affecting family relationships until family members share their perspectives.

Tip

Attorneys should be aware that chronic pain is a life-changing condition. In many cases when functionality is assessed there will be a significant decrease in ability and a need for assistance with daily activities. The value of this loss is individual to each patient and his family. When trying to determine the extent of functional loss, it is necessary to question the family about the effect of the chronic pain on the other family members.

For example, children may indicate they have been asked to take on family responsibilities the affected parent may have performed prior to the chronic pain. Spouses may describe how the pain has increased the family workload for them. Additionally, there will be a financial strain due to decreased income and a potential for lost conjugal companionship since sexual functioning may be limited due to pain or medication side effects. Depression is common with chronic pain; some antidepressants, such as Prozac and Effexor, and tricyclics, such as Elavil and Desipramine, have the potential to lower libido.

A. Location

There are several different methods for having patients describe the location of their pain. The usual method of determining location is to ask the patient where the pain is or to have the patient indicate by pointing to where the pain is located. Gentle palpation by the healthcare practitioner can also be used to determine the area that is painful. Using a body diagram is helpful for chronic pain patients. If the patient marks in a painful area in the low back and pain down one leg it could be an indication of a radicular pain caused by a ruptured disc. Using the diagram to hypothesize potential causes determines what types of tests are ordered and what types of interventions are available. Attorneys should review these diagrams and ask questions about what further examinations such as MRIs or myelograms were ordered and obtain these results as well.

Some practitioners will have the patient color in the area of pain and may even include a color interpretation (e.g., red being a high level of pain). At the same time, radiation of the pain may be determined by asking the patient if the pain extends beyond the painful area or if the pain moves to another body area after she moves (e.g., pain that radiates down a leg when the patient stands).

B. Intensity

Pain intensity is most commonly assessed by determining a number on a 0–10 rating scale. This is considered to be an 11-point Likert-type format where there is a 0 through 10. This Visual Analog Scale (VAS) format is used in both research and clinical settings. In research settings, the patient may be asked to mark on a 100 cm line where she feels her pain is located. In clinical settings pain intensity rating is determined by asking the patient to rate his or her pain by giving the healthcare provider the number that best describes the pain; 0–3 being mild pain, 4–6 being moderate pain, and 7–10 being severe pain.

A variation on this type of rating is a slide rule that has a 0 (no pain) at one end and a 10 at the other end indicating the most pain ever. The patient slides the indicator to the level he feels is indicative of his pain. This tool may be used with a blank line or a numbered line facing the patient depending on the patient, or if there is a need for the healthcare provider to blind the patient to the numerical ratings. For patients who have difficulty with numerical rating, using a line with 0 at one end and a 10 at the opposite end and asking the patient where the pain falls on the continuum may be the best approach. For convenience, some scales are double sided with a numerical rating on one side for the person assessing the pain and the line without the numbers facing the patient. This allows the patient to use the tool as it best fits her needs and gives the healthcare professional the numerical pain rating they need.

Additionally, there has been research that shows that elderly patients do best with a pain scale that is vertical, similar to a thermometer that has the 0 pain rating at the base and the 10 or most severe pain rating at the top. It is felt that the elderly patient conceptualizes the meaning of the rating scale best when it moves from bottom to top, low pain ratings at the bottom and higher pain ratings at the top.[10,18]

C. Duration

Questions that are answered related to duration are "when did the pain start" and "how long does the pain last?" By determining when the pain begins or ends, it is possible to determine when it is worse or better. It is an important part of a pain assessment to determine the onset of pain and how long the pain lasts.

Tip

Attorneys should pay particular attention to this question. Unrelieved pain is unacceptable, and the attorney should review charts and documentation carefully to determine if high pain intensities were allowed to remain untreated for long periods of time.

D. Description

The description of the pain as the patient relates it is one of the best ways for the patient to convey a picture of the pain to the healthcare provider. The attorney reviewing the medical records may read the patient's exact words, quotes, or complaints. It is a powerful element of the pain assessment when the patient indicates the pain "feels like a knitting needle stuck in a leg" or that the pain is like "an electric shock" moving down an arm. The type of pain descriptor a patient uses may be an indication of whether the pain is musculoskeletal or neuropathic. Musculoskeletal pain is often described as achy or dull. Neuropathic pain may be best described as needles and pins, numbness, burning or tingling.

Another way to describe pain is for the healthcare provider to offer a list of common pain descriptors. These descriptors are found in lists on the multidimensional pain instruments used to assess chronic pain.

Tip

Terms such as *burning, numbness, tingling, shooting,* or *electric* are more indicative of neuropathic pain. Descriptors such as *achy, dull,* and *throbbing* most often indicate a musculoskeletal pain.

The attorney should be aware that treatment plans differ by the type of pain. For neuropathic pain, there should be not only a pain medication but the recognition that neuropathic pain requires the addition of medication to treat neuropathic pain such as an antidepressant or Neurontin. Nerve blocks provided through the services of an anesthesia pain clinic are additional neuropathic treatment modalities. Careful analysis of the verbal descriptors used by the patient when speaking about his pain may be helpful in determining if the correct combination of treatment options was offered to the patient.

E. Aggravating or alleviating factors

Asking the patient to list things that make the pain worse or better is helpful when assessing pain. Identifying these factors is useful in determining treatment options. Included in this section of the assessment are complementary methods such as heat, cold, relaxation, topicals, or herbal remedies. Very often patients use these methods and overlook telling their healthcare provider that they are employing this type of assistance for pain control.

F. Functional impairment

Determining the impact of pain on function is an important piece of the pain assessment process. If pain is not well controlled, patients will not be able to care for themselves or pursue their normal daily activity patterns. Pain is a dynamic entity. It usually increases with activity. The assessment process should include an assessment of the pain at rest as well as with activity. In this way it is possible to see if pain relief continues as the patient moves and engages in normal daily activities. If pain control is not sufficient for activity, medication doses may need to be adjusted or additional medication may be needed prior to activity.

Part of the function assessment is to ascertain the patient's sleep and rest pattern. If the patient is not sleeping, pain control may be insufficient. If patients do not sleep they will not have the energy to continue with a normal daily activity pattern. Adjusting pain medication doses or adding a medication for sleep may be an important piece of an adequate pain management regimen.

The attorney should pay particular attention to the functional component of the pain assessment. If the patient cannot function, income is affected. Careful chart review should determine what types and doses of pain medication were used to treat the pain, and if they were effective enough to help the patient maintain his functional status.

G. Case study: Adam

Adam, twenty-four, was a driver of a car that was hit from behind while stopped at a red light. Medical examination revealed a spinal injury with ruptured discs severe enough to require an anterior-posterior approach to spinal rodding and stabilization with plates. After the surgeries and partial recovery, Adam spoke about the effect of the pain on himself and his young family:

> You know I will never be the same. I can't do anything like I did before. I can't work any more, and my wife has to pay all the bills. They are retraining me for a computer job but I can't sit long enough to do the class work. My physician won't give me an opioid medication to use even once or twice a day. She thinks I should only be taking Motrin. I know if I could have even one or two Percocet a day I could tolerate the sitting time I need to do the computer training.
>
> I have an eighteen-month-old baby too. I can't even hold her on my lap any more, the weight is too much. I'll never be able to push her on a swing or slide down a slide with her. This whole thing makes me so sad. I cry when I am alone. I don't want my wife to see me. We can't even go out to dinner anymore so our friends have kind of given up on us. I wish I had never been in the car that day. I wish my doctor would listen to me about how I think I could do better with just a little better pain medication. I just want my old life back and I get tired of talking about the whole thing.

This case illustrates the type of issues surrounding the complexities of assessing chronic pain. Attorneys who are questioning clients about their chronic pain need to ask questions not only about the pain but functionality, loss of income, and quality of life which are important aspects of a complete pain assessment. Very often patients will be reluctant and embarrassed to expose the true depth of how chronic pain affects their life until it is too late and families and marriages are destroyed. The plaintiff's lawyer should be very careful to explore the complete scenario at all levels to ensure that full damages are considered.

H. Pain goal

It is particularly helpful for the healthcare professional to establish a pain goal as a point of reference with chronic pain patients. In the hospital, patients can determine what pain intensity allows them to participate in physical therapy or ambulation. For chronic pain patients, the pain goal is an agreed upon pain intensity level where the patients can function at an acceptable level.

For example, if a patient with a pain goal of 4, which would mean a pain of 4 out of 10, can function at an acceptable level of activity. However, if subsequent assessments have the same patient rating his pain at a 7 that would mean that the patient has more pain and that functionality would be impaired. It may also mean that the patient needs more pain medication or that he or she has been more active than the pain goal would allow. If the pain rating given by the patient is a 4 or less, that would mean that the pain goal is being met and the patient is receiving adequate pain relief and can function at the level he feels tolerable. The best outcome with a pain goal is to have the patient and the healthcare practitioner agree on the pain goal and for the pain rating from the patient to fall at or under the agreed upon pain rating. This would be an indication of stable pain with stable doses of pain medication.

2.3 Pain Instruments

There are a variety of instruments or tools that have been developed to measure the various elements of pain. Some instruments are a one-dimensional measurement such as intensity, and other instruments combine elements and are considered to be multidimensional. The one-dimensional instruments are used most commonly with acute pain assessments and are combined with the other elements of a pain assessment for chronic pain.

Tip

The multidimensional tools most often are used for assessing chronic pain and combine a pain intensity scale, assessment of functionality, and aggravating or alleviating factors.

No matter which pain instrument is being used to assess pain, it should be reliable and valid as well as quick and easy to use. Pain instruments are usually developed for use with a certain population such as pediatric patients or adults. Accordingly, pain assessment tools for adults should be used only with adults, and pediatric pain assessment tools should not be used with adults. If the scale is used in other than the population that it is designed for, it would not be possible to say that the outcome derived from the measurement was accurate.

For patients who do not speak English, pain instruments need to be adapted so that they are easy for these individuals to use. There are sources that provide translations into many different languages. The AHCPR (now AHRQ) *Management of Cancer Pain*[17] and *Acute Pain Guidelines*[15] are available in Spanish. In the assessment chapter of *Pain: A Clinical Manual* there are selections of pain scales in a variety of languages.[8] The AHCPR pain guidelines are available over the national website and include the clinician's manual, a quick reference guide, and a patient education pamphlet.

It is difficult for healthcare providers to assess cognitively impaired or nonverbal patients. For example, a patient with Alzheimer's disease may not be able to communicate pain in the standard fashion. However, if the patient is moaning or restless and calms once pain medication is tried, then pain should be presumed present and pain medication given on a regular basis. For the same Alzheimer's patient with a broken hip, pain should also be presumed present and pain medication administered. Chart documentation should indicate the pain behavior and a decrease in the behavior when pain medication is given. See Chapter 15, "Pain and Suffering in the Elderly Population," for additional information.

A. Case study: Bonita

Bonita was thirty-nine-year-old female patient who had surgery the previous day after being injured in a head-on collision. Her family contacted a lawyer to represent her interests. When the attorney entered the room he saw that the windows were darkened and the patient was tearful. She stated the pain "just cuts into my stomach like a knife." Bonita had a pink emesis (vomit) basin on her chest. She was nauseated and related that her pain was an 8 out of 10—severe pain—despite her continued use of a Demerol PCA (patient controlled analgesia). She stated that Demerol always made her nauseated and she did not feel the pain medications were working. She related that the pain was located in her abdomen, at the surgical site. She also said that the nurses were telling her she needed to walk in the halls twice today. She said she just did not think she could do it. Bonita felt too sick and hurt too much.

When the attorney received the medical records for this admission, he reviewed the nurse's notes to determine how Bonita's pain was described. When the nurses asked the patient to rate her pain, she assigned an 8 to the pain, which signified a severe level.

The verbal descriptor of knife-like pain identified the pain as sharp and stabbing and was useful for the overall pain assessment. When the patient said the pain was at 8, that was the level of pain and it should have been treated accordingly.

This was acute pain that was the result of trauma. The patient was anxious related to the uncontrolled pain, and she was upset and tearful. Despite her telling the physician that she did not get good relief with Demerol, that was the pain medication she was given. This medication choice was an additive element to her distress and pain.

The pain was made worse with movement and she felt she could not comply with planned walking that was required of her as a postoperative patent. Her overall functionality was impaired and it was most likely that she would have to stay longer in the hospital than she planned since the unrelieved pain may have set back her discharge time by at least one day.

B. One-dimensional pain instruments

1. Numeric Pain Scale (NPI)

The case study described above refers to measuring pain on a numerical scale. The most common one-dimensional scale is the Numeric Pain Intensity (NPI) Scale (see Figure 2.1). This scale is made up of a horizontal line with a beginning point marked 0 or "no pain" and a 10 at the opposite end marked "worst pain possible." When using this pain rating tool, the patient reports the number that she feels best represents the pain that she feeling. Generally, pain in the 1–3 category is ranked as mild pain, 4–6 as moderate pain, and 7–10 is the highest level or severe pain.

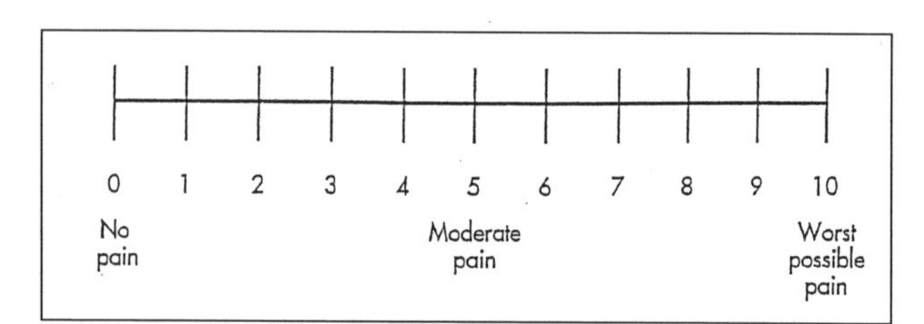

Figure 2.1 Numeric Pain Intensity (NPI) Scale

There is no right or wrong number for rating pain. Most often 3 is considered by practitioners to be the number where patients can participate in activity, but with chronic pain patients a higher number may be tolerable pain. No matter what number the patient chooses as the pain level that is the pain rating that should be accepted. Reassessment of pain should be aimed at measuring the efficacy of pain interventions by a decrease in the rating of the pain.

2. Visual Analog Scale (VAS)

The visual analog scale is a 100-millimeter horizontal line with 0 as the anchor at one end of the scale and 10 at the opposite end of the scale. Although this is a very simple form of pain assessment, there are some drawbacks. For most patients this type of pain assessment is adequate. However, for patients who have visual or cognitive impairment, this scale is hard to use. Clinicians found that some elderly patients had difficulty marking on the line and at times marked above or below the line rather than directly on the line.[17,18] See Figure 2.2.

3. Verbal Descriptor Scale (VDS)

The verbal descriptor scale uses words such as no pain, mild pain, moderate pain, or severe pain to help patients describe their pain intensity. Comparison of improvement in pain is made by asking for a descriptor after a pain relief intervention, such as medication, and comparing it to the previous pain rating by the patient. If the pain was rated by the patient as moderate when first asked, and then as mild after pain medication, the pain intensity would be considered to be decreased and the intervention effective. Feldt, Ryden and Miles found a 73% completion rate for this scale in a group of cognitively impaired patients.[19] Additionally, some studies have shown that adults actually prefer this scale.[18]

Problems with this rating scale are that the patients must have a functional level high enough to understand

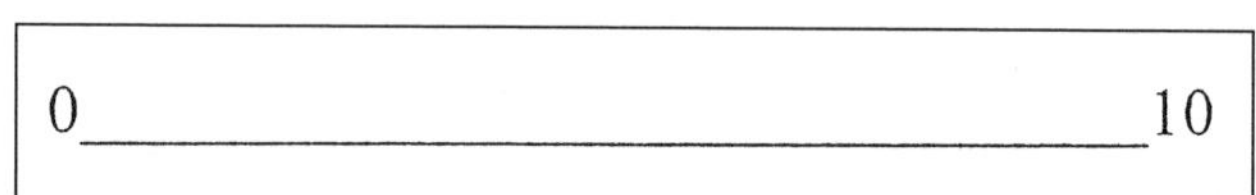

Figure 2.2 Visual Analogue Scale (VAS)

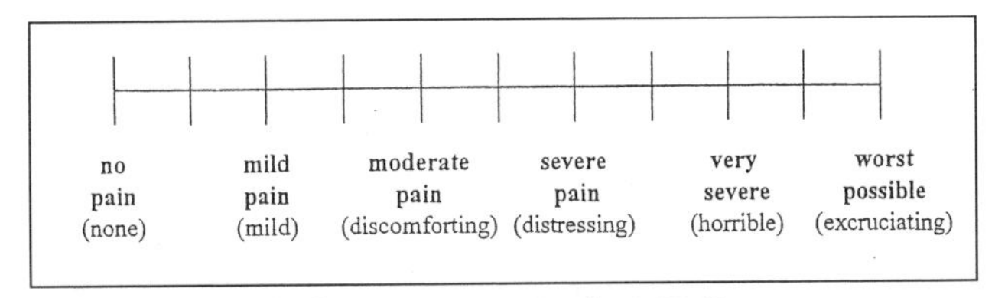

Figure 2.3 *Verbal Descriptor Scale (VDS)*

the use of the words and their meaning. This would eliminate patients such as pediatric patients, cognitively impaired patients, intubated patients, or geriatric patients with impaired mental functional status. See Figure 2.3.

4. Combined scale

There have been attempts to combine the features of these one-dimensional scales into a configuration that conveys all the options combined. This can be done as a horizontal line or a vertical rotation of the scale. One such use is the thermometer pain scale. This is a vertical presentation of the NPI combined with the verbal descriptor scale in a thermometer configuration. See Figure 2.4.

C. Behavioral pain rating scales

Behavioral scales are used to assess pain when the patient is unable to rate her pain using a standard pain rating scale. Behaviors that are used by the healthcare professional to identify pain as being present are facial expressions, vocalization, or movement. Although behavioral indicators are not ideal for assessing pain, they do give an indication of whether pain is present or not.

There is current research being conducted on the use of behavioral instruments to assess pain in this population. These scales consist of lists of recognized pain behaviors, such as grimacing, moaning, or guarding the painful area. When these behaviors are noted the chart documentation should reflect that this is a recognized pain behaviors and the pain relief action should be implemented. All attempts should be made to use a standard pain intensity measure, but should this prove impossible, a scale such as the CNPI, a checklist of nonverbal pain indicators for cognitively impaired patients, or the use of the Observational Indicators of Pain, a list of recognized pain behaviors, may be helpful.[10,20] Behaviors that are commonly thought to indicate pain are guarding, grimacing, withdrawal, and crying. These patient populations are difficult to assess even for skilled pain management practitioners. Herr and Garand have proposed this list of behaviors that might indicate the presence of pain in cognitively impaired patients such as those with Alzheimer's disease or strokes.[10] See Chapter 15, "Pain and Suffering in the Elderly Population," for more information.

1. FACES

The FACES scale is one of the older behavioral pain intensity scales. It was originally developed for use in pediatric patient populations who were unable to use the numerical pain rating scales. The six faces are aligned with a happy (or no-pain) face at the left and the tearful (or most-pain) face at the right. The patient is asked to point to the face that best represents the

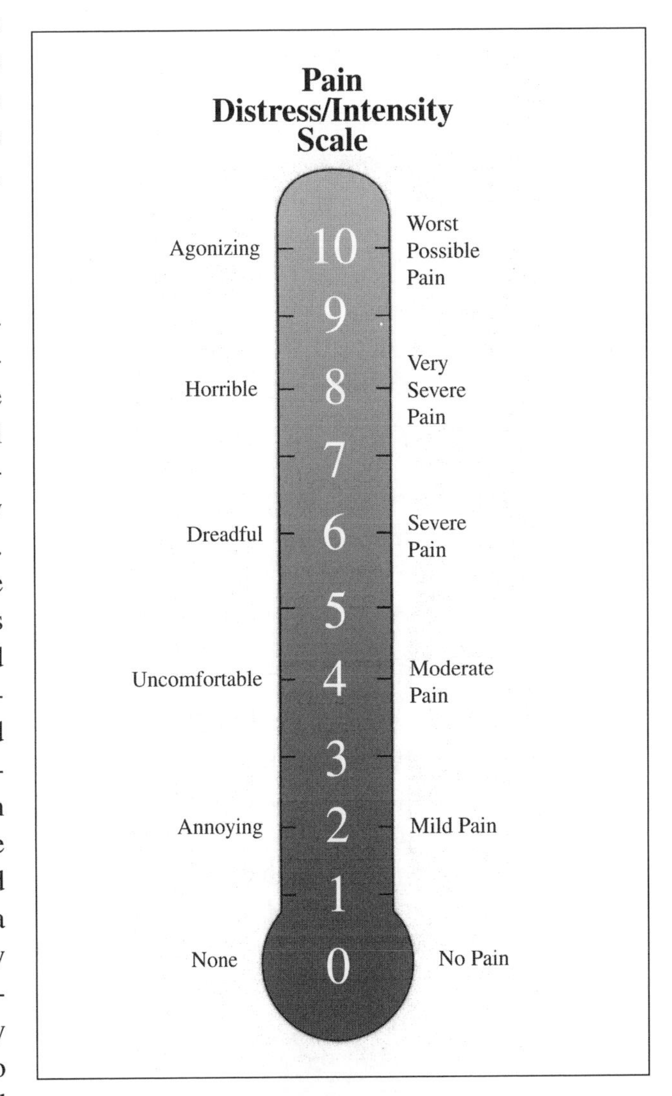

Figure 2.4 *Thermometer-combined verbal descriptor and numeric pain intensity scale*

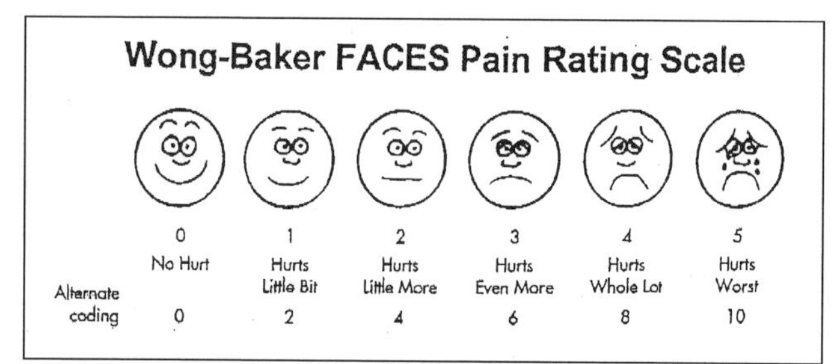

***Figure 2.5** FACES, reprinted with the permission from Wong DL, Hockenberry-Eaton M, Wilson D, Winkelstein ML, Schwartz P:* Wong's Essentials of Pediatric Nursing, *ed. 6, St. Louis, 2001, Mosby, p. 1301. Copyright Mosby.*

patient's pain. This will not convert to a numeric rating but it does indicate if there is pain and how severe the pain may be. See Figure 2.5.

2. CRIES

The CRIES scale is used with neonates and is based on a group of observations and physiologic indicators. The behaviors are rated and scored with the higher score indicating the greater distress and pain. It is specifically designed for use with neonatal postoperative pain. See Figure 2.6.

D. Multidimensional pain scales

There are two multidimensional pain scales that are used for pain assessment: the *McGill Pain Questionnaire* (MPQ), short form (SF-MPQ), and the *Brief Pain Inventory* (BPI). These scales not only measure the intensity of pain but have diagrams for pain locations, verbal descriptors, and an indicator of mood. These tools are used clinically as either a self-report tool or an interview format.

1. *McGill Pain Questionnaire* (MPQ)

The *McGill Pain Questionnaire* has both long and short forms. The original version of the tool has three classes of verbal descriptors that are scored and weighted. There is a pain intensity scale and a body diagram for locating the pain. Gracely and Graham report that the MPQ is useful for determining some elements of the pain experience but lacks the ability to translate the meaning of the verbal descriptors from the list of words that are more descriptive of syndromes.[21,22]

Both the long and short forms of the MPQ have been widely used, and there are many studies to support the reliability and validity of the instrument. The instrument has also been translated into several languages for use in a variety of settings. Clinically, it has been used to study post-procedural pain, experimentally induced pain, and a large number of medical and surgical areas with children over the age of twelve. For multidimensional pain assessment it is undoubtedly the standard against which other instruments are measured. See Figure 2.7.

2. *Brief Pain Inventory* (BPI)

The *Brief Pain Inventory* (BPI) is a simpler and easier to use instrument than the MPQ. It has been determined to be reliable and valid.[23] Clinically, the instrument has been used as an interview and in a self-report format. The instrument has a pain intensity rating: present pain, worst pain, and best pain in the last month, and a body diagram to locate pain. There is a functional assessment and questions related to pain medication efficacy.

The BPI has been used extensively outside the United States and with a variety of patient populations. The instrument is not designed for assessing acute pain, but it is very suitable for patients with chronic malignant and benign conditions. A major drawback to the instrument is the requirement that the patient have a functional level that allows for responding independently or to questions that require more complex answers. See Figure 2.8.

Tip

Attorneys should question whether the pain scale being used to assess pain has reliability and validity with the patient population being assessed. Adult scales should not be used with pediatric patients and pediatric pain scales should not be used with adult patients.

2.4 Assessing Pain in Specialty Populations

There are several groups of patients that may need special attention when pain is being assessed. Pain assessment in the pediatric population is difficult unless pediatric pain scales or pediatric assessment techniques are used. See Chapter 6, "Pain and Suffering in Children," for more information. Geriatric patients also have problems with standard pain scales if they have physical or cognitive barriers. See Chapter 15, "Pain and Suffering in the Elderly Population," for more information. Both groups of patients require extra time and attention when pain assessment is being performed.

Patients who are intubated, or in critical care settings, are considered challenges for pain assessment. Some critical care patients are able to self report their pain levels. However, those who are intubated or comatose are much more difficult to assess. The use of behavioral scales has been tried with modest success. D'Arcy and Puntillo found that critical care patients experienced a high level of pain and that these patients

CRIES Scale

	0	1	2
Crying	No	High pitched	Inconsolable
Requires O_2 for sat >95	No	<30%	>30%
Increased vital signs	HR and BP = or <preop	HR or BP ↑ <20% of preop	HR or BP ↑ >20% of preop
Expression	None	Grimace	Grimace/grunt
Sleepless	No	Wakes at frequent intervals	Constantly awake

Neonatal pain assessment tool developed at the University of Missouri-Columbia.

CODING TIPS FOR USING CRIES

Crying	The characteristic cry of pain is *high pitched.* If no cry or cry that is not high pitched, score 0. If cry high pitched but baby is easily consoled, score 1. If cry is high pitched and baby is inconsolable, score 2.
Requires O_2 for sat >95%	Look for *changes* in oxygenation. Babies experiencing pain manifest decreases in oxygenation as measured by Tco_2 or oxygen saturation. If no oxygen is required, score 0. If >30% O_2 is required, score 1. If <30% is required, score 2. (Consider other causes of changes in oxygenation, such as atelectasis, pneumothorax, over-sedation)
Increased vital signs	NOTE: Take blood pressure last as this may wake child, causing difficulty with other assessments. Use baseline preoperative parameters from a nonstressed period. Multiply baseline HR × 0.2 and then add this to baseline HR to determine the HR, which is 20% over baseline. Do likewise for BP. Use mean BP. If HR and BP are both unchanged or less than baseline, score 0. If HR or BP is increased but increase is <20% of baseline, score 1. If either one is increased >20% over baseline, score 2.
Expression	The facial expression most often associated with pain is a grimace. This may be characterized by brow lowering, eyes squeezed shut, deepening of the nasolabial furrow, open lips and mouth. If no grimace is present, score 0. If grimace alone is present, score 1. If grimace and noncry vocalization grunt are present, score 2.
Sleepless	This parameter is scored based on the infant's state during the hour preceding this recorded score. If the child has been continuously asleep, score 0. If he or she has awakened at frequent intervals, score 1. If he or she has been awake constantly, score 2.

Figure 2.6 *CRIES, reprinted with permission from Judy Beldner, RN, CNS, MS, University of Missouri—Columbia*

McGill Pain Questionnaire (MPQ)-Short Form

Short-Form McGill Pain Questionnaire

PATIENT'S NAME: ______________________ DATE: ____________

	NONE	MILD	MODERATE	SEVERE
THROBBING	0) ____	1) ____	2) ____	3) ____
SHOOTING	0) ____	1) ____	2) ____	3) ____
STABBING	0) ____	1) ____	2) ____	3) ____
SHARP	0) ____	1) ____	2) ____	3) ____
CRAMPING	0) ____	1) ____	2) ____	3) ____
GNAWING	0) ____	1) ____	2) ____	3) ____
HOT/BURNING	0) ____	1) ____	2) ____	3) ____
ACHING	0) ____	1) ____	2) ____	3) ____
HEAVY	0) ____	1) ____	2) ____	3) ____
TENDER	0) ____	1) ____	2) ____	3) ____
SPLITTING	0) ____	1) ____	2) ____	3) ____
TIRING/EXHAUSTING	0) ____	1) ____	2) ____	3) ____
SICKENING	0) ____	1) ____	2) ____	3) ____
FEARFUL	0) ____	1) ____	2) ____	3) ____
PUNISHING/CRUEL	0) ____	1) ____	2) ____	3) ____

VAS NO PAIN |————————————————| WORST POSSIBLE PAIN

PPI

0 NO PAIN ____
1 MILD ____
2 DISCOMFORTING ____
3 DISTRESSING ____
4 HORRIBLE ____
5 EXCRUCIATING ____

The short-form McGill Pain Questionnaire (SF-MPQ). Descriptors 1–11 represent the sensory dimension of pain experience and 12-15 represent the affective dimension. Each descriptor is ranked on an intensity scale of 0 = none, 1 = mild, 2 = moderate, 3 = severe. The Present Pain Intensity (PPI) of the standard long-form McGill Pain Questionnaire (LF-MPQ) and the visual analogue scale (VAS) are also included to provide overall intensity scores.

Figure 2.7 McGill Pain Questionnaire, *reprinted with the permission from R. Melzack. © R. Melzack, 1984.*

BRIEF PAIN INVENTORY

Date______/______/______ Time:__________

Name:______________ ______________ ______
Last First Middle Initial

1) Throughout our lives, most of us have had pain from time to time (such as minor headaches, sprains, and toothaches). Have you had pain other than these everyday kinds of pain today?

   1. Yes 2. No

2) On the diagram, shade in the areas where you feel pain. Put an X on the area that hurts the most.

   Right Left Left Right

3) Please rate your pain by circling the one number that best describes your pain at its WORST in the last 24 hours.

   0 1 2 3 4 5 6 7 8 9 10

   No Pain — Pain as bad as you can imagine

4) Please rate your pain by circling the one number that best describes your pain at its LEAST in the last 24 hours.

   0 1 2 3 4 5 6 7 8 9 10

   No Pain — Pain as bad as you can imagine

5) Please rate your pain by circling the one number that best describes your pain on the AVERAGE.

   0 1 2 3 4 5 6 7 8 9 10

   No Pain — Pain as bad as you can imagine

6) Please rate your pain by circling the one number that tells how much pain you have RIGHT NOW.

   0 1 2 3 4 5 6 7 8 9 10

   No Pain — Pain as bad as you can imagine

7) What treatments or medications are you receiving for your pain?

   ____

   ____

8) In the last 24 hours, how much relief have pain treatments or medications provided? Please circle the one percentage that shows how much RELIEF you have received.

   0% 10 20 30 40 50 60 70 80 90 100%

   No relief — Complete relief

9) Circle the one number that describes how, during the past 24 hours, pain has interfered with your:

   A. General activity

   0 1 2 3 4 5 6 7 8 9 10

   Does not interfere — Completely interferes

   B. Mood

   0 1 2 3 4 5 6 7 8 9 10

   Does not interfere — Completely interferes

   C. Walking ability

   0 1 2 3 4 5 6 7 8 9 10

   Does not interfere — Completely interferes

   D. Normal work (includes both work outside the home and housework)

   0 1 2 3 4 5 6 7 8 9 10

   Does not interfere — Completely interferes

   E. Relations with other people

   0 1 2 3 4 5 6 7 8 9 10

   Does not interfere — Completely interferes

   F. Sleep

   0 1 2 3 4 5 6 7 8 9 10

   Does not interfere — Completely interferes

   G. Enjoyment of life

   0 1 2 3 4 5 6 7 8 9 10

   Does not interfere — Completely interferes

Brief Pain Inventory (Short Form). Source: Pain Research Group, Department of Neuro-Oncology, The University of Texas MD Anderson Cancer Center. Used with permission. Adapted to single page format.

Provided as an educational service by Endo Laboratories

Figure 2.8 Brief Pain Inventory, *reprinted with permission from Charles S. Cleeland, PhD., ©1991 Charles S. Cleeland, PhD.—Pain Research Group. All rights reserved.*

had recall of their critical care pain experiences[24,25] In a study, procedures commonly employed in ICUs such as chest tubes were rated by patients as painful and that medications, if given, were not effective for pain control.[25] A rule of thumb with patients who are unable to report pain is to assume that pain is present if the patient is experiencing a condition which is normally painful. See Chapter 14, "Pain and Suffering in the Intensive Care Unit," for more information.

Another group of patients that has problems with pain assessment are addicted patients, or those patients with a history of substance abuse. The term substance abuse covers not only illicit drugs but alcohol. Addicted patients have the same right to have their pain assessed and treated as those patients without substance abuse issues. Often healthcare professionals are reluctant to provide opioids to patients with addiction histories because they fear readdiction or contributing drugs to an active addiction. This fear of addiction, and fear of opioids, colors the whole pain assessment process for these patients.

Addicted patients can be treated effectively and have their pain adequately managed. Assessment of these patients by healthcare providers requires an open and honest discussion of the issues and a complete drug history. A good working knowledge of the appropriate definitions for addiction, dependence, and tolerance is helpful for use in assessing pain in these cases.[26] These terms are defined in Figure 2.9.

Because there is so much misunderstanding of what addiction is, patients who are dependent on pain medication to maintain function are often mistakenly classified as addicts. Chronic pain patients who require opioids daily for pain relief so that they have a higher function and quality of life are correctly classified as dependent, and not addicted.

Tip

Attorneys who represent plaintiffs should be aware of the correct terminology and check charts to evaluate if the patient has been mislabeled as addicted when he is really dependent. Additionally, patients who are labeled as addicts often have difficulty getting the pain medication they need based on caregiver bias against them.

Patients who require dose escalations may be experiencing tolerance but may often be labeled as drug seeking. Once stable pain control is achieved the pain medication dose should also remain stable; however, some patients experience reluctance on the part of their healthcare providers to escalate doses until pain is adequately relieved. Attorneys should be aware of this pattern and discuss the issue with the clients.

True addiction is a less common occurrence. Real addicts would take pain medication whether they have pain or not. They enjoy the feeling the drug provides and crave the drug they favor. Addicts are dependent on pain medication, but not all opioid-dependent patients are considered addicts.

Tip

Healthcare professionals can have a difficult time continuing to prescribe opioids for patients they feel are addicted. This reluctance can be partially explained by opiophobia,[11,26,27] or fear of opioid medications and fear of regulatory overview.

tolerance. "Tolerance is a state of adaptation in which exposure to a drug induces changes that results in a diminution of one or more of the drugs effects over time."[25]

physical dependence. "Physical dependence is a state of adaptation that is manifested by a drug specific withdrawal syndrome that can be produced by abrupt cessation, rapid dose reduction, decreasing blood level of the drug, and/or administration of an antagonist."[25]

addiction. "Addiction is a primary, chronic, neurobiologic disease, with genetic, psychosocial, and environmental factors influencing its development and manifestations. It is characterized by behaviors that include one or more of the following: impaired control over drug use, compulsive use, continued use despite harm, and craving."[25]

***Figure 2.9** Terminology related to pain medication*

Because healthcare professionals are unsure of pain assessment and misunderstand what true addiction means, the risk of undertreating pain is very real. This bias against opioids can be found in all areas of medical practice but is especially problematic in emergency rooms where patients have short interactions with medical staff and need repeat visits for pain control.

Some pain medications, especially some sustained release opioids, have recently been used recreationally and have been publicly labeled as highly addictive. Attorneys are advised to determine how the drugs were taken and what other drugs were used in conjunction. To chew a sustained release pain medication means that the entire dose of medication is delivered at one time. This is outside of manufacturer's recommendations and attorneys should be aware of how these drugs work when they are abused.

Attorneys should remember that even if a patient is truly addicted to opioids or has a history of addiction to street drugs, he is entitled to the same level of pain management as any other patient. To do otherwise is to fall outside of the recommended practice outlined in the JCAHO pain standards.

2.5 Case Study: Carlos

Carlos was a middle-aged patient with a diagnosis of colon cancer and heroin addiction. He was admitted to the hospital with uncontrolled abdominal pain eighteen hours after last using heroin. The assessment should have included an open discussion of the amounts and types of drugs being used in a non-judgmental fashion. No attempt should have been made to dismiss the patient's pain, and he should not have been treated differently because of his addiction. He needed enough pain medication to account for his heroin use and additional pain medication to treat his abdominal pain.

Since the opioid conversion from heroin to a standard pain medication is unknown, a morphine patient-controlled intravenous analgesia (PCA) was used to determine the amount of pain medication needed to control the pain which, the patient related, was quite severe.

Carlos used the PCA for several days and found his pain was able to be well-controlled. The staff encouraged Carlos to use the PCA to maintain his comfort. When the conversion from IV pain medication to oral pain medication was calculated, the dose required for pain relief was 500 milligrams of extended-release morphine twice a day. Since the patient was opioid-dependent from his heroin use when he was admitted, a higher dosage of pain medication was needed to compensate for the street drug use as well as the opioid required to control the chest wall pain.

Tip

Extended-release pain medications such as MS Contin or methadone are often used for addicted patients because the sustained action of the medication does not allow wide variation in blood opioid levels. These medications provide a steady method for long-term pain relief.

2.6 Case Study: Diane

Diane was a fifty-year-old woman diagnosed with breast cancer after a lengthy delay. A plaintiffs' attorney filed an action against her primary care physician, who had consistently dismissed the plaintiff's concerns without referring her to a surgeon. When her attorney called Diane to see if she was all right, she said,

> Well, you know, I have cancer and it's so bad now I really can't get out of my house. My side aches just like a toothache all the time. I can't do anything I used to do, and I can't seem to get the doctor to give me anything that helps the pain. I keep telling her my pain is severe. I rate it 8 out of 10 at every visit. Every morning I wake up and know that I will have pain all day. I can't sleep well and I am just so depressed.

The pain Diane was suffering arose from a tumor pressing on her side. It was chronic pain that had no real cure except surgery or radiation. Even so, since the pain had been allowed to go on for such a long time and the level was so intense, it would take a long time to get the pain to a reasonable level. Her verbal descriptor of toothache was helpful for the pain assessment. The decrease in quality of life Diane was experiencing was significant. The attorney should involve Diane's husband in the pain-assessment process to get the best picture of how this pain was affecting not only the patient but the functioning of the family.

Despite her repeated pain rating of 8, Diane had not been given any medication that was helpful for pain relief. The attorney reviewed the medical records to see how Diane's pain was assessed at her medical office visits and question why she had not been given adequate pain medication for her pain. The lack of surgical referral caused considerable pain and suffering for both this patient and her family. The attorney assisted Diane in asserting her rights to adequate pain management. Additionally since the pain was allowed to go on for so long, if Diane had surgery it might be much more difficult to control her pain.

2.7 Summary

Pain assessment is critical to the delivery of adequate pain management. If the assessment does not lead to a good evaluation of the patient's pain, undertreatment will result. The national guidelines for pain management give directions for assessment. In order for all patients to receive the pain management they need, all caregivers need to learn, develop, and use pain assessment skills that will help patients communicate their pain levels and the effect that their pain has on their lives. Attorneys will find the clues regarding pain assessment in medical records. This information is useful in establishing the presence or absence of pain.

Endnotes

1. Joint Commission on Accreditation of Healthcare Organizations, *Pain Assessment and Management: An Organizational Approach.* Oakbrook Terrace, IL: Joint Commission, 2000.

2. Laska, L., editor, "Failure to Diagnosis and Treat Unstable Angina—Death of a Fifty-Year-Old Man—$200,000 California Settlement with Initial Internist—California Dismissal for Subsequent Internist." *Anonymous Decedent v. Anonymous Internists,* _____County (CA) Superior Court, Case No. ______, *Medical Malpractice Verdicts, Settlements and Experts* May, 2002, 9.

3. Laska, L., editor, "Failure to Timely Diagnose and Treat Ischemia Following Lumbar Laminectomy—Leg amputated but Sepsis Leads to Organ Failure and Death—1.3 Million North Carolina Settlement." *Anonymous Decedent v. Anonymous Emergency Room Physician and Anonymous Hospital,* _____County (NC) Superior Court, Case No. ______, *Medical Malpractice Verdicts, Settlements and Experts.* May, 2002, 18.

4. Angolara, R.T., and Donato, B.J., "Inappropriate Pain Management Results in High Jury Award." *Journal of Pain and Symptom Management*: 6(7): 407: 1991.

5. Pasero C., and McCaffery M., "The Undertreatment of Pain." *American Journal of Nursing*: 101(11): 62: 2001.

6. La Ganga, M.L., and Monmaney, T., "Doctor Found Liable in Suit over Pain. *Los Angeles Times.* June 15, 2001: A1, A34.

7. Yi, M., "Doctor Found Reckless for Not Relieving Pain." *San Francisco Chronicle.* June 15, 2001: A1, A18.

8. McCaffery, M., and Pasero, C., *Pain: Clinical Manual.* St. Louis: Mosby, 1999

9. American Society of Pain Management Nurses, *Core Curriculum for Pain Management Nursing.* Philadelphia: W.B. Saunders, 2002.

10. Herr, K.A., and Garand, L., "Assessment and Measurement of Pain in Older Adults." *Clinics in Geriatric Medicine*: 17(4):1–22: 2001.

11. American Pain Society, *Principles of Analgesic Use in the Treatment of Acute Pain and Cancer Pain*, Fourth Edition. Glenview, Il, American Pain Society, 1999.

12. Choiniere, M., Melzack, R., Girard, N., Rondeau, J., and Pacquin, M., "Comparisons between Patients' and Nurses' Assessment of Pain and Medication Effects in Severe Burn Injuries." *Pain*: 40: 143–152: 1990.

13. Dudley, S., and Holms, K., "Assessment of Pain Experience in Relation to Selected Nurse Characteristics." *Pain*, 18: 179–186: 1984.

14. Harrison, A., "Assessing Patients' Pain: Identifying Reasons for Error." *Journal of Advanced Nursing*: 16: 1018–1025: 1991.

15. Agency for Health Care Policy and Research. *Acute Pain Management Guidelines.* AHCPR Pub.No. 92-0019. Rockville, MD: Public Health Service. U.S. Department of Health and Human Services, 1992.

16. Ferrell, B., Grant, M., Padilla, G., Vemuri, S., and Rhiner, M., "The Experience of Pain and Perceptions of

Quality of Life: Validation of a Conceptual Model. *Hospice Journal*: 7(3): 9–25: 1991.

17. Agency for Health Care Policy and Research, *Management of Cancer Pain.* AHCPR Pub. No. 94-0592. Rockville, MD: Public Health Service. U.S. Department of Health and Human Services, 1994.

18. Herr, K.A., and Mobily, P., "Comparison of Selected Pain Assessment Tools for Use with the Elderly." *Appl Nurs Res*: 6(39): 1993

19. Feldt, K.S., Ryden, M.B., and Miles, S., "Treatment of Pain in Cognitively Impaired Compared with Cognitively Intact Older Patients with Hip Fractures." *Journal of the American Geriatrics Society*: 46:1079–1085: 1998.

20. Feldt, K.S., "The checklist of Non-Verbal Pain Indicators (CNPI)." *Pain Management Nursing*: 1(1),13–21:2000.

21. Gracely, R.H., "Evaluation of Multi-Dimensional Pain Scales." *Pain: 48*: 297–300: 1992.

22. Graham, C., Bond, S., Gerkovich, M., and Cook, M., "Use of the McGill Pain Questionnaire in the Assessment of Cancer Pain: Replicability and Consistency." *Pain*: 8: 377–387: 1980.

23. Daut, R.L., Cleeland, C.S., and Flanery, R., "Development of the Wisconsin Brief Pain Questionnaire to Assess Pain in Cancer or Other Diseases. *Pain*: 17:197–210: 1983.

24. D'Arcy, Y.M., "Patient-Controlled Analgesia (PCA) with Fast-Track Coronary Artery Bypass (CABG) Patients." *Proceedings at the 9th World Congress on Pain*, Vienna Austria. August 22–27, 1999. p.76.

25. Puntillo, K.A, and Weiss, S.J., "Pain: Its Mediators and Associated Morbidity in Critically Ill Cardiovascular Patients." *Nursing Research*: 43(1), 31–36: 1994.

26. American Academy of Pain Medicine, American Pain Society, American Society of Addiction Medicine. *Definitions Related to the Use of Opioids for the Treatment of Pain. Consensus Statement,* 2001.

27. Weissman, D.E., and Haddox, J,D., "Opioid Pseudoaddiction—An Iatrogenic Syndrome." *Pain,* (36):363–366: 1989.

Additional Reading

American Geriatrics Society Panel on Chronic Pain in Older Persons, "The Management of Pain in Older Persons." *Journal of the American Geriatrics Society*: 46: 635–651: 1998.

Bates, B., *A Guide to Physical Examination and History Taking*, Fifth Edition. Philadelphia: JB Lippincott Company. 1991.

Camp, L.D., and O'Sullivan, P.S., "Comparison of Medical, Surgical and Oncology Patients' Description of Pain and Nurses' Documentation of Pain Assessments." *J. Adv. Nurs*: 12:593–598:1987.

D'Arcy, Y.M., *Implementation of a Pain Resource Nurse Program*. Unpublished thesis. Winona State University: 1995.

Faries, J.E., Mills, D.S., Goldsmith, K.W., Phillips, K.D., and Orr, J., "Systematic Pain Records and Their Impact on Pain Control." *Cancer Nursing*:14(6):306–313:1991.

Grossman, S.A., Sheidler, V.R., Swedeen, K., Mucenski, J., and Piantadosi, S., "Correlation of Patient and Caregiver Ratings of Cancer Pain." *Journal of Pain and Symptom Management*: 6(2):53–57.

Higginson, I.J., "Innovations in Assessment: Epidemiology and Assessment of Pain in Advanced Cancer." *Proceedings of the 8th World Congress on Pain, Progress in Pain Research and Management*, Vol.8, edited by Jensen, T.S., Turner, J.A., Wiesenfeld-Hallin, Z. Seattle: IASP Press, 1997.

JCAHO web site: Pain Management Standards. Web site: http//www.jcaho.org; vol 2000, JCAHO 2000.

Kehlet, H., "Effect of Pain Relief on the Surgical Stress Response." *Regional Anesthesia*: 21(6S):35–37: 1996.

Manz, B.D., Mosier, R., Nusser-Gerlach, M.A., Bergstrom, N., and Agrawal, S., "Pain Assessment in the Cognitively Impaired and Unimpaired Elderly." *Pain Management Nursing*: 1(4):106–115, 2000.

McCaffery, M., and Ferrell, B., "How Would You Respond to These Patients in Pain?" *Nursing* 91 :21(6):34–37, 1991.

McCaffery, M., Ferrel, B.R., "Patient Age: Does It Affect Your Pain Control Decisions?" *Nursing* 91: 21(9):44–48, 1991

McCaffery, M., and Ferrell, B.R., "Does the Gender Gap Affect Your Pain Control Decisions?" *Nursing* 91: 22(8): 48–51, 1992.

McGuire, D., "Comprehensive and Multidimensional Assessment and Measurement of Pain." *Journal of Pain and Symptom Management*: 7(5): 312–316: 1992.

Melzack, R., "The McGill Pain Questionnaire: Major Properties and Scoring Methods." *Pain*: 1: 277–299: 1975.

Melzack, R., "The Short-Form McGill Pain Questionnaire." *Pain:* 30: 191–197: 1987

Puntillo, K.A., White, C., Morris, A.B., Perdue, S.T., Stanik-Hutt, J., Thompson, C.L., and Wild, L.R., "Patients' Perceptions and Responses to Procedural Pain: Results from the Thunder Project II." *American Journal of Critical Care*;10(4), 238–251: 2001

Zalon, M.L., "Nurses' Assessment of Postoperative Patients' Pain." *Pain*: 54: 329–334: 1993.

Chapter 3

Pain Management

Dorene A. O'Hara, MD, MSE

3.1 Acute Pain: Introduction

A. Assessment

It is critical for the healthcare practitioner to assess acute pain properly. Errors in fundamental assessment procedures, that is, history, physical examination, and testing, can be negligent errors. (See the case examples throughout this chapter.) Attorneys handling personal injury cases understand that pain is one of the largest components of damages. Appropriate pain management following an injury can improve the quality of the plaintiff's life, whereas ineffective pain management leads to added misery.

B. Pain as a signal of injury

The official definition of pain from the IASP (International Association for the Study of Pain) is: An unpleasant sensory and emotional experience associated with actual or potential tissue damage or described in terms of such damage.[1]

Tip

Pain is first and foremost a signal of injury or impending injury and should be evaluated thoroughly and promptly.

"Pain" occurs when a person processes stimuli from (or which appear to come from) peripheral sites in the body which are identified as unpleasant. Biologically, we are designed to react in an aversive fashion to tissue injury, for our own survival. Pain behavior includes immediate attempts at avoiding the injury, physical attempts to modify the response (i.e., putting ice on a sprain to decrease the pain of inflammation), crying out for help, and learning for future avoidance.

Thus, because of the rapidity of learning from previous pain and injury, the patient with pain, even the very young patient, will have insights into the severity of the noxious injury. The patient must be listened to! (With children, the parents must also be listened to.)

Pain signals are carried along nerve pathways into the spinal cord. Many local, systemic, and central nervous system neurotransmitters and hormones carry or modulate pain signals, as described below.

C. The neurobiology of pain

After injury, chemical mediators of pain are released locally in the injured area, causing localized swelling, pain, and redness, and setting off a chain reaction for more plasma factors and white blood cells to come to begin the healing process. Substance P (named P for pain) helps carry the pain message to the spinal cord.

In the cord, pain signals are transmitted up via the dorsal horn along several types of pathways at varying speeds (see Figure 3.1). Some receptors in the spinal cord "remember" this pain and can recall the response later, especially if the area is injured again. These are called N-methylD-aspartate receptors (NMDA) for the chemicals they bind to. These receptors are critical for general learning and memory in the brain, as well,

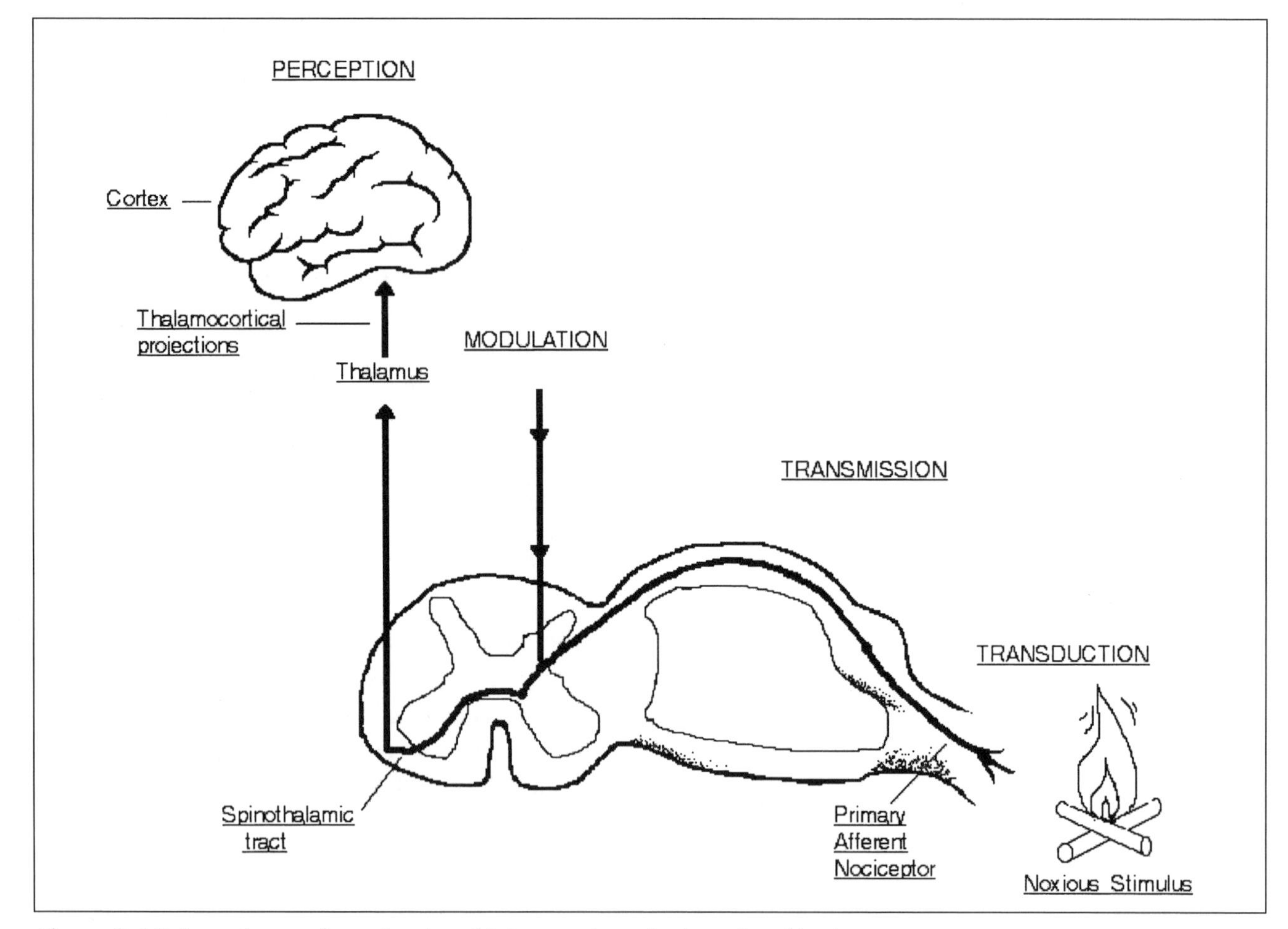

Figure 3.1 *Pain pathways from the site of injury to the spinal cord and brain*

which indicates how important the acute pain response can be in survival. Chemical factors or hormones for the "fight or flight" response are released from both the central nervous system and glandular structures, including epinephrine, to increase heart rate and breathing, and improve muscle strength. Treatments for both acute and chronic pain are often designed to inhibit these complex responses at varying levels in the body and brain.

Many of the chemicals released increase the pain and inflammatory response as a part of healing and injury avoidance. These generally act at peripheral sites such as in the skin or muscle. Other chemicals modify the response or even inhibit the pain response, for example, the endorphins. These factors generally act centrally, in the spinal cord or brain. See Table 3.1.

Receptors have been identified for the action of many of the body's chemical factors. In turn, drugs have been developed to act at these receptors and to stop the pain and injury cascade. Drugs such as the narcotics, or opiates, work as natural endorphin receptors in the body. See Table 3.2. Endorphins and opiates modify pain responses in several locations via inhibition.

Acute pain from peripheral structures tends to be localizable. (The patient can identify the site of injury.) Sites on the skin can serve as markers for the location of deeper nerve injury, since precise nerve pathways send fibers to the skin. This is called "innervation," and a classic diagram is used in clinical practice to identify the nerves involved when pain from the spinal cord or major nerves occurs in the skin. This is called the diagram of "skin dermatomes," shown in Figure 3.2.

Inflammation plays an important role in peripheral pain. Examples of this type of injury include muscle

Table 3.1
Neurobiology of Pain

Central Inhibition of Pain	Peripheral Activation of Pain
endorphins	Substance P
gamma-amino benzoic acid (GABA)	bradykinin
serotonin (central brain, mood effects)	serotonin (tissues, pain-causing effects)
melatonin	histamine
enkephalins	prostaglandins

Table 3.2
Nervous System Activity in Chronic Pain

System	Likely Effect	Drugs Acting on System
NMDA receptor	triggers pain memory	Ketamine
Substance P	chemical pain signal	Capsaicin
stress response (e.g. epinephrine)	multiple	Clonidine (by inhibition)
prostaglandins	inflammatory response	aspirin, non-steroidal anti-inflammatory drugs, COX-2 inhibitors
histamine	inflammatory response	antihistamines
central nervous system	neuroexcitation	anticonvulsants
brain serotonin, other substances	low levels facilitate pain	antidepressants

Note: Endorphins and opiates modify pain responses in several locations via inhibition.

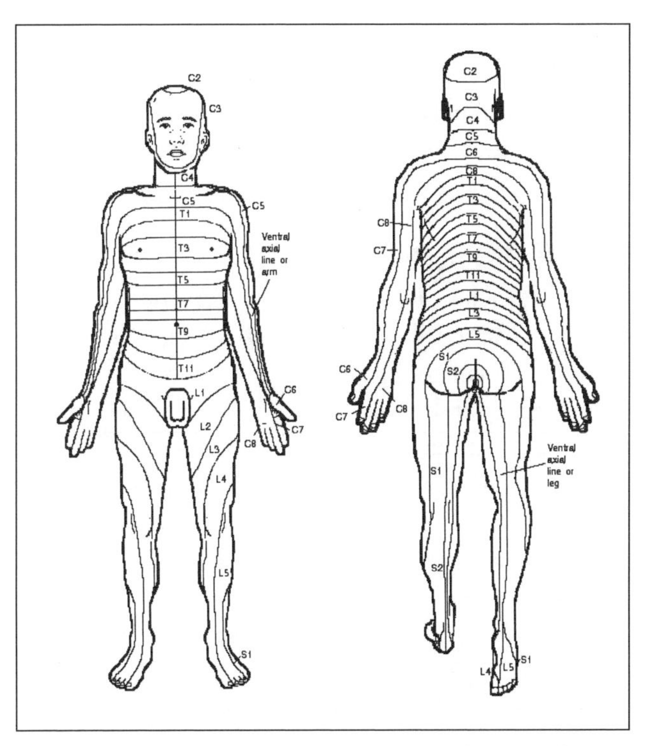

__Figure 3.2__ The skin dermatomes, sites corresponding to spinal cord innervation

injuries, fractures, and burns. Visceral pain comes from deeper internal structures, and is usually poorly localized and not represented by the dermatomes. Examples include the early abdominal pain of acute appendicitis, heartburn, or stomach cramps.

The goal of pain interventions is therefore twofold: (1) to assess the pain as a signal of tissue damage, stop the damage, and preserve life, and (2) to relieve suffering.

3.2 Types of Acute Pain

A. Headache

Headache is one of the most common pain complaints, responsible for billions of dollars each year in medical costs (U.S.).[2] Features of headaches are shown in Table 3.3. Headache is considered a type of chronic pain, however severe headaches can be acute and signal not a chronic process, (no matter how severe the pain) but rather an acute process. For this reason, all headaches must be evaluated and taken seriously. They can signal a chronic benign (i.e., noncancerous) process, brain tumor, undiagnosed trauma or an acute vascular event.[3,4] See Table 3.4.

Assessment of headache includes history and physical, and may include MRI or CAT scan, EEG, vascular studies of the brain, skull and neck x-ray films.

B. Acute backache

Acute backache can occur with sudden ruptured disk, muscular strain, and trauma or falls. Sometimes it occurs for no anatomically understood reason at all. Acute back injuries are common in those who lift or sit for prolonged periods for their jobs—construction workers, repair workers, nurses and nurse's aides, truck and bus drivers, and delivery staff. However, many people injure themselves at home and can usually cite the onset of the event.

Acute backache can also occur with metastatic cancer and spinal lesions. Patients with osteoporosis can fracture vertebral bodies with otherwise minor slips and falls.

Assessment includes history and physical, lumbar or other spine x-ray films, and usually includes CAT scan or MRI if pain persists. Spinal tap or EMG may be indicated, depending on the likely diagnosis.

Table 3.3
Types of Common Headache and Facial Pain

Headache Classification	Features
common migraine	one-sided, pulsatile quality, sensitivity to light and sound, nausea, more common in women than men
classic migraine	"common" features, plus aura (foreknowledge headache is coming) and sometimes visual changes (lights, etc.)
tension headache	pain in back or sides of head, bilateral, pressing quality
trigeminal neuralgia	severe facial pain, shock- or knife-like, sensitivity to touch
cluster headache	severe facial pain, 30–90 min long, awakes patient from sleep, behind the eye, tearing and nasal congestion, sensitivity to alcohol consumption, more common in men than women
temporal arteritis	fever, general fatigue, weakness, body stiffness, mostly in elderly patients, tender at temples
post-traumatic	variable character, usually fades with time

C. Trauma

Acute pain with trauma requires thorough and complete assessment by an emergency medicine trained physician or other physician trained in trauma care. Patients may not recall all events, especially if there is head trauma.

Patients with moderate to severe acute pain after trauma should be sent to the ER by the healthcare provider, even from the doctor's office or by the doctor's triage nurse after phone consultation. If in doubt, the patient should be sent by ambulance, as ambulance arrival alters the triage order in many ERs. (That is, patients who are sent by ambulance are usually evaluated first, and patients who walk in may be incorrectly assumed to be low priority. It is the responsibility of the triage nurse and physician to evaluate these cases properly.)

D. Surgical pain

Postoperative patients typically suffer from inadequately treated pain. The reasons for this persistent

Table 3.4
Severe Headaches
(Those Requiring Immediate Intervention)

Underlying Pathology	Features
brain tumor	lethargy, protracted vomiting, visual changes, various physical signs depending on type
vascular event (arteriovenous malformation, aneurysm, subarachnoid bleed)	severe headache (worst ever), neurologic changes, fainting
meningitis	headache with stiff neck, history of fever or infection, skin rash, lethargy
special	positional headache after spinal tap, epidural or spinal anesthesia, or back surgery: requires assessment by anesthesiologist

failure of medical care include inadequate education of physicians, nurses, patients, and the public, fears of drug overdose (these fears vastly overrate the risk of overdose), sparse staffing of nurses on the hospital units, and, sadly, indifference.

In this era of cost controls, insurers do not choose to reimburse most anesthesia services for postoperative pain control. Many medical practitioners do not know the appropriate doses and dosing intervals for analgesic drugs. However, rarely does this kind of error of omission reach the level of medical malpractice.

Surgical patients can receive IV, IM, or oral medications, regional techniques, patient-controlled analgesia, and even alternative or complementary techniques to relieve pain.

E. Angina/chest pain

This type of pain can signal a severe cardiac event such as a myocardial infarction (MI), pathology in the lung, disease in the gastrointestinal (GI) tract, anxiety, or musculoskeletal inflammation of chest wall structures.[5] The patient with new acute chest pain is always sent immediately for emergency workup, and the less serious or life-threatening diagnoses then can be evaluated over time. See Table 3.5 for symptoms of angina and other chest pain. Patients with known angina who may be having MI are now encouraged to take an aspirin immediately (in some cases this may be modified if they have severe bleeding at the same time). Cardiac damage due to ischemia (reduction in blood supply causing tissue death) can be prevented with rapid anticoagulant therapy in the hospital, so early referral to the hospital is critical. Failure to diagnose a myocardial infarction correctly is a common cause of liability in the emergency department.

F. Abdominal pain

Moderate or severe acute abdominal pain can signal a host of serious internal problems, many of which require speedy surgery. Although gastroenteritis can present like an acute surgical abdomen, such infection or food-related diagnosis is the diagnosis of exclusion. Patients with acute abdominal pain (see Table 3.6) should seek immediate medical attention. See Silen[6] for an excellent medical review. (Note: the information in Table 3.6 is not meant to be an exhaustive list or to replace having the patient fully examined by a physician.) The history and physical exam are extremely important—thus, the medical practitioner or triage nurse should err on the side of caution when evaluating abdominal pain complaints. The location of the pain, associated tenderness, appetite, nausea, vomiting, or diarrhea, onset with types of foods or between meals,

Table 3.5
Angina Compared to Other Types of Chest Pain

Symptoms	Primary Diagnosis	Rule-Out Diagnoses
chest heaviness, especially spreading to left arm, jaw, back	angina	thoracic/aortic aneurysm, pericarditis, pulmonary embolism, tumors of chest wall or breast, herpes zoster, GI causes
heartburn related to meals, relieved with antacids	ulcer, gastrointestinal reflux disease	angina, systemic causes listed above
chest pain, worsened when one presses on chest wall	musculoskeletal costochondritis, rarely, neck injury	life-threatening diagnoses listed above

previous surgical history, obstetric/gynecologic history, urinary symptoms, for example, are all important clues.

Tip

Abdominal pain is one of the most challenging problems in medicine.

G. Invasive cancer pain

Cancer pain is usually considered under the heading of chronic pain. It is dealt with more fully in Chapter 11, "Cancer Pain and Suffering." When a tumor invades soft tissue or bone, the destruction of normal tissue and pressure causes release of inflammatory pain mediators. New pain in any patient with a history of cancer (or any chronic pain) must be evaluated thoroughly. Tumors may be treated with radiation therapy or chemotherapy; inflammatory components respond well to combinations of anti-inflammatory drugs, narcotics, and regional anesthesia.

The World Health Organization (WHO) has published a recommendation (called the pain treatment ladder as shown in Table 3.7) for achieving freedom from cancer pain.[7] In the table, non-opioid drugs refer to agents such as aspirin and the nonsteroidal anti-inflammatory drugs (NSAIDs). Opiates refer to drugs such as morphine and oxycodone, and adjuvants refer to agents which can enhance pain relief, such as the antihistamines. Since there are safe ways to treat even severe pain, there is no longer an excuse for clinicians to let cancer patients suffer.

H. Labor pain

The pain of labor for childbirth has little or no intrinsic value to the mother or the baby, despite biblical references to the contrary. It is a side effect of the essential uterine contractions which allow birth. (Vaginal birth has intrinsic value over cesarean section to both mother and baby. Cesarean section is performed when vaginal delivery is dangerous for the mother or the baby.)

Anesthesiologists have developed excellent techniques for easing the pain of labor, especially the epidural anesthetic, which allows the mother to rest during the middle phase of labor and decreases the tendency for hyperventilation and decreased uterine blood flow. Intravenous narcotics, given often in early labor, pass via the placenta to the baby. They are withheld late in labor because they will depress newborn respiration. Thus, a woman who, for one reason or another, does not have an epidural and, near delivery, experiences pain, may not be able to have any pain relief at that point for her delivery other than a local injection or block by the obstetrician.

For cesarean section, the ideal anesthetic is either spinal or epidural, allowing the mother and father (or birth coach) to experience the baby's birth together. General anesthesia is more dangerous to the pregnant patient because of the large abdomen, effects on lung function, increased risks and difficulty with intubation, and full stomach. General anesthesia also relaxes the uterus and can contribute to postpartum bleeding. The baby does receive small amounts of general anesthesia

Table 3.6
Typical Features of Abdominal Pain and Source

Symptom Complex	Likely Diagnoses
localized pain, worse with movement, cough or touch, often associated with muscle spasm	perforation of internal organ, bacterial source, pelvic inflammatory disease, pancreatitis
cramping, intermittent, usually poorly localized pain	obstructed intestine, ureter, or part of the biliary tree (i.e. gallbladder)
cramping in suprapubic (i.e. bladder) area, tenderness with firm tapping over back near kidneys, flank pain	obstructed ureter or kidney stone
sudden or slow onset pain, often diffuse, usually not tender, continuous pain	vascular embolism or thrombosis or rupture

*These are the most common diagnoses, but abdominal pain can be difficult to evaluate.

Table 3.7
WHO 3-Step Ladder for Cancer Pain Treatment

Step 1	non-opioid +/– adjuvant drug therapy
Step 2	opiate for mild to moderate pain + non-opioid +/– adjuvant as needed
Step 3	opioid for moderate to severe pain +/– non-opioid +/– adjuvant as needed

*The goal: freedom from cancer pain. See Endnote 7

during a cesarean section; however, intravenous narcotics and benzodiazepines are avoided until after delivery.

I. Pediatric pain

Pain in children has become a major concern for healthcare professionals. Pediatric patients cannot understand painful events, thus, they experience intense fear and anxiety with any painful procedure. Presence of the parent is generally beneficial, which explains recent trends toward twenty-four-hour stays for parents in pediatric wards, parents in the OR for anesthetic induction, and rapid return of the parent to the child in the surgical recovery room.

Numerous medications and techniques are now available, so painful injections should be kept to a minimum. A topical local anesthetic (EMLA—eutectic mixture of local anesthetics) can eliminate the pain of an IV insertion. EMLA cream or ethyl chloride spray can be used in the pediatrician's office to minimize the pain of vaccinations. Regional or local anesthesia can and should be used during surgical procedures whenever possible for postoperative pain control. See Chapter 6, "Pain and Suffering of Children," for more information.

Tip

Minimizing pain and suffering for children and adolescents is a major concern of modern pediatric care in hospitals and clinics.

J. Sickle cell crisis

Patients with sickle cell anemia may undergo "crisis" in which red blood cells collapse to a sickle shape in large numbers, clumping in capillaries, bones, and joints and causing intense pain. Cold temperature, decreased levels of blood oxygen, dehydration, and recent infection increase risk of this event. Treatment is geared to improving red cell function and reversing the process while relieving pain and preserving organ function.

3.3 Acute Pain: Conclusion

How does the clinician know the difference between a critical event and one less serious? This can be difficult. However, it is a part of all general medical training for physicians. Nursing professionals are also trained to evaluate pain and emergency patients, to make an assessment and "triage" the critical injuries. Table 3.8 lists some symptoms which require immediate attention.

Often patients will find self-help remedies, adding these to the pain relievers given, and manage their pain at home. It is better for the patient if he or she feels comfortable speaking about extra or alternative therapies with the doctor or nurse.

Acute pain should be considered a sign of tissue injury until proven otherwise, and once the etiology is discovered, therapy should be directed both at elimination of further injury and direct relief of the pain.

3.4 Acute Pain Cases

The anesthesiologist, especially one who works with the hospital-based pain service, may be called to assist with most of the patient problems listed above, usually as a consultant. The anesthesiologist must thoroughly understand the differential diagnosis of acute pain, so as not to miss life-threatening disease and mask the symptoms with analgesics. Unfortunately, clinicians tend to err on the other side with acute pain, undertreating even once a diagnosis is made and pain can and should be relieved.

Attorneys involved in evaluating alleged medical malpractice may find that the sudden onset of acute pain is a common variable. In the following cases pain was the common denominator. (These are real cases modified so as not to identify any patient, physician, or institution.)

A. Albert

1. Fact pattern

Albert, a forty-five-year-old male weighing 450 pounds, underwent successful stomach stapling for morbid obesity. Intubation was difficult but was safely accomplished, and the patient initially did well. He was placed on a PCA intravenous pump (patient controlled analgesia) using IV morphine in appropriate doses with good pain relief. Albert began ambulating and taking fluids on the fourth day. On the sixth day, the PCA was discontinued as the patient was tolerating oral pain medication and had decreased pain. On the tenth day, discharge planning was nearly complete; however, the patient complained of increased abdominal pain when walking. He seemed out of sorts. He had no fever. In the afternoon he collapsed with a wound dehiscence (opening) and was rushed for emergency surgery.

In the operating room intubation was very difficult due to neck swelling. The patient suffered a hypoxic event and cardiac arrest. Resuscitation was unsuccessful and chest compressions were complicated by the large chest size. The patient expired on the operating table.

2. Analysis

No suit was filed in this case. The patient was carefully observed, and the dehiscence was not predictable. A large body weight entails risks of difficult postoperative recovery and difficult intubation, facts which were disclosed in the consent. No negligence occurred. In retrospect, the only signs of the event were the increased pain and the patient feeling unwell.

Table 3.8
Summary Table: Pain Symptoms Requiring Immediate Medical Attention

In children: Any severe or continuing pain complaints
In adults: New headache, different from previous headaches
Severe headache, especially with any of the following: throbbing, explosive sensation, protracted nausea or vomiting, visual changes, dizziness, loss of consciousness, or a statement that "this is the worst headache of my life"
Back pain associated with weakness or numbness in legs, or with loss of bladder or bowel control
New back pain in any patient with a history of cancer
Severe abdominal pain, especially with loss of appetite, fever, nausea and vomiting, diarrhea, chills, night sweats, bloody or black stools
Chest pain, heaviness or tightness with or without shortness of breath, especially associated with exercise, cold weather, or after heavy meals
Unexplained continued indigestion, arm pain (especially on the left), or shoulder pain that does not respond immediately to over-the-counter medicines
Severe pain associated with a traumatic physical injury, accident or fall

B. Ben

1. Fact pattern

Ben, a fifteen-year-old retarded male with chronic bowel obstructions, had been in the hospital for one month with bouts of obstruction treated with laxatives and enemas. The patient could only make himself understood to his mother. The patient developed severe abdominal pain on a Friday of a holiday weekend. He moaned and his mother told the doctors that she thought her son was very sick. X-rays of the abdomen were ordered, then a barium enema, but the films were not reviewed by the physicians on call. There was a change of physicians over the weekend with a lack of communication regarding the need to follow up on the films. The attending doctor's notes indicated that he rarely saw the patient himself, leaving the care to unsupervised residents. Ben stopped eating. He began screaming and crying and was restrained. His mother became upset with the nursing staff over the care and was thrown out of the hospital.

After two days of severe pain, no oral intake, and minimal IV fluid administration, the x-rays were finally read. The patient now had sunken eye sockets, appeared severely dehydrated, and screamed when touched. A GI consult was called. Ben had necrotic bowel. He died, massively dehydrated, separated from his mother, and in pain.

2. Analysis

This case settled in favor of the plaintiff (mother) for both negligent medical care and pain and suffering. The grossest medical errors included lack of proper follow-up, failure to review x-rays in a timely fashion, inadequate resident supervision, ignoring new pain, ignoring legitimate parental concern, and failing in even routine testing, vital sign and fluid monitoring.

C. Carol

1. Fact pattern

Carol, a twenty-six-year-old female, was in labor with her first child. The patient was small in size and the obstetrician expected a possible forceps or cesarean delivery due to cephalopelvic disproportion (i.e., the baby's head might be too large to pass the mother's bony pelvic opening). The anesthesiologist was called for an epidural. Carol initially did not want an epidural.

The obstetrician and anesthesiologist explained together the risks of urgent cesarean section or forceps delivery with possible injury to the baby or risk under general anesthesia. (Urgent general anesthesia under these circumstances entails additional risk, including aspiration of stomach contents, failed intubation and hypoxic injury to mother or baby, and increased blood loss due to anesthetic effects on uterine relaxation.) The patient refused the epidural.

At a cervical dilation of 7 cm (10 cm is full dilation) Carol was in severe pain, and labor was not progressing well. She agreed to an epidural injection. During placement of the catheter, the patient was in severe pain and was unable to sit still. A wet tap occurred on first attempt. (The needle nicked the dura, causing a CSF, or cerebral spinal fluid, leak and headache.) The patient began to complain of headache. The anesthesiologist made a second attempt at another interspace and placed the epidural without further problems. The headache was somewhat relieved with the epidural.

The patient eventually had a cesarean section twelve hours later, and the same epidural was re-dosed successfully for surgery. The baby was blue on delivery but the second Apgar score was 8 (with 10 the highest possible score) and the baby pinked up. The baby went to the regular nursery.

On the first postoperative day, Carol again had a headache which occurred when she sat up or walked and disappeared if she was flat. The anesthesiology service did an epidural blood patch. This was performed by placing an epidural needle in the site of wet tap. A second assistant removed sterile blood from the patient, which was injected into the epidural needle. The patient had immediate relief of the headache and went home on the fourth day. She sought the services of an attorney with a claim of a severe headache after delivery.

2. Analysis

There was no medical negligence in this case. This is a typical case with expected risks, well-managed by nursing, obstetrics, pediatrics, and anesthesia.

D. David

1. Fact pattern

David, a fifty-year-old male, had spinal anesthesia for hernia surgery. He was not informed of the risks or alternatives, including general or even local anesthesia with sedation. The patient had a spinal in the sitting position, and during the needle placement he felt ripping pain down one leg, then the other. David screamed loudly enough to bring the surgeon into the room from the scrub sink in the hall. The anesthesiologist continued without questioning the patient or stopping at all. The patient noted that the pain stopped, then he went numb from the waist. Postoperatively, David had leg weakness, bladder paralysis, and numbness along multiple nerve distributions.

2. Analysis

The documents showed that the anesthesiologist used a local anesthetic known to be associated with nerve damage in recent years. Negligence occurred also with lack of informed consent and with the anesthesiologist continuing despite the patient screaming in pain. The pain in this case was a sign of nerve injury. Injecting the local anesthetic caused toxic and traumatic permanent damage to the nerves supplying the cauda equina (nerve roots leaving the spinal cord). The patient received a very large settlement from both the doctor and hospital after one day of trial.

E. Edwin

1. Fact pattern

Edwin was admitted to a medical center for control of severe headache. The patient was given a PCA pump which administered morphine. Edwin died on the day after admission. The coroner ruled that the patient died due to human error because the pump was improperly programmed by the nursing staff. His death was presumably caused by morphine overdose. The surviving spouse obtained settlements against both the hospital (for the nurses) and the pump's manufacturer.[8]

2. Analysis

Properly programmed morphine PCA pumps should not cause a drug overdose. Nursing duties include frequent checks on the patient's vital signs during the first twenty-four hours of PCA use and review of medication usage and documentation on the pain flowsheet, as well as standard pump programming. All personnel using PCA pumps must receive instruction on safety and usage.

3.5 Chronic Pain

A. Assessment

Patients typically are asked to describe the location of the pain, whether it travels from one place in the body to another (medically termed "radiation"), and its character. The character of the pain is extremely important. Words such as sharp, dull, aching, burning, pressure, and so on give clues as to the pain's origins. The intensity of the pain should be rated on a scale of 0–10, with zero being no pain and 10 the worst pain imaginable, just as with acute pain.

However, it is important to recognize that chronic pain from any source has other features which make chronic pain a disease state unto itself. Most people who develop pain on a chronic basis, whether from an injury, a debilitating disease, a common complaint like headache, or without any obvious cause have certain similar features. This is called the "chronic pain syndrome." Assessment of chronic pain includes an evaluation of the complex features of this syndrome in addition to any identifiable root cause.[2]

B. Chronic pain syndrome

Once pain becomes chronic, the mind and body begin to manifest changes which tend to imprint both pain sensations and what clinicians call "pain behavior" on the central nervous system. Pain behavior may include decreasing activity, avoiding movement, sleeping more, and manifesting signs of depression. Reasons for these changes in sensations and behavior are only partly understood. Even if the patient's complaints and behavior seem excessive to the observer, they may be honest responses and not malingering. Malingering is not common, and distress is often misinterpreted as inappropriate behavior or overreaction. Physicians experienced in pain management and evaluation can usually tell the difference. Table 3.9 is a two-column list of chronic pain characteristics.

Tip

Pain exists if the patient says it exists.

Typically, on an acute basis, when receptors in the body react to a pain stimulus, they fire off signals to the spinal cord, triggering a cascade of hormone and neurotransmitter release, especially if danger is present (the fight or flight response). Avoidance behavior and learning about danger take place. The pain serves to remind the injured patient to rest while the body heals. There are generally no long-term ill effects from the pain itself, if the injury completely heals. See Figure 3.3.

The patient with chronic pain quickly learns that standard avoidance behaviors and rest only partly work. Chronic pain is aggravated by stress, lack of sleep, dietary factors, and personal problems at home or at work. Quick fixes are hard to come by, and the pain recurs, often unpredictably, profoundly affecting every aspect of the patient's existence. Relationships, work, and health suffer. The patient feels victimized. No one wants to hear the complaints anymore. Often the patient looks just fine on the outside but is suffering terribly on the inside.

Table 3.9
Chronic Pain Symptoms/Features of Chronic Pain

Commonly described features of the chronic pain syndrome are:	
severe pain, constant or waxing and waning	altered sleep
requirement for long term pain medication	anxiety
limitations in activity and mobility	depression
effects on social relationships	physical tension
effects on sexual drive, function, or both	anger
feelings of helplessness	changes in appetite
decreased job performance	alterations in bowel habits
frustration with doctors	focusing blame on self, family, the system

Tip

Chronic pain is a different phenomenon from acute pain, in its effects on the body and mind, and in the goals of treatment.

The gate control theory, developed by Wall and Melzack,[9] helps explain why a variety of treatment methods may affect both chronic and acute pain, and why the attorney may see the plaintiff undergo several pain treatment courses. The theory suggests that numerous stimuli can reach the spinal cord and then the brain from the sensors in the body. These stimuli can be modulated by chemical effects (internal hormones, neurotransmitters, or external drugs) in the brain, spinal cord, or peripheral receptors or the bloodstream; they can be modulated by cognitive and subconscious brain activity and by physical methods, including "alternative" methods. See Table 3.10 for a list of factors involved in control of the "pain gate."

Physical methods such as physical therapy and massage, psychological methods such as "talk" therapies and relaxation techniques, and patient self-help such as the pain diary are integral parts of treatment, along with judicious use of drug therapy and medical or surgical procedures. Figure 3.4 illustrates the many factors which interact in causing chronic pain.

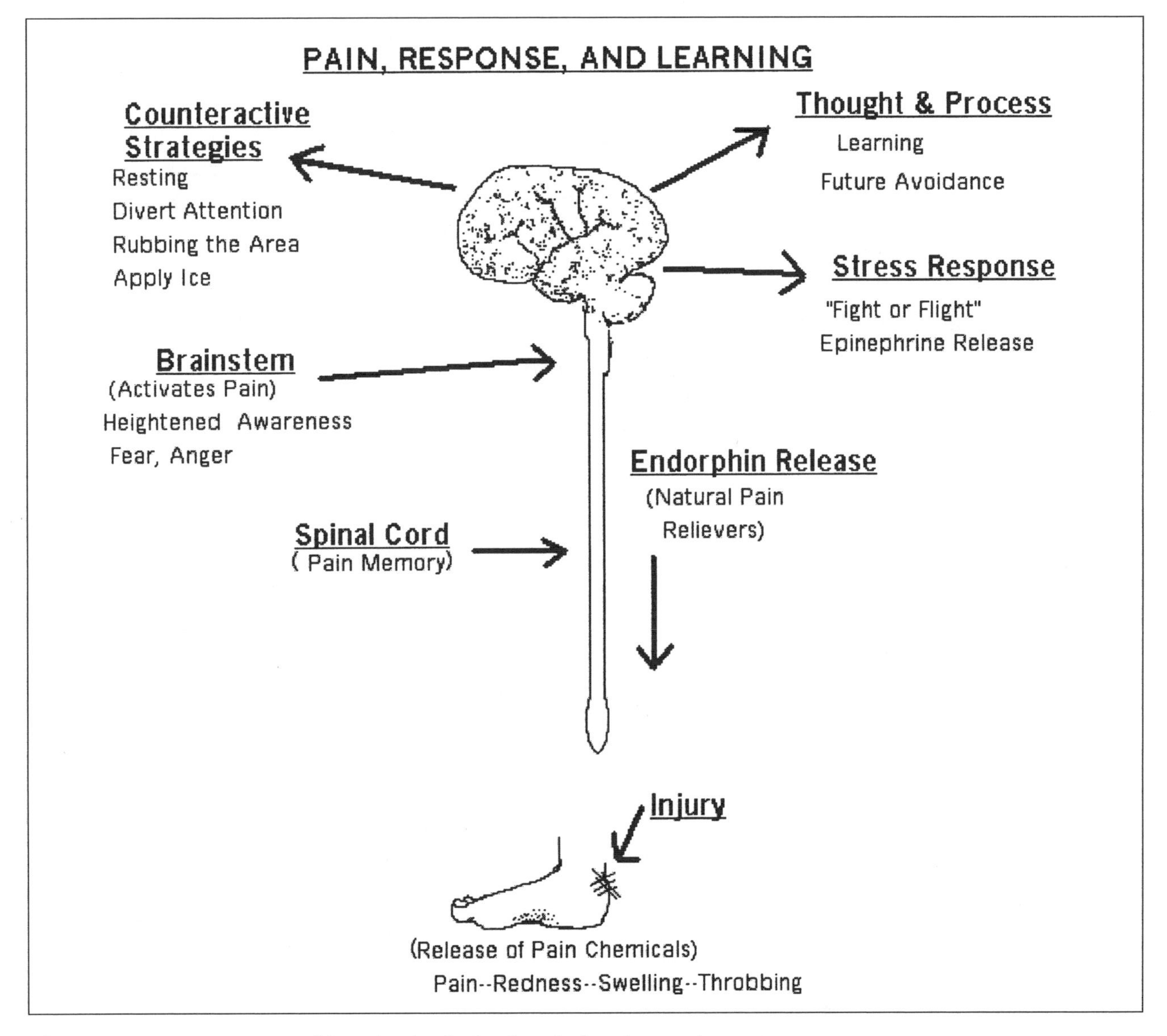

Figure 3.3 *Pain, response and learning in the body, mind and central nervous system*

C. Types of chronic pain

1. Headache

Headache may be an acute problem (see above), but more commonly it is a chronic one. Headaches range from minor tension or migraine-like types to major, debilitating conditions such as cluster headache or trigeminal neuralgia. Headache can also be the presenting symptom for temporomandibular joint (TMJ) or ophthalmalogic problems, impending stroke, aneurysm rupture, and brain tumor. Therefore, new headaches should always be evaluated.

The patient's description of symptoms is very important. Please refer to Table 3.3 for typical headache types and symptoms.

2. Low back pain

This is another common complaint. The anatomy of the spinal column is such that many activities—prolonged sitting or standing, lifting, reaching—can put the spinal column at risk for sudden muscle strain or intervertebral disc protrusion. Muscle strain is often deep and can involve nerves causing severe pain; disc protrusion can cause neurologic symptoms such as pins and needles sensation, numbness or weakness in the lower extremities, and bowel or bladder symptoms (via the lower sacral nerves). Most low back pain is nonspecific; that is, no anatomic basis for the complaint is identifiable.

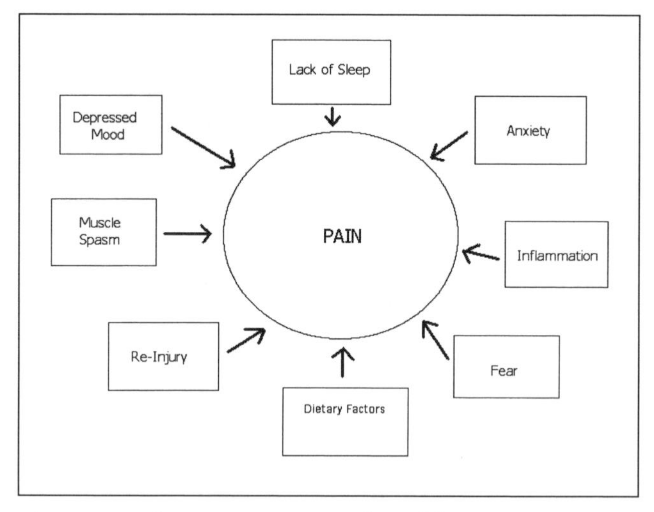

Figure 3.4 *The symptom complex of factors interacting in chronic pain*

Table 3.10
Factors that Close the Pain Gate

Method	Proposed Mechanism of Effect
rubbing the area	low-level stimulation
distraction, especially humor	endorphin release
electrical stimulation (TENS,* PENS,* electroacupuncture)	low-level stimulation
body massage, physical techniques (chiropractic, osteopathy)	endorphin release
exercise, especially stretching	low-level stimulation, endorphin release
heat and ultrasound	increased blood flow, release of tissue spasm
cold packs, ice	slowing of signal from tissue to brain, local factors (less swelling)
acupuncture, moxibustion (a heat form of acupuncture)	low-level stimulation, endorphin release, other factors (as yet unidentified)

*TENS is transcutaneous electrical nerve stimulation, with electrodes applied to the skin; PENS is percutaneous electrical nerve stimulation, with needle electrodes inserted into muscle and subcutaneous tissue. See Melzack and Wall (1965).[8] These techniques may act by means of more than one mechanism.

People who do not exercise regularly and who do not strengthen their abdominal muscles are at increased risk for back injury with even minor exertion. And most people do not know how properly to tilt the pelvis and use the legs to assist in lifting. People who are more physically fit are at lower risk for minor injury but can still do major damage if they are not careful with lifting.

Problems such as back pain (or headache, for that matter) are often accompanied by myofascial pain (also known as trigger points). These are knots of tightened muscle along a host of body points, many of which are also acupuncture points. Pain specialists, physical therapists, chiropractors, and doctors of osteopathy (D.O.s) who do manipulation, and massage therapists are well aware of the value of helping to release trigger points when they work on patients with back, head, or neck pain. Table 3.11 shows some features of back pain and potential causes.

3. Visceral abdominal pain

Pain from inside the body, often caused by abnormal contractions of the intra-abdominal structures, or viscera, is known as visceral pain. The pain tends to be nonspecific, does not feel as if it comes from anywhere in particular, and has a cramping quality. Many different body processes can present with this type of pain.

The chronic pain specialist usually sees patients referred from general surgeons, internists, family practitioners, gynecologists, or urologists who have had a full workup for major intra-abdominal or intrathoracic pathology. If the pain is chronic, these patients generally have many symptoms of the chronic pain syndrome. The evaluation must include a review of all the workup data (x-rays, scans, blood work, and so forth) and a detailed patient history. Dietary history, personal, social and work histories, history of ethanol intake, tobacco and drug use and, in many cases, the sexual history are critical to understanding the problem. See Table 3.12.

Nonspecific visceral pain can be difficult to treat. Often the patient has been frustrated in a futile search for a "physical" diagnosis, when one cannot be found. This fact does not lessen the reality of the pain. The approach will include multiple modalities.

4. Neuropathic pain

Pain associated with a variety of types of disease and injury can develop the unusual and unpleasant characteristics of neuropathic pain. The name hints at the etiology—damage to nerves. This can occur with demyelinating diseases such as multiple sclerosis, brain or spinal cord lesions, generalized diseases with end-organ damage such as diabetes mellitus, infectious processes such as AIDS or shingles, and inflammatory processes such as pancreatitis. It can also occur after surgical treatment of neck or back pain or any orthopedic surgery.

The hallmark of neuropathic pain is in the patient's description: words like burning, stabbing, tearing, agonizing, and cutting are typical. The pain has such an unpleasant quality to it that often people do not believe the patient. Many patients are labeled hopeless or crazy when they present with neuropathic pain.

Neuropathic pain appears to come from repeated and uncoordinated firing of nerve endings in the damaged area, plus chronic changes in the spinal cord receptors (especially pain receptors like NMDA) and in the central brain. However, the mechanisms are not entirely understood.

Recent advances in pharmacology and neuroscience are helping patients with neuropathic pain. In addition to traditional pain therapies listed in the next section, drugs originally developed for epilepsy have proven helpful. The mechanism of effect is likely the inhibition or slowing of nerve conduction.

Table 3.11
Contributing Causes of Back Pain

Type of Pain	Features
myofascial	tender muscle "knots" or trigger points, worse with movement
disk protrusion or nerve root irritation	postural changes, decreased straight leg raise, radiation of pain or numbness to extremity; may involve bowel/bladder (incontinence)
tumor	pain may not change with movement; may cause neurological changes in legs, bowel, bladder; night pain also is possible
arthritis	pain with movement, morning stiffness, may affect multiple spine levels and neck
infectious	stiffness, general signs (fever, weakness, fatigue) may be present; may have skin rash

*Note: More than one diagnosis may co-exist. A full workup is required to rule out all serious diagnoses. Many psychological and stress-related factors contribute to back pain.

5. Causalgia (reflex sympathetic dystrophy)

This is a severe type of neuropathic injury usually caused by trauma (major or minor). It has other names, including Sudeck's atrophy and, recently, complex regional pain syndrome. For unknown reasons the damaged nerves begin to fire repeatedly, causing not only severe pain of the neuropathic type but also skin, bone, and blood vessel changes.

The affected area is usually in an arm or leg, with an initial red inflammatory reaction that may be misdiagnosed as infection. This is followed in about six weeks with gradual atrophy of the skin and nails, muscle wasting, and blood vessel constriction, along with severe pain and sensitivity to touch and movement. The temperature of the extremity drops, and it often turns blue or white. The pain is so severe that even the lightest touch or motion triggers spasms of pain.

Table 3.12
Visceral/Abdominal Pain

Causes of Abdominal Pain		
appendicitis	cholecystitis	renal stone
pelvic inflammatory disease	aortic aneurysm	ischemia of abdominal vasculature
inflammatory bowel disease	pancreatitis	endometriosis
torsion of ovary	abdominal mass	bowel obstruction
gastroenteritis	herpes zoster	testicular pain
myofascial pain	nerve entrapment syndrome	angina
gastric ulcer	sickle cell crisis	anxiety-related
variety of metabolic and other causes		

*Note: Pelvic (in females) and rectal exams (all patients) are required in evaluating back pain. See Silen's book[6] on the acute abdomen.

Excessive release of stress hormones from the autonomic nervous system (sympathetic activation sets off fight or flight defenses) appears to contribute to RSD since nerve blocks and drugs which inhibit the stress response can help.

Patients with this type of lesion must see an anesthesiologist pain specialist as soon as possible to have the best chance of cure. Current treatment recommendations include sympathetic blocks and physical therapy.

3.6 Treatments for Chronic Pain

Chronic pain is expensive to treat and involves many hidden costs of lost work if associated with disability. Attorneys consider the costs of treatment and losses for disability in the litigation process. Table 3.13 lists some of the costs involved in lost workdays and the medical care of chronic pain problems.

A. Medications

Pharmacologic therapy is extremely important for chronic disease and is becoming more so. In the United States, the Health Care Financing Administration estimated an expenditure of $112 billion for prescription drugs in the year 2000.[10] Drug costs are the fastest rising component of medical expenditures, rising at 15% per year in the United States. The expenditures for prescription drugs in 1999 were $99.6 billion, up from $85.2 billion in 1998. This is close to 10% of the total amount spent in the U.S. on health care.[11]

Tip

Chronic pain is rarely cured with pharmacologic treatment alone, also requiring patient-initiated behavioral changes, reasonable exercise, and often psychological techniques for long-term results.

1. Nonsteroidal anti-inflammatory drugs (NSAIDs)

The first line of medications used to treat almost all types of pain are the nonsteroidal antiinflammatory drugs, commonly abbreviated as NSAIDs. Aspirin (acetylsalicylic acid), which is a derivative of a natural product from the bark of the willow tree, is the prototype of these drugs. This class also includes drugs such as ibuprofen (e.g., Motrin) and naproxen (e.g., Naprosyn). The anti-inflammatory drugs block the activation of the inflammatory mediators of pain at the site of injury and the enzyme cyclo-oxygenase, thus minimizing swelling and pain. They are usually tried, in various combinations, before resorting to narcotics/opioids.

Aspirin and the NSAIDs also prove beneficial for treating the autoimmune disease of rheumatoid arthritis, not only because they inhibit prostaglandins, but also because they inhibit overactivity of the T- and B-white blood cells. (In autoimmune diseases, the body's antibody and cellular defense system against foreign invaders such as bacteria begins to attack itself.)

Aspirin also has the feature of inhibiting clotting of blood platelets. This is one of the side effects of all NSAIDs and can be a potential problem in patients with bleeding disorders. Aspirin has a longer-lasting

Table 3.13
Pain Complaints and Costs

Type of Medical Cost	Amount ($U.S.)	Study
musculoskeletal injury—insurance costs	$40 billion	Snook and Webster (1987)
lost workdays—backache	$28 billion	Rizzo, Abbot and Berger (1998)
medical care (arthritis and rheumatic diseases)	$21 billion	Felts and Yelin (1989)
lost workdays (migraine)	$5–17 billion	Stang and Osterhaus (1993)
medical care (migraine)	$9 billion	Stang and Osterhaus (1993)
medical care, lost workdays, disability	$80 billion (minimum)	Haddox and Bonica (1998)
work-related injuries	$200 billion	Doleys and Doherty (2000)

See O'Hara[2] for further information on healthcare costs.

anticoagulant effect than the other NSAIDs, a property that can sometimes be used to advantage. For example, low doses of aspirin are now used to prevent heart attacks and strokes, since aspirin deters clotting within blood vessels—a major precursor of these catastrophic events. However, these drugs increase bleeding risk from gastric ulcers.

A new kind of cyclo-oxygenase inhibitor, called the COX-2, has turned out to be an excellent pain reliever with fewer side effects than the original NSAIDs. Two of these drugs now available on the market are celecoxib (Celebrex) and rofecoxib (Vioxx). The first type of cyclooxygenase enzyme, the general type described above, has multiple effects on both the inflammatory response and coagulation. The second type, called COX-2, is specifically released in the body in response to tissue injury. Therefore, inhibiting this enzyme does not generally cause side effects in the stomach, kidneys, or blood. Thus, these new drugs may be better for treating of chronic inflammatory pain, such as that of arthritis, than aspirin or another NSAID.

Side effects are much less common with these newer drugs. Because of their specific pain-relieving action and low incidence of side effects, the new COX-2s have become among the most widely prescribed drugs in the United States. However, for patients at risk for cardiovascular disease, taking a COX-2 inhibitor does not protect against stroke or heart attack, the way low-dose aspirin does.

2. Acetaminophen

Acetaminophen, also known as Tylenol, Panadol, or paracetamol, is another effective standard analgesic drug. First introduced in 1893, it did not come into widespread use until after World War II. It is not of the anti-inflammatory class like aspirin, so it has none of aspirin's bleeding or ulcerative side effects.

Acetaminophen is used for the same types of pain as NSAIDs and is quite effective, especially when used in combination with more powerful drugs of the narcotic class. Despite the fact that arthritis has a significant inflammatory component, acetaminophen has also been found to be useful in treating this disease. (However, acetaminophen offers no protection against heart attack or stroke.)

In high doses, acetaminophen can cause severe and even fatal liver damage. The daily adult dose should not exceed 4,000 mg (roughly ten regular-strength pills). This dose limitation poses a problem for patients with chronic pain who are used to taking high doses of the acetaminophen combination drugs (acetaminophen plus a narcotic) such as Percocet (which contains the narcotic oxycodone) or Tylenol #3 or #4 (acetaminophen with codeine in one of two strengths). As the patient increases the daily dose of the narcotic, the acetaminophen dose can reach toxic levels.

3. Narcotics or opiates

Opiates (also called narcotics because they can induce narcosis or sleep) may have been known among the ancient Sumerians and are first referred to in writing by the Greek botanist, Theophrastus, in the third century B.C. In 1806, the chemist Serturner isolated the active agent of the opium poppy, which he named morphine, after Morpheus the Greek god of dreams and son of Sleep.

Various combinations of morphine and the other active ingredients of opium have been used therapeutically throughout history. Opiates have also been known for centuries to have addictive properties. For this reason, chronic pain patients must guard against escalating doses and work with their doctors to limit tolerance. This usually includes substituting other analgesic drugs for narcotics, periodically reducing doses, and, in some cases, going off narcotics altogether.

In the 1980s, scientists discovered various peptides produced within the body and acting at the same sites as the opiates. These peptides bind to specific receptors in the brain, spinal cord, gut, and other tissues.[12] Both the opioid drugs and the internal opioid peptides act at specific receptors in the brain and spinal cord. Activation of the opiate receptors then activates a protein which slows release of neurotransmitters for the pain signal.

These endogenous (produced within the body) opiates are extremely powerful and in the long run prove more effective in modulating chronic pain than opioids taken in as drugs. This is because taking opiates causes changes in the body's receptors, usually by inducing the body to make more receptors. As a result, the response to the drug (based on the molecule of drug interacting with the receptor) is diluted. The body soon requires more and more drug to achieve the same pain-relieving effect—called tolerance.

For at least twenty years it has been known that opiates work in the brain; more recently active sites in the spinal cord were identified. It has been found that opiate receptors are located in other body sites as well. With every injury, new opiate receptors are generated at the site from peripheral nerve endings, so that opiates act right at the source of the pain and injury.

For both moderate and severe pain there are many oral combinations of opiates, including codeine, propoxyphene (Darvon), oxycodone (Percodan) and hydro-codone (Vicodin). For severe pain, oral morphine (such as MS Contin) is very helpful and available for once or twice per day dosing. More drugs continue to become available.

One drug in the opiate class, tramadol (Ultram), is especially useful for some patients with chronic pain due to its weak activity at the opiate receptor plus its effects on increasing serotonin in the brain. Tramadol's dual mechanism of action is associated with less potential for chemical dependence than with standard opiate drugs. It is still a powerful pain reliever, similar to the opiate meperidine (Demerol) in effect, but less potent than morphine.

The narcotic Oxycontin is an extended release painkiller for moderate to severe pain. Its effectiveness is in part the result of its sustained release, which avoids the peaks and dips in pain relief seen with the shorter-acting medications. Oxycontin is also an example of a drug with serious abuse potential. The drug is widely available by prescription for patients with severe pain; however, illegal use of this drug (e.g., intentional drug addiction) is on the rise. There are significant risks with all narcotic medications, especially for people taking other drugs which affect mood or the central nervous system.

4. Benzodiazepines

Often, patients who see a specialist for pain problems are already taking one of the benzodiazepines—drugs like diazepam (Valium), alprazolam (Xanax), lorazepam (Ativan), or triazolam (Halcion). These drugs are primarily intended to treat anxiety disorders and some forms of seizure disorder.[13] Their effects include sedation, loss of memory, muscle relaxation, and a calming effect. They bind to receptors (GABA, or gamma-aminobutyric acid) in the central nervous system and slow or inhibit transmission of nerve impulses. They have no pain relieving effects alone, although they can enhance the effects of opioids if used with them in combination. These drugs also alter normal REM sleep and can therefore cause residual daytime sleepiness which may seriously affect a person's physical and mental performance.

The side effects of the benzodiazepines are significant—long-term dependence is common, tolerance develops, and fatal interactions can occur if they are taken in combination with alcohol.

There is one recently developed nonbenzodiazepine sedative available specifically for sleep. Zolpidem (Ambien) has little effect on REM sleep and therefore is better for insomnia. However, it is only recommended for short-term use (up to several weeks), not chronically. Another new nonbenzodiazepine agent, zaleplon (Sonata) has also been approved for short-term treatment of insomnia. However, all these drugs can interact with other central nervous system depressants, causing severe side effects.

5. Antidepressants

Low doses of certain antidepressants are now well known for their pain-relieving effects. They can be used whether or not the patient is suffering from depression, so the mechanism of effect is not simply elevation of mood.[14]

Antidepressants are grouped in chemical categories by their structure or site of action, such as the tricyclics or the serotonin reuptake inhibitors. The tricyclic antidepressant amitryptilene (brand name Elavil) appears to be the most effective for this indication and is the most commonly used antidepressant for pain management. Another antidepressant, trazodone (Desyrel) is one of the atypical antidepressants (i.e., not a tricyclic or other major class) used sometimes in pain management. It has fewer effects on the heart than the tricyclics. Pamelor is also used in this context because it has fewer side effects.

In the brain, after neurotransmitters are released to initiate a nerve impulse, some of the active molecules are taken back up again into the cells, reaccumulated, and later released again. Reuptake stops the action of the neurotransmitter temporarily. Drugs that block reuptake, like most of the antidepressants, prolong the action of the neurotransmitters. In the brain, this potentially lifts mood. However, the exact mechanism of the effect on pain is unclear.

Because most of the general antidepressants have a sedative effect, they may also prove helpful for the pain patient who suffers from insomnia. The drug is typically taken at night as an aid to sleep. The most common side effects of these drugs are excessive daytime sleepiness, some potential heart rhythm effects, and weight gain.

The neurotransmitter serotonin seems to be important in several conditions, including chronic pain. The newer serotonin-reuptake inhibitors fluoxetine (Prozac), fluvoxamine (Luvox), paroxetine (Paxil), and sertraline (Zoloft) are also used in pain management. They may be helpful for patients who do not need a sedating agent; however, they can sometimes cause anxiety.

The new drug Sarafem for premenstrual syndrome (PMS) is in fact the same medication as Prozac, released with a new name for this new FDA-approved indication. The clinical trials showed that this drug was helpful for this medical problem.

It takes two to three weeks to see the effects of these drugs due to their slow onset of action, so one needs to be patient when starting out this therapy. Likewise, it takes a few weeks for the effects to wear off.

6. Anticonvulsants

Anticonvulsant drugs slow nerve transmission and are, therefore, used in the treatment of seizure disorders such as epilepsy.[15] Because chronic pain problems are often associated with abnormal excitation of nerve impulses, these drugs are also helpful in treating certain types of chronic pain. Examples of such drugs include carbamazepine (Tegretol) and phenytoin (Dilantin). These drugs are used to treat neuralgias (pains due to abnormal signals emitted from nerve bundles or nerve endings) and in pain after nerve injuries due to trauma or some degenerative diseases. They must be given under close medical supervision due to potentially serious side effects.

Anti-seizure agents such as gabapentin (Neurontin) are in common use in the United States for neuralgias and related pain problems. This drug slows nerve transmission by binding to excitatory tissues in the brain, although the exact site of action is yet unknown. It does not bind to the GABA (gamma-amino-benzoic acid) receptor but may affect GABA via an indirect mechanism by altering the speed of nerve signals through sodium or calcium channels in the cell membrane. These channels let charged ions pass to cause an electrical current that propagates the nerve signal. This drug has the benefit of being much safer than the other anticonvulsants in use for chronic pain, with fewer side effects. It has been shown to be helpful in treating particularly difficult problems such as the neuropathy of diabetes. Gabapentin is currently used for a variety of pains associated with nerve injury, including trigeminal neuralgia (a severe type of headache and facial pain), reflex sympathetic dystrophy (severe pain in the extremities), post-herpetic neuralgia (pain after shingles infection), and nerve entrapment syndromes (pain after trauma or surgery). The major common side effect of gabapentin is fatigue.

7. Alpha-2 agonists

The alpha-2 agonists, such as clonidine, block transmission of pain signals by interacting with specific receptors.[16] These are the same receptors involved in the stress response, in particular, in causing the increased pulse and blood pressure that occur when the stress response is activated. These drugs were first formulated as drugs to treat high blood pressure, so when used for pain, they can cause a drop in blood pressure. They block the pain response using a separate pathway from the opiate drugs. As a result, they do not induce opiate tolerance and can be very helpful in the treatment of patients who need high doses of morphine or other narcotics for severe pain, especially cancer pain. A new formulation of clonidine for epidural use, Duraclon, was recently approved as a pain reliever (for administration in an epidural and only by those trained in anesthesia). Another alpha-2 drug, dexmedetomidine, has just become available for use in anesthesia and critical care.

The pain-relieving qualities of the alpha-2 agonists are probably connected with the fact that they block the stress response, acting at the same receptors which respond to epinephrine and norepinephrine. One would expect then that mind/body techniques such as meditation or biofeedback, which help block the stress response, would also help relieve pain—and clinical experience shows this to be true.

8. Ketamine

There is one drug currently in use which acts at the NMDA receptors: those sites responsible for pain memory.[17] This drug, ketamine, has been in use for many years in anesthesia as an anesthetic and pain reliever. Unfortunately, this very powerful drug has several undesirable effects, including effects on the brain (in some cases it produces hallucinations as it is chemically related to LSD and mescaline). Under the right circumstances in anesthesia practice and for conscious sedation for painful medical procedures, it can be used very safely. For example, anesthesiologists and pediatric intensivists use it along with strong intravenous benzodiazepine sedatives for procedures such as bone marrow biopsies in adults and children.

Unfortunately, because of its side effects, this drug is rarely if ever appropriate in chronic pain treatment. As a research tool and a model for other drugs which might target the memory receptor for pain, it will continue to be useful.

9. Capsaicin

One of the primary mediators of pain is called substance P. A specific substance P inhibitor, capsaicin (Zostrix), is prescribed especially as a topical cream. Derived from pepper plants (the plant's scientific name is capsicum), this agent blocks substance P activation in the skin and in subcutaneous tissues. It is therefore very useful in the treatment of difficult pain conditions such as post-herpetic neuralgia (shingles) or other neuropathic pains.

Because an attack of shingles can be treated with antiviral medications and prescription pain-relievers, and because sometimes other tests are indicated to rule out any accompanying problem, persons suffering from shingles should consult a physician immediately.

10. Migraine-specific drugs

For migraine and cluster headache, the class of serotonin agonists such as sumatriptan (Imigran) and related drugs are often prescribed. (Serotonin agonists act as a subtype of the serotonin receptor.) These drugs seem to work by stimulating some constriction of blood vessels (alterations in blood flow are a major causative factor in these vascular headaches) and may also inhibit the release of substance P. They tend to act quickly, whether taken orally or by injection. However, they can raise blood pressure and cannot be used in patients with uncontrolled hypertension or angina.

See Table 3.14 for a list of drug treatments for chronic pain, and their actions.

B. Local anesthetics and nerve blocks

Local anesthetics are very powerful in inhibiting acute pain and in blocking many types of chronic pain, at least temporarily. Many personal injury attorneys are aware that plaintiffs are treated with a variety of local anesthetics and nerve blocks for pain relief.

Tip

Local anesthetic blocks can be very helpful as an adjunct to chronic pain treatment but rarely are 100% effective.

Local anesthetics can be delivered precisely to the site of a nerve which carries the pain signal to the brain, via a carefully performed injection. The needle tip is introduced to a spot just beside, but not within, the nerve sheath. Often the correct placement of the needle is signaled by the patient's reporting a "paresthesia" or electric shock sensation. Alternatively, a nerve stimulator can be attached to a regional block needle to verify correct placement. The stimulator is turned on to a low level, which causes the nerve to fire when the needle is in the correct area. If the needle goes in too far and invades the nerve sheath, the patient will report pain and not just an electric shock sensation. (Further explanation of the intricacies of performance of nerve is outside of the scope of this chapter. Interested readers are referred to texts on regional anesthesia and interventional pain management.)

For chronic pain, repeated nerve blocks can not only block the pain for a few hours but also stop the excitatory cascade (called wind-up) prominent in many types of pain due to nerve or tissue injury. This excitation causes pain to be more intense, to last longer, and to spread beyond the area of the initial injury. In patients with chronic pain, the excitation becomes linked with fear—fear of further injury, fear that the pain will last forever, and fear about the ability to function in the future.

For example, with even a simple skin burn, the area of pain extends past the site of the burn to a secondary circumferential area which has not been injured but is still tender to the touch. Emotional excitation and fear can increase the pain response via the same hormonal mechanisms as those of inflammation. Therefore, blocking of wind-up by both psychological techniques and physical techniques is a key part of minimizing pain after injury. Patients should be treated with respect and in a calm manner and assisted in developing reasonable expectations about their chronic pain and healing.

Simple local anesthetic injections can be given in a physician's office. More complicated blocks such as celiac plexus blocks for cancer pain, or lumbar sympathetic blocks for reflex sympathetic dystrophy, are

Table 3.14
Drug Treatments for Chronic Pain

Drug or Class	Actions	Typical Pain Type Treated
NSAID's (ibuprofen, naproxen, etc.)	anti-inflammatory, anti-coagulant (prostaglandins)	all
COX-2 inhibitors (Celebrex, Vioxx, etc.)	specific pain-related prostaglandin inhibition	arthritis, inflammatory pain
Narcotics (morphine, fentanyl, oxycodone, etc.)	bind to narcotic receptors, induce tolerance, sedation, respiratory depression	acute pain, cancer pain, severe pain, +/– chronic pain
antidepressants (Elavil, Prozac, etc.)	mood elevation, modulation of brain neurotransmitters	chronic pain, all types
anticonvulsants (gabapentin, Tegretol, Dilantin)	decrease signal transmission of pain sensations	neuropathic pain, RSD, trigeminal neuralgia, others
serotonin agonists (Imitrex, etc.)	affect blood vessels/flow (postulated effect)	headache, mainly migraine
local anesthetics (lidocaine, Marcaine, etc.)	block nerve impulses in deep nerve fibers, spinal cord or skin	back pain, nerve entrapment, RSD, cancer, acute pain, surgical pain

Note: Consult pharmacology texts for full information and side effects and precautions.

done in an anesthesia suite or minor surgical suite by an anesthesiologist trained in the techniques. Local anesthetic toxicity can cause serious injury, and blocks are not without risk. Risks can include permanent nerve injury or death. Nerve blocks should only be performed by an individual with specialized training in pain management. Often blocks require real-time x-ray guidance in order to verify correct placement of the needle. However, when used properly such injections can make an immense difference in pain and suffering.

Local anesthetic epidural injections with steroids prove helpful for certain kinds of back pain, most commonly radicular or nerve root pain, presenting as pain with numbness going down the leg. This type of block is rarely helpful for back pain that does not radiate into one or both legs, nor is it helpful for back pain due to myofascial irritation (pain primarily in the muscle) or joint problems. Once a patient has had surgery on the back, the efficacy of this treatment decreases. At most, a series of three injections, repeated every six months, may be appropriate if the first injection yields some relief.

If symptoms include bowel or bladder problems, weight loss, or paralysis of the legs, a full medical workup is mandatory. Studies such as x-rays and CAT scans or MRI should confirm the diagnosis prior to the treatment. (Unfortunately, too many patients undergo needless injections for pain problems. While these procedures are usually safe, they are not completely risk free.)

For some patients with severe pain problems—such as those caused by invasive cancers, post-herpetic neuralgia, and reflex sympathetic dystrophy—it is important to consult a pain specialist within the first few months of symptoms. The specialist can perform a series of nerve blocks or for long-term problems, can place a small plastic catheter in the epidural space for repeat dosing of analgesics. The catheter is then tunneled under the skin and attached to either an injection port or to a surgically implanted infusion pump to minimize the risk of infection. (A standard epidural catheter can only remain in place for three to seven days.)

Other advanced pain treatments involve the use of electronic devices implanted near the spinal cord or used externally to attempt to override and counteract abnormal nerve impulses. Spinal cord stimulators are implanted at many major medical centers, for example. These devices are programmed to deliver small electrical impulses to the spinal cord in the area of the perceived pain (such as the lower lumbar nerve roots). Although these stimulators are available for pain treatment, they have a significant failure rate and can cause infection or other injury. Stimulators can also be implanted in the brain by neurosurgeons who specialize in this technique. In the opinion of this writer, implanted stimulators should only be used along with intensive multidisciplinary pain management and after careful explanation of the risks to the patient.

3.7 Nerve Block Cases

A. Flora

1. Fact pattern

Flora, a forty-five-year-old woman, underwent a series of epidural steroid injections for low back pain. She had previous back surgery (microdiscectomy) for a ruptured disk with right-sided sciatica. The patient was out of work due to pain. After the second epidural injections the patient stated she developed muscle weakness and numbness in the right leg, as well as pain. The weakness and numbness resolved that night, but the pain remained. Flora sued the anesthesiologist, stating he caused injury doing the epidural. However, she did not report any unusual pain during the performance of the block. The EMG showed some mild right-sided muscle weakness. Her exam showed decreased straight leg raising on the right, mild motor weakness, and no sensory loss.

2. Analysis

There was no evidence of negligent technique with the epidural and no residual injury suggesting the epidural needle caused nerve damage, only pain and the mild deficits which was the patient's initial complaint. The law firm which took this case advised the plaintiff to drop the suit.

B. Gary

1. Fact pattern

Gary, a thirty-eight-year-old man with a history of smoking and heart disease, was in treatment at the clinic for abdominal pain after his gallbladder (not laparoscopic, but open) surgery. The pain was localized at the subcostal incision scar site, so local injections were repeated as needed over six months. The patient had a follow-up visit at the clinic after an injection and complained of abdominal pain again near the scar site by the right lower rib cage. Questioning revealed that the pain was more aching in character and sometimes worsened with breathing. Gary was sent for chest x-ray and EKG. The EKG was unchanged, but the chest film showed thickening on the right. The radiologist recommended a CAT scan and tomograms, which showed an early lung cancer. The patient had successful surgery and survived the lung cancer. Gary stopped smoking.

2. Analysis

For patients with ongoing pain problems, each evaluation and follow up requires close questioning about the pain, especially after interventions such as nerve blocks are made. One known medical problem does not preclude another one developing. This patient's life was saved because his pain was carefully evaluated.

C. Henrietta

1. Fact pattern

A dentist saw Henrietta, a middle-aged obese woman, who required treatment of a painful tooth. His pre-procedure evaluation noted that she had hypertension. The dentist performed a local anesthetic block, then immediately left the room. The patient's husband was directed to a waiting room; thus, no one was with the patient. When the dentist returned some minutes later, Henrietta was unresponsive and turning blue. With some difficulty the dentist and assistants moved the patient to the floor. The dentist's records stated that he was only gone a few minutes. EMS rescue was called. The dentist testified that he attempted to perform CPR; however, the EMS records noted that when they arrived no oxygen was being given and no ventilations were being performed. The crash cart had not been opened, no IV started and no drugs had been given. Henrietta's eyes were fixed and dilated when the code team arrived. She was pronounced dead on arrival to the hospital. EMS was present within ten minutes of the call; however, it was clear from the official call log that the call to EMS was later than the dentist had reported and that there had been a considerable delay between performance of the block and discovery of the problem. The patient's husband received a large settlement.

2. Analysis

The dentist violated a primary safety requirement of performance of local anesthestic block: the patient must be monitored. Local anesthetics can cause toxicity from either inadvertent intravenous injection or relative overdose and are more risky in those with cardiac disease. The negligence was compounded by failure to perform even the most basic of resuscitation efforts. Note that if the dentist had remained with the patient (or left a nurse) and the cardiac arrest had then occurred and if proper resuscitation had been done, even with a poor outcome, there would have been no negligence. Medical personnel are reminded not to try to improve the situation by misrepresentation of the facts in documents or in testimony.

D. Irving (Anesthesia case but the principles apply to pain blocks as well.)

1. Fact pattern

Irving, a twenty-five-year-old man, underwent spinal anesthesia for repair of bilateral inguinal hernias. During the performance of the spinal, the patient claimed he felt severe pain going down the right leg and screamed. Irving reported that the doctor reassured him, completed the spinal, and surgery proceeded. Within two hours after surgery, the patient developed left leg pain, back pain, and a foot drop. The EMG showed evidence of nerve injury. The anesthesiologist noted in the contemporaneous anesthesia record that the patient had a paresthesia on the left. Irving sued, and at trial he described the pain he felt during the spinal. The patient received a large settlement.

2. Analysis

A local anesthetic block may cause a paresthesia (an electric shock sensation) but should be discontinued if the patient complains of pain during placement of the needle. Injection of local anesthetic into a nerve or nerve root typically causes severe pain and irreversible nerve damage.

E. Jennie

1. Fact pattern

Jennie, a sixty-four-year-old female, had received mastectomy and chemotherapy for breast cancer, followed by reconstructive surgery. She complained of pain along the scar and pain down the left side of the chest where some muscle flaps had been taken and wanted to initiate a suit against the plastic surgeon. Review of the records showed that muscle flaps were taken along the latissimus dorsi near the long thoracic nerve; however, the consent clearly described possible nerve damage and that involvement of nerves in the flank was a known complication of the surgery. Jennie was referred to an anesthesiologist/pain specialist. She received nerve blocks (intercostal) and repeat injections along the scar which provided some temporary relief of the pain. A low dose antidepressant, gabapentin, and NSAIDs were added. It was clear from the evaluation in the pain clinic that the patient was angry about having cancer, and she was urged to see the pain clinic psychiatrist for at least a few visits. She refused but decided to continue with the pain specialist. After consultation with her attorney, she decided to drop the case.

2. Analysis

There was no evidence of negligence in this case despite the presence of some neuropathic pain, and it became clear to everyone except the patient that it would be better to redirect her anger and deal with her underlying cancer rather than sue the surgeon. It was fortunate that this patient found a good pain clinic where she had excellent rapport with the anesthesiologist, obtained some pain relief, and where she could expect to have gradual lessening of her pain over time.

3.8 Cancer Treatments

A. Radiation therapy and implanted pumps

Some of the pain of cancer is caused by the invasion of bone and other tissues by tumor cells. As an adjunct to chemotherapy, radiation may be used both to eliminate tumors and to treat pain. Studies estimate that 65%–90% of painful areas due to tumor can be helped by radiation therapy.[18] Highly sophisticated x-ray machines are used to destroy the proliferating cells, and thus prevent them from compressing nerves or internal organs. Radiation therapy may supplement various drug and nondrug therapies.

Physicians who are not familiar with cancer pain management should refer patients with moderate or severe cancer pain to a pain specialist, especially if the patient's pain appears to be out of control. In one California case, a plaintiff won a large settlement on behalf of her deceased father, who had alternate bouts of severe cancer-related pain and narcotic side effects while in the hospital and at home, with death due to respiratory arrest.[19] Failure to treat the pain properly was the main contention in the case.

Tip

Chronic pain treatment plans should be re-evaluated periodically with appropriate tests or x-rays to rule out new or extending disease presenting as pain.

B. Alternative medicine treatments

The past several years have witnessed a resurgence of interest in many therapies which were not formerly considered a part of mainstream Western medicine. The ancient art of traditional Chinese medicine (TCM), for example, has been practiced for thousands of years. Interest especially increased after Western physicians began visiting China in the 1970s and seeing these practices, including use of herbs and acupuncture in therapy, and information was publicized in the United States and other Western countries.

Together these treatments are called "complementary and alternative medicine" (CAM) or, in Dr. Andrew Weil's term, "integrative medicine." Paradoxically, many of these techniques now called "alternative" have in fact been part of the practice of pain management for many years.

Much of what CAM offers makes very good sense. It is unfortunate that some Western-trained physicians have little knowledge of these therapies and seem to be reluctant to accept even the best of them. By contrast, physicians who practice pain management have accepted alternative treatments for decades, especially the use of acupuncture, bodywork techniques such as massage and chiropractic, and mind/body techniques such as meditation and visualizations.

Tip

Alternative medical therapy can be very effective in pain treatment, as long as the practitioners offering the therapy are properly trained, credentialed, and licensed. Alternative medicine should be used along with conventional medical treatments.

According to a 1997 survey, patients in the United States made over 629 million visits to CAM practitioners that year.[20] Today, in Europe and Australia, between 20%–70% of patients (depending on the medical problem) use CAM. Most of the costs are paid by patients out of pocket. Yet only about 40% of patients discuss such alternative therapies with their doctors, at least in part because physicians do not ask about them. This rift between CAM and standard medical therapy can only be detrimental to physicians and their patients.

Physicians trained solely in Western medicine have on the whole been reluctant to accept alternative medicine, sometimes abruptly dismissing these treatments without even hearing the relevant evidence. Their bias is usually due to the "single cause-single effect" model of disease, a model which has serious flaws. Other divisive biases derive from an unfamiliarity with CAM and the inadequate scientific literature on the subject. But the field is rapidly changing. Nurses have often been more willing than physicians to try alternative methods.

1. Acupuncture

Perhaps the best known part of traditional Chinese medicine (TCM) is acupuncture, one of the standard therapies designed both to treat disease and to maintain general health. This ancient art—named in the West from the Latin *acu*, "needle," and *punctura*, "pricking"—has been practiced for more than 5,000 years. The Chinese doctrine teaches that health lies in the harmony of two complementary forces, the yin (dark, female) and the yang (light, male). Energy is thought to flow through meridians in the body which are named after bodily organs. These meridians or channels do not necessarily correspond to specific nerves, lymphatics, or blood vessels. The Qi, or chi, flows through the body along these meridians, and acupuncture is used as part of TCM to attempt to balance this flow. Specific points have been mapped on the skin to correspond with many internal body points.

Acupuncture is now practiced in the United States and Western countries with tiny, single-use, sterilized needles that are placed in several points in the skin and twirled on insertion. Sometimes the needles are stimulated with a very low level electric current (electroacupuncture) or the technique is performed with massage (no needles, called acupressure) or with heat (moxibustion). Usually the patient feels no pain, but rather a tingling at the site and perhaps all over.

In fact, many classical acupuncture points correspond to common trigger points for pain. These points often occur at the junctions of nerves and muscles (called motor points) or at points of soreness associated with neck, back, or facial pain or headache. Other acupuncture points may be sites on the skin where the electrical energy of the body can be modulated.

Still, we don't understand entirely how acupuncture works in Western terms, although scientific data give some clues as to how it might affect pain pathways and multiple organ systems. In addition, acupuncture practitioners may approach a medical problem in a very different way from that of standard medicine. Since many patients with pain derive a benefit from acupuncture, it is certainly worth trying for many, if not all, pain problems.

Practitioners are licensed in most U.S. states, and accredited training programs for both physician and non-physician acupuncturists are available. The National Institutes of Health (NIH), the World Health Organization, and many other agencies offer information about acupuncture for patients.

Pain problems treated with acupuncture include headache, trigeminal neuralgia, peripheral nerve injuries, musculoskeletal pains, low back pain, sciatica, and osteoarthritis; this is not an exhaustive list. Most patients experience a benefit within three to six treatment sessions and return for periodic "booster" sessions over the ensuing years.

Acupuncture also appears to produce relaxation and a sense of calm. The mechanism of effect is at least twofold: stimulation of the neurons in the brain and body which release endogenous opiates (endorphins) and closing the gate for pain transmission to the brain. The low-frequency stimulation of the tiny acupuncture needles is below the pain threshold (that's why it is nearly painless), but it suffices to stimulate the nervous system. Electroacupuncture and heat methods appear to strengthen this gate closing mechanism by increasing the intensity of the stimulation without causing pain.

2. Chiropractic therapy

Chiropractic therapy treats a variety of conditions, but it is associated primarily with manipulative therapy aimed at improved mobility of the joints and the relief of pain. First established in 1895 in Iowa, chiropractic has developed separately from standard medicine and at times has overly emphasized the importance of the spine in causing disease. Now it is a regulated profession. Chiropractic employs many types of manipulation, including the "joint crack," which is produced by a rapid thrust to a bony area, causing pressure across the joint and the bursting of a small bubble of nitrogen in the joint fluid.

Chiropractors also help their patients with information about health and how to prevent further pain and injury, especially for problems with the back.[21] Chiropractic treatment is intended to help counteract some of the physical forces which lead to low back pain in the first place. These include long hours of sitting at work with unrelieved stresses of weight bearing, stresses of driving including whole body vibration, sedentary lifestyle which helps "freeze" joints, muscles, and tissues, and inadequate rest (i.e., rest only when it fits into a work schedule).

In some studies, chiropractic treatment has been shown to be better than traditional medical therapy for low back pain and markedly better than bedrest.[21] The benefits for acute intervention appear to be long lasting, continuing from six months to one year after the treatment. This therapy is commonly used for head and neck pain complaints as well, although the evidence shows it is approximately as effective as other therapies, including various drugs.

Unlike massage, chiropractic does not stimulate release of brain endorphins. Rather, it relieves pain by both peripheral and central mechanisms, decreasing stimulation from painful interstitial (deep) tissues, and increasing the internal pain-relieving activity of the central nervous system (via inhibitory nerve cells in the spinal cord). This means that chiropractic manipulation works locally on painful tissues and also causes an increase in the spinal cord's control over painful stimuli which then limits the sensation of pain in the brain.

3. Herbal therapies

Herbal therapies have recently become very popular, as interest has been revived in natural products that were also popular about a century ago. In fact, about 30% of all medicines today are derived from plants. Many others are synthetic substances similar to the original plant material but purified or modified to increase potency.

Tip

Herbal therapies are not FDA-regulated for purity or content. Buyers should investigate the brand name for reliability, for example in the new *Physician's Desk Reference for Herbals, Prevention magazine,* or at AskDrWeil.com.

Many of the herbal products available in drugstores and health food stores have been shown to be effective in recent scientific studies. Others have questionable value. Table 3.15 lists some herbals used for pain and related conditions. Table 3.16 lists supplements, and Table 3.17, certain herbals known to be unsafe. Also, Andrew Weil offers excellent up-to-date reviews of herbal therapies in his books, his website, and his newsletter. Another excellent source for herbal medicine updates is *Prevention* magazine. For scientific references, also see the book by O'Hara.[2]

Herbals are active substances that may interact with each other or with drugs and may cause allergic reactions and side effects. Hence, a natural substance may not be better for everyone, and not all are safe. Unfortunately, not all physicians in the United States are familiar enough with herbal remedies to discuss them intelligently with their patients. This is slowly changing. Women who are pregnant or plan to be, or nursing mothers should discuss all herbals with their physician. Some may be toxic to the fetus or newborn or may induce premature labor.

Adults should consider taking basic vitamin supplements for health. Also, many of the most important nutrients are present in quantity in fresh fruits, vegetables, and other foods. It is always better to try to get some of the necessary supplemental vitamins and minerals through diet, although some nutrients (like calcium for older women) need an extra boost.

4. Mind-body techniques

a. Biofeedback. Biofeedback is an established, proven technique by which one learns to control automatic physiologic effects such as body temperature, heart rate, or blood flow into the hands. Often other sensations, such as intensity of pain, are controlled in

Table 3.15
Commonly Used Herbal/Supplemental Preparations

Herb names	Active Agent	Intended Use	Side Effects
aloe vera	gel or juice from live plant	topical anti-inflammatory for pain or burns	few; should avoid putting into open wounds
bromelain	2,000 mcu bromelain extract or 1,200 gdu	oral preparation 100–200 mg 4–6 x per day; inhibits bradykinin, anti-inflammatory	may cause allergy
feverfew (*Tanacetum parthenum*)	standardized to 0.2% parthenolide	migraine prevention—not effective as treatment	GI upset, mouth ulcers, clotting abnormalities
kava (*Piper methysticum*)	standardized to 70% kavalactones	relief of anxiety or stress	slows reaction time; may discolor hair, skin, nails; do not combine with sedatives, alcoholic beverages, antidepressants
St. John's wort (*Hypericum perforatum*)	standardized to 0.3% hypericin	antidepressant *proven effective for some patients.	sunlight sensitivity; not to be taken with anti-anxiety antidepressants, alcoholic beverages; not approved fo pregnancy; may decrease effectiveness of birth contr result in unplanned pregnancy
methyl salicylate	10–60% methyl salicylate ointments	"Ben-Gay" and other brands; pain relief by local anti-inflammation and heat	may overdose if used with heating pad; may irritate right after exercise.
peppermint oil	menthol 1.2616%	topical to forehead and temples for headache	may cause skin irritation
willow bark	1% salicin, as a tea (use 1 tsp. per cup)	pain relief, anti-inflammatory	not as effective as aspirin; may cause stomach irritation
valerian (*Valeriana officinalis*)	standardized to 0.8–1.0% valerenic acid	relief of insomnia, more gentle than most therapies	sedation; may cause headache, restlessness in some; do not combine with other sedatives
SAM-e (S-adenosyl methionine)	200-mg tablets, not standardized; usual dose is 400–1,600 mg per day	antidepressant; affects serotonin and dopamine systems; unclear how or how much it works.	few side effects; should not be used to replace ongoing antidepressant therapy without psychiatrist follow-up; not for bipolar (manic-depressive) disorder
glucosamine and chondroitin sulfate	variable doses	relief of arthritis pain, increase mobility; may reduce pain and breakdown of cartilage; unclear how well they work; not a cure for arthritis	decreased insulin secretion
capsaicin (capsicum)	capsaicin 0.025–0.075% creams	pain relief via activation or inhibition of substance-P pathways	prescription and natural forms available; skin rash, redness possible; do not get into eyes
melatonin	3-mg tablets most common dose	insomnia, prevent jet-lag	headaches, fatigue, confusion

the process. This is accomplished by using a device that measures a physiologic variable, such as the heart rate, then feeds back the information to the patient. The patient tries to slow the heart rate in an attempt at relaxation. Often mind-body imagery is an effective way to achieve this control. Soon the patient learns how to control automatic processes in the body, thus limiting the stress response from the autonomic nervous system. Eventually, the patient becomes so adept at this process that the device becomes unnecessary.

Table 3.16
Commonly Used Supplements

Supplement Name	Effects
vitamin C (200–500 mg/d)	cancer prevention, fighting colds, immune system boost
vitamin E (400–800 IU/d)	cancer prevention, anti-aging, prevent atherosclerosis
carotenoids (vitamin A, 25,000 IU or 15 mg)	cancer prevention, immune boost, improve sight
omega-3 fatty acids (found in salmon, sardines, mackerel and flaxseed)	cancer prevention, post-menopausal symptoms
selenium (200 mcg)	fight cancer (side effects: hair loss, nausea, fatigue)
gamma-linolenic acids (evening primose, black-currant oils)	essential fatty acids, postmenopausal symptoms
isoflavones (soy milk 1 c. or 30–50 mg/d)	post-menopausal symptoms, increase bone, decrease cholesterol

Biofeedback is effective for many types of chronic pain, especially headache, arthritis, muscle pain, and temporomandibular joint pain (TMJ). It has also been used to treat a variety of chronic conditions in which the autonomic nervous system plays a role and in treatment of drug or alcohol addiction. Biofeedback should always be learned with a certified instructor. It is intended as a supplement to continuing medical therapy.

b. Meditation. Herbert Benson and his colleagues in Boston have been studying meditation and the stress response for over two decades. According to Benson, 60%–90% of patient visits to the doctor involve stress and the mind-body realm.[22] He recognized that the stress response affects multiple organ systems, most immediately the cardiovascular system, but also on the brain and on chronic disease of all kinds. Meditation can be used to counteract chronic stress, which is endemic to modern life and wreaks havoc on the body. Dr. Benson coined the term "relaxation response" for the complex beneficial effects of meditation on the body.

By practicing meditation—whether with a group in a medical clinic, with audiotapes, or at one of many meditation centers throughout the world—a person may positively influence the course of cardiac disease, cancer, and all pain problems. This does not mean that these chronic diseases will necessarily be cured, but it is highly likely that there will be improvement in symptoms, and even in longevity.

Meditation appears to help better regulate cortisol secretion—allowing rapid release of cortisol under ini-

Table 3.17
Supplements of Questionable Efficacy and/or Dangerous Side Effects

Herbal Name	Purported Benefit	Other Effects
comfrey	topical anti-inflammatory, for arthritis, pulmonary disease	poison if taken internally; link to cancer and liver toxicity
DHEA	slow aging, decrease weight	hirsutism; linked to some cancers
ephedra (ma huang)	increased energy, decrease weight	hypertension, seizures, death; dangerous with anti-depressants; increased risk of death with anesthesia
chaparral (creosote)	anti-cancer, anti-acne	nonviral hepatitis
yohimbine	treat erectile dysfunction, general male aphrodisiac	weakness, paralysis, death
lobelia	treat asthma and bronchitis	respiratory depression, increased heart rate, coma, death
chitosan	weight loss (animal shells, absorbs fat in the gut)	may bind fat-soluble vitamins; no proven benefit

tial stress, but also causing a faster drop to low levels after the stressor has been encountered. This results in less hyperreactivity of the stress hormones epinephrine and norepinephrine. In people who practice meditation, the receptors to stress which normally raise blood pressure and heart rate (called the beta-adrenergic receptors) are less reactive than in controls.[23]

Conscious attention to repetitive, rhythmic motions uses our own autonomic nervous system in order to relieve pain. The effects of rhythmic breathing and soothing music or other sounds are at least partly mediated via alteration of the basic biological responses and release of stress chemicals. Since pain is increased by adrenergic activity and certain difficult pain syndromes are at least partly caused by overactivity of the stress response, one would predict that meditation would be a powerful tool for pain relief.

Meditation can be helpful for improving a variety of negative behaviors, habits, and addictions. Negative conditions and avoidance behaviors tend to generalize, so that, for example, avoiding fear of one particular situation may expand to overwhelming, crippling fears. (Think about the child getting back on the bicycle right after the fall. The longer he waits, the greater the fear. It's the same phenomenon.) Negative outlooks tend to persist.

Habits of smoking, overeating, or other addictive behaviors usually develop in response to real stresses in our lives, perhaps back into childhood. But later in life such habits prove counterproductive. Many negative behaviors that begin with a wish to avoid problems are then prolonged to avoid uncomfortable feelings in difficult circumstances. Denial is a powerful mechanism for avoiding the feeling of being out of control. Mind-body techniques put the control back where it belongs—within ourselves.

c. Hypnosis. Hypnosis has been used for analgesia since at least the early nineteenth century, when it was called "mesmerism," after the Austrian physician Franz Anton Mesmer, one of the founders of the field. Hypnosis has been used clinically to treat all types of pain, including headache, phantom limb pain (pain remaining after a traumatic or surgical amputation), low back pain, and postoperative pain. There is a similar response rate to hypnosis and biofeedback in clinical studies, indicating that central mechanisms are involved in modulating the pain response. However, the mechanism does not seem to be related to opiate receptors and endorphin release.

Hypnotic techniques can also be used in surgery and medical procedures with excellent results, making the experience more pleasant, allaying fear, and improving medical outcome.

5. Other alternative medicine disciplines

a. Homeopathy. Homeopathy is a truly alternative form of medicine, with a different approach to healing than that of mainstream medicine. Named from the Greek for "like the disease," it was developed by the German physician Dr. Samuel Hahnemann. Hahnemann suggested that symptoms may be attempts by the body to cure itself of disease, thus, the remedy would be to encourage the symptoms gently using a highly diluted solution of an agent that causes similar symptoms in a healthy person.

For example, Dr. Hahnemann noted that quinine (from cinchona bark) would produce fever and chills in a healthy person. But in a person with malaria, quinine is a cure of these same symptoms. From such evidence, Hahnemann developed two principles of homeopathy: (1) like cures like, or the law of similars, and (2) by extreme dilution, the remedy becomes more effective with avoidance of side effects, or the law of infinitesimals. A third overriding principle is that homeopathic medicines are given to treat the whole person.

Homeopathic remedies are made from plants, animals, or minerals, diluted with nine parts of water or alcohol a number of times (for twelve, it is then labeled 12X, which is equivalent to a one-in-a-trillion dilution). Thus unlike herbal remedies, these solutions are extremely dilute and have few if any side effects. The dilutions are vigorously shaken, so that, in theory, additional energy is added to the solution.

Homeopathy fell out of favor in the United States in the last 100 years or so with advances in allopathic (mainstream) medicine, but homeopathy is widely practiced elsewhere. There are many licensed practitioners of medicine (M.D. or D.O.), nursing (R.N.) or chiropractic (D.C.) who also sometimes prescribe homeopathic remedies. However, only Arizona, Connecticut, and Nevada have laws regarding licensing of homeopathy at this time.

Few clinical trials are available for homeopathic remedies. Some well-known remedies for pain include arnica, *Rhus toxicodendron*, *Ruta graveolens*, *Hypericum perforatum*, *Natrum muriaticum*, silica, and *Pulsatilla nigricans*. Despite lack of apparent side effects, the precaution to avoid medications in pregnancy still applies, but many homeopathic remedies can usually be given safely to children.

b. Magnet therapy. There has been interest in the possibility that the application of magnetic fields to parts of the body might influence the energy of the body and therefore, pain. Good scientific evidence showing the effectiveness of magnets will be important in determining when and how this treatment might be effective. For back pain, for example, magnets are taped over trigger points (or held in place with elastic bandages) for up to several days. Theoretically, the magnetic field may alter blood flow in the affected area.

In one small double-blind, placebo-controlled study, use of magnets for treatment of chronic low back pain was not shown to be better than placebo.[24] Although more work needs to be done in this area, a number of companies are now making and selling magnets for treatment of pain. Patients with pacemakers or implanted defibrillators should never use magnets, since they may alter the function of the cardiac device.

c. Therapeutic touch. Therapeutic touch is a type of energy therapy pioneered about twenty-five years ago by Delores Krieger, R.N., Ph.D., a professor at New York University. To what extent and how it works is still unclear. Some studies have been biased, making this therapy difficult to evaluate. However, therapeutic touch, which is not a hands-on technique, but rather a method in which the hands are held over the patient, is said to promote a sense of calm. This and other types of "distant healing," including prayer, have been shown to produce positive effects in medical patients.[25]

d. Aromatherapy. Aromatherapy is the use of scented concentrated oils, either inhaled or applied to the skin, in order to achieve health benefits. It is clear that some scents are helpful in inducing feelings of relaxation and calm, but other health benefits have not been proven. Commonly used scents include lavender, chamomile, and vanilla for calming effects, peppermint and eucalyptus for pain relief, and tea tree oil for skin eruptions. Aromatherapy oils should never be taken internally. People with skin allergies or asthma should be careful to avoid triggering allergic responses. Aroma-therapy is offered by some healthcare practitioners.

e. Ayurveda. Ayurvedic medicine is another holistic system which has been practiced in India for thousands of years. In Ayurveda, the physician determines which of three basic metabolic types fit the patient—kapha, pitta, or vata. One of these types may be considered dominant in an individual. Those who are mainly "vata" are thought to be thin, quick, and energetic; those of the "pitta" type are competitive and hot-tempered; and those of the "kapha" type are generally calm and stolid in personality. The physician prescribes diet, exercise, lifestyle changes and other therapies in order to balance the system and avoid disease. However, Ayurveda is not a recognized medical specialty in the United States at this time.

Some of the Ayurvedic practices, such as healthy eating, yoga and meditation, have obvious benefits for health and well-being. Others, such as the use of laxatives and purgatives, may be too harsh for many patients.

3.9 Chronic Pain Cases

A. Kevin

1. Fact pattern

Kevin, a fifty-five-year-old man, came to the pain clinic with severe one-sided headache that produced tearing and a knife-like sensation behind the right eye. The patient was feeling depressed and suicidal due to the pain but continued to go to work. He was diagnosed with cluster headache and given gabapentin and Zoloft. Given his suicidal thoughts, Kevin agreed to see a psychiatrist along with the pain treatment. The pain improved slightly. The patient was offered neurosurgical blocks but was concerned about the risk. The neurosurgeon felt strongly that the patient should have a block, but the patient wanted a second opinion. He instead opted for acupuncture with a local Chinese medical practitioner and had enough improvement with the combined treatments to avoid more invasive blocks at that time. In psychotherapy, Kevin began to work on his troubled marriage and problems with his employer.

2. Analysis

It is important for patients to recognize the risk of deep blocks and for alternative treatments to be offered. In addition, the psychological concerns for many patients with chronic pain are significant and should not be ignored. Blocks can always be added at a later time. Critical to this case was early consultation to the psychiatrist, use of antidepressants and anticonvulsants, and good communication with the patient. Cluster headache is a very serious pain problem.

B. Louise

1. Fact pattern

Louise, a sixty-year-old female, was referred to the pain clinic by her gynecologist for unexplained abdominal pain. She was evaluated for gallbladder pain two months before then had a cholecystectomy. A pelvic ultrasound and CT scan of the abdomen and pelvis were negative. Louise complained of an aching pain in her right upper quadrant near her surgical scar and moving to the back. There was concern about a pancreatic or liver source or an abdominal aneurysm, but evaluation and blood tests by a general/vascular surgeon were negative.

Louise complained of fatigue and depression since her husband's death two years before. She saw the clinic psychiatrist and began Prozac which appeared to help her mood. She began an exercise and low-fat diet plan which also seemed to help.

One evening the on-call physician heard from the patient. Louise had developed a pustular rash over the right upper quadrant in the area of her pain. A diagnosis of shingles (herpes zoster) was tentatively made, and the patient was told to get capsaicin cream that night and to come in the next morning. She was placed on antiviral therapy and had a rapid recovery. The patient's pain gradually got better and after one year she stopped the Prozac. She never developed the serious complication of post-herpetic neuralgia (PHN).

2. Analysis

Pain complaints in the abdomen are complex and often involve more than one active diagnosis. All avenues must be followed. Zoster (shingles) typically presents with pain up to two weeks before the lesions appear. Zoster should be treated quickly to minimize the risk of PHN.

C. Mark

1. Fact pattern

Mark was treated with Percocet by a general practitioner for a work-related back sprain. The patient continued to receive scripts for more than 100 pills at a time, renewing them over four years. The patient frequently "lost" his prescription. Mark became addicted to narcotics and later heroin, contracting hepatitis C. The GP never referred the patient to a pain specialist. Mark received a cash settlement in suit against the GP.[26]

2. Analysis

Giving long-term narcotic prescriptions for back sprain is improper, especially when the patient displays typical behaviors of addiction such as "losing" prescriptions. This indicates possible drug abuse or drug dealing. Patients who develop drug-seeking behaviors while being treated for chronic pain should be referred to pain or addiction specialists. It is within the standard of care to refuse to refill pain prescriptions if the prescriber feels uncomfortable with the patient's progress. Alternatively, patients may be asked to agree to taper off narcotics after long-term therapy.

D. Norris

1. Fact pattern

Norris, a patient with a toothache of two to three months' duration, saw an endodontist, who did a root canal, prescribing penicillin and Tylenol # 3 (with codeine) and scheduling a return visit in two weeks. The patient had continued pain, calling and visiting the office multiple times. The endodontist repeated the root canal and twice prescribed Vicodin (a narcotic) for pain. Within a few days another dentist in the office diagnosed periodontitis of another tooth and performed a root canal. More Vicodin was ordered. The next day Norris returned with swelling and continued pain of the left jaw. The first endodontist (the defendant) prescribed Lortab (another narcotic) and penicillin. One day later the patient was telephoned, and he reported swelling on the other side and difficulty swallowing, although overall improvement. Norris was not examined. The next morning the patient called complaining of difficulty breathing. He went to the dentist's office, then to an oral surgeon who had him admitted to a hospital for intubation and emergency surgery. The diagnosis was Ludwig's angina, that is, spread of tooth infection to the mouth and airway causing life-threatening swelling. The patient died during attempts to gain an airway by the hospital anesthesiologist and thoracic surgeon. The jury found for the plaintiff's estate, against the dentist but in favor of the anesthesiologist and surgeon.[27]

2. Analysis

Here chronic pain indicated an infection which was initially misdiagnosed, then continued pain and increased symptoms signaled inadequate control of the infection with the penicillin. Pain after dental work should subside over the subsequent days; thus the real problem was masked with numerous prescriptions for narcotic painkillers. Proper treatment would have been to refer the patient to an oral surgeon for hospital admission on either day two or three when the pain and symptoms continued.

3.10 Summary of Principles of Chronic Pain Management

Pain management can be a risky undertaking, because pain is at once a potential symptom of disease and a symptom to be treated. If the treatment masks the ongoing disease process, or if the treatment is invasive and causes injury, the result may be considered negligence. Each case has to be individually evaluated; however, often common sense and an effort to listen carefully to the patient and follow up after treatment go a long way toward avoiding an injury.

Endnotes

1. International Association for the Study of Pain, "Pain Terms: A List with Definitions and Notes on Usage Recommended by the IASP Subcommittee on Taxonomy." *Pain* 6, 249–252, 1979.

2. O'Hara, D.A., *Heal the Pain, Comfort the Spirit. The Hows and Whys of Modern Pain Treatment*, University of Pennsylvania Press, Philadelphia, 2002.

3. Ashburn, M.A., and Rice, L.J., eds., *The Management of Pain*. New York: Churchill Livingstone, 1998.

4. Adams, R.D., Victor, M., and Ropper, A.H., eds., *Principles of Neurology*, Sixth Edition. New York: McGraw-Hill, 1997.

5. Wilson, J.D., Braunwald, E., et al., eds., *Harrison's Principles of Internal Medicine*, 12th Edition. New York: McGraw-Hill, 1991.

6. Silen, W., *Cope's Early Diagnosis of the Acute Abdomen*, 17th Edition. London: Oxford Press, 1987.

7. World Health Organization, *Cancer Pain Relief*. Geneva: World Health Organization, 1986.

8. Laska, L., editor, "Lethal Morphine Dose Caused by Malfunction of Medicine Pump Causes Death—Failure of Nurses to Adequately Monitor Patient—Confidential Settlement in South Carolina," *Staci Lavender as Surviving Spouse of Randall Lavender, Deceased v. Baxter Healthcare Corporation and Spartanburg Regional Medical Center*, Spartanburg County (SC) Circuit Court, Case No. ____, *Medical Malpractice Verdicts, Settlements and Experts*, 13, April 2002.

9. Melzack, R., and Wall, P.D., "Pain Mechanisms: A New Theory," *Science* 150, 971–979, 1965.

10. Lentz, R., "Tight Leash: Drug Detailers Find Their Access Severely Limited," *Mod Physician*, 10, Nov. 1999.

11. Isenstein, H., "Out of Sight: Skyrocketing Drug Costs Threaten the Bottom Line of Medical Groups," *Mod Physician*, 35–43, Feb. 2000.

12. Pert, C., *Molecules of Emotion*. New York: Touchstone, 1997.

13. Baldessarini, R.J., "Drugs and the Treatment of Psychiatric Disorders: Depression and Mania." In Hardman et al., eds., *Goodman and Gilman's The Pharmacological Basis of Therapeutics*, 9th Edition. New York: McGraw-Hill, 1996.

14. Fishbain, D.A., Cutler, R.B., et al., "Do Antidepressants Have an Analgesic Effect in Psychogenic Pain and somatoform Pain Disorder? A Meta-Analysis." *Psychosomatic Medicine* 60, 503–9, 1999.

15. Borsook, D., LeBel, A., et al., "Central Pain Syndromes." In Ashburn and Rice, eds., *The Management of Pain*. New York: Churchill Livingstone, 1998.

16. Maze, R., and Fuzinaga, M., "Alpha-2 Adrenoceptors in Pain Modulation," *Anesthesiology* 92, 934–6, 2000.

17. Marshall, B.E., and Longnecker, D., "General Anesthetics: Ketamine." In Hardman et al., eds., *Goodman and Gilman's The Pharmacological Basis of Therapeutics*, 9th Edition. New York: McGraw-Hill, 1996.

18. Janjan, N., "Radiotherapeutic Management of Symptomatic Disease." In Loeser, J. D., ed., *Bonica's Management of Pain*. Philadelphia: Lippincott Williams and Wilkins, 2001.

19. Laska, L., editor, "Failure to Properly Manage Patient's Pain—Severe Pain Prior to Death—$1.5 Million California Verdict," *Beverly Bergman, Robert Bergman, and Alice Edlinger v. Wing Chin, M.D.*, Alameda County (CA) Superior Court, Case No. Hospital 205732-1, *Medical Malpractice Verdicts, Settlements and Experts*, 22–23, January 2002.

20. Eisenberg, D., et al., "Unconventional Medicine in the United States: Prevalence, Costs, and Patterns of Use." *NEJM,* 328, 246–52, 1993.

21. Cherkin, D.C., et al., "A Comparison of Physical Therapy, Chiropractic Manipulation, and Provision of an Educational Booklet for the Treatment of Patients with Low-Back Pain." *NEJM* 339, 1021-1029, 1998.

22. Herbert Benson, M.D., personal communication.

23. Mills, P.J., *Meditation, Science and Medicine*, Nov/Dec 1999, 38–41.

24. Collacott, E.A., et al., "Bipolar Permanent Magnets for the Treatment of Chronic Low-Back Pain," *JAMA* 283, 1322-28, 2000.

25. Astin, J.A., et al., "The Efficacy of 'Distant Healing': A Systematic Review of Randomized Trials," *Ann Int Med* 132, 903–10, 2000.

26. Laska, L., editor, "Over-Prescription of Percocet—Failure to Refer Patient to Specialist—Prescription Drug Addiction, Heroin Addiction, and Subsequent Contraction of Hepatitis C—$375,000 Massachusetts Settlement," *Medical Malpractice Verdicts, Settlements and Experts*, 29–30, February 2002.

27. Laska, L., editor, "Failure to Diagnose Pneumothorax during Complaints of Tooth Pain—Death—$500,000 Verdict in Rhode Island," *Estate of Antonio Fontes v. Salomone, et al.,* Providence (RI) Superior Court, Case No. 97-5362, *Medical Malpractice Verdicts, Settlements and Experts*, 8–9, February 2002.

Chapter 4

A Psychologist's View of Pain and Suffering

Lisa Stepp, Ph.D., M.S., R.N., APN, AOCN, CRNH

Synopsis

> ". . . all important things cannot be measured and all things that can be measured are not necessarily important . . . ."
>
> Albert Einstein

4.1 Introduction

In the mid-seventies, significant changes were taking place in the medical community. Cancer patients were being treated with cytotoxic agents capable of decreasing tumor size and providing limited promise of survival. Researchers were beginning to discover the importance of DNA in understanding human disease, and the first endorphins were identified. These hormonal substances, which are secreted by various cells in the body, were found to modulate pain perception and to be influenced by attitude. At this point, doctors began to realize the patient controls his or her outlook on life and that outlook influences his or her endorphins.[1] The role of patients in their recovery from illness and injury could no longer be ignored. This caused a paradigm shift from the omnipotent, omnipresent physician providing care to a team approach for treatment which included the patient as a part of that team.

It was during this philosophical development that physicians recognized pain as a multifaceted experience and began to recruit psychologists, nurses, social workers, physical therapists, and others to assist in the assessment, planning, treatment, and evaluation of chronic pain patients.[1] While the psychologist, as well as the other pain team members, find the pain and suffering of individuals a complex and challenging area of practice, the attorney is faced with the challenge of verifying or disputing psychological claims as part of damages.

Pain is a subjective experience that produces unpleasant sensory and emotional sensations, first associated with psychological and behavioral changes followed later by structural differences. The individual's perception of pain and appreciation of its meaning are complex phenomena that involve psychological and emotional processes in addition to activation of nociceptive pathways.[2] Revolutionary at the time of development, McCaffery's definition of pain, which is "whatever the experiencing person says it is, existing whenever he says it does," incorporates this multifaceted concept as well as challenges the pain management team to accept the patient's explanation and understanding of the experience.[3] While the anatomy, physiology, and pharmacology of pain and analgesia have been studied extensively, the full extent of the psychological, social, and spiritual impact from pain remains an enigma for healthcare professionals and attorneys.

Tip

Margo McCaffery's definition of pain challenges the clinician and attorney not necessarily to believe but to accept the patient's report of pain.

Pain is a virtually universal experience, and yet, extremely personal for the client. Ongoing research in pain continues to support the need for a framework of treatment that intervenes in all quality of life domains and is individualized for each client. In 1994, the Agency for Health Care Policy and Research (now called the Agency for Healthcare Research and Quality) published guidelines specifically designed for the management of cancer pain. While addressing a specific population of pain patients, this panel of experts identified four areas of quality of life that are affected by pain: physical, psychological, social, and spiritual. Patients with pain experience decreased functional capability, diminished strength and endurance, nausea, poor appetite, and poor or interrupted sleep. Psychologically, pain patients experienced diminished leisure enjoyment, increased anxiety, fear, depression, personal distress, difficulty concentrating, somatic preoccupation, and loss of control.[2] When pain reduces patients' options to exercise control, it diminishes their sense of well-being, adding to their sense of helplessness, hopelessness, and vulnerability. In the social domain, diminished social relationships, decreased sexual function, altered appearance, and increased caregiver burden can manifest in the patient experiencing pain that is uncontrolled or chronic. Spiritually, patients with pain may experience increased suffering, altered meaning in life, and begin a reevaluation of their religious beliefs. By recognizing the effect pain has on the entire existence of the patient, the psychiatrist and psychologist have become vital parts of the healthcare team. The plaintiffs' attorney's role to explore the implication of pain and help the fact finder appreciate the effect of the injury can also be critical for the patient to achieve a positive outcome.

Tip

Because of the psychological aspects of pain and suffering, the psychiatrist and psychologist contribute greatly to the evaluation and treatment of this patient population.

4.2 The Role of the Psychologist

There are several roles for the psychologist in pain management. From diagnostician and psychotherapist, to patient advocate, the mental healthcare professional functions at several levels and should be well versed in all forms of pain interventions. The most common approach used by psychiatrists and psychologists in pain management is the integrated response model.[4] Through this process the clinician works to establish both medical and psychiatric diagnoses stemming not only from the point when the patient is seen but including past perspectives of the patient. If patients in pain are assessed utilizing only the medical model, the evaluation is limited. This limited scope also disregards the possibility that the patient may have developed psychiatric problems as a result of the pain or that pre-existing problems may have precipitated the presenting chief complaint.

Tip

Pain can lead to the development of psychiatric problems, as well as exacerbating existing ones.

The medical community has come to recognize that individuals can experience physical, emotional, and spiritual pain. Any one of these can exist individually or, more commonly, in tandem. While not all patients with psychological pain are experiencing physical pain, most patients that experience physical pain do report psychological pain and suffering.

Researchers have further divided physical pain into two distinctive classifications, acute and chronic, and three subcategories, somatic, neuropathic, and bone.[5] While each of these categories is imperative to direct appropriate interventions, the major classifications best facilitate the psychologist's ability to understand the scope of the patient's needs. The definition, characteristics, psychological manifestations, and consequences of these two types of pain help to narrow the selection of necessary psychological therapeutic interventions. For the content of this chapter, acute and chronic refer to physical pain.

4.3 Acute Pain

Acute pain has long been recognized as a warning system which functions to alert of impending or existing physical damage. Individuals are prompted by this perception of discomfort to modify their activities and seek medical attention. In this way, pain can be understood as beneficial, heralding conditions that may be life-threatening. In the case of known tissue damage, such as trauma or surgery, pain can be utilized as a measure of healing. The perception of pain should lessen as the tissue is repaired or once the underlying cause of the pain has been treated, since the severity of acute pain and other symptoms is more or less in linear proportion to the extent of the basic pathology.[6] In the postoperative setting, an exacerbation of pain, such as increase of intensity or frequency or a change in pain character, may denote complications that require immediate intervention. For example, the patient who develops chest pain after abdominal surgery requires evaluation to rule out a myocardial infarction.

The characteristics of acute pain relate to cause, duration, and physiologic response. Some traumatic causes of acute pain may require psychological intervention if there is a potential for significant sequela. However, usually, the cause of acute pain can be assessed and treated, permitting the patients to return to their previous physical states.

Causes of acute pain can vary widely. Burns, childbirth, surgery, infection, and trauma are the most common causes of acute pain. Most importantly, in the case of diagnosed acute pain, the clinician is able to treat the underlying cause of the pain. Once the cause is treated, the symptom of pain should subside.

The duration of the pain process, the temporal perspective, is the most obvious distinction that is made when classifying pain.[6] Pain that is limited to less than thirty days is seen as acute. The exception to the duration distinction occurs when the underlying cause of the pain is not treatable. In the case of disease, such as cancer, even though the patient has experienced pain for less than thirty days, if the underlying cause can not be treated or removed, the patient should be diagnosed with chronic pain and treated accordingly. If the patient has not already been evaluated for the psychological impact of the pain state, she should be at this time.

Tip

Duration is a critical parameter to assess when classifying a patient's pain.

Attorneys are more likely to be involved in litigating cases involving either recurrent acute pain or chronic pain. Recurrent acute pain defines a pain pattern that persists over an extended period of time but is episodic in nature.[6] The patient will experience periods in which he is pain free interrupted by periods of pain. Sickle cell anemia crisis, headaches, gastrointestinal motility disorders, degenerative disc and joint disease, collagen vascular disease, and similar functional processes are examples of conditions which cause recurrent acute pain. These patients experience a wide range of symptomatology that would benefit from psychiatric or psychological intervention. Fear and anxiety are the most prominent psychological symptoms for individuals with recurrent acute pain. They fear the inevitable return of the acute pain, which is a natural progression in the course of their disease, as well as the effects on work status and potential sequela following the next episode.

The variability and unpredictability of recurrent acute pain make effective coping difficult and thus contribute to an adversary relationship so often observed between patients and healthcare professionals. Individuals fear dismissal, labeling of the pain as "not real," and being labeled as "mentally ill." While diseases such as sickle cell anemia seem neither to increase or decrease vulnerability to addiction, physicians continue greatly to overestimate the incidence of addiction in this patient population. This misconception leads to significant undertreatment of the pain and reinforcement of drug- seeking behavior. The vicious cycle continues until the patient receives adequate pain control and appropriate psychological interventions to repair the physician-patient relationship.

Tip

Fear and anxiety are the most common psychological symptoms in patients with pain.

Physiologically, the acute pain patient may experience numerous subjective, as well as objective, changes. Increases in blood pressure, heart rate, and respiration are commonly seen, along with nausea, profuse sweating, pallor, and vertigo. As acute pain is treatable and self-limiting in duration, patients experience these symptoms for a short period of time.

A. Management of acute pain

It is doubtful that most of us would survive without the protective mechanism of acute pain.[6] By warning of danger and limiting utilization of injured parts, pain prompts access to the medical system. However, some treatments of underlying pathology are pain-generating in and of themselves. Most notable is surgery. Postoperative pain is considered a specific type of acute pain that commonly requires the use of opioids or nonsteroidal anti-inflammatory drug medications.[6] The use of comfort measures, such as heat or cold, can also help relieve the discomfort, along with sentiments of concern from friends and family. See Chapter 3 for more information on pain management.

B. Complications of acute pain

One of the major complications of postoperative pain is its undertreatment. Attorneys and legal nurse consultants may see evidence of undertreatment of pain in medical records or elicit that testimony when questioning the plaintiff. Patients receive significantly less opioid analgesics than are ordered because the staff is overly concerned regarding opioid addiction, analgesics are irrationally selected, patients fear addiction and therefore do not request pain relief, and many physicians have inadequate knowledge about the pharmacology of analgesics.[6] While it is a widely held axiom that "no one ever died from pain," the physiologic effects of uncontrolled acute pain can be devastating. Therefore, although it is not practical or desirable to eliminate all postoperative pain, clinicians should be prepared to minimize its incidence and severity. Research has shown that pain increases cardiac work and metabolic rate, interferes with blood clotting, leads to water retention, impairs wound healing, and alters immune function. The psychological and emotional disturbances that can be caused by uncontrolled or undertreated acute pain can also lead to lifelong changes in the patient. Individuals may find themselves reluctant to seek the medical interventions necessary in the future to avoid the discomfort they experienced in the past.

C. Psychological issues in acute pain

Psychological manifestations are more commonly associated with chronic pain than acute pain. However, when they arise, symptoms such as fear, anxiety, anger, irritability, and restlessness can be seen. These symptoms, to a mild degree, are expected, but when they become more severe or interrupt the patient's recovery a psychological evaluation and treatment may become necessary. If left untreated, these symptoms can lead to profound changes in the patient's quality of life. These factors have been reported in the literature to influence the tolerance for pain significantly and may determine the amount of suffering and pain generated.[7] While the pain will subside with treatment of the underlying cause, the fear and anxiety may be sustained by the patient for long periods of time. Patients have reported fear of future injuries or medical procedures, mistrust of the healthcare system, unwillingness to return for subsequent treatments, and in extreme cases, withdrawal from leisure activities.

4.4 Chronic Pain

In contrast to acute pain, chronic pain lasts longer than six months, has lost any beneficial attributes, and is usually present because the body is not healing or because physical damage is ongoing. For some researchers, however, this six-month interval definition is inappropriate and too broad. Bonica, possibly more succinctly, defines chronic pain as that "which persists a month beyond the usual course of an acute disease or reasonable time for an injury to heal."[6] Whichever definition for duration the clinician utilizes, all agree that the characteristics of chronic pain are detrimental to the patient. When pain becomes intractable (cannot be reduced) and serves no useful purpose, it can be as destructive and pernicious to the life process as any disease entity.[6] Unfortunately, chronic pain is now considered to be one of the most common and difficult problems to manage. Substantial evidence indicates that neither acute nor chronic pain are managed adequately within most U.S. healthcare systems. If treated by using acute pain process strategies, chronic pain may eventually become more intense, with the patient experiencing increased disability and suffering.[6] Based on this information, most clinicians understand that the goal of chronic pain management is avoidance. Therefore, scheduled pain medication is utilized in place of an "as needed" time frame. Review of medical records by attorneys and legal nurse consultants will indicate that the pain medication was ordered "ATC" or around the clock. This regimen can decrease the amount of analgesic that is necessary, as well as the abuse potential of certain agents.

Tip

The goal of chronic pain management is avoidance. Therefore, any medical record should reflect that the patient is receiving scheduled medications or therapeutic interventions.

A. Impact of chronic pain

Chronic pain, in contrast to acute pain management, requires both physical and psychological strategies. While psychological treatment should supplement medical care and not replace it, the medical assessment of chronic pain without psychiatric assessment would compromise any medical diagnostic endeavor.[6] Pain and depression tend to co-occur irrespective of disease severity and whether or not there is an organic basis for pain. Emotional distress can actually increase the intensity of the pain, but the presence of emotional factors does not mean that the pain is imaginary. Psychometric testing can exclude or confirm existing psychopathology of dysfunctional traits allowing clinicians to identify patients at risk for serious psychological symptomatology.

Bonica states that in most cases apprehension, fear, guilt, depression, worry, and anxiety—all mental effects of pain—seem to have as much to do with the physical deterioration of the patient as does the pain itself.[6] The attorney questioning the plaintiff about chronic pain would be well served to ask questions to identify the coexisting mental effects of pain. These symptoms impose severe emotional, economic, physical, and social stresses on the patient. No matter what factors with which the pain experience consists or is associated, and regardless of etiology, the mind and body are connected, and therefore, affected together by the experience.[6] This bond between the physical and psychological gives rise to the concept of suffering.

B. Suffering in chronic pain

No discussion of pain would be complete without addressing the component of suffering. In a comprehensive study, Cassell (1991) states that "people in pain frequently report suffering from pain when they feel out of control, when the pain is overwhelming, when the source of the pain is unknown, when the meaning of the pain is dire, or when the pain is apparently without end . . . in these situations persons perceive pain as a threat to their continued existence—not merely to their lives but their integrity as a person."[6] Components of suffering include

- sadness,
- anger,
- loneliness,
- depression,
- grief,
- unhappiness,
- melancholy,
- rage,
- withdrawal,
- yearning,
- powerlessness,
- helplessness,
- hopelessness,
- isolation, and
- unremitting fear.

These symptoms are usually associated with the "chronic pain syndrome." Suffering is an intricate part of pain. As presented by Loeser, the multifaceted model of pain includes nociception, which is the transmission of the pain impulse, pain, suffering, and pain behavior.[8] After the pain impulse is transmitted to the brain (nociception) the perception of pain ensues. In turn, suffering is generated, leading to pain behaviors. Pain behaviors are defined as "any type of output from an organism that is commonly understood to suggest the existence of a tissue damaging stimulus."[8] Suffering, like pain, is a subjective complaint and can only be assessed through patient report and pain behaviors.

Tip

The suffering component of the pain process causes psychological symptoms.

Beyond the physical perception of pain, patients also have an understanding of what the pain represents through suffering. Therefore, it is actually this suffering component to the physical pain process that causes psychological symptoms. Through this definition of suffering, it is clear that not all clients who suffer are in physical pain, but all patients in pain are suffering. Further discussion of this concept is found in Chapter 5, "Suffering: A Multi-Dimensional Concept."

C. Losses in chronic pain

Patients with chronic pain potentially experience loss of function, employment, and financial security. Other losses experienced by the patient include self-efficacy, mobility, position in the family structure, and sense of well-being. This concept is demonstrated in the case of *Partner-Brown v. Bornstein*, where the plaintiff contended that due to malpractice on the part of his podiatrist he was experiencing loss of enjoyment of life. The court of appeals in Florida, found that physical pain and suffering can impair the enjoyment of life and can be considered by a jury separate from mental anguish. The court upheld the finding of the lower court and found for the plaintiff.[9]

In response to these losses the patient often becomes depressed and develops a sense of helplessness.[10] This helplessness results in lack of motivation and passive coping, which may affect physical recovery. The patient who loses motivation tends to be less compliant with treatment regimens resulting in extenuation of recovery time. This noncompliance with treatment may be misinterpreted by attorneys who conclude that the pain was not present or had been previously magnified. It is also crucial to note that when chronic pain results from physical trauma, it is a continuing reminder of the trauma and is thus re-traumatizing, serving as a reminder of the original event.[10]

The losses from the pain experience however, are not experienced alone. Spouses, children, and parents are also dramatically affected. A spouses may be required to increase his or her role as wage earner as well as assume more responsibilities in the home. Children may have to forego or abandon extracurricular activities due to financial changes or increase in house duties. While family members may adapt to these changes without difficulty, the pain patient usually reports an overwhelming sense of guilt related to the diagnosis and changes that have been required. Attorneys questioning of the person in chronic pain should include exploration of the effect of chronic pain on the rest of the family.

D. Psychological issues in chronic pain

The concurrent losses that are experienced by individuals diagnosed with chronic pain can lead to very specific psychological changes. These changes can be potentially devastating, not only for the patient but the family as well. Figure 4.1 provides a list of questions the attorney should ask family members to provide further insight to the patient's status and its familial effects.

1. Depression

Depression for the patient experiencing chronic pain can be overwhelming. Studies show that 20%–70% of pain patients also suffer from major depression.[11]

While there is a clear understanding that depression can precipitate physical pain, researchers point out, "it is equally as likely that pain may precede anxiety and depression."[11] The delineation of which is the antecedent symptom may seem confusing; however, it is clear that both must be treated concurrently to achieve a successful outcome. To complicate the situation, diagnosing depression can also be difficult. There are three main types of depression experienced by chronic pain patients; reactive or adjustment disorder

- Does the individual still participate in usual activities?
- Does the individual still participate in hobbies or leisure activities?
- Have you noticed any personality changes?
- Has the individual become aggressive in any way?
- Has the individual had hallucinations or delusions?
- Has the individual demonstrated anger or discouragement?
- How has the current situation changed your relationship with the individual?
- What impact has the current situation had on your life?
- What changes have been made in your life due to the individual's current state?

Figure 4.1 *Questions for attorneys to ask family members about psychological changes*

with depressed mood; depression not otherwise specified; and a major depressive episode. While most chronic pain patients will experience reactive depression, their symptoms may worsen over time, leading to a more clinically depressed state.

Reactive depression, also known as adjustment disorder with depressed mood, is temporary and related to some current event or loss. This is seen in patients who have lost a loved one or experienced a change in relationship, such as divorce, breaking an engagement, or leaving a job. The specific psychological symptoms have occurred in response to a specific and identifiable psychosocial stressor. The reactions of the client may go beyond feeling blue or down; however, they are a necessary part of the internal processing of the loss which the grieving person must go through before reorganizing her life. Reactive depression is a normal part of the grieving process even though the symptoms may be very deep. Clients should be evaluated frequently during this time and assessed for symptoms that are debilitating, last longer than is reasonable, or do not improve with time.

Depression NOS (not otherwise specified) is a diagnosis used to classify patients with serious depression that do not meet the criteria for major depression. This includes patients whose depressive symptoms have not lasted long enough to have dysthymic disorder (greater than two years) but continue to be depressed in response to some traumatic event longer than usually expected.[13] Most clinicians expect that depression will not last longer than six months after the stressor has ended. However, with chronic pain patients, the stressor does not end. For these clients, expectations are that they will begin to adapt to their circumstances and the depressive symptoms will resolve. Clients who are unable to adapt may find their depression lasting longer than six months.

A major depressive episode is more pronounced than reactive depression or depression not otherwise specified.[13] For a diagnosis of major depression, five or more of the following symptoms must occur during a two-week period almost daily and one of the symptoms must be depressed mood or loss of interest or pleasure in usual activities. The symptoms are

- depressed mood most of the day,
- markedly diminished interest or pleasure in all or almost all activities,
- significant weight loss when not dieting or weight gain, decrease or increase in appetite,
- insomnia or hypersomnia,
- psychomotor agitation or retardation,
- fatigue or loss of energy,
- feelings of worthlessness or guilt,
- diminished ability to think or concentrate or indecisiveness, and
- recurrent thoughts of death.[13]

Specifically related to individuals diagnosed with major depression is the risk of suicide. All intimations that a patient is having recurrent thoughts of death or suicide require complete documentation and intervention by a qualified clinician.

In an opinion in a case in New York, the appellate court recognized that the prediction of the course of an individual's mental disease is difficult. However, clinicians should apply a standard of care which includes the evaluation of symptoms and appropriate interventions to protect patients from self-harm. In this case, the patient had been released on a pass after threatening to end his life. He then committed suicide. The family claimed wrongful death, medical malpractice, and pain and suffering. While the wrongful death and malpractice judgments of the lower court were upheld in this case, the evidence remained insufficient regarding conscious pain and suffering.[14] Further exploration of the psychiatric history of the patient by the plaintiff's attorney, as well as a more complete explanation of the relationship between depression and pain and suffering may have altered this decision.

In this type of case, the attorney is faced with the difficult task of making clinical depression palpable for the layperson. The most effective way of achieving this goal is to utilize analogies that mirror experiences common to the human condition. Most of the population, at one time or another, has contracted the flu. A comparison between clinical depression and suffering flu symptoms emphasizes feelings rather than jargon, allowing the jury to empathize with the plaintiff. The attorney may even address specific symptoms that are shared by both disease states, such as insomnia or fatigue. This analogy can be expanded to include the family by discussing the impact that having an ill member can have on the routine and overall well-being of others.

Attorneys should remember that depressed patients and their families may be so exhausted from the effect of the disease that they are unable to communicate adequately with the jury. The fatigue, indecisiveness, and apathy that are a part of clinical depression may leave the patient unable to even answer simple questions about the disease. Therefore, the attorney should strive not only to broaden her understanding of the patient's experience but work to translate this information adequately and credibly to the layperson.

2. Anxiety

Along with depression, many chronic pain patients also experience anxiety. Anxiety occurs when an individual believes that the demands of a situation are greater than his abilities to cope with it. A certain amount of anxiety is expected in normal everyday life that prepares an individual to defend or escape a threatening situation. Researchers have found that anxiety can help with task performance by sustaining a heightened state of awareness. However, the anxiety is of short duration and resolves when the task is completed. Anxiety may be considered abnormal if it occurs in the absence of what most people would consider to be an adequate stress, or if it is so severe or longstanding that it interferes with day-to-day life.[15] Generalized anxiety disorder (GAD) is the worry and tension that is chronic, exaggerated, and seems to have no cause. These symptoms last at least two weeks. Individuals tend to anticipate the worst in every case and worry excessively about a variety of issues. The characteristic symptoms of GAD include

- chronic, exaggerated worry and tension that is unfounded,
- duration of six months or more,
- expectation of the worst,
- inability to relax,
- insomnia,
- fatigue, trembling, muscle tension, headaches, irritability, and
- depressed mood.

More women suffer from GAD than do men, however, the symptoms exhibited are the same. Fortunately, people who suffer from GAD do not experience severe social avoidance, yet the symptomatology will significantly interfere with their daily activities. There is considerable overlap between depressive disorders and anxiety disorders. If the diagnostic criteria of both are present, the depressive disorder takes precedence and anxiety symptoms are considered secondary.[15]

Guilt is another common complaint accompanying chronic pain. Patients report that "good days" are marred by feelings of guilt because they do not feel like they are ill. This leads to the perception that they are able to do more than they should. Guilt can also stem from their role change within the family since most patients recognize the burden their illness places on others.

To evaluate the level of psychological symptomatology that a plaintiff client is experiencing, the attorney may ask a few simple questions to help identify individuals in need of further psychological evaluation. Potential questions include:

- How did the pain that you now experience occur?
- Where do you experience the pain?
- How long have you had this pain?

- Do you ever have trouble falling asleep at night?
- What medications have you used in the past month?
- Do you feel that you worry excessively about many things?
- How long have you felt worried?
- Do you experience shortness of breath on occasion?
- Do you have fear of losing control of yourself or of "going crazy"?

These questions give the interviewer insight as to the duration of symptoms, as well as the effect of the symptoms on the patient's activities of daily living. More questions are listed in Figure 4.2 that help in the evaluation of the patient experiencing pain and suffering. Should the attorney find the cognitive triad of symptoms (i.e., helplessness, hopelessness, and lack of self-worth) or if the patient verbalizes thoughts of self-harm or suicide, an immediate referral to a psychiatrist or psychologist must be made.

- On a scale of 1–10, how would you describe the intensity of your pain?
- How would you describe your pain (i.e. sharp, burning, dull)?
- What makes your pain worse?
- What medications are you taking for your pain?
- Are these medications effective?
- Does your pain interfere with your ability to sleep, eat, dress yourself?
- How does your pain interfere with your ability to enjoy your normal activities?
- Have you noticed any change in your sleeping habits?
- Have you noticed changes in your eating habits? Weight gain or loss?
- Do you cry often or easily?
- Have you been more irritable?
- Have you had any changes in relationships with friends and family? At work?
- Do you have difficulty concentrating?
- Do you feel you have more or less control over your life?
- Do you feel responsible for your current situation?
- Do you feel you have less energy?
- Do you think you are pessimistic or optimistic about the future?
- Do you ever think about hurting yourself?
- Are you thinking about hurting yourself right now?

Figure 4.2 *Questions for attorneys to ask the client experiencing pain and suffering*

4.5 Common Treatment Problems

There are many ways in which clinicians and attorneys collect data regarding the patient. These include medical records, reports from friends and family, clinician assessments, and the patient's own words. With complaints such as pain and suffering, however, greater weight must be placed on self-report. Yet even with this understanding, the more evidence of outward quantitative signs of pain, the less dependence there is on the patient's complaints and feelings. Mobility testing is one tool that can quantitatively support patients' subjective reports. A thorough assessment, qualitative and quantitative, of all self-reported symptoms should be of paramount importance to the attorney to differentiate between individuals fabricating their illness and true pain patients.

A. Malingering and factitious disorder

1. Malingering

Due to the subjective nature of pain, pain patients are often challenged regarding the actual validity of the pain. Malingering and factitious disorder are often suspected when there is a dichotomy between physical findings and subjective patient reports. The patient may present with various exaggerated pain behaviors, such as limping, moaning, groaning, and grimacing while the physical examination and various tests may not reveal any obvious pathology.[16] Well-trained clinicians recognize that the extent of a patient's subjective complaints often have more to do with psychological factors than with physical pathology.[16] In order to obtain secondary gains from the pain diagnosis, the patient may participate in deliberate deception, known as malingering and factitious disorder. The causes may also be due to a process unknown to the patient, such as in somatoform disorders where mental states are manifested into bodily symptoms.[17]

Some plaintiffs are labeled as malingerers by their treating physicians or those who perform defense medical examinations. Malingering patients will exaggerate their illness to derive benefits, such as disability, compensation or to obtain controlled substances. If a patient is found to be untruthful regarding his disability, he may lose his benefits and face prosecution. In *Dollison v. Hayes*, the injured plaintiff sued the defendant for injuries sustained in a motor vehicle accident. The jury awarded $0 for past and future physical pain, rejecting the plaintiff's and physician's testimony regarding the severity of his condition. The decision was upheld upon appeal due to the jury's ability to reject offered subjective testimony.[18]

An individual with a history of unlawful, aggressive, or deceitful behavior may have a propensity for malingering. One significant characteristic of malingering is the lack of cooperation with evaluation and treatment. While some patients are found to be noncompliant with therapy, the clinician can usually identify the cause, such as lack of knowledge, limited access to therapy, or side effects of medications. However, the malingerer is unable to show reasonable cause for lack of cooperation. When plaintiffs are unfairly labeled as malingerers, it is usually due to the biases of physicians or to unreasonable expectations about how long it should take for the plaintiff to recover from an injury.

2. Factitious disorder

People with factitious disorder intentionally feign or actually induce physical or psychological illness in themselves, typically to garner the attention of others. These patients seek to satisfy internal needs and are hardly aware of external or material benefits. Unlike malingerers, factitious disorder patients are seeking medical attention and, therefore, comply with treatment regimens and agree to procedures they know are unnecessary.[16] Clients are aware that they are the direct cause of the signs and symptoms they are exhibiting. Some patients report that even though they are cognizant of their actions to induce symptoms they are unable to control the impulse to elicit compassion or interest from others. No single cause has been found for factitious disorder. The development of this condition is commonly linked to child abuse, underlying personality disorder, and a desire to deceive. In many cases the suffering of a major loss has been implicated.[16] Diagnosis of factitious disorder is usually based on the exclusion of medical or psychiatric conditions, together with a combination of signs and symptoms characteristic of the disorder. Such signs and symptoms include falsification of clinical examination, production of disease, or fabrication of false accounts.

This chronic illness is daunting and frustrating for clinicians to treat. Through a thorough assessment, healthcare professionals usually find a history of changing doctors frequently, extensive knowledge of medicine, negative results followed by further symptom development, symptoms that occur only when the patient is being observed, few visitors when hospitalized, and arguments with hospital staff. Treatment usually includes cognitive-behavioral therapy and, in some cases, antidepressant medications. Heavy-handed punitive confrontation does not work.

B. Psychogenic pain

Psychogenic pain (somatoform mental disorder) differs from both malingering and factitious disorder. Mental health consultants are frequently asked to evaluate patients with complaints that may not have a discernible physical cause. Attorneys may see this term used in reports of defense medical examiners. There are numerous subtypes of somatoform disorders identified in the *Diagnostic and Statistical Manual of Mental Disorders*, Fourth Edition.[13] The most common are somatization and pain disorder.

Tip

While somatoform illnesses are linked to mental processes, there still may be a viable medical diagnosis that requires appropriate intervention.

Somatization disorder involves a plethora of symptoms involving four different sites of pain, two gastrointestinal problems such as nausea or vomiting, at least one sexual symptom such as sexual indifference or excessive menstrual bleeding, and one pseudoneurological symptom. For this diagnosis, there must be symptoms in each of these areas that cannot be fully explained by the medical examination. In some cases of somatization disorder, a medical diagnosis can be made, but the resulting impairment is in excess of what is expected. Most importantly, the symptoms are not feigned as in malingering or self-induced as in factitious disorder.

Pain disorder is another subtype of somatoform illness. Patients present with pain in one or more anatomical sites that is severe enough to warrant medical attention.[19] While psychological factors are judged to play a role in the onset, maintenance, and exacerbation of the pain, there is clinically significant distress and impairment that accompanies the symptoms. It must be emphasized that even when psychological factors may initiate a painful condition, all pain is very real to the patient. Clinicians must be able to recognize emotional distress rather than pure nociception and understand that psychological mechanisms do intensify pain.

One study performed in 2002 by Young et al. evaluated the effects of stressful events on chronic pain perception. The study was significant based on the fact that the effect of disaster and trauma on physical pain had historically not been evaluated. He found that overt acts of mass aggression, terrorism, and other forms of disaster (both natural and man-made calamity) may exert a potent and enduring influence on physical pain perception.[19] By triggering an acute stress response, these acts of barbarism can amplify pain-correlated symptoms such as muscle spasms, jumpiness, jitteriness, twitchiness, irritability, and hyperarousal. This study supports the premise that emotional stress may influence an individual to adopt negative coping strategies and become less proactive in managing chronic pain.

A somatoform diagnosis does not mean there is no real medical illness or pathology. Unfortunately, somatizing patients can become passive and dependent as their symptoms increase. Clinicians must be wary of reinforcing the somatizing behavior. They may inadvertently send the message that being physically ill is acceptable but being depressed or anxious is not. Overall, this patient population remains very difficult to treat. Fueled by the increased attention from others, they resist psychiatric referrals and deny the possible role of psychological factors. The legal system's emphasis on the value of chronic pain may inadvertently reinforce the somatizing patient to continue to report pain.

C. Chronic back pain

The complaint of back pain continues to be problematic for patients, clinicians, and psychologists, especially when it stems from a work-related injury. The effective evaluation of a patient with chronic back pain requires the physician and pain management team to be thoroughly familiar with the physiologic characteristics of pain, as well as the social and psychological factors that influence an individual's response to a work injury.[16]

In 1980, Waddell and his associates developed a standardized assessment of behavioral responses that occur during a physical examination. Waddell's behavioral signs are grouped into five categories, including tenderness, simulation, distraction, regional disturbances, and overreaction.[16]

1. Tenderness should not be present as back pain does not render skin tender to light touch.
2. When pressure is applied to the top of the head of a standing patient or the shoulders and pelvis are rotated in unison, there is no pressure applied to the lower back. Therefore, the patient should not experience any discomfort during this simulation test.
3. The distracted straight leg raise can be performed with the patient seated with one knee extended.
4. The regional disturbances exam evaluates any sensory change or weakness that does not follow expected patterns. An example is the patient who complains of pain throughout an entire limb instead of pain that follows the nerve pathways originating in the spine.
5. A positive sign to overreaction is noted when the client is hypersensitive to touch at varying times during the examination.

A positive finding is defined as the presence of three or more of these signs. While Waddell's behavioral signs have been well documented in the literature, the purpose of the examination should be limited to aiding clinical assessment directing appropriate physical or psychological treatment, screening for illness behavior, and reducing unnecessary procedures. Clinicians and attorneys need to be aware that the presence of behavioral signs does not contradict or preclude physical findings.

Another assessment tool for evaluation of patients with back pain is the Mensana Clinical Back Test. This test is designed to measure the validity of the complaint of pain in patients who have had pain in their back, neck, arms, or legs for six months or longer, independent of pre-existing personality traits or psychological tests.[20] The test consists of fifteen questions and has a potential scoring of 60 points. Each question is asked by the examiner and should be administered by an individual trained in the test's administration and evaluation. A score of 17 points or less suggests that the patient is reporting a normal response to chronic pain. A score of 18–20 points identifies a chronic pain patient who may be exaggerating the symptoms. An exaggerating patient will score between 21–31, while a score of 32 or higher suggests that a psychiatric consultation is necessary. Physical and psychological therapy of the chronic pain patient remains a difficult task at best. However, with ongoing research, better assessment techniques, and appropriate interventions, improved quality of life for these patients can be achieved.

D. Locked-in syndrome and posttraumatic stress disorder

1. Locked-in syndrome

Beyond the challenges of treating malingering pain patients and those with factitious disorder, there are other special populations of pain patients that require adaptive methods of evaluation and treatment. One is the patient with locked-in syndrome, and the other is the posttraumatic stress disorder client.

Locked-in syndrome is a rare and devastating neurological disorder characterized by complete paralysis of voluntary muscles in all parts of the body except for those that control eye movement.[21] The brain damage is found in the ventral part of the rotral pons, or brain stem, where motor axons from both sides of the brain converge. Limbs, trunk, neck, and even the muscles in the face are affected. Breathing may or may not be affected; however, most patients will require some type of airway assistance. Causes of the disorder range from traumatic brain injury, vascular disease, and demyelinating disease to medication overdose. Brain stem stroke from basilar artery thrombosis is the most common cause.[22] Stroke victims and those suffering from amyotropic lateral sclerosis (Lou Gehrig's disease) are also at risk for developing this devastating disability.

Tip

Patients with Lou Gehrig's disease understand that they will experience locked-in syndrome. This understanding often leads patients to consider physician-assisted suicide.

Communication for these patients is almost nonexistent. In many cases, some facial movement remains, and patients are able to send messages through eye or jaw movements. In contrast to other brain injury and organic brain disorders, patients with locked-in syndrome remain completely aware and conscious of their surroundings. This may be ascertained by assessing the patient's ability to respond to simple commands, such as to look up or down. If eye movements are not spared, the electroencephalogram may be the only means of distinguishing this state from coma.

There is no cure for locked-in syndrome. While functional neuromuscular stimulation can activate some muscles, most care for these patients is supportive in nature. Initial care is directed toward the acute medical issue. Thereafter patients will require total care. The patient will require a feeding tube and assistance with all elimination processes and general activities of daily living. Most importantly, these patients need companionship and a variety of daily experiences as they are conscious and retain cognitive function.[21]

Scientists are currently investigating several creative computer-based communication strategies that appear to receive commands directly from the brain, bypassing the muscles. One type involves an electrode that is implanted in the brain and picks up electrical impulse activity and sends the message to a computer which prints out the message.

The consequences surrounding locked-in syndrome are devastating for the patient as well as the entire family. Patients find themselves trapped in a body that no longer responds to their wishes or commands. While communication may be tedious, these individuals must be given the opportunity to release the feelings of fear, anxiety, depression, anger, and grief that accompany this disorder.[21] The predominant fear for clients is that of another insult to the brain and death. This fear is not unfounded. Stroke victims are constantly faced with the potential for another stroke rendering even the smallest movements impossible. Also, patients and family members are informed at diagnosis that the most common cause of death of individuals with a history of stroke is another stroke. Therefore, medications for anxiety are usually ordered in low dosages to help the patient cope with their status.

While physical pain is not usually associated with muscle paralysis, patients must be continuously evaluated for their comfort level. Even though the signals for movement are no longer transmitted, the patients are still aware of sensory input and therefore are fully capable of pain perception. Many patients continue to suffer pre-morbid conditions, such as arthritis and migraine headaches. The pain from these disorders will continue to register with the patient just as procedural pain will. They will not be able to communicate even the greatest intensity of discomfort unless the caregiver is proactive in assessment of the patient. Most importantly, the patient's needs must be anticipated.

With an understanding that the prognosis for these individuals is poor and the majority do not regain function, family members are faced with the daunting task of a complete care patient for an indeterminate amount of time.[21] Changes in financial status, working arrangements, and living arrangements may all occur concurrently, causing a great deal of stress for all involved. Most commonly, these patients cannot be in the home. The care required for these individuals is intense and complicated. This issue can bring about feelings of abandonment, fear, anger, resentment, and depression in all those involved.

The patient and family should be psychologically evaluated by healthcare providers as soon as possible. Even conventional methods, such as cognitive and behavioral therapy, can be very useful and should be initiated immediately to help identify coping strategies and decrease feelings of isolation.

2. Posttraumatic stress disorder

Along with severe physical damage following a trauma, psychological problems may also emerge that were not present prior to the incident. Such is the case with posttraumatic stress disorder (PTSD). This syndrome is defined as a response to an extremely stressful event that would be distressing to anyone. The types of events that may be associated with personal injury litigation may include awareness of an unavoidable collision, witnessing the death of a fellow passenger in a vehicle, or observing one's child being hit by a car. That is, the threshold event is recognized to be capable of evoking significant symptoms in most people.

In a 2001 case, a jury awarded $1.64 million to a New York woman who witnessed an accident that killed her husband and who suffered serious injuries of her own. The couple's car was struck by a tractor trailer that was changing lanes. The couple got out of their car. Another car then struck the husband and his wife and propelled her twenty feet down the road, where she landed on a divider. Both people were taken to the hospital, where the husband died during surgery two hours later. The jury awarded the wife $1.295 million. This included $750,000 for her physical injuries, $100,000 for chronic pain and $95,000 for lost wages. The husband's estate received a $295,000 wrongful death award and $50,000 for conscious pain and suffering.[23]

The individual may experience, witness, or be confronted with an event or events that involved actual or threatened death or serious injury or threat to the physical integrity of self or others.

A Somerset, New Jersey, jury awarded $750,000 to a man who was traumatized when a UPS truck crashed into the living room of his condominium. Although he was not physically harmed, he was subsequently diagnosed with posttraumatic stress disorder and panic disorder. The plaintiff was upstairs and did not see the accident, but he heard it and rushed downstairs to check on the safety of his wife and ten-month-old baby who were in the rear of the unit and witnessed the accident. Neither was physically hurt. The wife was also a plaintiff and settled before trial. The husband claimed that the crash had made him nervous, irritable, and subject to sleep disturbances and pain attacks. The plaintiff rejected an arbitration award of $4,500. UPS plans to appeal the verdict.[24]

Recently, the *DSM-IV* deleted the requirement for the event to be outside the range of normal human experience.[25] The disease is more likely to occur after a man-made disaster than a natural one. There may be a delay of days or weeks between the stressful event and the initiation of symptoms. Individuals may function without difficulty during and immediately following the trauma in an almost eerily calm manner. However, once symptoms begin they are usually well-established within six months.

PTSD patients exhibit a myriad of symptoms that can range from mild to severe in intensity. This complex set of psychological and biologic problems can develop from an acute or chronic stressor. Clients may report sleep problems, depression, being easily startled, headaches, gastrointestinal disturbances, dizziness, and chest pain. There is also a tendency to lose interest in leisure activities and withdraw from others. The most common and life-altering symptoms include anxiety, reexperiencing the trauma, and avoidance behavior.

Reexperiencing the trauma, or flashbacks, can be triggered by sights, sounds or odors that remind individuals of the event.[25] During the flashback, patients can lose touch with reality, feel and believe that they are reliving the trauma, as well as actually see images, hear sounds, and distinguish smells that accompany the memory. These episodes usually last only a few seconds or minutes; however, on rare occasions they have lasted several days. Patients may also experience nightmares and disturbing thoughts related to the trauma.

Tip

Flashbacks can be so detrimental to the patient's functioning ability that remaining gainfully employed can become almost impossible.

Because of the perceived reality of the flashback, patients often identify triggers to the flashbacks and begin to avoid any possibility of coming in contact with them. For some patients, this activity of avoidance behavior may significantly interfere with their ability to live a normal life. Individuals may begin to see crowds or even small groups as triggers. Depending on the patient and the trauma experienced, one may find being outside intolerable, while another specifically avoids enclosed spaces.

A New York woman was the victim of a break-in. An intruder beat, raped, and sodomized her. Her six-year-old son witnessed the attack. The mother contended that she suffered psychological injuries including post traumatic stress disorder with nightmares, flashbacks, depression, and hypervigilance. The plaintiff son contended that he experienced post traumatic stress disorder with difficulty sleeping and a fear that someone will get into the house and assault his mother again. The jury determined that the defendant failed to maintain the building in a safe condition and awarded the plaintiffs a total of $5,852,000. To the mother, the jury awarded $5,151,000, which included $1,000,000 past pain and suffering, $1,000 past medical expenses, $4,000,000 future pain and suffering, and $150,000 future medical expenses. To the son, the jury awarded a total of $701,000, including $500,000 past pain and suffering, $1,000 past medical expenses, $200,000 future medical expenses, and $0 future pain and suffering. *Johnson v. NYCHA*.[26]

Risk factors for the development of PTSD include, but are not limited to, a history of mental illness, poor coping skills, and lack of social support. While PTSD is treatable, interventions should begin as soon as possible to minimize the personal impact of the disorder and increase the chances of recovery. At the onset of symptoms, patients may attempt to self-medicate with drugs and alcohol. To avoid this destructive behavior, early intervention is crucial.

Psychiatric treatment should include

- teaching patients to accept trauma,
- decreasing patients' need to rearrange life to avoid reminders of the event,
- allowing time for intense grief and mourning, and
- allowing time to verbalize feelings of fear, anger, grief, and rage.[27]

This can be accomplished through cognitive-behavioral therapy, group psychotherapy, and medications such as antidepressants. However, no amount of treatment can help individuals who do not participate in their therapy. Unfortunately, just due to the nature of the disease and symptoms, patients with PTSD have a very difficult time being compliant with treatment. It is vital that they receive support from family and friends to attend to all prescribed medications and therapies. Lawyers as well should support clients in doing what is necessary to get better.

4.6 Grief

Any discussion of pain and suffering would be incomplete without a discussion regarding grief. Loss is an inevitable part of human existence. Losses associated with death are complex and unique, as is the grief that accompanies the loss. Grief may be experienced whenever a survivor loses a family member or friend in an accident and may be associated with survivor guilt or the guilt from recognizing that one's life was spared.

A. Anticipatory grief

Researchers have identified several types of grief: anticipatory, grief, and complicated grief. Anticipatory grief refers to the process of mourning an impending loss.[33] Most commonly, this type of grief is noted in patients who are terminally ill, as well as in their families. As they prepare for the separation of death, they begin to grieve over loss of hopes, dreams, and expectations. Ill patients will begin to process their life and prepare for its ending.

However, death is not the only time individuals experience this type of grief. Losses resulting from medical malpractice can also lead to anticipatory grief.

In 2000, $550,000 was awarded to a New York woman when she contended that her gynecologist had failed to perform a pregnancy test after she complained of abnormal bleeding. She was subsequently diagnosed with a ruptured ectopic pregnancy and the left fallopian tube was removed. She contended that her history of endometriosis and loss of one fallopian tube greatly diminished her ability to conceive.[28]

The sequelae of the event in this case included not only the physical loss of reproductive health, but also an altered sense of well-being, the potential inability to procreate without assistance from medications or medical procedures, and the grief associated with perceived future loss in a life without children.

To a lesser extent feelings of sadness and loss may be processed before a graduation, a move, or any other significant life-changing event. Prior to surgery, such as mastectomy, hysterectomy, or amputation, the patient may begin anticipatory grieving for the whole body she had before she begins to accept the concept of what her new body will be like.

B. Grief

Grief relates to the feelings related to the loss. Patients may experience anger, frustration, sadness, guilt, or regret as they work through this process. While grief is an expected reaction, the emotions involved vary from person to person and are very real. Without question, grieving individuals require that their extremely personal perceptions be accepted for what they are.

C. Complicated grief

Complicated grief is the term used to describe grief intensified to the point of being overwhelming, leading individuals to maladaptive behaviors.[27] Several authorities on this topic agree that pathology is more related to the intensity and duration of the grief reaction rather than the presence or absence of specific suspect behavior.[29] Attorneys representing clients displaying the following symptoms should recommend that the client seek further evaluation and assessment for potential complicated grief:

- speaking of the event produces intense and fresh grief
- relatively minor events produce intense grief reaction
- loss is often the theme of discussions
- survivor unwilling to move items that belonged to deceased
- survivor develops symptoms similar to those of deceased prior to death
- radical life changes
- history of subclinical depression or low self-esteem; false sense of euphoria following loss
- compulsive need to imitate the deceased
- self-destructive behavior
- episodic unaccountable sadness
- fear of similar illness
- avoidance of death rituals[30]

Tip

Hope is a basic spiritual need which relates to the future. Clinicians and attorneys working with patients who are grieving or suffering should ask questions related to expectations for the future.

Failure to grieve is usually seen as another complication of the grief process. When a clinician determines that the patient is not exhibiting the symptoms associated with the normal grieving process, a diagnosis of failure to grieve may be applied. However, healthcare professionals and attorneys must remember that each person grieves differently. There should not be a hasty judgment that the client is not processing the loss until a thorough assessment is made, including the patient's coping mechanisms, available support, and past history of grieving.

D. Additional perspectives on grief

Mourning is actually the process one undergoes to resolve the grief.[31] This process relates to the deceased, the external world, and self. Culture plays an important role in how, when, where, and how long a person will mourn.

Sigmund Freud wrote about the grief process in his classic paper "Mourning and Melancholia." He believed that grief was a response to loss, including but not limited to death. Regarding duration of mourning, Freud recognized that the process was not complete until the ego became free and uninhibited again.[31]

Erich Lindemann addressed acute traumatic grief in a systematic way. He discovered that individuals may experience somatic symptoms, as well as feelings of guilt and anger, after the loss of a loved one in an unexpected manner. To bring order and insight to grief, Lindemann identified three stages of grief: shock and disbelief, acute mourning, and resolution of the grief process.[30] To work through these stages, survivors perform the tasks of grief which are: emancipation for the deceased, readjustment to life without the deceased, and formation of new relationships. Duration of grief depends on how efficiently the individual is able to complete each task.

Bowlby and Parks described four phases of mourning: numbness, yearning and searching, disorganization and despair, and reorganization.[33] The first phase of numbness is characterized by a generalized feeling of detachment. This dazed feeling functions as a protective mechanism during the first few weeks of bereavement and may be considered a form of denial. The yearning and searching phase denotes the period of time when individuals begin to realize that their loved one is gone. They may report sensing the deceased's presence or hear their foot steps. The bereaved may experience disbelief, tension, sobbing, or irritability. Characterized by giving up the search for the deceased, the disorganization and despair phase finds individuals apathetic and depressed. Clients begin to realize they have entered a world devoid of their loved one. As grieving individuals begin to seek ways to remake their lives they are considered to be entering the reorganization phase. They begin to break attachment to the lost loved one and establish new ties.

Kubler-Ross in 1969 developed the stages of death and dying.[31] After interviewing 200 terminally ill individuals, she began to formulate a picture of the grief process of the dying. Interestingly, over the intervening years, these stages have been found to mirror the grief process of the non-terminal person as well. While these stages are not intended to be viewed as sequential processes through which individuals pass, the grieving person will experience each of these.

The identified stages are denial, anger, bargaining, depression, acceptance, and hope.[31] In the beginning of the grief process, the individual tends to separate himself from the grief process. He tends to separate himself from the event by refusing to believe that it is happening to him. This denial is often used as a coping mechanism to make the situation more manageable. Once the individual realizes that this is truly the situation, anger usually follows. Here the client may make statements such as "Why me?" and "What did I ever do to deserve this?" The client also may exhibit signs of irritability and aggressive behavior as a manifestation of anger. Bargaining involves a realization that anger is counterproductive for the individual. Patients begin to attempt to make contracts and agreements with a higher power. While clinicians or attorneys may or may not be informed regarding these deals, the behavior of the client changes dramatically as if part of the bargain is to "be good." The client usually has a very positive attitude and outlook on the situation. Following the bargaining stage is depression. During this stage individuals usually experience reactive depression and not clinical depression.[27] They express feelings of sadness regarding their situation and may experience episodes of crying. Patients have reported a great deal of introspection during this time involving self-evaluation and may withdraw from loved ones for quiet time alone. During the acceptance stage, individuals come to terms with the situation, and while there may be periods of sadness, they begin to reintegrate into social situations and significant relationships. The final stage is hope. Clients begin to alter their hopes from what they were to what is reasonable following their loss. This relates to the reorganization phase identified by Bowlby and Parks; however, individuals may be seen to move back and forth through the stages of death and dying as they mourn.

Tip

Grief has no timetable.

One of the major changes in grief theory over the past few years is the shift from the concept of stages to tasks.[27] Mourning is an active and unique experience. By focusing on the client's objectives, the dimension of time is removed and therefore more universally applicable. Worden identified four tasks that incorporate the work of grief. They are

- accept the reality of the loss,
- work through the pain of grief,
- adjust to the environment in which the deceased is missing, and
- relocate the deceased emotionally and move on with life.[27]

Normal grief remains an enigma for healthcare professionals due to the high variability of symptomatology between patients. Many of the theories already discussed come from anecdotal data and public perception regarding grief and bereavement. However, to understand this phenomenon fully, attorneys, researchers, and clinicians need to have common knowledge of the wide range of behaviors manifested by an individual's mourning. These symptoms are grouped into four categories: feelings, physical sensations, cognitions, and behaviors.

Feelings accompanying normal grief include sadness, anger, guilt or self-reproach, anxiety, loneliness, fatigue, helplessness, yearning, emancipation, relief, and numbness. If these feelings persist, they may herald the development of complicated grief, and patients should be evaluated for treatment.

Physical sensations are very common yet often overlooked. These symptoms include hollowness in the stomach, chest and throat tightness, over sensitivity to noise, a sense of unreality, feeling short of breath, muscle weakness, lack of energy, and dry mouth. Clinicians should perform a thorough assessment and investigation of these symptoms to ensure there is no underlying pathology.

Cognitions refer to the thought patterns that are characteristic of the grief process. Disbelief, confusion, obsession, as well as visual and auditory hallucinations are common after a major loss.

Sleep disturbances, dreams, avoidance, restlessness, and over-activity are also associated with grieving. These behaviors often correct themselves over time. Crying is possibly the most puzzling behavior, not for the clinician but for the client. When an individual cries, there are normally identifiable precursors. These include a lump in the throat, overwhelming emotions, and headache. Curiously, patients who have experienced a significant loss find that some crying episodes begin with no warning signs. The individual may only become aware that she is crying when she finds tears on her cheek.

Most importantly for clinicians is the ability to differentiate between grief and depression. The following gives some guidance in this difficult task. Grief is characterized by

- no clear history of depression,
- recognizable loss,
- mood states are labile,
- variable behavior,
- open anger and hostility,
- sporadic weeping,
- preoccupation with loss,
- vividly clear dreams,

- episodic sleep disturbances, and
- self-blame.

Individuals experiencing grief usually respond to warmth and reassurance.[29]

Depression is marked by

- history of mental problems,
- loss seen as punishment,
- prolonged sense of sadness,
- withdrawn,
- anger internalized,
- weeping may be inhibited or uncontrolled,
- preoccupation with self; sees self as bad for being depressed, and
- moderate to severe insomnia.

Individuals suffering from depression respond to pressure and urgings.[29]

The following is a list of questions that might be asked by the attorney or clinician to ascertain the client's current state:

- How do you feel this loss has affected your life?
- Based on previous losses, how would you compare this loss?
- Have you noticed any change in your sleeping or eating patterns?
- In relation to the grief you have seen in others, tell me how you would compare your grief.

These questions seek out information regarding physical and emotional components of the grief process. By having clients compare the current loss to previous experiences and to the grief they have seen in others, the attorney can better identify breaks with reality and refer the individual for further evaluation.

E. The role of the attorney in helping the grieving client

While grief has no time table, there are identifiable stages when individuals may seek legal counsel following a loss. Commonly, this is during the anger stage of grief. As individuals perform the task of seeking understanding for why the loss has occurred, the client may seek to lay blame or assign responsibility. In some instances, a direct causal relationship can be established and the negligent party should be held accountable. However, the attorney should try to maintain an objective and reasonable attitude when evaluating a situation for potential litigation.

A California man who had been incorrectly informed that he had acquired immune deficiency disease (AIDS) was appropriately awarded $200,000 for pain and suffering. Based on the diagnosis, the man had undergone seven years of unnecessary treatment, been unable to engage in sexual contact, and had postponed his marriage. The most compelling issue in this case is that he had been seeing two physicians over the intervening seven years and neither had reviewed the results of his HIV test which clearly reflected inconclusive results.[32]

Experienced medical malpractice attorneys recognize that angry clients tend to exaggerate circumstances or connect facts that have no relationship. In more severe cases, the client may be delusional or paranoid, believing the loss is related to some elaborate conspiracy. These individuals should be referred immediately for evaluation and treatment.

When a loss or death is traumatic and unexpected, there is a certain lack of closure experienced by the survivor. There was usually no time for the patient to express her wishes or make any arrangements. The survivor, while beginning his task of grieving, is forced to make decisions that he is not prepared to make. Acute feelings of unreality, disbelief, and shock are common. In the event of a violent or wrongful loss, anger, and frustration at the injustice may be added to grief over the loss.[30] Treatment for those suffering from a loss should focus on the tasks of grief. For the patient who is struggling to accept the reality of the loss, clinicians and attorneys should

- listen actively,
- encourage discussions of the future,
- assess and encourage social attachments,
- offer opportunities to discuss loss,
- normalize grief through personal contacts and literature, and
- avoid platitudes.

F. Therapy for grief

Working through the pain of grief may be more difficult for some than others. Patience and compassion are the attributes most useful for clinicians at this time. Allowing patients to express their feelings in a safe environment is extremely important, To facilitate the process, caregivers should normalize these feelings for the client. Statements that reflect these emotions as a common experience of individuals in the same circumstances can reassure the patient of the universality of the grief experience.

To adjust to the environment in which the deceased is missing may take more time for some. The amount of dependence the survivor had on the deceased can be a mitigating factor impeding the completion of this task. If the loved one was the sole financial provider or the dominant decision maker, the grieving individual may have a knowledge deficit that will need to be corrected before being able to orient fully to the new environment. To assist with this transition the clinician should

- assist with role evaluation, discovering what functions have been vacated and how life has changed,
- provide practical assistance in developing skills, and
- advise minimal change.

When clients are attempting to move on with their lives, nonjudgmental support is invaluable. Clinicians can also help by

- validating and normalizing feelings,
- facilitating expression of feelings,
- interpreting "normal" grief while allowing for individual differences,
- continuing support, and
- identifying pathology and referring to a psychiatrist when appropriate.

Over the past few years, researchers have begun the task of exploring disaster grief. Numerous debates in this pursuit have been dedicated to defining and measuring disasters.[30] The most common definition used today is:

> [A]ny emergency that requires the implementation of special arrangements by one or all of the emergency systems for rescue and transport of a large number of casualties, the identification of directly or indirectly involved large numbers of people, response to large numbers of inquires, utilization of large-scale combined resources, and mobilization and organization of supporting and emergent services.[30]

Examples of disasters include airplane crashes, the collapse of buildings, train wrecks, entertainment or sports event injuries, and so on. Following the identification of an event as a disaster, the next step is to identify the victims. The most direct victims are those individuals killed or injured. It is assumed that those close to the event are the ones most severely affected. Legally and psychologically, however, this may not be so. Proximity is often used to dismiss claims for compensation for posttraumatic stress disorder (PTSD).[30] Yet, research has shown that individuals may exhibit signs of PTSD after witnessing the event or observing the aftermath. Today these victims, along with rescue workers, are more vocal about their condition. Taylor has identified six categories of victim. They are

- those directly exposed,
- those with close family ties to primary victims who themselves have vicarious grief,
- rescue and recovery workers,
- concerned people in the community,
- those not directly involved but with underlying psychopathology, and
- individuals who but for chance might have been primary victims.[29]

People in any of these categories should have post-event evaluation and treatment.

For members of the community affected by the tragedy, post-disaster rituals can aid in recovery. Following disasters, individuals may visit the site laying flowers and mementos, hold official memorial services, set up permanent memorials, or observe anniversaries. These rituals may be spontaneous and start within hours of public notification. Upon notification of the death of John Lennon, Princess Diana, and at the World Trade Center disaster, individuals began to place flowers and hold candlelight ceremonies. People feel the need to do something to express their sorrow. These are vitally important for psychological well-being. While we all grieve differently, we do all grieve. Sharing the heavy feelings and emotions through public displays can start individuals down the road to recovery.

4.7 Conclusion

Medical and legal professionals have long understood the difficulty of evaluating subjective information. The mere fact that an individual has experienced an injury does not prove compensable pain and suffering. Numerous juries have awarded medical expenses while simultaneously failing to award damages for pain and suffering due to a lack of persuasive evidence. To ensure that each client receives the appropriate award, the clinician and attorney should use the diagnostic tools available to them to quantify such a subjective loss. Furthermore, the attorney should familiarize himself with the concepts of pain and suffering to be able to clearly articulate to laypeople their devastating effects.

Endnotes

1. Weiner, R.S., editor, *Pain Management:A Practical Guide for Clinicians*, Fifth Edition, Vol 1. Boca Raton: St. Lucie Press, 1998.

2. Jacox, A., Carr, D.B., Payne, R., et. al. *Management of Cancer Pain*, Clinical Practice Guideline No. 9, AHCPR Publication #94-0592. Rockville, MD: Agency for Health Care Policy and Research, U.S. Dept. of Health and Human Services, Public Health Services, March, 1994.

3. "Innovative Hospice Care." *Pain Management Formulary*. Florida: Vitas Hospice Corporation, 1994.

4. Shealy, C.N., and Cady, R.K., "Historical Perspectives." In Weiner, R.S., editor, *Pain Management: A Practical Guide for Clinicians,* Fifth Edition, Vol. 1. Boca Raton: St. Lucie Press, 1998.

5. "Innovative Hospice Care." *Pain Management Formulary*. Florida: Vitas Hospice Corporation, 1994..

6. Thienhaus, O., and Cole, E.B., "Classification of Pain."In Weiner, R.S., editor, *Pain Management: A Practical Guide for Clinicians*, Fifth Edition, Vol. 1. Boca Raton: St. Lucie Press, 1998.

7. McCaffery, M., and Beebe, J., *Pain Clinical Manual for Nursing Practice*. St. Louis: Mosby, 1989.

8. Shealy, C.N., and Cady, R.K., "Multidisciplinary Pain Clinics." In Weiner, R.S., editor, *Pain Management: A Practical Guide for Clinicians,* Fifth Edition, Vol. 2. Boca Raton: St. Lucie Press, 1998.

9. *Partner-Brown v. Bornstein*, 734 So 2d 555; 1999, FLA. App. LEXIS 7454, 24, *Fla. L. Weekly*; 1329.

10. Moser, R.S., "The Psychologist's Role in the Chronic Pain of Reflex Sympathetic Dystrophy." *New Jersey Psychologist*, 24–25, 1999.

11. Ruoff, G.E., "Depression in the Patient with Chronic Pain," *Journal of Family Practice* (6) 525–534.

12. Hendles, N., "Psychiatrist Role in Pain Management." In Weiner, R.S., editor, *Pain Management: A Practical Guide for Clinicians*, Fifth Edition, Vol. 1. Boca Raton: St. Lucie Press, 1998.

13. American Psychiatric Association Diagnostic Criteria, *DSM-IV-TR*. Chicago: RR Donnelley and Sons, 2000.

14. *Fiederlein v. New York Health and Hospitals Corp.*, Supreme Court of New York, Appellate Division First Department, 80. A.D. 2d 821;437 N.Y.S. 2d 321; 1981 N.Y. App. Div. LEXIS 10629, March 31, 1981.

15. Dinsmoor, R.S., "Generalized Anxiety Disorder." *Gale Encyclopedia of Medicine*. Farmington Hills, MI: Thompson Corporation, 2002.

16. Feinberg, S., and Mott., K. "From Injured Worker to Chronic Pain Patient." *CWCE,* Jan/Feb, 177–182, 2000.

17. Frey, R.J., "Factitious Disorders." *Gale Encyclopedia of Medicine*. Farmington Hills, MI: Gale Research, Thompson Corporation, 1999.

18. *Dollison v. Hayes*, Court of Appeals of Texas, Sixth District, 29-258-CC; 2002, Tex. App. LEXIS, 4188.

19. Young, M.A., Young, B.J., Stiens, S.A., Hoffberg, H., Cassius, D., Narrow, C., and Kornhauser, S., "Terrorism's Effect on Chronic Pain Perception: An Analysis of a Multi-Center Cohort." *Practical Pain Management*, Mar/Apr, 9–12, 2002.

20. Harsha, W., "Understanding and Treating Back Pain." In Weiner, R.S., editor, *Pain Management: A Practical*

Guide for Clinicians, Fifth Edition, Vol. 1. Boca Raton: St. Lucie Press, 1998.

21. Kibiuk, L. *Unlocking Locked-In Syndrome.* Society of Neuroscience, Washington, DC, 1–3, 1999.

22. Valenstein, E. and Nadeau, S.E., "Conditions That Resemble Coma." *Neurological Examination,* 1–4. 1998.

23. "1.64 Million for PTSD Following Witness of Accident and Injury." Suits and Deals, *New Jersey Law Journal,* December 17, 2001.

24. "$750,000 for Violent UPS Delivery." Suits and Deals, *New Jersey Law Journal,* August 5, 2002, 8.

25. Holmes, L., "Facts about Post-Traumatic Stress Disorder." *Mental Health Resources,* 1–5, 2002.

26. Zarin, I., editor, "$5,852,000 Verdict." *New Jersey Jury Verdict Review and Analysis,* 23, (3), August, 2002, 25

27. Kubler, K.K., Berry, P.H., and Heidrich, D.E., *End of Live Care: Clinical Practice Guidelines.* New York: WB Saunders Company, 2002.

28. Laska, L., editor, "Unexplained Bleeding Following Laparoscopy—Failure to Diagnose Ectopic Pregnancy." *Donna Ann Riley v. Niels Lauersen, MD.,* Kings County (NY) Supreme Court, Index No. 31675/97, *Medical Malpractice Verdicts, Settlements and Experts.* Feb. 2001, 23.

29. Becvar, D.S., *In the Presence of Grief: Helping Family Members Resolve Death, Dying, and Bereavement Issues.* New York: Guildford Press, 2001.

30. Hockey, J., Katz, J., and Small, N., *Facing Death, Grief, Mourning and Death Ritual.* Philadelphia: Open University Press, 2001.

31. Kubler-Ross, E., *On Death and Dying.* New York: MacMillan, 1969.

32. Laska, L., editor, "Sixty Year-Old Man Incorrectly Informed He Has AIDS—Unnecessary Treatments for Seven Years—$200,000 Settlement California." *Richard P. Hancsak and Lilliana Witz-Hancsak v. Friendly Hills Healthcare Network, Friendly Hills Healthcare, CIGNA Health Plans, Inc., CIGNA Health Care of California, L.A. Health Care Center, Elaine Jones, M.D., Tiberio Lindgren, M.D., Robert J. Coutron, Ph.D.,* Los Angeles County (CA) Superior Court, Case No. _____, *Medical Malpractice Verdicts, Settlements and Experts,* Jan. 2002, 26.

33. Bowlby, J., *Loss: Sadness and Depression,* Vol. III. New York: Basic Books, Perseus Books Group, 2000.

Additional Reading

Albin, R., "The Psychology of Injury." *Trial,* 52, September, 1999.

Chapter 5

Suffering: A Multidimensional Concept

Leta Truett, PhD, RN and Patricia Iyer, MSN, RN, LNCC

Synopsis

5.1 Introduction

Suffering is a common experience of individuals with chronic debilitating disease or injury. While suffering has been addressed in relationship to the patient's response to chronic illness and death, the concept has not been well described in terms of how patients perceive it. Authors have addressed suffering by writing around the topic or using examples to describe suffering. This chapter will present an overview of suffering and its effect on quality of life. The authors refer to the suffering of patients. It is understood that not all plaintiffs were the patients affected by the disease or injury that gave rise to the litigation. The plaintiffs' attorney's job is to discover the suffering the plaintiff experienced as a result of the injury and to ensure that the trier of fact understands the effects of the suffering. The defense attorney's job is also to determine how much the plaintiff suffered and to minimize the effect of the suffering when presented to the trier of fact.

Patients with chronic debilitating disease or injury, by the nature of the illness and its treatment, are at a high risk for suffering. Not only is the diagnosis a threat to the integrity and existence of an individual, but the resulting need for multiple modalities of treatment such as surgery, chemotherapy, radiation, and rehabilitation can have a dramatic effect on the individual as well. The length of treatment varies depending on the diagnosis and different modalities used. Patients can undergo many adverse physical and emotional reactions during this extended time period. Patients may opt for experimental procedures as well as experimental drugs with unknown efficacy. These trends have exciting research potential but may affect the patient's quality of life (QOL) significantly and lead to prolonged suffering.

The diagnosis of a debilitating disease or injury affects one's life significantly and can result in profound changes in the family dynamics, gainful employment, financial security, emotional stability, and overall QOL. One can make the case that the same principles apply in acute injury and life-threatening events when one's existence or integrity is at risk. Injuries leading to disabilities that affect QOL would result in the same human responses that occur in the area of chronic debilitating disease or cancer. The need for prolonged rehabilitation for disabilities may also predispose the patient to situations resulting in a suffering experience.

Unfortunately, there is little in the way of research findings on the subject of suffering. One of the difficulties has been the lack of a solid conceptual foundation for exploration of the phenomenon. Rodgers and Cowles[1] used a method of concept analysis to enhance the existing understanding of suffering. Their analysis provided a definition of the concept of suffering as an individualized, subjective, and complex experience characterized by persons assigning to a situation or a perceived threat an intensely negative meaning.

Kahn and Steeves[2] formulated a number of succinct tenets about suffering that outline the innumerable sources of suffering and suggested that understanding the sources of suffering can lead to understanding behaviors, attitudes, and responses of the person who is suffering. They maintained that suffering has a basic structure and is a universal aspect of human nature.

5.2 Pain and Suffering Defined

When referring to the concept of suffering, many people think of it only in terms of a direct relationship to physical pain. An accepted approach is to believe that if the pain is adequately relieved the relief of suffering will follow. This concept presents a one-dimensional portrait of suffering. Suffering is a multidimensional concept that needs to be described apart from the usual coupling phrase "pain and suffering." The concept of pain is explored elsewhere in this text. This chapter will focus on suffering.

Tip

Attorneys and experts use the term "pain and suffering", but suffering can occur in the absence of pain.

In his classic article on the nature of suffering, Cassell[3] describes suffering as, "a threat to the person's continued existence or integrity as persons, a fear that goes beyond and is distinct from pain" (p. 640). He suggests the intensity of a physical symptom does not necessarily correlate with the suffering one experiences, and in some situations, a person may suffer without the presence of physical symptoms. Sometimes suffering is associated with pain. In these instances, the person feels out of control when the pain is overwhelming such as in chronic pain, or when the meaning of the pain is dire.

In elaboration on the nature of suffering, Cassell[3] makes the point that suffering is experienced by the whole person, occurs when an impending destruction of the person is perceived, and can occur in relation to any aspect of the person. Cassell[3] and Kahn and Steeves[2] maintain that suffering is a phenomenon that cannot be reduced beyond the whole person.

Tip

Suffering is experienced when some crucial aspect of one's own self, being, or existence is threatened.

The meaningfulness of such a threat is to the integrity of one's experience of personal identity. For example, a woman suffers while waiting for the results of a breast biopsy. Pain may or may not evoke suffering. Whether or not this would be the case would depend on the meaning the individual gives to the pain. Kahn and Steeves[2] state, "Any threat to personal integrity, whether painful or not, can invoke suffering" (p. 626).

Chapman and Gavrin[4] discuss the underlying physiology of suffering as resembling that associated with threat, principally arising from noradrenergic mechanisms in the brain. Prolonged stress disturbs circadian (sleep/wake) rhythms and produces disequilibrium that pervades every aspect of life as described in the statement, "Relentlessness is the cardinal feature of suffering" (p. 11).

Morse and Carter[5] maintain that the concept of suffering is poorly developed. They elaborate by saying "much of the research into suffering has also been unsuccessful in developing a definition of the concept and the void has not gone unnoticed" (p. 43). Lacking a clear definition of suffering causes many authors to write around the topic rather than specifically defining the nature of suffering. Philosophical explorations of suffering have produced findings that are too abstract for clinical use and not helpful in assisting attorneys present or refute suffering claims as part of damages. The investigators suggest that delineating the characteristics of the experience and identifying related concepts would increase the understanding of suffering.

The phenomenon of suffering in cancer and chronic disease patients has been examined through a number of qualitative research studies. These studies have identified characteristics and themes of suffering (Battenfield;[6] Benedict and Bird;[7] Charmaz;[8] Dildy;[9] Flaming;[10] Lindholm and Eriksson;[11] Pollock and Sands[12]). Several quantitative studies have been conducted to examine suffering from a statistical model (Benedict;[13] Copp[14]). A methodological study to test the validity and reliability of a tool to describe the characteristics of suffering has been conducted (Truett[15]). Unfortunately, research about the experience of suffering is scarce. Copp[14] states, "suffering, like death, is often not studied because it is intrinsically linked to one's own existence; once acknowledged it becomes a personal threat" (p. 491).

According to Watson[16] the level of suffering, tragically, determines the quality of human existence. Suffering is universal but the level, intensity, or duration of suffering is not.

Tip

Suffering is often borne silently and alone. The evolution of this attitude has resulted in a continued "silent conspiracy" to keep suffering a private matter and forces the sufferer to remain alone to deal with the unspeakable.[17]

There is a tendency in certain cultures as well as in specific gender characteristics that encourage individuals to exhibit stoic patterns of behavior and interfere with the seeking of assistance. To do so would communicate weakness on the part of the individual. The attorney should keep this in mind when eliciting testimony from the stoic plaintiff. Family members may be better sources of examples of the kind of suffering the stoic patient has undergone.

Kahn and Steeves[2] contend that nurses have a moral obligation to speak out about the suffering they witness. Coyle[18] describes suffering as something that happens within a person and only through direct communication of the suffering by the individual can we actually know what the suffering entails. Plaintiffs' attorneys find that some of their clients are reluctant to discuss their suffering and need encouragement to describe what are highly personal aspects of their reactions to illness or injury.

Graneheim, Lindahl, and Kihlgren[19] studied nine healthy individuals with the goal of understanding the connection of suffering in life values and their reflections on active euthanasia. The fear of suffering (i.e., torment, dependence, physical pain, abandonment, hopelessness, and frailty) were the foremost considerations for active euthanasia. Fifty percent of nurses agreed suffering provided sufficient justification for physician-assisted dying.

Tip

The reason most frequently cited as justifying requests for active termination of life is the fear of prolonged suffering with pain and other distressing symptoms.[20]

Given the universality of the suffering experience coupled with the conspiracy to keep suffering silent, it is inevitable that patients would become depressed and hopeless. According to Knight,[21] depression and hopelessness is the lethal combination in wishing to take one's life. Given the possibility to open the communication of the suffering experience, coupled with the caring presence of family, friends, and healthcare professionals, the wish for death may not be necessary. Attorneys should be sensitive to signs of depression in the clients they represent and be prepared to suggest that professional counseling be sought.

5.3 The Meaning of Suffering

Suffering has historically been viewed in a spiritual orientation and many of the world's religions have incorporated suffering as a part of human experience and nature itself. The Buddhist, Christian, and Jewish religions view suffering as an inevitable component of human life. According to Byoch,[22] each reflects a different approach to dealing with suffering, ranging from severing attachments and achieving a desire-less state, offering one's suffering for the sake of others as a sacrificial act, or acceptance of human suffering in congruence with God's eternal plan.

Along a more secular orientation, much has been written regarding the meaning of suffering. Several authors have concluded that new meaning in life can come through a suffering experience (Starck;[23] Starck and McGovern;[24] Steeves and Kahn[25]). Frankl[26] wrote in his discussions of the holocaust experience that meaning is found through self-transcendence. He asserts that choice and responsibility are available to the sufferer, and one is free to choose how to respond. Ultimately, suffering is viewed as a challenge to find meaning. While these views are acknowledged and respected, the underlying premise of the author is that suffering is an undesirable state or condition.

A. Effects of diagnosis

The diagnosis of a debilitating disease or injury changes patients' lives and propels them into a world of unknowns. Quality of life is affected because the disease or treatment of disease may disable, disfigure, or cause considerable misery from treatment side effects even though they may be life-saving. Patients differ in their ability to cope with the changes in their lifestyle. Many patients need support from a caring person to adjust and move beyond the limitations brought about by suffering. Healthcare providers and attorneys need to be knowledgeable about the multidimensional aspects of suffering and be able to assess the suffering in patients so that intervention can occur.

B. Patient perceptions of suffering

Much of what is revealed in the literature regarding the phenomenon of suffering is assumption and conjecture. Very little is documented regarding how persons who have experienced the phenomenon describe it. There have been several qualitative studies and one quantitative study that have attempted to provide patient perspectives. These will be reviewed as to their findings.

In a classic article Copp[14] suggested that "no one has markedly enriched our awareness of the phenomenon of suffering" (p. 471). In a descriptive study of 148 patients interviewed in five hospitals, suffering is defined as "the response to pain" (p. 492). Suffering included many anticipatory fears being more acute than actual pain. The value of Copp's study was to highlight the lack of knowledge in the area of suffering and to provide more information from the patient's perspective. A limitation of this study was that the author failed to differentiate the concept of suffering from pain, addressing it instead as a response to pain.

Tip

The language of suffering is similar to the language of loss.

Charmaz[8] interviewed fifty-seven chronically ill patients regarding the sources of their suffering. The subjects identified losses due to the illness such as restricted lives, social isolation, being discredited, and burdening others. The length of suffering was identified as a factor in that those subjects who had improved viewed their suffering as being enlightening while those who continued to suffer expressed a sense of loss. Length of time is an intriguing aspect, and leads one to wonder if those who were able to improve were better able to identify the sources of suffering and seek help to cope or if they were able to conquer suffering on their own.

Battenfield[6] interviewed nine adults using an open-ended interview technique to establish a schema of attitudes toward suffering and to identify an optimal stage of relief for the sufferer. Human responses were identified and stratified into a progressive schema from initial impact, turmoil with resolution, coping, accepting and understanding, and finding meaning. She set out to describe suffering but ended up developing a schema that looks more at the process of suffering. The process affects the sufferer from the initial impact to the apex of the suffering phenomenon that has been described by Frankl[26] as finding meaning in suffering. A value emphasized in this study was the identification of human responses to suffering outlined in the schema (immobility, shock, hurt, agony, disbelief, denial, fear, anger, depression, guilt, shame, hopelessness, despair, feeling of abandonment, and helplessness). These responses closely approximated themes identified in other qualitative studies (Dildy;[9] Lindholm and Eriksson[11]).

Benedict[13] conducted structured interviews with thirty primary lung cancer patients to investigate the incidence of suffering in the lung cancer patient. This research was based on a previous work of Benedict and Bird[7] identifying experiences associated with suffering as reported by a group of adults with various types of cancer and categorizing them into physical, psychological, and interactional aspects. The highest levels of suffering for the lung cancer patients were in the area of physical and psychological domains. The greatest suffering was associated with disability, pain, anxiety, changed daily activities, weakness, and fatigue. The group with known metastatic disease differed significantly in reporting greater suffering in the domain of psychological issues.

To increase understanding and discover ways to alleviate suffering, Lindhom and Eriksson[11] conducted qualitative interviews with eleven nurses and five patients. Significant statements were developed into main categories or themes. Patients tended to describe the "what" of suffering as lack of freedom, immobility, lack of strength, despair, disappointment, pain, fear, a longing for another human being, and a threat to existence. The nurses tended to describe the 'why' or reason for suffering and were hesitant and uncertain when describing what patients really experience as suffering.

The investigators maintained they captured what the informants felt about suffering rather than a specific definition of suffering. This study provided a distinction between the "what" and the "why" of suffering and was a valuable contribution to the concept.

Dildy[9] conducted a study to describe the nature, meaning, and effect of suffering from the perspective of patients with rheumatoid arthritis. Using a semi-structured questionnaire, fourteen recorded interviews were conducted in which the experience of suffering was described as struggling, loss of dreams, restructuring a future orientation, and withdrawing. The phases of disintegration of personhood (loss of independence and self-sufficiency), the shattered self (mental anguish, pain, activity limitation or being "locked in," and fatigue), and reconstruction of self (feeling hopelessness and in some cases considering suicide) were key characteristics of the suffering experience.

Pollock and Sands[12] explored the meaning of suffering through semi-structured interviews with twenty subjects who had multiple sclerosis. The goal was to obtain descriptions from subjects about the characteristics of the suffering experience, strategies used to cope, and meaning found in their experience. Suffering experiences included numerous stressors and problems within physiological, psychological, and sociological domains. These included problems with inability to carry out activities of daily living, fatigue, fear of exacerbation, changes in lifestyle, fear of being a burden, and decreased social contact. Subject responses about suffering experiences followed a hierarchical progression from shock and denial through acceptance and understanding and ultimately to finding meaning in their suffering.

Qualitative research on experience of suffering has described themes of suffering such as, "agonizing heaviness prompted by being with and apart from others, objects and situations" (Daly,[27] p. 50). The core concepts derived from interviewing eight patients were identified as paralyzing anguish, entanglement of engaging and disengaging, and struggling in pursuit of fortification.

C. Defining attributes and characteristics of suffering

In order to interpret and understand the phenomenon of suffering, one of the authors (L.T.) conducted a phenomenological study of the suffering of seven cancer patients who identified they were currently experiencing or had experienced suffering. The following themes emerged from the qualitative study: change in lifestyle, lack of understanding by family and friends, unrelieved pain, withholding information, loss of control, overwhelming loss, and anger and frustration. The themes found in this study were combined with other characteristics related to suffering derived from qualitative and quantitative studies, and these were consolidated as follows.

The following section describes these dimensions and provides the reader with specific questions that may be asked of the plaintiff or patient to explore aspects of suffering.

1. Change in lifestyle. The inability to accomplish activities of daily living such as inability to complete tasks, care for self, participate in family activities, participate in creative activities, loss of stamina and energy, and being forced to stay at home.

- How is your life different now than before the accident?
- What can you no longer do for yourself that you could do before?
- What do you miss about your life before the diagnosis of ____?

2. Unrelieved pain. Pain that is not adequately relieved by pain medication or alternative treatment measures such as rest, heat or cold, and interferes with activities of daily living.
   - How has the unrelieved pain you are experiencing affected your ability to perform activities of daily living?
   - How has this interfered with your enjoyment of life?

3. Lack of understanding by family and friends. Family and friends' inability to accept the aftermath of the patient's disease and treatment if the problems linger and the patient does not improve in the time frame expected.
   - How have your relationships with family member and friends changed as a result of your disability?
   - How has this affected you physically and emotionally?

4. Withholding information and isolation. Feeling of not being able to give or share information regarding his disease or treatment in order to protect family and friends and to avoid the discomfort and insecurity of others which forces a self-imposed isolation.
   - How has the present disability affected your ability to communicate openly with family members and friends?
   - What effect has this had in your relationships?

5. Loss of control or powerlessness. Loss of control over the ability to direct her life and feeling powerless to deal with the overwhelming forces such as the treatment and the side effects of treatment as well as the possibility of recurrence or failure of treatment.
   - How do you view your ability to control your life circumstances?
   - What effect does this have on your self esteem and feeling of being able to determine your own fate?

6. Anger and frustration. Feelings of anger were projected at multiple sources such as family and friends, God, and the medical community. The frustration of trying to deal with his present circumstances and being unable to control events created most of the anger.
   - How have the negative feelings of anger and frustration interfered with your outlook or mood?
   - How do you release your feelings of anger and frustration?

7. Sense of loss. Loss expressed in relationship to multiple losses such as loss of job, role in the family, health, creative ability, to function as she had done in the past.
   - What do you perceive as personal losses related to the disability?
   - How does the loss affect in your life?

8. Anxiety. Constant feelings of uneasiness, sense of impending doom.[13]
   - Can you describe your feelings of anxiety or nervousness?
   - How have these feelings affected in your ability to function?

9. Depression. Dense of sadness or unhappiness at not being able to experience joy and sense of well-being.
   - Describe how your depression or sadness has affected your ability to function as compared your ability prior to the disability.
   - Has your enjoyment of life decreased because of these feelings?

10. Fear. Dread of death, future disability, and recurrence of disease.
    - What fears do you have in relationship to your disability?

- How have your fears interfered with your daily life?

11. Hopelessness and despair. Giving up the feeling of being able to deal with the present circumstances involving the cancer and its treatment.
    - Have you had feelings of hopelessness or despair in dealing with your present circumstances?
    - Have you ever thought of suicide as a result of these feelings?

12. Feelings of abandonment and alienation. Feeling alone in the fight to save his life and that no one understands what he is going through.
    - Describe the feelings you have related to isolation and abandonment due to your disability.
    - How have these feelings affected your relationships with family and friends?
    - How has this affected your mood and behavior as compared to prior to the disability or injury?

13. Financial and job problems. Problems related to income and expenses related to disease, inability to continue to work to provide income to make ends meet.
    - How does the disability affect your ability to work and maintain financial independence?
    - How have the financial problems related to your disability changed your standard of living?
    - How has this affected your feelings of self worth as compared to prior to the disability, and how has this affected in your relationships with family, friends, and coworkers?

14. Lack of information about disease. Not being informed about the aspects of disease and treatment and not being able to deal with problems successfully.
    - Can you describe how not being fully informed about the aspects of the illness, treatment, and undesirable outcomes affected your overall sense of security?
    - How has this affected your subsequent recovery?

Once these basic characteristics of the suffering experience were extracted, Truett[15] developed an instrument, "The Description of Suffering Instrument" (DSI), to further define and describe the characteristics of suffering on a larger scale. A sample of 155 cancer survivors responded to the questionnaire. A factor analysis was performed along with other statistical testing of validity and reliability, and six factors were identified. They appear in Figure 5.1. The importance of these data is that patients confirmed the multidimensional nature of suffering. The clustering of characteristics through factor analysis assists in identifying various aspects involved in the individual dimensions.

The research findings of these qualitative and quantitative studies attempt to describe and define suffering as well as to identify relief for the sufferer. However, the literature continues to identify a need to define and describe the concept of suffering from the patient's perspective.

5.4 Suffering's Relationship to Quality of Life

The multidimensional aspects of suffering are similar to the dimensions found in the QOL (quality of life) model. Examining this conceptual model for underpinning the multidimensional structure of suffering can assist in understanding the complex nature of the experience. Quality of life is a concept dating back to antiquity. Defined as a "good life" it has undergone many transformations. The equation of QOL and performance status has proven to be too limiting, and the need to incorporate other dimensions into the conceptual framework has received much attention by researchers.

Tip

QOL has evolved into a multidimensional construct consisting of biological, physical, psychological, social, and spiritual factors.

Many other dimensions have been identified, but as Cella[28] indicates at least three dimensions must be examined to describe the conceptual framework adequately. It has moved from a global perspective to specified and measurable domains.

Factor 1. Existential issues
threat to existence
fear of recurrence
anxiety
sense of doom
dread of procedures
depression
hopelessness

Factor 2. Functional and physical issues
side effects
loss of independence
fatigue
inability to perform ADLs
loss of control
change in appearance

Factor 3. Emotional and feelings issues
disbelief this has happened
feeling sorry for self
feeling of being alone
helplessness
anger associated with disease
feelings of guilt

Factor 4. Impact of disability issues
frustration due to limitations
fear of being disabled
sense of loss due to changes
financial problems

Factor 5. Illness support issues
unrelieved pain
lack of information
problems with HCP
change in belief system

Factor 6. Family support issues
inability to share information
lack of understanding

Figure 5.1 *Factors associated with the multidimensional aspects of suffering*

A definition of QOL adopted by Cella and Cherin[29] states, "Quality of life refers to patients' appraisal of and satisfaction with their current level of functioning as compared to what they perceive to be possible or ideal" (p. 69). This would be adequate for carrying out the constructs of QOL.

Quality of life is a broad concept. Its use as an outcome is especially relevant to the evaluation of medical care and damages that have resulted from trauma or disease. Healthcare providers need to be concerned about the patient's response to disease and.

Ferrell[30] discusses a model for QOL that she and colleagues have developed for cancer patients that incorporates the domains of physical, psychological, social, and spiritual. The following section defines each dimension of quality of life and provides examples of associated damages.

A. Physical domain

The physical domain includes the maintenance of function and independence. Physical characteristics of suffering include inability to perform activities of daily living as well as recreational activities, fatigue, and unrelieved pain.

A sixty-five-year-old driver was awaiting delivery of steel stabilizer bars at a truck rental company. An employee got into the cab of the truck and began to move it, knocking the plaintiff to the ground. He suffered a severe ankle injury, and during the course of the next year, he underwent four operations and had screws and plates inserted into his ankle. He also had a bone graft to close a fracture and underwent a fifth operation to remove a screw from his ankle. He still suffers from nerve damage and progressive posttraumatic arthritis. Although he had planned to work another five to ten years, the ankle injury prevented that. The case settled for $688,500 including $150,000 for pain and suffering, $272,000 for future lost wages, and $182,206 for past lost wages. The balance of the award was allocated to out-of-pocket medical expenses and for his wife's damages.[31]

Many of the cases reported in the legal literature describe clear-cut physical damages. These cases are often attractive to plaintiffs' attorneys because it is easy for the jury to understand how the plaintiff was harmed. Examples of physical damages include:

1. Unnecessary surgery: Loss of organs, mutilation, exposure to complications from surgery

A woman with a history of successfully treated breast cancer underwent genetic testing to determine if she was at increased risk for breast and ovarian cancer. The test was interpreted as positive. She had her remaining breast, ovaries, and uterus removed. A second genetic test showed that the plaintiff did not have the mutation after all. The action settled for $2,000,000.[32]

2. Loss of senses: Sight, hearing, taste and smell, sensation

An Arizona prison inmate was denied treatment for hydrocephalus. He alleged that he developed hydrocephalus (an accumulation of cerebrospinal fluid) for no apparent reason. He slowly developed headaches, dizziness, vomiting, blurred vision, strabismus and loss of sight. He requested medical treatment numerous times, but the defendant failed to provide care. The jury awarded a verdict of $6,000,000.[33]

3. Nerve damage: Peripheral nerve damage, such as foot drop, or the development of reflex sympathetic dystrophy (complex regional pain syndrome) or central nervous system damage resulting in paralysis

An orthopedic surgeon performed a multilevel laminectomy on the plaintiff. Plaintiff alleged that the surgeon was under the influence of cocaine and was impaired during the time he treated her, and that during surgery he severed a nerve root in her back. When the surgeon's drug test was positive five days after surgery and he was suspended, no attending physician was assigned to oversee the plaintiff's care for the next seven days. A hematoma developed in the operative site, resulting in partial paralysis, loss of bladder control and sexual function, and chronic severe pain. The suit settled for a confidential amount.[34]

4. Abdominal complications: Peritonitis, obstruction, adhesions, colostomy, incontinence, persistent nausea, vomiting, and diarrhea

A Georgia man, age thirty at the time, suffered a rectal tear in a motor vehicle collision. The surgery to repair the tear was properly performed, and then the plaintiff underwent a laparoscopic diverting loop colostomy. The wrong end of the colon was stapled, resulting in total obstruction of the plaintiff's digestive tract. Seven days later, the tract ruptured, causing a massive infection. The plaintiff lost a significant portion of his large bowel and his abdominal wall and was left with no abdominal muscles and only a thin layer of skin covering his intestines. The plaintiff was also restricted to lifting no more than 20 pounds and suffered from constant diarrhea. The defendants admitted liability prior to trial, and the case proceeded on the issue of damages. The plaintiff alleged that he suffered significant permanent injuries which rendered him totally disabled from employment as a direct result of the negligence of the defendants' employees. The plaintiff's wife also claimed loss of consortium. The defendants contended that the plaintiff was not totally disabled and the plaintiff would be able to seek some employment in the future. The jury returned a verdict for the plaintiff, awarding $6,250,000, including $1,000,000 for loss of consortium.[35]

B. Psychological domain

The psychological domain includes a sense of control in the face of life-threatening illness characterized by emotional distress, altered life priorities, and fears of the unknown, as well as positive changes such as heightened appreciation of life and significant relationships. Psychological characteristics of suffering include anxiety, depression, anger, and multiple losses related to disease.

A delayed diagnosis of breast cancer occurred when Karen Karavanas alleged that the defendant pathologist advised her that the lump was benign. Karavanas married and became pregnant shortly after the biopsy but, still bothered by the lump, consulted another doctor in December 1999. A second biopsy by a new doctor showed a rare cancer. Karavanas had a mastectomy in January 2000 while pregnant, but further tests and treatment were delayed until after she gave birth to a daughter in March 2000. The cancer had not spread by April or May, but further testing showed that it had metastasized by October 2000. In the suit against the pathologist, the plaintiff claimed that because of the metastasis she cannot have reconstructive surgery. She says she cannot bear to look at herself or allow her husband to see her with one breast. She also claims that her cancer treatments interfere with her ability to care for her baby and that she tries to keep her daughter from bonding with her so that the child will not be devastated when she dies. This suit resulted in an $825,000 settlement.[31]

Much of this chapter addresses the psychological aspects of suffering. Emotional claims are often part of the damages alleged in a suit. They may include the following.

1. Fear, anxiety, embarrassment, humiliation, and grief over lost opportunities, body parts or self-image

A Philadelphia fireman claimed that he was sexually harassed by employees for almost two years. A fireman who worked under his supervision confronted him with gay material. The damages award was $1,237,500. It included back pay of $225,000, front pay of $512,500, and pain and suffering of $500,000.[36]

2. Rape trauma syndrome

A thirty-eight-year-old female was a patient in the psychiatric division of the hospital. Restrained by leather straps at her wrists and ankles, she was allegedly molested twice by a nurse's assistant employed by the hospital. She alleged extreme emotional distress resulting from digital sexual penetration and oral contact with the perpetrator's genitals. The defendant contended that the plaintiff consented to the sexual activity by screaming about sex and suggesting sex. The defendant also claimed it was not liable because the perpetrator's actions were outside the scope of his employment. The perpetrator was jailed, convicted, and sentenced to two to five years, and the jury awarded the plaintiff $1,250,000.[37]

C. Social domain

The social domain provides a way to view not only the disease and its symptoms but also the person with the disease. It is the means by which we recognize people with disease, their roles, and relationships. Social characteristics of suffering include changes in the role in the family, isolation from family and friends, and lack of understanding of family and friends.

In a New Jersey case, the failure to prescribe Coumadin, a blood thinner, resulted in a severe stroke. After the stroke, the patient needed assistance to walk, was rendered incontinent, did not recognize her grandchildren, and underwent a personality change that made her combative at times. She died of unrelated causes two years later. The jury awarded $850,000. The defense attorney has moved for a new trial, calling $850,000 for two years of pain and suffering excessive. He said he will appeal if the motion failed.[31]

A nurse employed in a hospital contracted hepatitis C when she was inadvertently stuck with a needle. She claimed that the hospital wrongfully advised her over a five-year period, during which period three blood tests were positive for the disease, that the testing was negative. During this five-year period she suffered extensive fatigue without knowing the cause, which severely disrupted her family life. The plaintiff also maintained that when she ultimately learned that the test results had been positive for five years, she suffered severe emotional distress for her own health and that of her family. This distress was driven by the knowledge that the delay in treatment occasioned an increased risk of permanent liver damage as well as liver cancer or other liver disease. The fear was heightened by the failure of the first round of Interferon. The second round of Interferon was successful, and there was no evidence of permanent injury. The couple ultimately divorced, and the former husband brought an independent action, contending that notwithstanding the fact that he was not a patient he was owed a duty to be informed of such results through reporting to his wife. It was foreseeable that the failure to diagnose or communicate a positive test result could cause harm to him. The plaintiff was permitted to proceed against her employer notwithstanding the Workers' Compensation bar. The jury found that the conduct of the hospital through its employees rose to the high level required for an employee to sue an employer in a third party case. The jury then rendered a gross award to the plaintiff of $1.5 million for emotional distress and $1.5 million for increased risk of harm. The jury also awarded $500,000 to the husband for his claim prior to the divorce.[38]

D. Spiritual domain

The spiritual domain relates to aspects of the meaning of illness, transcendence, uncertainty of life as well as religious ideology. Spiritual well-being is the ability to maintain hope and derive meaning from the illness experience that is characterized by uncertainty. Spiritual characteristics of suffering include fear of recurrence, fear of death, loss of control, and hopelessness.

A thirty-two-year-old man suffered left testicular pain and swelling. Misdiagnosed as having epididymitis, the patient lost blood flow to the left testicle from torsion (twisting), resulting in tissue death. This was the second testicular torsion suffered by the plaintiff. He had experienced torsion several years before on the right side. He was fearful he would suffer torsion of his remaining testicle, resulting in loss of the testicle, sterility, loss of natural hormone production, loss of sexual function, and loss of energy. He claimed past and future pain and suffering due to his fear of losing the remaining testicle. The jury returned a verdict awarding the plaintiff $200,000 against the defendants, including $100,000 for disfigurement. He received $100,000 for pain and suffering.[39]

Each of these domains affects QOL as a whole and the inclusion of the aspects within each domain yields a greater understanding of the total QOL of the individual. Through the inclusion of aspects from all domains, thorough assessment of the individuals QOL is more likely. Ferrell[40] has indicated suffering transcends all the domains of the QOL mode. The graphic in Figure 5.2 attempts to depict the delicate balance involved in the relationship of QOL and suffering. With a decrease in QOL, suffering would theoretically increase, and with a decrease in suffering, QOL would be increased.

5.5 Assessment Measures

Patients are routinely assessed when they enter a healthcare setting. Depending on the setting and the extent of the disease or injury, this assessment could range from minimal to thorough. In the hospital setting, the accreditation bodies such as the Joint Commission Accreditation for Healthcare Organizations (JCAHO) have mandated specific criteria for hospitals to follow to complete the accreditation process successfully. As of 2001, the JCAHO has been surveying the implementation of a new standard on pain management. There are specific policies and procedure being put into place to meet these new requirements. This has made a major impact on how institutions regard a very important part of healthcare assessment. In response to these new standards, the Veteran's Administration hospitals have implemented pain as a fifth vital sign along with temperature, blood pressure, pulse, and respira-

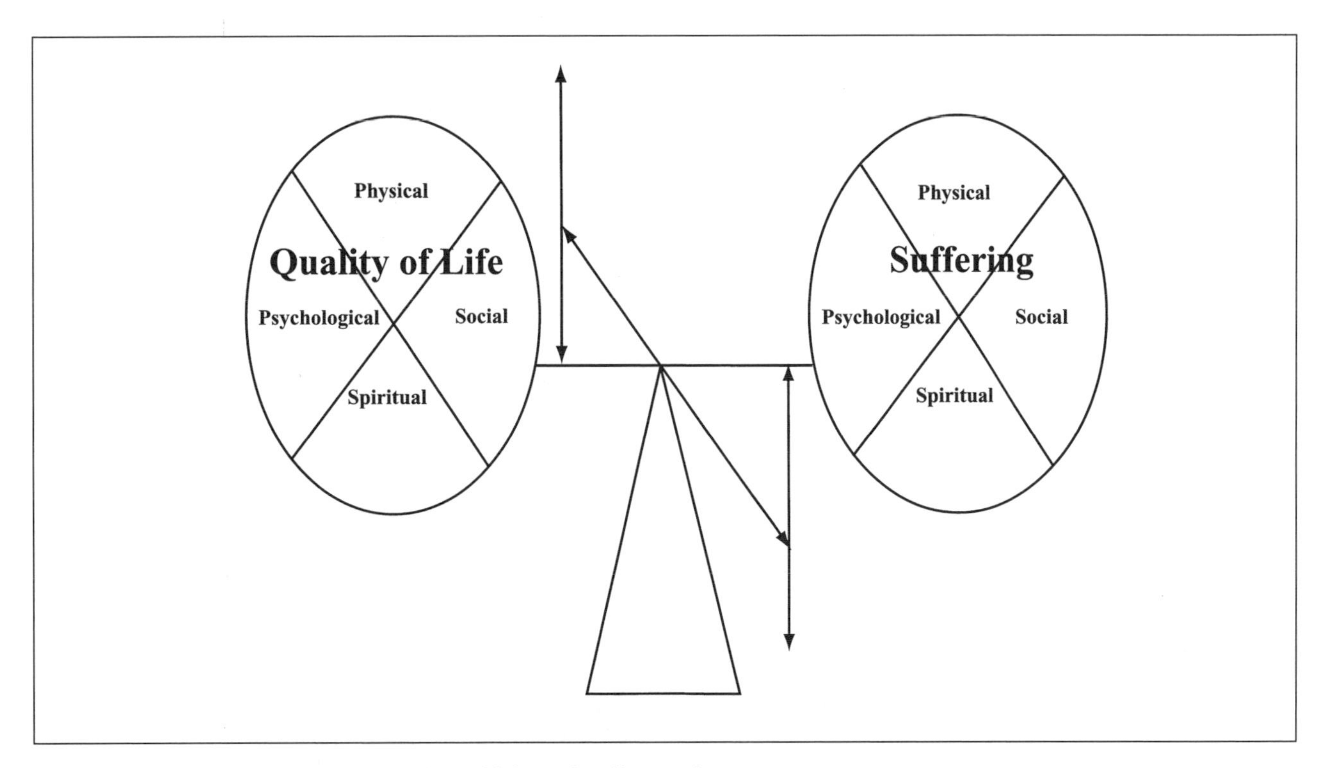

Figure 5.2 *Delicate balance of quality of life and suffering domains*

tion. This is mentioned because of the huge impact in all VA hospitals throughout the U.S. whereas other hospitals have had this in place for over ten years. Getting adequate attention to these critical aspects of care takes an act of Congress. So what are the chances of getting a valid, reliable tool in place for QOL that is used routinely? The answer of course is not very good.

Quality of life instruments range from a one-dimensional construct to more multidimensional constructs that include physical, psychological, social, and spiritual domains. In a meta-analysis of multiple instruments to determine the relationships among two constructs (QOL and perceived health status), and three functioning domains (mental, physical, and social functioning)) in twelve chronic disease studies, the results indicate that QOL and perceived health status are distinctive constructs from the patient's perspective. Patients give greater emphasis to mental health than to physical functioning when evaluating QOL versus health status. This underscores the need to use a multidimensional instrument.[41]

There are numerous instruments to measure quality of life. The following are just a few that have been used and may be more generalizable than some of the others.

- Medical Outcomes Study SF-20 (MOS SF-20)
- European Organization for Research and Treatment of Cancer Quality of Life Questionnaire (EORTC QLQ-30)
- General Health Survey (SF-36)
- Functional Assessment of Cancer Therapy-General (FACT-G)
- Assessment of Quality of Life (AQoL)

5.6 Documentation of Suffering

While healthcare providers (HCPs) recognize that suffering is a common occurrence, it is difficult to describe or quantify, making the assessment a complex issue. The reluctance to address these issues is evident in clinical practice when just the mention of the topic of suffering generates feelings of discomfort on the part of HCPs. This discomfort may be related to the lack of information regarding the concept as well as the feeling of not being able to address the issue adequately. It is common for medical records to note the presence or absence of pain and to rate it on a scale from 0–10. It is less common to see specific conclusions documented in the medical record that the patient is suffering. The attorney and damages experts often have to be able to draw inferences from the documentation of specific physical and psychological symptoms that are associated with suffering. For example, the medical records may document that the patient experienced physical symptoms such as nausea, vomiting, diarrhea, itching, and incontinence, loss of sensation, dizziness, skin breakdown, or foul-smelling drainage from wounds. The records may document psychological responses associated with suffering, such as crying, agitation, anxiety, anger, depression, or withdrawal.

The reality of the practice setting is that QOL is addressed in an erratic fashion. There are assessment tools specific to pain (Brief Pain Inventory), depression (Beck Depression Scale), anxiety (State/Trait Anxiety Scale), performance (Karnovsky Scale), and fatigue (Brief Fatigue Inventory). Each gives a glimpse of a one-dimensional perspective but falls short of the whole picture. What allows an adequate assessment of QOL and the presence or absence of suffering? The answer of course is a valid, reliable instrument relative to specific patient populations that would address the different domains from the impact of the specific disease or injury. It is difficult to imagine an instrument that could generalize across the varied patient populations without addressing some of the critical aspects of the disease or injury. An example of this comes from the work of Ferrell et al.[42] in an attempt to validate QOL measures for patients undergoing bone marrow transplant. There are so many unique experiences this patient population undergoes that a generic instrument may not capture the essence of the problems. Another example might be a head-injury patient and the need for a valid, reliable instrument focused on the unique experiences this patient population would likely experience.

Specific questions such as pain measurement may be integrated into the generic assessment forms on admission and on subsequent office visits, or patients may be asked how things are going. The burden falls to the patients as to how comfortable they feel in taking up the physician or nurse's time with issues they may be reluctant to discuss due to the lack of time. Time is always the issue, and QOL issues are always sensitive and need personalized attention. The "silent conspiracy" at work in the healthcare industry is the hustle and bustle of meeting all the demands. Very few patients are assertive enough to feel comfortable in putting forth their own agenda, and few healthcare professionals are brave enough to open Pandora's box.

5.7 Intervention Approaches

In order to be able to intervene effectively in QOL issues one must be willing to assess the area of concern. While HCPs espouse the mission to treat disease and relieve suffering of patients, it is another matter to integrate that philosophy into practice. The treatment of disease states has long been the target of medical care. Curing versus caring is an age-old dichotomy that has erred on the side of the former. Little in the way of resources has been allotted to the caring of patients to address the additional domains of QOL.

An intriguing study of 271 people was conducted to obtain oncologists' views regarding QOL information, to describe their willingness to use QOL information, and to propose interventions to facilitate the use of QOL information in clinical decision making (Bezjak, et al.[43]). The most striking aspect of the study is that 76% of physicians surveyed agreed that they did not discuss QOL issues with patients unless the patients asked about it first. The use of QOL questionnaires was primarily limited to patients in clinical trials, and only 26% of respondents indicated they use formal QOL questionnaires in their practice. On the other hand, the statement was made that there is nothing that should prevent the use of the already available QOL instruments to help gather and use information about individual patients in the clinical setting.

Realizing that QOL and suffering aspects of care are not likely to be assessed routinely in the foreseeable future, it is therefore important to establish what was communicated to the healthcare providers and what follow-up was made. The medical record may or may not provide an insight to this information.

5.8 Role of the Attorney in Evaluating the Effects of Disease or Injury on Quality of Life

Attorneys must address these issues during discovery and trial to understand the effects on the plaintiff's life. Plaintiffs need to be evaluated for the effects of their disease or injury and subsequent treatment on QOL. One way to evaluate QOL is by asking the plaintiff directly. This is probably the best way, but probably the most time consuming. Patient stories yield the best picture of what the patient is experiencing, and with the right environment the patient can express his or her concerns and benefit from a caring presence. Many healthcare providers and attorneys may feel inadequate to tackle these types of interactions, and many really may not have time in their day. Some attorneys involve legal nurse consultants and paralegals in obtaining this type of information. Some type of self-assessment by the patient as a screening instrument may in fact be the most pragmatic way to identify areas needing follow up with appropriate resources. Some plaintiffs' law firms send out questionnaires every few months to determine if new symptoms, treatment, or suffering is occurring.

In the best of all possible scenarios, the patient would be assessed as to level of QOL to assist HCPs to monitor and possibly modify treatment goals in an ongoing manner. Once the areas of decreased QOL are identified, specific interventions may be recommended. These may be as varied as the problems identified.

Many plaintiffs' attorneys are placed in the position of seeing the overview of the effect of the injury or disease on the quality of life of their client. Inevitably, over the course of the three to five years typically associated with litigation the attorney may be placed in the position of advising the client to seek help to deal with the multidimensional aspects of suffering. The following section provides guidance on how to intervene in each of the four major areas of quality of life.

A. Physical domain

In the area of performance or functional disabilities that create limitations that affect a patient's ability to perform activities of daily living, job-related activities, and recreational activities, resources such as physical medicine and rehabilitation services which include physiatrists, physical therapists, occupational therapists and recreational therapists can be consulted. These specialized services can implement specific treatments, exercises, and equipment to assist patients in overcoming many of the limitations of their disease or injury. The diagnosis of physical dysfunction and the recommendation of specific treatment measures is a highly specialized field of medicine and should be used more in the areas of improving QOL.

Tip

Suffering transcends all the domains of the QOL model.

Pain syndromes related to disease, treatment of disease, or injury are of the utmost importance to assess and intervene effectively. While it is clear pain and suffering are different concepts, unrelieved pain will most definitely cause extreme suffering. It is imperative for patients to be treated with appropriate pharmacological and non-pharmacological treatment modalities to maximize their ability to participate in a lifestyle that is meaningful. Complicated or intractable pain syndromes must be referred to pain experts who can do a thorough evaluation and provide definitive treatment measures utilizing a multidisciplinary approach. While the majority of pain syndromes can be treated successfully through the use of pharmacological agents, a small percentage will require some type of invasive procedure to provide relief. The barriers that exist in effective pain management can be overcome with proper education of HCPs, adequate assessment, and utilization of appropriate treatment measures.

The controversial issue of physician-assisted suicide may well be tied to the problem of ineffective pain management in our society. It is a commonly held belief among pain experts that if pain were adequately treated, patients would not have to resort to this extreme measure. The emphasis should be on preventing the depression and hopelessness associated with unrelieved pain through effective pain management.

B. Psychological domain

In the area of psychological dysfunction, there are multiple resources available, such as psychiatrists, psychologists, social workers, and counselors. Wellness centers are more prevalent today, and many focus on relaxation and coping strategies to deal with the multitude of stressors in patients' lives as they seek to overcome their disease or injury. Being present for patients allows them to express their innermost feelings and fears and subsequently work to resolve conditions such as depression, anxiety, hopelessness or fear of death. Patients may need more thorough evaluation for the addition of medications such as antidepressant and anti-anxiety drugs. Combining pharmacological and non-pharmacological interventions may provide the best solution for the patient's problem. The evaluation and follow up of response are critical to the success of the treatment plan.

C. Social domain

Social problems related to roles, friend and family relationships, and work-related and financial concerns can have an enormous effect on patients' lives. Social isolation and reluctance to share information with family and friends may need to be addressed before patients can return to normal interaction. Intimacy issues such as sexual activity are extremely difficult areas for patients to communicate as well as for the HCPs and attorneys to assess for loss of consortium claims. Having questions related to sexual activity as a component of the QOL instrument may be a less threatening way to bring this issue to light. Opening the channels of communication is of primary concern. As Cassell[44] states, recovery may require the assistance of a caring person. The chance of that being a family member or close friend is very likely. The willingness to communicate is the key to opening up to others in order to receive assistance to move beyond the present. Resources such as social workers, counselors, and support groups can encourage patients to express their feelings in order to receive the support they need.

D. Spiritual domain

Spirituality consists of many concepts. Religious beliefs and tenets on one hand can be tremendously comforting for some, whereas others may need to look beyond formalized religion to more universal concepts. Concepts such as the interconnectiveness of all living things and finding peace through quieting of the mind can provide similar support in the spiritual domain. Finding meaning through religious beliefs or through a transcendental experience can allow for moving beyond the limitations of the present. This is a personal journey, but one that is crucial as one is confronted with a threat to one's existence or integrity. Identifying patient conflicts in the area of spiritual domain can provide interventions from resources ranging from ministerial pastors, priests, rabbis, church groups, lay groups, and meditation groups. With the increase in diversity in our society, we must be more open to the differences in cultures, and we must be willing to explore the various resources available in the community to assist in this effort.

5.9 Legal Implications of Suffering

Awards for pain and suffering have come under increased scrutiny in recent years. Tort reform efforts have focused on this component of damages, with limitations being placed on the amount of the award that can be granted in some states. Conversely, some states have placed limitations on punitive damages, leading creative attorneys to shift their attention to pain and suffering. Liptak, quoting Victor Schwarz, a coauthor of a leading law school textbook on torts, noted that "Plaintiffs' lawyers are repackaging their punitive damages claims to put the money load into pain and suffering damages.[45]

Some states may allow recovery for pain and suffering even in the absence of physical injury. A New Jersey Appellate division held in *Willis v. Ashby*, that the parents of a stillborn child had a claim for severe emotional harm. This met the threshold for pain and suffering damages under the Tort Claims Act. The statute, NJSA 59:2 (d), bars such damages except where there is "permanent loss of a bodily function, permanent disfigurement or dismemberment" and where medical expenses exceed $3,600. The three-judge panel rejected the state's argument that psychological harm without physical symptoms does not suffice under the Tort Claims Act without an invasive assault. The panel held that psychological and emotional injuries should be treated the same as physical injuries under the Act's threshold provision when they arise in this context of a stillborn infant.[46]

The suffering experienced by a bystander who observes an accident may be a valid claim in some jurisdictions. This claim was the basis of a $2.2 million settlement in New Jersey in *Cafasso v. Atco Rubber Products*. The family of a woman injured by a truck received the settlement. The decedent suffered for up to eight seconds before she died. Her son witnessed the agony and has never recovered from post traumatic stress disorder. The defense position was that the woman died instantly and that her son had recovered from the emotional effects of the accident. The parties settled after mediation.[47] Connecticut has addressed this issue through their insurance policies. Connecticut uninsured and underinsured motorist coverage provides coverage for persons who suffer consequential damages as a result of bodily injuries sustained to an insured. This clause allows a person who incurs medical expenses on behalf of an insured, or has a cause of action for loss of consortium, to assert a claim under the uninsured motorist provisions of the policy. This claim would also seem to allow an insured to make a claim for bystander emotional distress under *Clohessy v. Bachelor*, 237 Conn. 31 (1996).[48]

5.10 Plaintiffs' Attorney's Presentation of Suffering in the Courtroom

The role of the plaintiffs' attorney is to present the suffering of the client in a meaningful way without either overemphasizing or underemphasizing it. Suffering may be discussed during voir dire. Jurors may be asked if they believe that family values are extremely important and if they recognize that injury to one family member tends to inconvenience and hurt the rest. The multi-dimensions of suffering may be introduced during voir dire. Jurors may be asked about their feelings about laws that provide for money damages for loss of earnings, medical bills, loss of companionship or society, and past and future pain and suffering. This line of questioning, carefully used, helps to identify potential jurors who will not be willing to award damages for these types of claims.[49]

Ball[50] suggests preparing three lists of harms suffered by the plaintiff. The immediate harms are the physical injuries. The consequences of the immediate harms constitute the second list. They may be the symptoms, losses, emotional effects, and other aspects of suffering. The last list contains the measures to fix or help the harms, such as treatment (surgery, hospitalization, nursing care, appliances, wheelchairs and braces.) The harms lists are used during voir dire, opening, testimony, and closing statements.

Suffering should be specially presented. Consider the case of the plaintiff who experiences post traumatic stress disorder. Analogies may be found to describe it such as "If you have ever woken up from a nightmare terrified, that is how John feels whenever he hears a car horn." Or when representing a client with panic attacks: "Try to remember the most panicked you have ever known anyone to be. That's how Jane feels all the time." When representing a person who has mobility problems, note that the client cannot escape or defend himself. The client knows this makes him a magnet for thieves. When he hears a noise at night, he cannot investigate. All he can do is lie there alone, helpless, and terrified. The jury will understand the terror of being alone, trapped in a fire and unable to escape.[50]

Tip

The attorney should examine the client's situation to identify the sources of suffering and the safety hazards and then determine how most effectively to present this information to the jury.

The role of jury is to consider suffering as a component of the intangible damages sustained by the plaintiff. While it is simple to calculate the cost of medical care and lost wages, it is often difficult to put a price on pain and suffering. According to Ball,[50] if medical bills and lost wages total $125,000, jurors are likely to use that figure as an anchor for pain and suffering, arguing that the plaintiff should get half of that amount, or double, or the amount exactly. They begin with the anchor of the tangible figure and argue to adjust it one way or the other. Ball argues that the attorney should use the term "intangible losses." Lawrence[49] stresses that the plaintiff attorney should avoid asking for damages for pain, suffering or mental anguish because those terms are often misinterpreted as connoting "lawyer greed." Instead, the closing argument should focus on the value of what the plaintiff has lost. The following closing argument was made in a case involving a permanently immobile plaintiff injured by a doctor's negligence.

Sometimes bad people break the law. Sometimes, not always, we catch them, and then we convict them. They are put in jail, and you know the rest: They get to stay in a cell of a constitutionally guaranteed size. They are given literature to read and access to the library. They get time in the yard and in the gym. More often than not, after a few years, they are released and paroled.

The plaintiff, Ellen Jones, is a prisoner of her injuries. They will hold her hostage for the rest of her life. She is unable to walk to the yard or the library. No early release or parole is possible. What she has lost is what we all cherish the most—her essential freedom.

5.11 Conclusion

The view that suffering cannot exist without an "invasive assault" is very shortsighted and demonstrates a lack of knowledge and understanding of the underpinnings of a suffering experience. Although it is a highly personal matter and only the individual can identify the meaning of the experience, there are qualitative methods to describe the "lived experience" of people and how this experience has affected their quality of life. Identifying the multidimensional aspects of suffering, allows for more thorough assessment of the impact of the experience and how it has altered an individual's life either temporarily or in some cases permanently. The most credible witness in this situation is the client. How she relates the effects of the suffering experience will determine the legitimacy of her claim.

Endnotes

1. Rodgers, B., and Cowles, K., "A Conceptual Foundation for Human Suffering in Nursing Care and Research." *Journal of Advanced Nursing*, 25, 1048–1053, 1997.

2. Kahn, D., and Steeves, R., "The Experience of Suffering: Conceptual Clarification and Theoretical Definition." *The Journal of Advanced Nursing*, 11, 623–631. 1986.

3. Cassell, E., "The Nature of Suffering and the Goals of Medicine." *New England Journal of Medicine*, 306(11), 639–648, 1982.

4. Chaplin, R., and Gavrin, J., "Suffering and Its Relationship to Pain." *Journal of Palliative Care*, 9(2), 5–13, 1993.

5. Morse J., and Carter, B., "The Essence of Enduring and Expression of Suffering: The Reformation of Self." *Scholarly Inquiry for Nursing Practice,* 10 (1), 43–60, 1996.

6. Battenfield, B., "Suffering—A Conceptual Description and Content Analysis of an Operational Scheme." *Image: The Journal of Nursing Scholarship*, 16 (2), 36–41, 1984.

7. Benedict, S., and Bird, J., "Suffering Reported by Adults with Cancer." *Journal of Alabama Academic Science*, 53(3), 80, 1982.

8. Charmez, K., "Loss of Self: A Fundamental Form of Suffering in the Chronically Ill." *Sociology of Illness and Health*, 5, 168–195, 1983.

9. Dildy, S., "Suffering in People with Rheumatoid Arthritis." *Applied Nursing Research* 9 (4), 177–183, 1996.

10. Flaming, D., "Patient Suffering: A Taxonomy from the Nurse's Perspective." *Journal of Advanced Nursing*, 22, 1120–1127, 1995.

11. Lindholm, L., and Eriksson, K., "To Understand and Alleviate Suffering in a Caring Culture." *Journal of Advanced Nursing*, 18, 1354–1361, 1993.

12. Pollock, S., and Sands, D., "Adaptation to Suffering." *Clinical Nursing Research*, 6(2), 171–185, 1997.

13. Benedict, S., "The Suffering Associated with Lung Cancer." *Cancer Nursing*, 12 (1), 34–40, 1989.

14. Copp, L., "The Spectrum of Suffering." *American Journal of Nursing*. 74(3), 491–495, 1974.

15. Truett, L., *Development of a Tool to Describe the Phenomenon of Suffering*. Unpublished doctoral dissertation. Denton, TX: Texas Woman's University, 1999.

16. Watson, J., "Human Caring and Suffering: A Subjective Model for Health Sciences." In Taylor, R., and Watson, J., eds., *They Shall Not Hurt: Human Suffering and Human Caring*. Boulder: Colorado Associated University Press, 1989.

17. Goldberg, J., "Concerning Human Suffering." *The Psychiatric Journal of the University of Ottawa*, 11, 97-104, 1986.

18. Coyle, N,. Suffering in the First Person: Glimpses of Suffering through Patient's and Family Narratives." In Ferrell, B., editor, *Suffering*. Boston: Jones and Bartlett, 1996.

19. Graneheim, U., Lindahl, E., and Kihlgren, M., "Descriptions of Suffering in Connection with Life Values." *Scandinavian Journal of Caring Sciences*, 11,145–150, 1997.

20. Thorpe, D., *An Analysis of Oncology Nurses' Statements Regarding the Association of Pain snd Suffering with Requests for Assistance in Dying*. Unpublished doctoral dissertation. Denton, TX: Texas Woman's University, 1993.

21. Knight, J., "The Suffering of Suicide: The Victim and Family Considered." In Starck, P., and McGovern, J., eds., *The Hidden Dimension of Illness: Human Suffering*. New York: National League for Nursing Press, 1992.

22. Byock, I., "The Nature of Suffering and the Nature of Opportunity at the End of Life." *Clinical Geriatric Medicine*, 12 (2), 237–252 1996.

23. Starck, P., "The Human Spirit: The Search for Meaning and Purpose through Suffering." *Humane Medicine*, 8 (2), 132–137, 1992.

24. Starck, P., and McGovern, J., "The Meaning of Suffering." In Starck, P., and McGovern, J., eds., *The Hidden Dimension of Illness: Human Suffering*. New York: National League of Nursing Press, 1992.

25. Steeves, R., and Kahn, D., "Experience of Meaning in Suffering." *Journal of Nursing Scholarship*, 19 (3), 144–116, 1981.

26. Frankl, V., *Man's Search for Meaning*, Third Edition. New York: Simon and Schuster, 1963.

27. Daly, J., "The View of Suffering within the Human Becoming." In Parse, R., editor, *Illuminations: The Human Becoming Theory in Practice and Research*. New York: National League for Nursing Press, 1995.

28. Cella, D., and Tulsky, D., "Measuring Quality of Life Today: Methodological Aspects." *Oncology*, 4 (5), 29–38, 1990.

29. Cella, D. and Cherin, E., "Quality of Life during and after Cancer Treatment." *Comprehensive Therapy,* 14 (5), 69–75, 1988.

30. Ferrell, B., "The Quality of Lives: 1,525 Voices of Cancer." *Oncology Nursing Forum*, 23 (6), 907–916, 1996.

31. Suits and Deals, *New Jersey Law Journal*, November 12, 2001.

32. Laska, L., editor, "Negligent Positive Finding of Breast Cancer Gene." *Anonymous Female Patient v. Anonymous Hospital and Anonymous Corporation,* Cuyahoga County (OH) Court of Common Pleas, case no. _____, *Medical Malpractice Verdicts, Settlements and Experts,* September 2002, 16.

33. Laska, L., editor, "Failure to Provide Prison Inmate Medical Treatment of Hydrocephalus." *Valdez v. State of Arizona*, Maricopa County (AZ) Superior Court, case no. CV 2000-000205, *Malpractice Verdicts, Settlements and Experts*, March 2002, 23.

34. Laska, L., editor, "Woman Claims Laminectomy Performed by Impaired Surgeon under the Influence of Cocaine." *Loleta Horner and Clarence Horner v. Garland Community Hospital, Ltd., Bruce S. Hinkley, M.D. and Ross Curtess, M.D.*, Dallas County (TX) District Court, case no. 00-00748-A, *Medical Malpractice Verdicts, Settlements and Experts*, July 2002, 60–61.

35. Laska, L., editor, "Negligent Technique in Performance of Colostomy following Repair of Rectal Tear Results in Bowel Rupture, Peritonitis and Permanent Abdominal Wall Support Weakness." *Krenson Edward Kniphfer, et al. v. Memorial Health University Medical Center, Inc. and MPPG, Inc.*, Chatham County (GA) State Court, case no. 101057F, *Medical Malpractice Verdicts, Settlements and Experts*, June 2002, 61.

36. Zarin, I., editor, "$1,237,500 Verdict." *Bianchi vs. City of Philadelphia, et al.,* Civil Action no. CA 99-CV-2904, *New Jersey Jury Verdict Review and Analysis.* July 2002, 23 (2): 25.

37. Laska, L., editor, "Hospital Aide Sexually Assaults Restrained and Confused Patient." *Mary Zsigo v. Hurley Medical Center*, Genesee County (MI) Circuit Court, case no. 99-66504-CL, *Medical Malpractice Verdicts, Settlements and Experts*, July 2002, 55.

38. Zarin, I., editor, "$3,580,000 Verdict Including $1.5 Million for Increased Risk Reduced by 5% under Scafidi." Docket no. L-2395-99, *New Jersey Jury Verdict Review and Analysis*, 23 (2), August 2002, 3–4.

39. Laska, L., editor, "Failure to Timely Diagnose Testicular Torsion Results in Loss of Man's Testicle." *Timothy Washington v. Dr. Michael Wilczynski, D.O., Radiology Imaging Associates, S.C.*, Cook County (IL) Circuit Court, case no. 97L-9044, *Medical Malpractice Verdicts, Settlements and Experts*, February 2002, 56.

40. Ferrell, B., "To Know Suffering." *Oncology Nursing Forum*, 20 (10), 1471–1477, 1993.

41. Smith, K., Avis, N., and Assmann, S., "Distinguishing between Quality of Life and Health Status in Quality of Life Research: A Meta-Analysis." *Quality of Life Research.* 8 (5), 447–59, 1999.

42. Ferrell, B., Schmidt, G., Rhiner, M., Whitehead, C., and Forman, S., "The Meaning of Quality of Life for Bone Marrow Transplant Survivors, Part 1: The Impact of Bone Marrow Transplant on Quality of Life." *Cancer Nursing*, 15 (3), 153–160, 1992.

43. Bezjak, A,, Ng, P., Skeel, R., DePetrillo, A., Comis, R., and Taylor, K. "Oncologists' Use of Quality of Life Information: Results of a Survey of Eastern Cooperative Oncology Group Physicians." *Quality of Life Research*, 10,1–13, 2001.

44. Cassell, E., "The Relief of Suffering." *Archives of Internal Medicine*, 143 (3), 522– 523, 1983.

45. Liptak, A., "Pain and Suffering Awards Let Juries Avoid New Limits." *The New York Times*, October 28, 2002.

46. Gallagher, M., "Tort Claims Act Damages Allowed for Medical Malpractice Pain and Suffering." *New Jersey Law Journal*, July 15, 2002, 5.

47. Suits and Deals, *New Jersey Law Journal*, September 2, 2002, 8.

48. *Connecticut Uninsured and Underinsured Motorist Coverage Issues*, Donovan & Morello, LLP, February 2000, www.findlaw.com, accessed December 4, 2002.

49. Lawrence, R., "What Good Will Money Do?" *Trial*, September 2002, 28.

50. Ball, D., *David Ball on Damages: A Plaintiff's Attorney's Guide for Personal Injury and Wrongful Death Cases*. Notre Dame, IN: NITA, 2001

Chapter 6

Pain and Suffering of Children

Sally A. Lambert, PhD, RN and Diane C. Hudson-Barr, PhD, RN

Synopsis

6.1 Introduction

The concept of pain has emerged over the last few years as a major concern for healthcare professionals. Traditionally the goal for healthcare has been to cure disease and reduce suffering. The concentration on understanding and curing disease has sometimes managed to leave pain and suffering in the background. However, consumer advocates, attorneys, healthcare professionals, and professional organizations have brought the issues to the foreground, and currently the healthcare climate mandates improved management of the client's pain and suffering.

Tip

Those caring for children or attorneys litigating personal injury cases involving infants and children face special challenges. Pain is an elusive and subjective concept. It cannot be precisely and scientifically measured in quantifiable terms.

Pain is self-reported, and therefore healthcare professionals differ on whether the patent experiences pain, how much pain there is, and how to treat it. This is especially true for the pediatric patient.

Myths about children's pain have influenced healthcare providers for many years. Many of these unfounded assumptions result from children's inability to report or express their pain and suffering in a meaningful way. Many practitioners and lay people mistakenly believe that children are simply small adults. Thirty years ago healthcare providers believed that infants could not feel pain because of immature nerves. This was based on the concept that nerves in infants were not able to transmit pain impulses, and therefore pain was not real. When children were perceived to have discomfort, it was thought to be unimportant and quickly forgotten. Pain was believed to do no harm to a child, and in fact, some believed that pain helped build a child's character.

Since some children seemed to handle pain better than adults, treatment was not advised. Healthcare professionals feared that administering narcotics for severe pain caused many harmful side effects and would lead to addiction; therefore narcotics were rarely given. In recent years these myths have been proven to be untrue, and current research has demonstrated that treating children's pain leads to quicker recovery from illness and injury.[1] The myths still prevail, however, and only recently have there been efforts to improve the art of pain management for children.

Tip

Even though the science of pain measurement and treatment has advanced, there continue to be many barriers to adequate pain treatment.

Pain may not be identified as a priority in health care, even though there is a clear medical duty to alleviate suffering. Other factors contributing to the undertreatment of pediatric pain include: educational deficiencies in the current methods of pain assessment and treatment, difficulties in quantifying pediatric pain, lack of standards for pain relief, the reluctance of family members to give children narcotics, and the scarcity of resources.[2] All of these factors can add up to inadequate pain relief and prolonged suffering of children, which contribute to the damages in a personal injury suit.

This chapter will review

- a historical perspective of pain management,
- reasons to treat pain (including consequences of untreated pain),
- child development (including development of concepts of illness and pain),
- pain assessment by developmental level, and
- management of pediatric pain (pharmacologic and nonpharmacologic).

The goal of this chapter is to provide a useful reference for the attorney, healthcare professional, or legal nurse consultant in understanding the problems and promise for the relief of pain and suffering for children of all ages. This chapter will provide information that will help in the analysis of medical records for evidence of pain and suffering in neonates and children.

6.2 Historical Perspective

A. Early History

Pain and suffering are a fact of life. Evidence from fossilized bones and tools from 40,000 B.C. and rock paintings from 2,000 B.C. indicate primitive man was bothered by many of the same pains that afflict modern man.[3] The two most common sources of pain for the child historically and today are injury or disease and childrearing practices.[4] The sources and treatment of childhood pain throughout time are intertwined with the role children played in the world at the time. Three excellent references that chronicle the child's pain experiences and its relationship to childrearing practices throughout history have been written by Brodie,[5] McGrath and Unruh,[4] and Ross and Ross.[3]

The importance of children to society has changed greatly since primitive times. Primitive man was not overly attentive to child welfare concerns because the struggle for existence was crucial for all, and only the strong could survive.[5] Ancient Greeks encouraged their children to excel in academic and athletic endeavors. Strength, vigor, masculinity, and beauty were all characteristics strongly valued, leaving little room for puny, sickly, or female children, who often were victims of infanticide.[5] The first law on a child's relationship to society was written by the ancient Romans, giving the father absolute rule over his children. Children were the property of their fathers; they could be sold to pay a debt, beaten, or even killed.[5]

With the decline of the Roman Empire, the Middle Ages were characterized by indifference and cruelty towards children with limited influence by the legal and religious prohibitions of the day.[4] During the Renaissance, childrearing advice was divided between restrictive and punitive methods and a more compassionate approach to care. As governments began to stabilize in the 13th century, the merchant and noble class system developed, and parents were newly aware of their children as future heirs of the family name, fortune, title, and power.[5] Increased attention to providing education and training opportunities for the children occurred. The 15th century brought a glimmer of humanism, and foundling homes were started for abandoned children by the church and state. With migration to the New World in the 1700s, children were seen as assets to the community because the expansion of this country depended on the growth of colonists' families.[5] The concept that children had special needs different from the adult led to the establishment of community schools (the foundation of our current system of education). During the 18th and 19th centuries, child welfare became a political issue at the same time that incorporation of hygienic practices in hospitals and foundling homes occurred.

All ancient civilizations believed pain resulted from intrusions in the body of magic fluids, evils spirits, or demons and could be released through prayers to the gods or by creating openings in the body for the sources to escape.[3,4] Aristotle (4th century B.C.) believed pain was an emotion, a passion felt by the heart that occurred when the intensity of sensation encountered by touch interacted with factors of the heart.[3,4] This view of pain prevailed until the Roman Galen (around 150 A.D.) proposed three classifications of nerves, including one that relayed pain messages. His idea was dismissed as an unwarranted attack on Aristotle.[3] During the Middle Ages, Christianity strongly influenced beliefs about pain, and the Roman Catholic Church suggested pain originated from the wrath of God and could be healed through religious worship.[4]

B. 1900s to present

Brodie[9] labels the period between 1901–1920 as the spirit of progressivism in the United States because of the increased interest of society and scientists in the welfare of children.[6] Both the private and public school systems enlarged to include greater numbers of students. The first White House Conference on Children and Youth was sponsored by President Theodore Roosevelt because more was known about fish, wildlife, and the boll weevil than the nation's children.[5] This conference led to the establishment of the Children's Bureau in 1912.[5] In 1916, child labor laws were enacted by Woodrow Wilson to protect children from harsh labor conditions, only to be revoked a year later by the Supreme Court and not enacted into legislation until 1940.[5]

Around the turn of the century, the topic of children's pain made an appearance in the healthcare literature. Children were believed to be unskilled at locating pain accurately, but they had the ". . . fortitude with which to bear severe pain . . . , the fortitude of little heroes."[7] Human pain was described as "a subjective experience which is most often accompanied by objective symptoms"[8] and its absence was not always a favorable indicator since the presence implies life and reaction to life. Although healthcare professionals were told they needed to be able to tell if an infant is in pain, be it hunger or discomfort, there were no suggestions on how to accomplish this. Pain was described in association with conditions and treatments without any suggestions on how to manage it.[9]

During the years 1920–1940, a focus on the normal growth and development principles for children evolved. The federal government's continued interest in the nation's children, the identification of the need to learn about the healthy child,[10,11] and the beginnings of the work on family dynamics, particularly separation,[6] probably all contributed to this change. Children were perceived as bearing pain better than adults, with Spartan endurance, forgetting the experience until the next time it occured[12] and demonstrating a recovery "[that] was rapid and often seemed miraculous."[13] Newborn pain was perceived to be less acute than what it would be as the infant aged.[14]

The most influential socio-political factor of the years of 1940–1960 was adoption of legislation in 1940 to protect children under sixteen years of age from being employed in hazardous environments. Children previously had worked long hours for little pay under dangerous conditions in factories with poor temperature regulation (too hot in the summer, too cold in the winter), dirty and noisy surroundings, and in the presence of hazardous materials associated with the particular industry.[5] Advances in knowledge of both applied and basic sciences continued to flourish during this time[5] and the availability of new technology led to increased burdens and responsibilities for those caring for pediatric patients.[6] A change in parental involvement in the care of the hospitalized child also occurred during this time: from limited and controlled involvement to the "rooming-in" practices that began in the 1950s.[6] The ongoing work of eminent psychologists of the day was responsible for these changes in parental involvement with the goal of reducing the child's pain and suffering.

Advances in the field of pain knowledge were practically nonexistent from 1850–1950 until Bonica changed the field with his publication of *The Management of Pain* in 1953.[3] Innovations regarding care of the patient in pain and practitioner education were the two most significant contributions of this work, that is held in high esteem to this day.[3] Other textbooks of this period described pain as "a feeling of discomfort that can be psychological or physiological in origin"[15] with the following signs and symptoms:

- facial expression changes (frown, drawn lips, furrowed brow),
- pallor,
- clenched teeth,
- decreased activity,
- increased blood pressure or pulse
- dilated pupils

Treatment of pain was described as palliative and supportive, but the authors did not identify specific intervention, except to say it was based on individual needs.[15]

Munson[16] recommended using play before painful procedures to minimize the child's unpleasant memories associated with that procedure. Play therapy, as a way for children to cope with the hospitalization experience, was described by several authors.[17,18] Wessel[19] stressed the honest approach when working with a child who will experience a painful procedure—admitting to the child that it will hurt. When discussing pain experiences, the approach used is brought back to that psychosocial and emotional focus. Petro[20] described the sense of pain to be poorly developed in little children although "they probably respond with some distress to many stimuli that can cause pain in adults."

Many exciting changes occurred in the world of pediatric care in the next decade from 1960–1970. Comprehensive care was taught with a focus on systematic processes and coordination between the healthcare team and the child with his or her family.[6] At the same time, a broad social mandate focusing on the health and welfare of all citizens, but specifically children and the elderly, swept the nation.[5]

In 1965, Melzack and Wall suggested pain was the result of more than one action of the nervous system modulated at successive synapses and the perception of pain was influenced by psychological factors.[3] These authors have continued to modify their "gate control" theory of pain by developing this theory through continued research. Gate control theory proposes that a neural mechanism in the spinal cord acts as a gate to increase or decrease the flow of nerve impulses from nerve fibers in the periphery of the body to the central nervous system. Additional (descending) controls of the gate result from cognitive mechanisms like anxiety, attention, past experience, and anticipation. This theory resulted in the development of pain control techniques like transcutaneous electrical nerve stimulation and has provided a physiological explanation for the psychological factors that have an influence on pain.[4]

Recommended treatment of pain in children included attempts to decrease the trauma (read "pain") of hypodermic injections through "best injection taker today" medals given to children[21] and the use of supportive approaches to decrease pain like parents' presence, a calm and skilled nursing approach, and honest communication. (For example, healthcare professionals were not to ask the child if he wanted to take his medicine now. If he says no, then he shouldn't have to take it. Instead, they ask if the child wants to take his medicine with water or with orange juice.) Indicators of pain were described as immobility, grimacing with movement, irritability, whimpering, whining, favoring the site in pain, and anorexia.[22] Webb[22] recommended postoperative medication administration for twenty-four to thirty-six hours after surgery. However, none of these suggestions was supported by empirical study.

In the decade that began in 1970, some educators suggested that children should no longer be viewed and treated as small adults.[23] In the early 1970s, the study of pain emerged as a separate field of scientific inquiry. This change of status has resulted in an exponential growth of empirical and clinical knowledge about pain.[3] Pain was described in association with specific disorders, and the use of analgesics was recommended.[23] McKee[24] suggested that children's coping with nerve-related body pain could be enhanced through the development of trust in the nurse. Schultz[25] examined the perception of pain in ten- and eleven-year-olds and described the emotional, psychological, and physical reactions of these children to include anxiety, hostility, anger, anguish, changes in posture and gait, and changes in blood pressure and heart rate values.

The late 1970s also saw the first acknowledgment of limited knowledge of pediatric pain and the beginning of more serious research into the topic. Pediatric nurses paved the way for the surge of interest in pediatric pain. McCaffery[26] identified factors that influence assessment of pediatric pain and suggested both analgesic and nonpharmacologic relief measures. Eland compared the amount of pain medication given to children after surgery to the amounts of medication given to adults undergoing similar procedures. The results demonstrated that children received significantly less medication. Unfortunately she only reported this information in a chapter found in a pain source book.[27] Two studies done in the 1980s confirmed her findings of the undertreatment of postoperative pain in children.[28,29] Possible explanations for the undertreatment include: (1) belief that children feel less pain, (2) challenges in interpreting the child's pain communication, (3) fear of possible side effects associated with medication administration, and (4) limited knowledge of the pharmacokinetics of pain medication in the pediatric population.[28,29]

Later research began to demonstrate that pain, in fact, had a detrimental effect on the child. Anand and colleagues demonstrated that neonates had increased levels of stress hormones and delayed healing with untreated pain.[30,31] These early studies of pediatric pain management brought attention to the fact that children experience pain and that this pain is usually undertreated and may lead to later consequences such as delayed wound healing, infection, prolonged hospitalization, and enhanced reaction to future painful events.

Professionals caring for children began to notice and become interested in the treatment of children's pain. Researchers realized that in order to treat pain, tools must be designed to measure the pain experience. Although the research on the pediatric patient's pain experiences increased dramatically in the past two decades, translation of this research into practice has not been as rapid.

Tip

Attorneys are still likely to encounter situations in which an injured child has received inadequate pain management.

In 1996, Broome and colleagues published the results of a survey that examined how healthcare providers in U.S. teaching hospitals assess and manage children's pain.[32] A total of 227 questionnaires were sent to 212 pediatric hospitals, and 113 were returned. Sixty percent of the respondents indicated that they had standards of care or protocols for pain, but only one-quarter reported that the standards were followed. Seventy three percent of the sample used formal pain assessment tools and only 35% reported that was "likely" or "very likely" that parents would be involved prior to a painful event.[32] Obstacles to pain management identified included inadequate recourses and knowledge deficits.

The study of pediatric pain has broadened to look at assessment tools, physiologic and behavioral indicators of pain, management strategies, and nursing and medical management behaviors. It has emphasized the interdisciplinary approach to research and patient care. Journals exclusively devoted to the continuing study of pain include *Clinical Journal of Pain*, *European Journal of Pain*, *Headache*, *Journal of Pain and Symptom Management*, *Pain*, *Pain Research and Management*, and *Pain Reviews* to name a few. These journals include the work of professionals in nursing, medicine, and psychology and help to establish the standard of pediatric pain management.

By the 1990s, pediatric pain received considerable attention in the professional literature, yet physicians were reluctant to prescribe pain medications and nurses were not measuring pain consistently. Several factors may account for this apparent gap between knowledge and practice. Studies concerning children's pain were published to limited audiences and thus not widely disseminated. Pain assessment and treatment was not covered in professional education programs, and there were limited tools available to measure pediatric pain. In addition, the myths surrounding children's pain continued with no public advocacy for pediatric pain treatment. The pain children experienced continued to be undertreated.

During this decade the healthcare climate began to change, and pain started to be noticed by government and consumer advocate groups. The U.S. Department of Health Education and Human Services' Agency for Health Care Policy and Research published *Acute Pain Management in Infants, Children and Adolescents: Operative and Medical Procedures* in 1992.[33] These guidelines became the first public policy statement mandating treatment of children's pain.

In general, the guidelines address the assessment and management of postoperative and procedural-related pain in children. The guidelines acknowledge that untreated pain has negative physiological and psychological consequences. "Prevention being better than treatment," the goal is to reduce pain to an acceptable level. Assessment and treatment (pharmacological and non-pharmacological) and reassessment at regular intervals meet this goal. Healthcare providers are encouraged to involve children and their families in the assessment and management of the child's pain experience.[33] Although the guidelines were widely disseminated to consumers and healthcare professionals, pain management practices in healthcare institutions were still lacking. Many factors may have lead to this resistance to change, including the still held beliefs that children did not feel the same pain as adults, healthcare providers were not educated on treating children's pain, and measures to evaluate children's pain were not readily available.

In 1998, the World Health Organization in collaboration with the International Association for the Study of Pain published Cancer Pain Relief and Palliative Care in Children.[34] The recommendations contained in this monograph urge comprehensive management of cancer pain and suffering. They called for practitioner education and explicit public policy aimed at alleviating suffering in those diagnosed with cancer.

In 2000, the American Academy of Pediatrics and the Canadian Paediatric Society published a policy statement, "Prevention and Management Pain and Stress in the Neonate."[35] Its objective was to increase awareness that neonates experience pain, provide a physiological basis for neonatal pain and management of pain by healthcare professionals, and to recommend effective and safe interventions. The policy guidelines specifically address the management of acute pain following surgery or painful procedures.[35]

In 2001, the American Academy of Pediatrics and the American Pain Society published a policy statement addressing the management of acute pain in infants, children, and adolescents.[36] This statement was published jointly "to underscore the responsibility of pediatricians to take a leadership and advocacy role to ensure humane and competent treatment of pain and suffering in all infants, children, and adolescents." See Figure 6.1 for a summary of the recommendations. The policy statement addresses specific treatment principles for procedural pain, surgery, trauma, and acute illness. The statement also recommends increased research and dissemination of knowledge of pediatric pain.[36]

The *Pain Assessment and Management: Guideline for Practice from the National Association of Neonatal Nurses*[37] describes the interdisciplinary nature of policy development, education, and competency validation, and hot to monitor the appropriateness and effectiveness of neonatal pain management. The guideline also recommends reassessment at regular intervals throughout the infant's hospitalization and describes nonpharmacologic and pharmacologic interventions for pain relief in neonates.

Other sources of the standard of pediatric pain management support the patient's right to pain assessment and treatment with statements interspersed within their own practice guidelines and missions. For example, the American Academy of Pain Management supports pain management activities provided with an "overriding concern for the patient and above all with the recognition of the patient's dignity as a human being."[38] The American Society of Pain Management Nurses also speaks to the role of the nurse in pain assessment, administration of treatment, and reassess-

- Incorporate the assessment and treatment of childhood pain into everyday practice.
- Anticipate painful experiences and use both comfort techniques and pain medication to minimize
- Use reliable and age-appropriate pain assessment tools.
- Encourage the self-report of pain whenever possible.
- Include physiologic measures, such as heart rate and breathing rate, in the assessment of pain.
- Ask the child's parents about their perceptions of their child's comfort status and to describe changes in typical behavior.
- Recognize that cultural and language differences may influence the child's experience and expression of pain.
- Pain assessment in children with cognitive, developmental, or emotional impairments is challenging; match your assessment technique with the special needs of the child.
- Look for special circumstances that may influence the child's ability to communicate and be understood.
- Recognize your biases and do not to allow those biases to interfere with the pain assessment process.
- Technically competent professionals should perform procedures so that pain is minimized.
- Both pharmacological and non-pharmacological comfort measures are used to treat pain.
- Children and parents should receive explanations prior to painful procedures to minimize the stress of the experience.
- Use a multidisciplinary approach that individualizes the management for each child and involves families in the process.
- Provide a calm physical environment that reduces distress-producing stimulation.
- Advocate for the effective use of pain medication to ensure compassionate and competent management of pain in children.

Figure 6.1 *Summary of AAP and APS recommendations for the management of pain in infants, children, and adolescents*

ment. See Figure 6.2 for websites of organizations that may be helpful to the reader.

The Joint Commission on Accreditation of Health Care Organizations (JCAHO) evaluates and accredits healthcare organizations and programs in the United States. Begun in 1951, this independent, not-for-profit organization is the primary standard-setting and accrediting body in health care. Their mission is to improve the safety and quality of health care provided to the public. Accreditation by JCAHO helps to ensure that patients are receiving a standard level of quality health care. Accreditation also is important to organizations because it is required for certain third-party reimbursements, educational programs, managed care contracts, and it enhances the image of the organization.

The JCAHO pain management standards state that patients have the right to pain assessment and treatment and are to be involved in all aspects of their care. Patients must be educated about their pain and managing pain must become part of their treatment plan. To date the JCAHO standards are the strongest and possibly the most influential in effecting changes in pain treatment for patients. The fact that JCAHO accreditation is shared with consumers as confirmation of quality of care provided and also is necessary for reimbursement has made institutions responsive to the JCAHO pain management mandate.

Tip

In July 2001, the JCAHO standard for pain management became mandatory.

Healthcare institutions are also mandating their own standards. Increasing attention to the education of healthcare professionals in pain management is beginning to occur. Pain management teams and consultative services are a part of many institutions.[39] In addition, pediatric hospitals have developed unique approaches to improve pain management. For example, Schechter and colleagues[40] describe the "Ouchless Place" at St. Francis Hospital and Medical Center in Hartford, Connecticut. Weisman and colleagues built on that concept and developed a pain-free hospital model.[41] The Comfort Zone™ is a comprehensive ini-

Agency for Health Care Policy and Research:
http://www.ahcpr.gov/research/resact.htm
American Academy of Pain Management
http://www.aapainmanage.org/
American Academy of Pediatrics
http://www.aap.org (search under 'pain')
American Pain Society
http://www.ampainsoc.org/
American Society of Pain Management Nurses
http://www.aspmn.org/html/membappnew.pdf
Canadian Pediatric Society
http://www.cps.ca/
International Association for the Study of Pain
http://www.iasp-pain.org/
MayDay Pain Project—pediatric links
http://www.painandhealth.org/pediatric-links.html
National Association of Neonatal Nurses
http://www.nann.org/ (search under "position statements")
Partners Against Pain
http://www.partnersagainstpain.com/html/main/
Pediatric Pain—Science Helping Children
http://is.dal.ca/~pedpain/pedpain.html
World Health Organization
http://www.who.int/en/ (search under "pain")

Figure 6.2 *Websites of organizations concerned with pain management*

tiative developed to increase awareness and improve pain management practices. Through education, development of treatment protocols and procedures, and ongoing monitoring, the Comfort Zone concept demonstrated practice improvements.[41]

Tip

The attorney or legal nurse consultant should check to see if the institution has a standard for pain management. If the institution does have a standard, the patient's medical record should reflect documentation that the providers have met the standard.

The publication and dissemination of these standards to the public and professionals is beginning to improve pain management practices. Consumer knowledge and advocacy have increased attention to pain and suffering of patients leading to changes in healthcare practices and environments.

6.3 Consequences of Pain in Children

As noted earlier in the chapter, pain once was conceptualized as a systematic response that included stimulation of pain receptors leading to specific responses within neurons in the spinal cord that were communicated to the brain.[42] The type of noxious stimuli, the context in which it occurred, and the behavioral state of the child are some of the other factors that influence the child's pain experience.[42] Additionally, acute and ongoing pain experienced by a child during hospitalization result in behavioral and physiological responses to the pain. Surgery or trauma also triggers the release of stress hormones leading to the breakdown of protein, fat, and carbohydrate stores. Research in psychoneuroimmunology also suggests these stress hormones play a role in immune suppression.[43] This immune suppression may cause a child to be more vulnerable to infection. The magnitude of stress hormones secreted can be decreased by the use of intraoperative opioids.[42] The pain experienced by children is interpreted differently depending on the age of the child. The following section presents information on the consequences of pain for the premature infant, older infant, child and adolescent.

1. Premature infants

Premature infants (infants born at thirty-seven weeks gestation or younger) experience many invasive procedures during their stay in the neonatal intensive care unit (NICU). Types of invasive procedures experienced by premature infants include simple procedures such as

- obtaining blood samples by using a heel lancet,
- IV insertion,
- feeding tube insertion,
- immunization (injection),
- inserting a needle to obtain blood and so on,

- more complex procedures (intubation [insertion of a breathing tube]),
- bladder tap,
- chest tube insertion,
- cut down procedure for IV insertion, etc.,
- the most complex (surgery, ECMO [extracorporeal membrane oxygenation or being placed on a heart-lung bypass machine]), and
- resuscitation.

Tip

One study estimated that as many as two to ten procedures were completed each day on premature infants;[44] another reported 488 procedures experienced by one infant born at twenty-three weeks gestation.[45]

Lower pain thresholds in neonates compounded by further decreases in the threshold after experiencing painful stimuli,[42] have implications for the cumulative effects of pain and stress in the premature infant.

Little data exist on the long-term effects of early pain on these developing infants, but researchers have explored the potential consequences of repeated and prolonged pain experienced during the NICU stay. Experts suggest that the pain experienced by these infants may result in changes to future pain responses and impact long-term developmental and emotional functioning.[46,47,48] More frequent clinical and subclinical neurobehavioral and neurological disorders and psychosocial problems have been noted during infancy, childhood, and adolescence in prematurely born infants.[48] Pain is not the only potentially harmful stimuli in the extra-uterine environment, yet pain exposure is considered to be the most salient aspect of NICU care that may affect brain differentiation and later development. Future problems may include learning disorders, cognitive deficits, behavioral problems, attention deficits, and poor motor coordination.[49]

Although statistically significant differences have been reported in those studies comparing prematurely born infants with full-term born infants, compensation to the infant's pain system may occur over time and with little adverse effect on function.[48] On the other hand, the indirect and direct effects of early pain on overall cognitive, social, and behavioral development may be substantial.[46,49] Less is known about the consequences of untreated pain on full-term infants due to the paucity of research in this area. It would not be appropriate to extrapolate from the studies conducted on premature infants because of the developmental differences between the two.[48]

2. Older infants, children, and adolescents

Infants, older children, and adolescents can experience pain from a variety of sources that include trauma, physical abuse, emotional distress, medication, and surgery. In the pediatric healthcare environment, children are subject to the same sources of pain experienced by the premature infant:

- simple procedures (IV insertion, feeding tube insertion, immunization [injection], venous/arterial stick for blood draw, etc.)
- more complex procedures (intubation [insertion of a breathing tube]),
- chest tube insertion
- cut down procedure for IV insertion
- the most complex painful experiences (surgery, ECMO [extracorporeal membrane oxygenation or being placed on a heart/lung bypass machine], and resuscitation)

The impact of untreated pain in children may go beyond the effect on the nervous system and subsequent development described for the premature infant. Invasive and painful procedures are particularly distressing to children; repeated procedures are often described as more distressing than any other aspect of illness or treatment.[27,50–52] Unlike older children, adolescents, and adults, infants and young children may not understand why a painful procedure must be performed. They may not participate in decision making, and they may not understand the time-limited nature of the pain experience. Providing the child opportunities to participate in decision making, using medical play for educating the child about future experiences, allowing for the presence of a parent, and using comfort measures and analgesia are just some of the interventions that help manage the pain experienced by the child. When these interventions are not used, the child most likely will be agitated during the procedure, the procedure will take longer and may not be successful, and subsequent procedures will be anticipated with dread and anxiety. The attorney or legal nurse consultant should review the medical records for documentation of which interventions were used before, during, and after painful experiences.

Evidence that repeated procedures and hospitalization influence the child's pain response has been reported by Savedra and colleagues.[53] Children with previous hospital experience described their pain differently from children who had not been previously hospitalized. When shown pictures of painful experiences, the children with hospital experience rated the pain less than the children without hospital experience. The children with hospital experience also related pain to illness more often than children without hospital experience.

Tip

Hospitalization and the subsequent suffering that may occur can lead to regression and behavior problems for the child long after the hospital stay. The attorney or legal nurse consultant should ask parents about changes in the child's behavior occurring after hospitalization.

Many hospitals have special programs to help children cope with these experiences. These include childlife services (professionals trained in helping children and families cope with illness and hospitalization), music therapy, art therapy, and psychology.

Chronic and recurrent pain occurs in pediatric patients. Children often experience headaches, migraines, and abdominal pain. Chronic diseases such as sickle cell disease, arthritis, and hemophilia also are associated with intermittent pain. Children who suffer these and other painful conditions often have difficulties in everyday functioning as a result. These difficulties may include missed school, depression and other psychiatric problems, reduced participation in peer activities, sleep disturbances, and problems within the family.[54] Children who suffer from painful chronic conditions may have additional problems if they experience acute pain due to injury or hospitalization for another problem. These children should continue their chronic pain regimen and may require additional treatment measures to manage the acute pain.

3. Summary

Pain has an impact on the physiologic and emotional development of the child, regardless of the age at which the pain is experienced. Untreated pain can have an impact on the current health of the child and has been suggested to impact on subsequent development and future health.

Tip

When reviewing the medical record, the attorney or legal nurse consultant should look for descriptions of the child's behavior and reaction to being in the hospital.

6.4 The Developing Child and Understanding of Illness and Pain

Although there are many theorists who have described the human's intellectual development, the stage theory developed by the Swiss psychologist Jean Piaget has contributed most towards our understanding of children's intellectual activity. The developmental stage has direct bearing on the amount of suffering experienced by the child as a result of trauma or illness. The capacity to understand pain and suffering is governed by intellectual development. Piaget described four periods of cognitive development: sensorimotor (birth to two years), preoperational (two to seven years), concrete operational (seven to eleven years) and formal operational (eleven-plus years). Each of these stages represents qualitative change in the way the child thinks or behaves and is experienced by every child in the same order without skipping any stage.[55] This section will review the four stages of the child's intellectual development and the child's evolving perception of illness and meanings ascribed to pain. Examples of pain and suffering resulting from injuries are presented through descriptions of outcomes of litigation.

A. Premature infants

Infants are categorized as premature if they are born before thirty-seven weeks gestational age. Premature infants therefore complete their physical development in a more stressful environment than the womb. The premature neonate and family must adjust to the unexpected, cope with the technology that supports physiological development, and create an emotional and physical attachment among all members of the family. The challenges are many, and the subtleties often overlooked. For example, through aversive learning, the premature infant associates touch (like a wipe on the skin and then a painful stick to the spot) with a hurt that the infant may not be able to differentiate between painful and comforting touches. Consequently, the infant may begin to consider all touch as painful.

Birth-related injuries affecting premature infants can result in brain damage, nerve damage, and other devastating consequences. These children may require a lifetime of care.

In a Kings County, New York, case, the plaintiff contended that the physician negligently failed to treat a woman who went into premature labor. The plaintiff contended that the failure to administer corticosteroids led to neonatal respiratory distress syndrome. This caused severe cerebral palsy with resulting severe brain damage that will permanently leave the child with a mental capacity of a four-year-old, prevent him from walking, and will have a permanent, severe impact on his ability to speak. The plaintiff also contended that the child requires round the clock care and will ultimately require permanent custodial care. The jury awarded $94,812,240. This included $3 million for past pain and suffering, $28,333,333 for future pain and suffering, $9,112,000 for future medical expenses, $44,000,000 for future custodial care, $4,288,000 for future rehabilitative services, and $6,078,907 for impairment of earning capacity.[56]

B. Birth to two years of age

Using Piaget's framework, the first two years of life are categorized as the sensorimotor period. The infant learns about self and the environment through the use of senses and motor activities. The infant starts with self-awareness and self-action about his own body and how his actions affect it. With maturity, the infant develops reflexes to identify the consequences of self-behaviors. Behavior modification, both positive and negative, begins to develop. Infants respond to pain with crying and body movements. They do not recognize the cause of pain, and they do not have the ability to "run away" from the pain source.

At around twelve months of age, the infant starts to develop simple problem-solving skills and begins anticipating actions and their consequences. For instance, a dropped spoon will elicit a look down. During the second year of life, the toddler develops rudimentary trial-and-error behaviors to accomplish goals. At the end of this stage of development, the young child has a basic understanding of causality.

Bibace and Walsh[57] describe children less than two years of age as incapable of conceptualizing illness. Young children do not understand the illness or its effects on behavior. If the younger child was questioned about health and illness, the child would either respond with answers that indicate he does not understand the question or give a response that is irrelevant to the question asked. The child at this age may have some special words for pain but is unable to describe intensity and type of pain sensation. The child is egocentric and cannot understand why caregivers cannot see the apparently obvious pain. Toddlers respond to pain with increased physical activity. They exhibit more behavioral distress during invasive painful procedures than older children.[51] Completing procedures as quickly and efficiently as possible and including parents as support to the child are important with this age group.

In a New York case, a two-year-old girl fractured her leg when she fell from her stroller at home. Marked skin and muscle necrosis (death) resulted from a tight cast. She developed compartment syndrome and underwent four separate fasciotomies (slicing the leg open) to remove dead skin, muscle, and tissue. The plaintiff was left with a pronounced deformity of her leg resulting from removed muscle, skin, and tissue with extensive scarring. She was outfitted with an orthotic brace, which permits her to walk relatively normally, but her foot is chronically inverted and will require periodic surgeries. The action settled for $2 million before jury selection.[58]

Injuries involving an infant's extremity can result in differences in the length of the legs, causing a pronounced limp. The child who walks differently from her classmates may be teased or ridiculed, resulting in withdrawal, anger and other negative coping mechanisms.

This case identifies the need for healthcare professionals to assess the fit of the cast, check circulation of the affected extremity, and ask and observe the child for pain or discomfort once the cast has been applied. Family members should be taught how to make these assessments before the child is discharged.

The permanency of damages was an issue in another New York case.

The plaintiffs contended there was a delay in diagnosis of cancer. The aggressive type of chemotherapy the child was required to undergo resulted in short-term toxicity, nausea, infections, and bleeding. The plaintiffs contended that the child developed a heart condition, was sterile, had kidney damage, had diminished hearing, and was expected to grow only to a height of four feet, ten inches (fifth percentile of normal height range) because her growth rate had been stunted by the long-term toxicity of the drugs. Defendants claimed that the plaintiff's heart and kidney functions were normal and that she would have a normal height. The defendants also denied that she was sterile and maintained that her hearing loss was in the high-pitch range only, which would not affect her daily activities. The jury awarded $3 million total with $1.5 million for past pain and suffering and $1.5 million for future pain and suffering.[59]

The delay in diagnosis resulted in a more aggressive treatment plan for the child, and that resulted in more pain and suffering of the child.

C. Preschool and early school-age

Piaget's preoperational period typically occurs between two and seven years. The child continues an egocentric orientation. The world exists only for the child. Thinking expands to include animism (attributing life and intention to all objects, such as toys), artificialism (believing all things are designed by human beings), realism (everything, including dreams, is considered real), and magic omnipotence (just by thinking it, the child can make it happen).[55] The child thinks in absolute terms. There are only opposites to explain all existence (it is black or white). The child also believes others have similar world views and knowledge.

During the preconceptual stage (two to four years), thought begins to include symbolism and abstraction (mental images for things that cannot be seen). The child interprets instructions literally and needs expected behaviors to be identified or she will not be able to follow instructions. Children in the perceptual or intuitive stage (four to seven years) demonstrate prelogical thinking, where thinking is based on the appearance and results of experiences and objects. A demonstration of five apples and five raisins will prompt the conclusion there are more apples because they are bigger in size. The child begins to exhibit centration, the ability to focus only on one aspect of a situation (even though his image may attribute many properties to the situation). The child also demonstrates transductive reasoning (from particular to particular without considering the general situation). This kind of reasoning can lead to assumptions about unrelated events (e.g., "When I opened the curtains, I made the sun come up in the sky.").

Bibace and Walsh[60] describe the two-to-six-year-olds' conceptualization of illness as built on their inability to distance themselves from their environment. Location and recent events influence children. Phenomenism is defined as the childhood belief that cause of illness is external to and separate from the body (i.e., the child has no responsibility for the illness). Illness is a present state that is not connected to the past or future.

As the child matures, the contagion explanation replaces phenomenism. Contagion expresses the belief that the cause of the illness is close to the child, something near the body, either a person or object (but not coming in direct contact with the body). The object or person is responsible for the child becoming ill. If the child assumes responsibility for the illness, it is because of some single activity, typically unrelated to the illness ("I was bad at school, that's why I'm sick.") The cure for the illness is believed to be a singular external event or action (for example, an injection), and the child does not understand how this event is curative. The illness time frame continues to be in the present, and the child is unable to differentiate between degrees of severity of illness.

The preschool child can give a more detailed description of pain.[61] At this age the child still may blame someone for the pain or think it is the result of some wrongdoing. Pain is a physical experience and unrelated to other emotions. The preschool child cannot understand the concept that a painful procedure might be beneficial.[62] It is important that the preschool-aged child be given simple information when a painful event is about to occur. Healthcare providers and family should praise the child after the procedure and reinforce the explanation. Preschool children often benefit from "playing" out the event, for example by being allowed to perform the procedure on a doll.

In a New Jersey case, the four-year-old plaintiff was too small for an amusement park ride. He fell 35–40 feet through an opening in the cage and fractured his femur. The fracture necessitated a few weeks of traction, eight weeks in a body cast, and several months of physical therapy. The plaintiff contended that the leg injury will permanently cause pain upon fatigue and changes in the weather. The infant plaintiff also suffered a concussion, which the plaintiff indicated has substantially resolved. The plaintiff related that he experiences nightmares about the event, which although more frequent in the past, had continued intermittently up until the time of trial. The jury found that the ride was not defective, but that both defendants failed to provide adequate warnings. They then awarded $400,000.[63]

Allegations of brain damage and loss of the tips of toes were the damages in an Ohio case. The plaintiffs alleged that the five-year-old boy was not timely diagnosed with Rocky Mountain spotted fever. He endured a long convalescence and sustained significant central nervous system and brain impairment. His septic condition, coupled with the treatments to save his life, caused him to lose portions of the tips of several toes on both feet. The defense disputed the degree of future brain injury to the child. The case was settled for $900,000.[64]

D. School-age

Piaget's concrete operations period typically occurs between seven and eleven years. The child begins this period using inductive logic (from particular to the general) but ends the stage using more deductive thinking (from the general to the particular). Language skills have improved, prompting explanations of pain in some detail, including intensity and location. Preteens can specifically describe pain using sensory information and can understand concepts like bleeding.[61] The child shifts from a more magical way of thinking to one that is based on science (facts). Thus the child can begin to understand that certain illness and injuries may cause pain.

The concrete-logical conceptualization of illness typically begins between seven and ten years of age.[57] The child is differentiating between self and others and can distinguish between what is internal and what is external to self. The child defines health and illness in terms of general categories of illness. The child also views self as responsible for activities that lead to health and illness. The cause of illness is due to the body coming in contact with external agents or the child has engaged in a "bad" activity that is morally contaminated (contagion explanation). Illness can now be differentiated between its cause and its transmission. Separation or avoidance of the causative agent or stopping the causation will result in a cure. Illness is believed to have a brief past and future (the time frame has broadened). Illnesses also can be differentiated into degrees based on how long it lasts, how much it hurts, and how much it limits the child's activities.

The internalization explanation is held by the more mature child and occurs when the child perceives health and illness as related to the physical condition of the body or the state of the internal organs and body system. Illness is believed to be caused by a contaminant or harmful object entering or affecting the body, the quality of the body system, or both. Cure occurs when an external object or activity enters the body and affects it in a positive way. The child may believe the body heals itself. The illness is perceived to have a temporal duration. The child understands that a developmental cause or condition can be responsible for an illness—illnesses caused by heredity can be explained to the child in this stage.

Between the ages of ten and twelve years children begin to establish connections and logical structures.[65] A child can understand that "if you take your pain medication you will feel better." Children can begin to understand the connection between psychological factors and pain. They begin to realize that attitudes can affect health and illness. Therefore, a child may understand that a headache gets better with an aspirin while it gets worse if you worry. Nine-to-twelve-year-olds can recall and identify experiences that have caused them pain. This is especially true for children who have had repeated hospital experiences.[53]

Control is important to the school-age child. Often when school-age children are faced with a painful procedure they hold themselves rigid in an attempt at bravery. There are few coping strategies to draw from at this age. It is important for the professional not only to explain the painful procedure, but also to help the child cope. Parental presence is helpful, as are relaxation techniques and other interventions discussed in the treatment section of this chapter.

A young boy from Florida injured his leg when he fell on a King Sago palm which had been cut down by landscapers. The plaintiffs alleged that the defendant doctor did not perform appropriate debridement and that other treatment errors occurred. The boy sustained permanent growth plate damage causing a current leg length discrepancy of over one inch with a predicted overall discrepancy of four to six inches, requiring future leg lengthening procedures and significant arthritic changes of the knee requiring future arthroscopic surgery and ultimately a total knee replacement. The jury awarded $1,016,306.[66]

Improper attention to wound care resulted in the need for surgery and the associated pain and suffering described here.

E. Adolescence

Piaget described formal operations as the period from 11 years of age onward. Logical reasoning and the ability to think about the hypothetical and the abstract occur during this period. Mental problem-solving includes more than concrete objects or problems: abstract problems can be analyzed and solved. The adolescent can separate abstraction from reality. Understanding the past, present, and future is part of the thought process.

Formal-logical explanations of illness categorize the child who is eleven years of age and older.[57] The child has reached the greatest level of differentiating between the external and internal world. Initially, physiological explanations across multiple dimensions are used to describe illnesses: stimulation and functioning of the internal parts of the body define illness and health. The immediate cause of an illness is related to the malfunctioning of an internal organ or process. Although an external event may have contributed to the illness, immediate and remote causes can be distinguished. There is a sequence of events that cause illness and that cure illness.[57]

There is a recognition that course and severity of illness may vary between individuals. As the child matures, the psychophysiological explanation of illness dominates and is coupled with the awareness that attitudes and mental actions as well as physiological function influence health and illness. Regardless of cause, children in this developmental stage believe a physiological cure is necessary to resolve the illness. Awareness of a broader definition of the types and severity of illness also develops during this stage. The perception that the child has a reasonable amount of control over the onset and cure of the illness also exists.

Adolescents can describe pain in great detail and can equate the pain to other experiences or metaphors like "elephants dancing in my head."[61] They go beyond what they can see and feel and can understand a physiological explanation of the pain. Coping skills may be improved at this age, but the adolescent still lacks experience and can benefit from a professional's support when facing a painful experience or illness. Adolescents can understand the value of pain in diagnosing an illness or injury. Adolescents and school-age children also suggest and solicit professional care.[53] The adolescent, like the school-age child, fears loss of control, understands that psychological actions and attitudes influence pain, and benefits from thoughtful and thorough explanations of pain and illness.

In general, a child's concept of pain follows a linear progression from being unable to verbalize pain and a reason for hurting, to being able to give a general external cause, and finally to include physiological and psychological causes.[61]

A Minnesota teenager suffered bilateral posterior hip dislocations in a motor vehicle accident. He alleged that there was a delay in diagnosis of the hip dislocations, which resulted in bilateral hip necrosis. Several surgeries were attempted, including a remodeling of the joint surface and revisualization procedures. All procedures failed. In the summer of 2000 at age fifteen, the young man had his first total hip replacement. Later that year he had his second hip replaced. In addition to the injuries sustained in the motor vehicle accident, plaintiff claimed that the delay in diagnosis and treatment of the bilateral posterior hip dislocations will require four to five hip replacements on each side throughout his lifetime. Depending on the success of the hip replacements and their longevity, he may ultimately end up in a wheelchair if there is insufficient bone surface in which to place a prosthesis. The action settled through mediation for $1.6 million.[67]

This is another example of improper treatment resulting in numerous painful procedures that otherwise would have been unnecessary.

A Pennsylvania teenager alleged that her surgeon performed inappropriate surgery to treat a foot disorder caused by Charcot Marie tooth disease. She suffers pain whenever she walks on her foot, has trouble balancing, and can only wear soft sneaker shoes. When not wearing shoes, she must walk on tiptoe to avoid placing pressure on her callous toe. This places significant, daily strain on her legs and entire back and spine. The jury awarded the plaintiff $1.2 million.[68]

F. Summary

Tip

Age influences how children understand illness and pain. Age also influences what strategies help the child deal with hospitalization and the pain experience.

For all ages, anxiety and stress enhance the feelings of pain. Fear and loss of control increase the anxiety and reduce the child's ability to cope. Developmental milestones are only guidelines and, when faced with painful events, children will regress to a more simplistic understanding of pain. Awareness of this regression influences the development of an individualized pain management plan by healthcare professionals, the child, and family.

Tip

The child's developmental age influences the child's response to illness and ability to describe pain. The parents may be asked how the hospital personnel treated their child, and if age-appropriate explanations were give for painful events or treatments. Parents also may be asked if their child's behavior reverted to a less mature stage and if the hospital personnel helped them understand the cause and strategies to deal with the behavioral changes.

6.5 Pain Assessment

The terms measurement and assessment are often used interchangeably in the pain literature. Measurement is usually used in a research context, whereas assessment is a broader clinical concept and implies information gathering from multiple sources.[69] This section will focus on the assessment of pain in infants, children, and adolescents. Since "pain has sensory, emotional, cognitive, and behavioral components that are interrelated with environmental, developmental, sociocultural, and contextual factors,"[36] multiple factors are used to assess the child's pain experience. Professionals should consider the specific pain experience or the noxious stimulus, the child's self-report (if able), physiological and behavioral responses observed, parent's report, the environment, and the current situation.

A. General assessment guidelines

Clinicians caring for infants, children and adolescents have both an ethical and professional obligation to assess and manage pain, thus eliminating suffering as much as possible. Professional standards mandate both assessment and treatment of pain (see standards section). In addition, recent research has demonstrated that untreated pain in infants and children has both short-term and long-term consequences. Untreated pain delays healing and may affect future response to painful experiences.[70] Pain assessment should not be limited to a measurement score alone. It should include the presence or absence of pain, the possible impact of pain on the individual, a decision to provide pain relief measures, and finally reevaluation to monitor the effects of the interventions.

Tip

Since pain assessment is a relatively new practice, professionals must understand and manage their own biases that may influence their interpretation of the child's experience, including discounting the myths about children's pain.

See Figure 6.3 for questions the attorney may want to ask the child to obtain a description of pain.

The successful assessment and treatment of pediatric pain requires a multidisciplinary approach. Healthcare professionals (physicians, nurse practitioners, dentists, and so forth) must be current in their knowledge of pain assessment and treatment. Also, professionals must have an understanding of the multiple dimensions of the pain experience and the obligation to prescribe appropriate pharmacological treatments for pain management. All are responsible for advocating for the child. In addition, non-pharmacological interventions to alleviate pain and suffering should be learned and practiced by all healthcare professionals caring for children. Education and involvement of families in pain and its management are essential elements of the treatment process. Finally, the pain treatment plan should be documented in the patient's records.

Tip

The attorney or legal nurse consultant should review the medical record for (1) pain medication order (if appropriate), (2) standing orders or unit standards of care that reflect pain management (i.e., use of sucrose in infants before painful procedures), (3) documentation about comfort or pain management interventions in the child's plan of care, (4) documentation of pain assessment scores on the daily record or specialized pain flowsheet, and (5) ongoing documentation in progress notes about the assessment and management of the child's pain.

Pain should be assessed at every healthcare visit and routinely at least once a shift when the child is hospitalized (more often if pain is noted to be present).

- Where does it hurt?
- How does it hurt (burns, stings, throbs, etc.)?
- How much of the time does it hurt?
- Does anything make it hurt more or less?
- Is the hurt keeping you from doing things you normally would do?
- What works to make the hurt less or go away?

For parents:

- Is your child behaving differently than he or she usually behaves? Please describe how the behavior is different than usual behavior.

Figure 6.3 *Questions healthcare professionals ask the child or parent to assess pain*

Pain is assessed more frequently after surgery and procedures. Comfort measures or medication administration should occur for pain scores that exceed minimal pain (this varies depending on the metric of the pain scale: for a 0–10 point scale, it is typically a score of 4; scales with other metrics should specify what score suggests a need for intervention). If interventions are undertaken to treat pain, reassessment is routine within thirty to sixty minutes. Tools used to assess pain must include self-report whenever possible, be age-appropriate, and clinically sensitive with demonstrated evidence of validity and reliability. Assessment and its written documentation should include behavioral observations, physiological data, the illness or painful event experienced, the child's cognitive level, the parent's perceptions, and the child's environment and cultural experiences.[36] The analysis of the medical records and discussion with the child's parents will assist the attorney or legal nurse consultant in understanding the child's pain experiences and responses.

Tip

Physicians, nurses, and other healthcare professionals will document the child's comfort level (often by use of a pain score), describe interventions used to alleviate the pain (medication prescribed, use of comfort measures), and variations in care provided (medication dosage increased, other medications added to the regimen, consultations for pain not responsive to intervention).

The following section describes pain assessment methods used with different age groups.

B. Pain assessment: Observation method (preverbal and nonverbal children)

Infants and young children have no or limited verbal communication skills and cannot report their pain experiences in words. Proper care for these younger children must rely on physiological and behavioral cues to suggest the presence of pain. Children with developmental delay or physical limitations also can be assessed using nonverbal pain cues. For all children who cannot verbalize their pain experience, it is important to obtain parental input about what indicators they typically see that suggest their child is in pain. The plaintiffs' attorney should ask the parents of a young child to describe the painful experiences their child suffered while receiving care. It also is important to ask the parents what they expected to be done for their child and if they felt their child received adequate pain treatment.

Physiological cues of pain include increased heart rate (tachycardia), increased respiratory rate (tachypnea), increased blood pressure (hypertension), decreased oxygen saturation (as evidenced on a pulse oximeter), increased serum cortisol levels (not routinely obtained), and increased intracranial pressure (not routinely measured). In premature or critically ill infants with sustained pain, the heart rate and respiratory rate may decrease as their limited physiological reserves become depleted. Unfortunately, these changes in physiological parameters are associated with other clinical conditions besides untreated pain: decreased circulating blood volume (shock, hypovolemia), infection (sepsis), and impaired respiratory function leading to decreased oxygen delivery (hypoxia). These indicators are not to be used as the only cues of pain.

Behavioral cues of pain in preverbal and nonverbal children include negative facial expressions (grimaces, deep frowns), changes in body movements (thrashing, flailing of extremities, or keeping too still), vocalizations (crying, moans, simple words for pain like "ouch" or "owie"), changes in interactions with caregivers and friends (withdrawn, overly quiet, increased clinging to parents), changes in sleep and wake patterns (sleeping more to escape the pain to restless and interrupted sleep), and self-consoling behaviors (sucking of thumb, rubbing affected area, curling up into fetal position). Extremely premature infants may not demonstrate these cues due to limited physiological reserves and may show more subtle versions of what is described above or may become flaccid and unresponsive to any stimuli. As the preverbal child ages, the number of behaviors in each of the categories expands as cognitive and motor skills advance.

The pain assessment tools used with the preverbal or nonverbal child may include behavioral measures or a combination of behavioral and physiological measures. In addition, some tools assess contextual indicators such as the ability to be consoled or the quality and presence of sleep. The healthcare provider observes the preverbal child for a specified period of time, scores individual categories, and sums the category scores into a total score. The ranges for the total score are typically divided into three categories: no or minimal pain, mild pain, and moderate to severe pain. When scores exceed a no or minimal pain range, comfort measures are typically attempted first, unless the pain is in the moderate to severe range. Typically in that situation, a combination of comfort measures and analgesia is warranted. Figure 6.4 lists observational pain assessment tools available and specifies the developmental age for each tool.

Tip

The attorney or legal nurse consultant should ask the healthcare professionals to describe how they were trained to use the observational pain assessment tool. It is important for the healthcare professionals to demonstrate competency in the use of the tool.

C. Pain assessment: Children's self-report pain measurements

The most reliable measure of pain is self-report—having the child tell the healthcare provider how much it hurts, where the pain is located, how long it lasts, what makes it better or worse, and so on. Children can provide a self-report of their pain by using words, num-

Developmental Age	Tool	Physiological Indicators	Behavioral Indicators	Contextual Indicators
N	Behavioral Pain Scale[71]		X	X
I, N	Clinical Scoring System (CSS)[72]		X	X
A, N, T, Pr, S, T	COMFORT Scale[73]	X	X	X
N	CRIES[74]	X	X	X
N	Distress Scale for Ventilated Newborn Infants (DSVNI)[75]	X	X	
P	Echelle Douleur Inconfort Nouveau-Ne (EDIN)[76]		X	X
N, P	Modified Infant Pain Scale (MIPS)[77]		X	X
N, P	Neonatal Facial Coding System (NFCS)[78]		X	
N, P	Neonatal Infant Pain Scale (NIPS)[79]	X	X	X
N, P	Neonatal Pain, Agitation, & Sedation Scale (N-PASS)[80]	X	X	X
N, P	Pain Assessment in Neonates (PAIN)[81]	X	X	X
N, P	Premature Infant Pain Profile (PIPP)[82]	X	X	X
N, P	Scale for Use in Newborns (SUN)[83]	X	X	X
I, Pr, S, T,	Children's Hospital of Eastern Ontario Pain Scale (CHEOPS)[84]		X	
I, Pr, S, T,	FLACC[85]		X	X
Pr, S, T	Nursing Assessment of Pain Intensity (NAPI)[86]		X	
T	Preverbal, Early Verbal Pediatric Pain Scale (PEPPS)[87]	X	X	X
I	Riley Infant Pain Scale (RIPS)[88]		X	X
T, Pr	Toddler-Preschool Postoperative Pain Scale[89]		X	
Adolescents	Objective Pain Scale (OPS)[90]	X	X	

A = Adolescent I = Infant N = Neonate P = Premature Infant Pr = Preschool S = School-age T = Toddler
See Chapter 2, *Pain Assessment*, for the CRIES tool.

Figure 6.4 *Observational pain assessment tools*

bers, pictures, or mechanical devices that reflect how much pain they feel at any given point in time.[91]

By the age of three to four years, the child begins to be able to self-report pain. This may be as simple as "I hurt" or use of special words such as "ouchy." The child may be able to point to an area of the body that hurts and describe a little or a lot of hurt but is unable to provide a detailed description of the pain. Behavioral and physiological measures, as well as parental reports are the most useful at this age.

The young child's underdeveloped cognitive abilities and language skills limit the use of self-report pain scales. Selection of a scale depends on the child's cognitive ability and ability to understand the pain rating tool. Reliability of the scale usage depends on the child's ability to estimate, classify, match, and apply the concept of numerical relationships that signify gradations or quantity. For example, just because the child can count to 10, does not mean that she knows the difference in quantity between 1 and 10.[91] When children are unable to complete these cognitive tasks, they will usually not be able to discriminate their pain and tend to pick the same number or a consistently high number. It is important for the healthcare provider to validate that the child understands how to use the tool and not assume that age alone will ensure validity and reliability—just because the child falls into the correct age group does not mean the tool is appropriate for that child's individual developmental level.

1. Poker chip tool

The poker chip tool[92,93] was developed for children age four years and older. The tool consists of four poker chips each corresponding to "pieces of hurt." The child is asked to evaluate his pain by choosing one to four pieces of hurt.

2. Pain thermometer

Another tool suggested for use with younger children is the pain thermometer.[94] This tool consists of a vertical graphic representation of a thermometer with a 0–10 numeric scale, 0 being no pain and 10 the worst pain possible. See Chapter 2, "Pain Assessment," for an example of this tool.

3. Color scales

Color scales have been developed to measure pain. The simplest is a horizontal representation of graded colors with red usually at the end representing severe pain. Eland[95] developed a more comprehensive color scale. The child is given eight colors and chooses what color represents what degree of pain, then using a body outline the child draws where her hurt is located.

4. Faces scales

One self report measure often used for school-age children is a faces scales. Faces scales are a series of children's faces either as photographs or drawings. The faces depict various states of distress from happy or no expression to severe crying and distress. The child is asked to pick which face best describes the amount of pain that he is currently experiencing. The faces have corresponding numbers so that a score may be assigned to reflect the child's pain. Most of the scales have a 0–10 score and include five to ten faces.

One of the most commonly used faces scale is the one developed by Wong and Baker.[96] See Chapter 2, "Pain Assessment," for an example of this tool.

This scale consists of six drawings of faces: the no pain is a smiley face and the worst possible pain is a crying face. The Oucher[97] consists of six photographs of the same preschool child depicting varying degrees of distress. The photographs are placed vertically and along side is a numeric line with numbers 0–100 in increments of 10. With this scale the child may use the faces or the numbers. The major criticism of this type of scale is that the child may not understand that the feelings of sad and happy may not be the same as the amount of pain or hurt that he is experiencing. When using these scales it is important that the child have a thorough explanation and time to practice with the scale, demonstrating proper use.

Tip

The attorney or legal nurse consultant may ask the child to demonstrate the use of the pain tool. For example, "If you skinned your knee while playing ball, can you show me how much hurt you had?" The parents may be asked if they thought their child understood when the healthcare provider asked the child about his or her pain or hurt.

5. Metric scales

The most common scale used with older school-age children and adolescents is some variation of a visual analogue scale (VAS). The most common type of VAS is a straight line with numbers (0–10) and word anchors no pain at the extreme left, little pain, medium pain, large pain, in the middle, and worst possible pain, at the right with the corresponding number 10.[98] Some clinicians may use just a straight line with only numbers. The child using this scale must understand the difference in numeric quantities and a careful explanation should be given prior to using the tool.

A numerical scale asks children to rate their pain on a scale of 0–10 with 0 being no pain and 10 being the worst pain possible. The child must then be able to imagine the scale and be able to quantify the difference in numbers. The drawback of this scale is the lack of visual clues and reference points.

6. Other tools

Other more complex tools for pain measurement in children are generally used for research purposes or chronic pain. For example, the child keeps a pain diary, usually of numerical pain ratings and other information relevant to the pain experience over time.[99]

7. Summary

There are valid and reliable tools that have clinical value for the child's self-report of pain. It is important that the healthcare provider explains the tool to the child and evaluates the child's ability to use the tool. Children who are able to report their pain must also be asked to locate the site, duration, and if possible the quality of the pain (e.g., sharp, burning, dull, or intermittent). If the child is old enough to describe pain, this description also should be documented in the medical record.

Tip

There will be institutional variation in how the pain score is documented; some may include the pain tool as part of the daily record, and some may simply record a pain score on the daily record. The attorney or legal nurse consultant should request information on the institution's standard of practice from the healthcare providers (e.g., a copy of the tool, instructions for use, and suggested age ranges and cognitive levels that are appropriate).

6.6 Management of Pain

Children's pain management integrates both pharmacological and nonpharmacologic measures (i.e., cognitive and behavioral strategies) that are discussed in detail in the next section. The goal of pain management is to reduce the pain and suffering to a level that is acceptable to the child patient. In general, for children who cannot verbally express their pain, the pain score obtained on the observation scale should decrease and the infant or child should be able to be involved in appropriate activities of daily living such as eating, sleeping, and playing. Some institutions set arbitrary levels beyond which pain interventions are required. For example, if a pain score is equal or greater than 4 out of a 0–10 scale, pain treatment is required.

Pharmacological pain management is addressed in Chapter 3, "Pain Management," so the discussion in this section will be limited to some general principles. First and foremost, professionals treating pain in children must be knowledgeable about the use of analgesics and dosage in children. Also, they must believe that narcotics are safe for children when used appropriately.

The decision of what interventions are appropriate depends on the severity and cause of the pain. Acute pain from operations, trauma, and illness is generally treated with medications. Mild pain may be adequately controlled with comfort measures: for example, repositioning the child or providing a favorite object and may not require pharmacological treatment. It is the opinion of these authors that all pain responds best to a combination of both comfort and pharmacological management. Chronic pain also requires a combination of approaches and, sometimes, the addition of such drugs as tricyclic antidepressants (Elavil, Tofranil) to enhance the effect of opioids. Antidepressants also produce some direct analgesic effect separate from the antidepressant action.[100]

A. Pharmacological pain treatment

For mild to moderate pain non-opioid analgesics are commonly prescribed. Non-opioid analgesics include nonsteroidal anti-inflammatory (NSAIDs) such as ibuprofen and aspirin. This class of drugs also may be used as an adjunct to reduce the total dose of opioids needed to treat more severe pain. NSAIDs are also used in combination with local or regional block for ambulatory surgery.[101] In general these drugs are safe when prescribed and used appropriately. There are limited data concerning the use of NSAIDs in infants.[35] Use of ibuprofen is not recommended in infants under one month of age.[102]

Acetaminophen (Tylenol) is also useful for mild to moderate pain. However, it is a weak analgesic and has a ceiling effect (i.e., more doses do not produce more analgesia).[103] In combination with NSAIDs or a weak opioid like codeine, Tylenol may be used to treat moderate pain.[101] The prolonged use of Tylenol must be closely monitored by a healthcare practitioner because Tylenol is metabolized in the liver and may cause liver damage.

Moderate to severe pain usually requires the use of opioids. Opioid use is indicated in children of all ages for the relief of postoperative pain, procedural pain, and the treatment of painful conditions.[35] Some general principles for opioid administration must be followed in order to achieve adequate pain relief. The child's anxiety contributes to the pain experience, therefore opioids are administered intravenously and not intramuscularly, thus avoiding the anxiety and pain associated with injections. To maximize the effect of medication and provide pain relief, opioids should be administered "around the clock" rather than a PRN "as needed" basis for postsurgical pain. Continuous intravenous infusions may be used, or the medication should be prescribed routinely at designated times. This method of administration avoids the intermittent pain relief that occurs when medications are given only upon patient request. For older children, usually above the age of seven years, patient controlled analgesia (PCA) may be appropriate. This method of administration provides a constant dose of the drug, while the child may obtain additional doses by pressing a button and receiving an additional dose. The PCA is programmed so that the total amount of medication that may be received is within the recommend dosage. The child may press the button to receive medication but the machine is programmed only to release a specific amount in a limited time period. Thus the child cannot receive a medication overdose.

Tip

Although parent and nurse-controlled PCA has been described,[103] it is increasingly becoming an unacceptable practice since pain is subjective and the child is the best judge of when pain medication is needed. Often opioid effect may be enhanced with the use of intravenous NSAIDs for short periods of time.

Healthcare providers who administer opioids to children must be aware of potential side effects, especially respiratory depression, and monitor the child closely. It is important that emergency equipment is near and if the child experiences respiratory depression, the dosage is adjusted accordingly. For the child who requires prolonged use of narcotics, a physical dependence may develop, and gradual weaning will be required.[36]

Regional anesthetic techniques such as peripheral nerve blocks and central neuraxis blockade (spinal, epidural) are used to provide pain relief during and after surgical procedures.[36] Regional analgesia provides intense analgesia with minimal physiologic alterations and thus is being used with increasing frequency for children.[104] Careful observation and monitoring during the postoperative period are essential. When used appropriately these methods provide effective relief from postoperative pain.

The use of topical anesthetics such as EMLA cream (eutectic mixture of local anesthetics; Astra Pharmaceuticals) has become a standard of care for procedures such as venipuncture (insertion of needle to start an intravenous line or obtain blood) and minor surgical procedures.[105] When EMLA is applied to the skin and covered by an occlusive (non-permeating) dressing at least 60 to 90 minutes prior to the procedure, local anesthesia of the area results. Unfortunately healthcare providers may not have an hour before performing a painful procedure. A child's anxiety and previous negative experience also affect the outcome of EMLA use. In a sample of 258 children aged five to eighteen years, Lander and colleagues found EMLA to be successful 84% of the time for venipuncture and 51% for IV cannulation (inserting a hollow tube over a needle into the vein).[106]

TAC, a solution of tetracaine, Adrenalin, and cocaine is a common topical anesthetic for wound repair. The TAC solution is placed on a cotton ball and applied directly over the wound and held in place with firm pressure for ten minutes. The use of TAC leads to effective anesthesia for wound repair and is safe for children.[107] Similar solutions—LET (a mixture of lidocaine, epinephrine, and tetracaine) or ELA-max (another lidocaine-containing preparation) are increasingly being used.[108]

B. Non-pharmacological pain treatment

This section describes the importance of parental involvement in the child's care and the preparation for painful events. Examples of specific non-pharmacological measures that have been used to reduce children's pain will also be reviewed. Many articles have been published in the nursing, psychological, and medical literature addressing non-pharmacological techniques to reduce pain and anxiety for children. To include every technique described would be overwhelming; therefore this section will be an overview of some of the common themes. A general summary of non-pharmacological interventions can be found in Figure 6.5.

Parents and the child must be involved in the child's pain management. First and foremost, both deserve preparation for painful procedures whenever possible. Preparation becomes the first step to successful pain control. Research has demonstrated that preparation prior to surgery and other painful procedures reduces postoperative pain. The child who understands the need for the treatment or procedure will be more cooperative and willing to learn to use behavioral and cognitive strategies to manage the discomfort. Explanations should be simple, age-appropriate, and truthful (refer to the section on children's development). Education is of equal importance for the child with a painful illness. If the child is too young for a verbal explanation, it is important for healthcare professionals to explain the procedure carefully to the parents and provide information concerning the expected responses of the child.

Parents are usually the greatest source of comfort for the child and should be encouraged to be present for painful experiences to provide comfort and support for their child. The child is encouraged to take part in the procedure whenever possible and given simple choices and sense of control. For example, the child may select a favorite toy to hold or pick music to listen to. Engaging children in some decisions will increase their cooperation. Playing with and handling medical equipment and learning about the procedure through this use of play is also an effective method. Many children's hospitals have child life specialists who are skilled in preparing children for painful events and procedures.

Painful procedures should be performed in a calm, comforting environment. Toys and other distraction materials should be available. The healthcare professionals performing the procedure should also be calm and explain what is happening as the procedure progresses. Medical equipment should be covered until it is needed to avoid frightening the child. When the procedure is completed the child is praised for a "job well done." Stephens and colleagues describe in detail how to promote a child's comfort during painful procedures. They include preparation of families and a detailed way of positioning children to encourage their participation and allow the procedure to be completed successfully with minimal stress for all.[109]

1. Infants

Neonates in intensive care units experience multiple painful and invasive procedures. The unit itself is usually busy and noisy, and the need for constant monitoring creates a stressful and stimulating environment. Gentle handling, efficient provision of treatments and minimizing the stimulation the infant encounters all contribute to the infant's comfort.[110] Containing, positioning, and swaddling also decrease the infant's distress. The infant is "contained" by positioning with blanket rolls in a comfortable flexed position. This provides "gentle stimulation simultaneously across the proprioceptive, thermal, and tactile sensory systems."[111] In simple terms, the infant feels safe and is reminded of the gentle confines of the uterine environment.

Physical comfort measures are also important to the full-term and older infant. Techniques such as massage, gentle touching, speaking in a soft, calm voice, music, and rocking can calm an infant and reduce pain. Non-nutritive sucking or the use of a pacifier also provides relief. The use of sweet-tasting substance such as sucrose has been demonstrated to provide pain relief for single invasive procedures.[112]

AGE	PHYSICAL INTERVENTIONS	BEHAVIORAL INTERVENTIONS	COGNITIVE INTERVENTIONS
INFANT	Rocking, pacifier, swaddling, sucrose, massage		Music
TODDLER	As little physical restraint as possible	Play, distraction like bowing bubbles, favorite stories, pop-up books, favorite toy/security object	Music, positive reinforcement, blowing the pain away
PRE-SCHOOL	As little physical restraint as possible	Behavioral rehearsal with play, distraction, favorite stories, TV/videos, post procedural play, favorite toy,	Blowing the pain away, relaxed breathing, shrinking the pain
SCHOOL-AGE	Exercise, heat, cold, TENS	Seeing the equipment before the procedure, video games, TV, biofeedback	Relaxation, counting, imagery, hypnosis, self-hypnosis, positive self talk, thought stopping
ADOLESCENT	Protect privacy, exercise, heat, cold, TENS	Biofeedback	Relaxation, imagery, hypnosis, self-hypnosis, positive self talk, word games
ALL AGES	Parental presence, give adolescents and older school age children a choice, comforting touch, allow child to sit up when possible	Provide a calm, soothing environment, talk slowly in a soft voice, provide positive reassurance to child, praise for a job well done in all instances	Age appropriate preparation, ask the child what would help reduce the pain

Figure 6.5 *Summary of non-pharmacological interventions for pain control*

2. Toddlers

Toddlers like to move and be active, and thus any procedure or pain that decreases mobility adds to the distress. Distraction helps the toddler focus away from the pain and therefore lessens the pain and distress of the procedure. Distraction works best if presented by the parent, who at the same time can provide comfort for the child. The distraction method chosen must be simple and of interest to the child; for example, a moveable object or pop-up books. At all ages having the parent present and providing comfort to the child will help.

3. Preschoolers

The preschool child also responds to distraction. The use of favorite stories can distract and calm the child. Physical touch from a parent provides comfort and support. Young children may also enjoy music or singing favorite songs. Watching TV, if possible, can allow the child to focus on something besides the pain experience. Relaxation is another important aid in pain control. For the preschool child such exercises as blowing bubbles will encourage taking deep breaths and at the same time provide a distraction. This technique is often used with the phrase "blowing the pain away."[113] At about the age of three years, the child can begin to use imagination and be engaged in more complex distraction techniques. For example, the child may be taught to imagine a switch that can turn off the pain and with the proper coaching from a parent or healthcare professionals, the child may actually turn an imaginary switch and reduce the pain.[114]

4. School-age children

The school-age child is able to understand an explanation about painful procedures and events. It is important for all children to know what is going to happen to them and how it might feel. The way that procedures or painful experiences are framed is important for this age child. Healthcare professionals should allow children to draw their own conclusions about painful experiences. Rather than tell a child the procedure will hurt, the professional may say that the procedure may have some discomfort but the medicine and other techniques like deep breaths will make it feel better. The child is encouraged to talk about and describe the event after it is performed. This positive approach and encouragement will enhance the pain control measures used.

School-age children respond well to simple relaxation techniques such as deep breathing. Often a child can be asked to imagine being a rag doll or some other floppy toy. Relaxation can be learned by tensing and then relaxing a body part. School-age children can also use distractions such as music, TV, video games, reading, solving problems, and word games.

Imagery is a useful tool for pain reduction as it encompasses both distraction and relaxation. Imaging is spontaneous and natural for children. The use of imagery focuses away from the pain or changes the perception. The child must have the cognitive ability to engage in fantasy. A coach is required to help the child maintain a pleasant image and direct attention away from the painful event.[115]

Children should also be asked what they think would help their pain. Often they are able to identify some simple environmental changes that would make them feel better. The more involved the child becomes, the more powerful the suggestions and pain reduction strategies become.

5. Adolescents

It is essential that adolescents be involved in their pain management and treatment choices. At this stage of development the child is capable of abstract thinking and is able to understand complex explanations of illness and the need for painful procedures. Adolescents are concerned about their bodies and self-image; therefore professionals are urged to provide privacy. This age group is capable of complex mental and cognitive coping strategies such as understanding cause and effect. As opposed to the younger child, the adolescent can understand that the use of distraction may relieve pain and can become more involved in the process. Some of the techniques that are used with the younger child continue to be effective for the adolescent such as music, TV, video games, etc.

Hypnosis has been used as an effective strategy to reduce pain for adolescents.[116,117] Hypnosis is an altered state of consciousness and requires a trained professional as coach or teacher. Adolescents and even younger children can be taught hypnosis to manage pain successfully.

Tip

Parents may be asked if they were "invited" or encouraged to be present with their child during painful procedures and if they were given suggestions to help their child cope with the procedure:

Were you encouraged to be with your child while he or she was in the hospital?

Were you encouraged to be with your child while he or she was experiencing a painful procedure?

Did the staff suggest ways you could comfort your child?

How did the staff respond to your child's pain or discomfort?

C. Summary

Preparation for painful events and explanation of illness are the most important beginning steps in pain management. Pharmacological pain management is enhanced by the use of non-pharmacological approaches. Most approaches are easily learned by all healthcare professionals and should be incorporated into daily practice.[116] Although the methods described above are discussed by age, they do cross developmental lines, and the child's interest and ability should be the prime consideration in choosing a strategy. Many of these strategies are so ingrained in the behavior of pediatric healthcare professionals that they are not considered noteworthy and thus are not documented. The attorney, healthcare professional, or legal nurse consultant may simply see a reference to use of distraction to reduce pain without details explaining what strategies were used.

Additional strategies for pain control include the use of physical therapy including heat, cold, whirlpool, manual techniques and exercise. One specific technique is transcutaneous electrical nerve stimulation (TENS). TENS delivers electrical stimulation to specific muscle fibers producing pain relief by causing endorphin release to modify the pain input into the spinal cord. Acupuncture is increasingly being used for pain control, although there is little information concerning its use with children. The school-age and older child have successfully used biofeedback to manage chronic pain. Finally the outcome depends on the creativity of the practitioner to select and combine appropriate modalities to improve and manage the child's pain.

6.7 Plaintiffs' Attorney's Perspective on Pediatric Pain and Suffering

Keenan[118] suggests that success at a trial involving pediatric pain and suffering depends on helping the jury see the world from the eyes of a child. As this chapter has explained, a child reacts to pain and suffering in ways different from an adult. Adaptation to injuries is often dependent on the child's developmental stage and the permanency of injuries. Several principles help the plaintiff attorney present damages.

A. Walk a mile in the child's shoes

The jurors should be helped to understand the impact of the injuries. Questions can be asked such as "How many of you have changed the diaper on a twelve-year-old who has no bowel or bladder control?"

B. Counter the parents' and treating doctors' optimism

The attorney must temper the optimism of these individuals by presenting a realistic view of the injuries and their permanency. Review of the medical literature by an experienced legal nurse consultant will help identify the expected realities and probabilities of permanency.

C. Discuss damages in your opening statement

Help the jury understand the impact of the injuries by telling a story of the life of the child, both before and after the injury.

D. Present damages witnesses first

Consider having the paramedic or helicopter life support technician testify first. This witness can provide powerful testimony regarding the severity of injuries and the extent of damages. This testimony can also be presented by an expert fact witness, as described in Chapter 17, "The Expert Fact Witness."

E. Let the evidence speak for itself

As discussed in Chapter 19, "Trial Exhibits: Preparation and Use," a piece of medical equipment can be a poignant symbol of the child's injuries.

6.8 Conclusions

Knowledge about the management of the pain and suffering of infants, children, and adolescents has increased, and healthcare professionals have both professional and ethical obligation to decrease the individual child's pain as much as possible. Reliable and valid pain assessment tools are available for bedside use, and effective pharmacologic and nonpharmacologic interventions also have been reported. Accreditation requirements currently include a program for assessing and managing pain during each healthcare contact, and institutions should have a standard of practice in place that describes the specific procedures followed at that institution. As healthcare professionals, parents, and the child himself become more experienced using these assessment and management strategies, the overall comfort of children will improve. Attorneys presenting evidence of pain and suffering in children should recognize the pain management that was used and find evidence of the effectiveness of treatment documented in the medical records.

Endnotes

1. Schechter, N.L., Berde, C.B. and Yaster, M., *Pain in Infants, Children, and Adolescents*. Williams and Wilkins, Baltimore, MD, 1993.
2. Kenny, N.P., "The Politics of Pediatric Pain." In Findley, G.A., and McGrath, P.J., eds., *Acute and Procedure Pain in Infants and Children, Progress in Pain Research and Management*, 20. Seattle: IASP Press, 2001.
3. Ross, D.M., and Ross, S.A., *Childhood Pain: Current Issues, Research, and Management.* Baltimore: Urban and Schwarzenberg, 1988.
4. McGrath, P.J., and Unruh, A.M., *Pain in Children and Adolescents.* Amsterdam: Elsevier, 1987.
5. Brodie, B., "Yesterday, Today, and Tomorrow's Pediatric World." *Children's Health Care,* 14, 168–173, 1986.
6. Fairchild-Lem, E.A., *Evaluation of the Validity and Reliability of the Pediatric Nursing Goals and Functions Questionnaire*. Unpublished master's thesis. Lawrence, KS: University of Kansas, 1985.
7. Kelley, S.W., *About Children: Six Lectures.* Cleveland: The Medical Gazette Publishing Company, 1897.
8. Weeks-Shaw, C., *A Textbook of Nursing*. New York: Appleton and Company, 1902.
9. Myles, F.A., "Preparation and Uses of Infusions." *American Journal of Nursing,* 13, 89–93, 1913.
10. Shearston, A.D., "Do You Understand Children?" *American Journal of Nursing,* 37, 486–487, 1937.
11. Smith, R.M., "Difficulties Encountered when Employing Nurses Inadequately Trained in Pediatrics." *American Journal of Nursing,* 23, 1201–1203, 1923.
12. Grace Ann, Sister, "The Child and Adult as Patients." *American Journal of Nursing,* 34, 854–856, 1934.
13. Harmer, B., *Textbook of the Principles and Practice of Nursing*. New York: MacMillan, 1923.
14. Sellew, G., *Pediatric Nursing*. Philadelphia: W.B. Saunders, 1934.
15. Armstrong, I.L., and Browden, J.J., *The Nursing Care of Children*. Philadelphia: F.A. Davis, 1958.
16. Munson, B.A., "Pediatric Nurse Need Psychiatric Training." *American Journal of Nursing*, 45, 50–53, 1945.
17. Erickson, F., "Play Interviews for Four-Year Old Hospitalized Children." *Society for Research in Child Development*, 23, 7–77, 1958.
18. Schiff, S., "Gaining a Child's Confidence." *American Journal of Nursing*, 59, 1748–1749, 1959.
19. Wessel, M.A., "Pediatric Nursing and Human Relations." *American Journal of Nursing,* 47, 213–216, 1947.
20. Petro, M., "Communicating with Little Children." *American Journal of Nursing,* 57, 693–694, 1957.
21. Tips, *American Journal of Nursing*, 62, 18, 1962.
22. Webb, C., "Tactics to Reduce a Child's Fear of Pain." *American Journal of Nursing,* 66, 2698–2671, 1966.

23. Pillitteri, A., *Nursing Care of the Growing Family.* Boston: Little, Brown, and Company, 1977.

24. McKee, K., "Neurotic Bodily Pain in Children." *American Journal of Nursing*, 70, 130–131, 1970.

25. Schultz, N.V., "How Children Perceive Pain." *Nursing Outlook*, 19, 670–673, 1971.

26. McCaffery, M., "Pain Relief for the Child: Problem Areas and Selected Nonpharmacological Methods." *Pediatric Nursing,* 3(4), 11–16, 1977.

27. Eland, J.M., and Anderson, J.E., "The Experience of Pain in Children." In Jacox, A., editor, *Pain: A Source Book for Nurses and Other Professionals.* Boston: Little, Brown, Boston, 1977.

28. Beyer, J.E., DeGood, D.E., Ashley, L.C., and Russell, G.A., "Patterns of Postoperative Analgesic Use with Adults and Children Following Open Heart Surgery." *Pain,* 17, 71–81, 1983.

29. Bush, J.P., Holmbeck. G.N., and Cockrell, J.L., "Patterns of PRN Analgesic Drug Administration in Children Following Elective Surgery." *Journal of Pediatric Psychology,* 14, 433–448, 1989.

30. Anand, K.J.S., Sippell, W.G., and Aynsley-Green, A., "A Randomized Trial of Fentanyl Anesthesia in Preterm Babies Undergoing Surgery: Effects on Stress Response." *Lancet,* 1, 243–248, 1987.

31. Anand, K.J.S., Carr, D.B. and Hickey, P.R., "Randomized Trial of High Doses of Fentanyl Anesthesia in Neonates Undergoing Cardiac Surgery: Hormonal and Hemodynamic Stress Responses." *Anesthesiology,* 67, A502, 1987.

32. Broome, M.E., Richtsmeier A., Maikler, V., and Alexander, M.A., "Pediatric Pain Practices: A National Survey of Health Professionals." *Journal of Pain and Symptom Management*, 11, 312–320, 1996.

33. Acute Pain Management Guideline Panel, *Acute Pain Management in Infants, Children, and Adolescents: Operative and Medical Procedures. Quick Reference Guide for Clinicians.* Rockville, MD: Agency for Health Care Policy and Research, Public Health Services, U.S. Department of Human, Services, Publication 92-0020, 1992.

34. World Health Organization in collaboration with the International Association for the Study of Pain, *Cancer Pain Relief and Palliative Care.* Geneva: World Health Organization, 1998.

35. American Academy of Pediatrics and Canadian Pediatric Society, "Prevention and Management of Pain and Stress in the Neonate" (RE9945). *Pediatrics,* 105, 454–461, 2000.

36. American Academy of Pediatrics and American Pain Society, "The Assessment and Management of Acute Pain in Infants, Children, and Adolescents" (0793). *Pediatrics,* 108, 793–797, 2001.

37. National Association of Neonatal Nurses, *Pain Assessment and Management: Guideline for Practice.* Glenview, IL: The Author, 2002.

38. American Academy of Pain Management. http://www.aapainmanage.org/, 2002.

39. Miaskowski, C., Crews, J., Ready, L.B., Paul, S.M., and Ginsberg, B., "Anesthesia-Based Pain Service Improve the Quality of Postoperative Pain Management." *Pain,* 80, 23–49, 1999.

40. Schechter, N.L., Blankson, V., Pachter, L.M., Sullivan, C.M., and Costa, L., "The Ouchless Place: No Pain, Children's Gain." *Pediatrics,* 99, 890–894, 1997.

41. Weisman, S.J., "Toward a Pain-Free Hospital." In McGrath, P. J., and Finley, G. A., Eds., *Acute Pain in Infants and Children, Progress in Pain Research and Management 20.* Seattle: IASP Press, 2001.

42. Fitzgerald, M.and Anand, K.J.S., "Developmental Neuroanatomy and Neurophysiology of Pain." In Schechter, N.L., Berde, C.E., and Yaster, M., Eds., *Pain in Infants, Children, and Adolescents.* Baltimore: Williams and Wilkins, 1993.

43. Page, G.G., and Ben-Eliyahu, S., "The Immune-Suppressive Nature of Pain." *Seminars in Oncology Nursing*, 13, 10–15, 1997.

44. Johnston, C.C., Collinge, J.M., Henderson, S. and Anand, K.J.S., "A Cross-Sectional Survey of Pain and Analgesia in Canadian Neonatal Intensive Care Units." *Clinical Journal of Pain,* 13, 308–312, 1997.

45. Barker, D.P. and Rutter, N., "Exposure to Invasive Procedures in Neonatal Intensive Care Unit Admissions". *Archives of Disease in Childhood,* 72, F47–F48, 1995.

46. Anand, K.J.S., "Long-Term Effects of Pain in Neonates." In Jense, T.S., Turner, J.A., and Wiesenfeld-Hallin, Z.,

eds., *Progress in Pain Research and Management*, Vol. 8. Seattle: IASP Press, 1997.

47. Anand, K.J.S., Grunau, R.E., and Oberlander, T., "Developmental Character and Long-Term Consequences of Pain in Infants and Children." *Child Adolescent Psychiatric Clinics of North America,* 6, 703–724, 1997.

48. Grunau, R.E., "Long-Term Consequences of Pain in Human Neonates." In Anand, K.J.S., Stevens, B.J., and McGrath, P.J., eds., *Pain in Neonates,* Second Revised and Enlarged Edition. Amsterdam: Elsevier, 2000.

49. Aynsley-Green, A., editorial, "Pain and Stress in Infancy and Childhood—Where to Now?" *Pediatric Anesthesiology,* 6, 167–172, 1996.

50. Fowler-Kerry, S., "Adolescent Oncology Survivors' Recollection of Pain." In Tyler, D., and Krane, E., eds., *Advances in Pain Research and Therapy: Pediatric Pain, Volume 15.* New York: Raven Press, 1990.

51. Jay, S.M., Ozolins, M., Elliott, C.H. and Caldwell, S., "Assessment of Children's Distress during Painful Medical Procedures." *Health Psychology*, 2, 133–147, 1983

52. Weekes, D., and Savedra, M., "Adolescent Cancer: Coping with Treatment-Related Pain." *Journal of Pediatric Nursing,* 3, 318–328, 1988.

53. Savedra, M., Gibbons, P., Tesler, M., Ward, J., and Wegner, C., "How Do Children Describe Pain? A Tentative Assessment." *Pain,* 14, 95–104, 1982.

54. Palermo, T.M., "Impact of Recurrent and Chronic Pain on Child and Family Daily Functioning: Practical Review of the Literature." *Developmental and Behavioral Pediatrics.* 21, 58–69, 2000.

55. Anderson, J.J., "Developing Children." In Foster, R.L. R., Hunsberger, M.M., and Anderson, J.J.T., eds., *Family-Centered Nursing Care of Children*. Philadelphia: W.B. Saunders, 1989.

56. Zarin, I., editor, "$94,812,240 Verdict." *New Jersey Jury Verdict Review and Analysis*, 23 (2), 19, July 2002.

57. Bibace, R. and Walsh, M.E., *Developmental Conceptions of Illness: Scoring Categories Manual.* Worcester, MA: University of Massachusetts Medical School, 1980b.

58. Laska. L., editor, "Negligent Treatment of Leg Fracture." *Latoya Wheeler, indiv., and as m/n/g of Tyra Wheeler v. NYCHHC*, New York County (NY) Supreme Court, Index No. 101650/99, *Medical Malpractice Verdicts, Settlements and Experts*, 49, September 2002.

59. Laska, L., editor, "Failure to Timely Diagnose Neuroblastoma." *Della McMurray, as m/n/g of Katelyn McMurray v. Staten Island University Hospital, Dr. Daniel Potaznik, Dr. Grace Matthew, Dr. Steven Schwartzberg, and Concord Neurological and Neurosurgical Assoc., P.C.*, Richmond County (NY) Supreme Court, Index No. 13366/96, *Medical Malpractice Verdicts, Settlements and Experts*, 11, May 2002.

60. Bibace, R. and Walsh, M.E., "Development of Children's Concepts of Illness." *Pediatrics,* 66, 912–917, 1980a.

61. Harbeck, C. and Peterson, L., "Elephants Dancing in My Head: A Developmental Approach to Children's Concepts of Specific Pains." *Child Development*, 63, 138–149, 1992.

62. Bush, J.P., and Harkins, S.W., *Clinical and Research Issues from a Developmental Perspective.* New York: Springer-Verlag, 1991.

63. Zarin, I., editor, "$400,000 Verdict." *New Jersey Jury Verdict Review and Analysis*, 23 (2), July 2002, 8.

64. Laska, L., editor, "Failure to Timely Diagnose Rocky Mountain Spotted Fever Causes Brain Damage and Loss of Tips of Toes for Five-Year-Old Boy." *James Doe v. Anonymous Physicians,* Athens County (OH) Common Pleas Court, Case No. ____, *Medical Malpractice Verdicts, Settlements and Experts*, 16, February 2002.

65. Hurley, A., and Whelan, E.G., "Cognitive Development and Children's Perception of Pain." *Pediatric Nursing*, 14, 21–24, 1988.

66. Laska, L., editor, "Failure to Properly Treat Fungal Infection." *Alexander Conwell, a minor, through his natural parents and legal guardians, Kent and Julie Conwell, and Kent and Julie Conwell, individually v. Carroll A. English, M.D.*, Collier County (FL) Circuit Court, Case No. 99-1512 CA 01, *Medical Malpractice Verdicts, Settlements and Experts*, 46, February 2002.

67. Laska, L., editor, "Failure to Timely Diagnose and Treat Bilateral Posterior Hip Dislocations of Motor Vehicle Accident Patient." *Anonymous Minor Patient v. Anonymous Hospital, Anonymous Emergency Room Physician, Anonymous Radiologist, and Anonymous Family Practitioner,* _____ County (MN) District Court, Case No. ____, *Medical Malpractice Verdicts, Settlements and Experts*, 15, June 2002.

68. Laska, L., editor, "Complications Following Childhood Foot-Arch Surgeries." *Bernadette Scarduzio v. Dr. Michael Downey*, Philadelphia City (PA) Court of Common Pleas, Case No. ____, *Medical Malpractice Verdicts, Settlements and Experts*, 50, March 2002.

69. Beyer, J.E., and Wells, N., "The Assessment of Pain in Children." *Pediatric Clinics of North America*, 36, 837–854, 1989.

70. Taddio, A., Katz, J., Ilersich, A.L., and Koren, G., "Effect of Neonatal Circumcision on Pain Response during Subsequent Routine Vaccination." *Lancet,* 349, 599–603, 1997.

71. Pokela, M., "Pain Relief Can Reduce Hypoxemia in Distressed Neonates during Routine Treatment Procedures." *Pediatrics,* 93, 379–383, 1994.

72. Attia, J., Amiel-Tison, C. and Mayer, M.N., "Measurement of Postoperative Pain and Narcotic Administration in Infants Using a New Clinical Scoring System." *Anesthesiology,* 67, 532A, 1987.

73. Ambuel, B., Hamlett, K.W., Marx, C.M., and Blumer, J.L., "Assessing Distress in Pediatric Intensive Care Environments: The COMFORT Scale." *Journal of Pediatric Psychology,* 17, 95–109, 1992.

74. Krechel, S.W., and Bildner, J., "CRIES: A New Neonatal Postoperative Pain Measurement Score: Initial Testing of Validity and Reliability." *Paediatric Anaesthesia,* 5, 53–61, 1995.

75. Sparshott, M., "The Development of a Clinical Distress Scale for Ventilated Newborn Infants: Identification of Pain and Distress Based on Validated Behavioral Scores." *Journal of Neonatal Nursing,* 2, 5–11, 1996.

76. Debillon, T., Zupan, V., Ravault, N., Magny, J.F., and Dehan, M., "Development and Initial Validation of the EDIN Scale: A New Tool for Assessing Prolonged Pain in Premature Infants." *Archives of Disease in Childhood Fetal Neonatal Edition,* 85, F36–F41, 2001.

77. Buccholz, M., Karl, H.W., Pomietto, M., and Lynn, A.M., "Pain Scores in Infants: A Modified Infant Pain Scale versus Visual Analogue." *Journal of Pain and Symptom Management*, 15, 117–124, 1988.

78. Grunau, R.V.E., and Craig, K.D., "Facial Activity as a Measure of Neonatal Pain Expression." In Tyler, D.C,. and Krane, E.J., eds., *Pediatric Pain: Advances in Pain Therapy and Research, Vol. 15.* New York: Raven Press, 1990.

79. Lawrence, J., Alcock, D., McGrath, P.J., Kay, J., MacMurray, S.B., and Dulberg, C., "The Development of a Tool to Assess Neonatal Pain." *Neonatal Network*, 12(6), 59–66, 1993.

80. Hummel, P., and Puchalski, M., *N-PASS: Neonatal Pain, Agitation, and Sedation Scale.* Chicago: Loyola University Health System, Loyola University, 2000

81. Hudson-Barr, D., Michel, B., Lambert, S., Palermo, T. M., Morbeto, K., and Lombardo, S., "Validation of a Modified Pain Assessment in Neonates (PAIN) Scale with the Neonatal Infant Pain Scale (NIPS)." *Neonatal Network*, 21(6), 1–7, 2002.

82. Stevens, B.J., Johnston, C.C., Petryshen, P., and Taddio, A., "Premature Infant Pain Profile: Development and Initial Validation." *Clinical Journal of Pain,* 12, 13–22, 1996.

83. Blauer, T. and Gerstmann, D., "A Simultaneous Comparison of Three Neonatal Pain Scales during Common NICU Procedures." *Clinical Journal of Pain*, 14, 39–47, 1998.

84. McGrath, P.J., Johnson, G., Goodman, J.T., Schillinger, J., Dunn, J., and Chapman, J.A., "CHEOPS: A Behavioral Scale for Rating Postoperative Pain in Children." In Fields, H.L., Dubner, R. and Cervero, F., eds., *Advances in Pain Research and Therapy*, Vol. 9. New York: Raven Press, 1985.

85. Merkel, S.I., Voepel-Lewis, T., Shayevitz, J.R., and Malviya, S., "The FLACC: A Behavioral Scale for Scoring Postoperative Pain in Young Children." *Pediatric Nursing,* 23, 293–297, 1997.

86. Stevens, B., "Development and Testing of a Pediatric Pain Management Sheet." *Pediatric Nursing,* 16, 543–548, 1990.

87. Schultz, A.A., Murphy, E., Morton, J., Stempel, A., Messenger-Rioux, C., and Bennett, K., "Preverbal, Early Verbal Pediatric Pain Scale (PEPPS): Development and Early Psychometric Testing." *Journal of Pediatric Nursing,* 14, 19–27, 1999

88. Joyce, B.A., Schade, J.G., and Keck, J.F., "Reliability and Validity of Preverbal Pain Assessment Tools." *Issues in Comprehensive Pediatric Nursing,* 17, 121–134, 1994.

89. Tarbell, S.E., Cohen, T I., and Marsh, J.L., "The Toddler-Preschooler Postoperative Pain Scale: An Observation

Scale for Measuring Postoperative Pain in Children Aged 1–5." *Pain*, 50, 273–280, 1992.

90. Broadman, L.M., Rice, L.J., and Hannallah, G., "Comparison of a Physiologic and a Visual Analogue Pain Scale in Children." *Canadian Journal of Anaesthesiology,* 35, S137, 1988.

91. Champion G.D., Goodenough B., von Baeyer C.L., and Thomas, W., "Measurement of Pain by Self-Report." In Finley, G.A., and McGrath, P.J., eds., *Measurement of Pain in Infants and Children, Progress in Pain Research and Management, 10.* Seattle: IASP Press, 1998.

92. Hester, N.K.O., "The Preoperational Child's Reaction to Immunization." *Nursing Research,* 28, 250–254, 1979.

93. Hester, N.O., Foster, R., and Kristensen, K., "Measurement of Pain in Children: Generalizability and Validity of the Pain Ladder and Poker Chip Tool." In Tyler, D.C,. and Krane, E.J., eds., *Pediatric Pain Advances in Pain Research and Therapy, 15.* New York: Raven Press, 1990.

94. Szyfelbein, S.K., Osgood, P.F., and Carr, D.B., "The Assessment of Pain and Plasma B-Endorphin Immunoactivity in Burned Children." *Pain,* 22, 173-182, 1985.

95. Eland, J. M., *Children's Communication of Pain.* Unpublished master's thesis. Ames, IA: University of Iowa, 1974.

96. Wong, D., and Baker, C., "Pain in Children: Comparison of Assessment Scales." *Pediatric Nursing*, 14, 9–17, 1988.

97. Beyer, J.E., *The Oucher: A User's Manual and Technical Report.* Evanston, IL: Hospital Play Equipment, 1984.

98. Sinkin-Feldman, L., Resler, M, and Savedra, M., "Word Placement on the Word-Graphic Rating Scale by Pediatric Patients." *Pediatric Nursing,* 23, 31–34, 1997.

99. Zeltzer, L., Bursch, B. and Walco, G., "Pain Responsiveness and Chronic Pain: A Psychobiological Perspective." *Developmental Behavioral Pediatrics*, 18, 413–422, 1997.

100. Heligenstein, E., and Gerrity, S., "Psychotropics as Adjuvant Analgesics." In Schechter, N.L., Berde, C.B. and Yaster, M., eds., *Pain in Infants, Children, and Adolescents*. Baltimore: Williams and Wilkins, 1993.

101. Morton, N.S., "Acute and Procedure Pain in Infants and Children." In Finley, G.A,. and McGrath, P.J., eds., *Progress in Pain Research and Management, 20.* Seattle: IASP Press, 2001.

102. Anand, K.J.S., Menon, G., Narsinghani, U. and McIntosh, N., "Systemic Analgesic Therapy." In Anand, K.J.S., Stevens, B.J. and McGrath, P.J., eds., *Pain in Neonates,* Second Revised and Enlarged Edition. Amsterdam: Elsevier, 2000.

103. Golianu, B., Krane, E.J., Galloway, K.S., and Yaster, M., "Pediatric Acute Pain Management." *Pediatric Clinics of North America*, 47, 559–587, 2000.

104. Yaster, M., Tobin, J.R. and Maxwell, L.G., "Local Anesthetics." In Schechter, N.L., Berde, C.B. and Yaster, M., eds., *Pain in Infants, Children, and Adolescents.* Baltimore: Williams and Wilkins, 1993.

105. Finley, G.A., "Pharmacological Management of Procedure Pain." In Finley, G.A,. and McGrath, P.J., eds., *Acute and Procedure Pain in Infants and Children, Progress in Pain Research and Management, 20.* Seattle: IASP Press, 2001.

106. Lander, J., Hodgins, M., Nazarali, S., McTavish J., Ocullette J. and Friesen, E., "Determinants of Success and Failure of EMLA." *Pain,* 64, 89–97, 1996.

107. Selbst, S.M., "Pain Management in the Emergency Department." In Schechter, N.L., Berde, C.B. and Yaster, M., eds., *Pain in Infants, Children, and Adolescents*, Baltimore: Williams and Wilkins, 1993.

108. Chen, B.K. and Cunningham, B.B., "Topical Anesthetics in Children: Agents and Techniques That Equally Comfort Patients, Parents, and Clinicians." *Current Opinion in Pediatrics,* 13, 324–30, 2001.

109. Stephens, B.K., Barkey, M.E. and Hall, H.R., "Techniques to Comfort Children during Stressful Procedures." *Advances in Mind-Body Medicine,* 15, 49–60, 1999.

110. Franck, L.S., "Clinical Evaluation and Treatment of Infant Pain in the Neonatal Intensive Care Unit." In Schechter, N.L., Berde, C.B. and Yaster, M., eds., *Pain in Infants, Children, and Adolescents*, Baltimore: Williams and Wilkins, 1993.

111. Stevens, B., Gibbons, S., and Franck, L.S., "Treatment of Pain in the Neonatal Intensive Care Unit." *Pediatric Clinics of North America,* 47, 633–650, 2000.

112. Blass, E.M. and Watt, L.B., "Suckling and Sucrose-Induced Analgesia in Human Newborns." *Pain,* 83, 611–623, 1999.

113. French, G.M., Painter, E.C,. and Coury, D.L., "Blowing Away Shot Pain: A Technique for Pain Management during Immunization." *Pediatrics,* 93, 384–388, 1994.

114. Kachoyeanos, M.K. and Friedhoff, M., "Cognitive and Behavioral Strategies to Reduce Children's Pain." *Maternal Child Nursing,* 18, 14–19, 1993.

115. Lambert, S.A., "Distraction, Imagery, and Hypnosis Techniques for Management of Children's Pain." *Journal of Child and Family Nursing,* 2, 5–15, 1999.

116. Wall, V.J. and Womack, W., "Hypnotic versus Active Cognitive Coping Strategies for Alleviation of Procedural Distress in Pediatric Oncology Patients." *American Journal of Clinical Hypnosis,* 31, 181–191, 1989.

117. Zeltzer, L., and LeBaron, S., "Hypnosis and Nonhypnotic Techniques for Reduction of Pain and Anxiety during Painful Procedures in Children and Adolescents with Cancer." *The Journal of Pediatrics*, 101, 1032–1035, 1982.

118. Keenan, D., "When a Child is Your Client." *Trial*, 38, September 2002.

Chapter 7

Pain and Suffering in Pediatric Neurology

Michael A. Pollack, MD, Michael R. D'Lugo, Esq., and Richard H. Ford, Esq.

"May I never see in the patient anything but a fellow creature in pain."
from the Oath of Maimonides

Synopsis

7.1 Introduction

Impairment and disability, which are targeted by the physician, correlate imperfectly with pain and suffering, which are important issues for the legal system. Pain complaints are not always associated with objective manifestations of disease. In young children or other nonverbal patients, the presence of pain can only be inferred by the observations of family members or medical personnel, and each observer may come to a different conclusion.

Suffering, which includes mental anguish associated with pain, impairment, or disability, is also difficult to evaluate in an objective fashion. In similarly impaired individuals, suffering may vary because of different coping strategies, family support systems, age, cognitive integrity, and financial status. Depression, which is one form of suffering often associated with chronic disease, can sometimes be quantified by various reported symptoms and physical findings. Treatment of depression represents an attempt to alleviate suffering even if the term is not often used in medical records. "Suffering" implies a subjective point of view and is less tangible than other data which physicians use in managing their patients. One poignant aspect of pediatric neurological practice is that many young children with overwhelming illness appear to be free of the depression or anxiety encountered in adults with comparable conditions. As neurologically impaired children mature and compare themselves with their peers, anger and depression may develop.

Suffering also occurs in the families of patients. Parents' personalities, coping strategies, psychological support systems, and financial circumstances affect their responses to minor and catastrophic illness in their children. It seems likely that different degrees of suffering may occur in families of children with identical conditions.

Tip

Suffering occurs not only in patients but also in their families.

This chapter reviews three conditions that often lead to litigation: cerebral palsy, head trauma including post-traumatic epilepsy, and obstetric brachial palsy. In each section, the presentation includes the following elements:

- definition of essential terms
- incidence and causes
- key physical findings and diagnostic procedures
- range of outcomes associated with the condition

Each section reviews the long-term physical, psychological, and social impact of the condition. Inevitably, the perspective offered in this chapter reflects the experience and interests of its authors. Most of the chapter is written from the perspective of a pediatric neurologist (MAP). At the end of each major section, we have included "The Legal Perspective" (ML and RF), which reflects the viewpoint of the malpractice attorney.

Information from health-related quality of life (QOL) studies, which have become more frequent in the past ten years, is presented at the end of each section. These studies attempt to evaluate outcome more broadly than traditional medical research. Although definitions of QOL vary, there appears to be a consensus that it must include psychological and social as well as physical function. This view is consistent with the definition of health offered by the World Health Organization: "a state of complete physical, mental, and social well-being and not merely the absence of disease or infirmity."[1] The broad evaluation of outcome implied by QOL studies implies the need for viewpoints other than those of the physician. QOL studies usually include assessments of the perceptions and feelings of the patient or family. There are potential conflicts between patient responses and external criteria. Various instruments have been devised in an attempt to classify and quantify these subjective responses.[2] Both generic and disease-specific inventories have been used. Complex statistical issues arise in QOL studies, and these difficulties are multiplied when QOL studies are carried out in children.[1,3,4]

In pediatric studies, an interview or inventory completed by a caregiver often substitutes for direct ascertainment of the patient's perceptions. An additional caution is that results of QOL studies may vary from one culture or country to another even when study groups appear comparable.[5] Despite these limitations, QOL studies are likely to be a permanent part of the medical landscape. They also provide a potential bridge between the medical and legal perspectives: QOL studies describe aspects of patient outcome that may be of great interest in the courtroom but not always available in the traditional medical record. There are at least two potential applications of QOL studies in the courtroom.

1. If a previously validated quality of life instrument is administered to the plaintiff or family members by a psychologist or other qualified professional, the results allow the functional significance of the individual's injury to be presented to the court with scientific credibility.
2. Even if the plaintiff does not undergo a formal QOL evaluation, the medical literature can be used to make inferences regarding the probable functional consequences of his injury.

7.2 Cerebral Palsy

A. Definitions

Cerebral palsy (CP) refers to "a group of chronic disorders impairing control of movement that appear in the first few years of life and generally do not worsen over time."[5] As used above, "nonprogressive" refers to the pathological cause of the impairment. One task of the pediatric neurologist is to identify uncommon, progressive brain disorders that, early in their course, may masquerade as cerebral palsy. Spinal cord lesions and various disorders of the peripheral nervous system (nerves and muscles) are also mistaken for cerebral palsy on occasion.

Tip

"Cerebral palsy" refers to a mixed group of neurological disorders occurring early in life and interfering with movement and coordination.

Although the term "cerebral palsy" implies a fixed lesion, which will not worsen with the passage of time, clinical manifestations change as the brain matures. In addition, patients whose symptoms are constant may appear more handicapped to their parents with the passage of time as maturation of healthy siblings and peers produces a different set of expectations. Secondary effects and coexisting conditions may also result in increased impairment and disability. For example, a child who walks short distances with a walker or other supportive devices may lose this ability as the result of weight gain, dislocation of the hip, or injury resulting from a fall.

As used by American neurologists, "cerebral palsy" refers only to motor (movement and posture) impairment. The terms "nonprogressive encephalopathy" and "static encephalopathy" imply that multiple functional domains may be affected in children with cerebral palsy. Although many children with CP are normal except for motor impairment, others display one or more additional manifestations of central nervous system dysfunction: mental impairment, seizure disorder, or special sensory (vision and hearing) deficits. As a general principle, children with the most severe motor impairment are also the most likely to have deficits in other areas of function.

Not all disturbances of posture, locomotion, and coordination attributable to early brain lesions merit the diagnosis of cerebral palsy. Rather, the term is used to refer to the following, well-defined patterns of motor impairment.

quadriplegia. Weakness of all four limbs

diplegia. Weakness chiefly affecting the lower extremities

hemiplegia. Weakness confined to the left or right extremities

monoplegia. Weakness limited to one extremity

choreoathetosis. Certain patterns of involuntary movement

ataxic. Balance and coordination difficulties due to cerebellar (hindbrain) involvement

mixed. Choreoathetosis associated with one of the preceding forms.

The root "-paresis" (e.g., hemiparesis) is sometimes used in preference to "-plegia" as the former term implies that voluntary movement of the affected part is at least partially preserved. In practice, the two terms are used interchangeably. The modifiers "spastic" or "hypotonic" are often applied when referring to children with diplegia, hemiplegia, or monoplegia. Spasticity implies stiffness, increased resistance to passive movement, and hyperactive tendon reflexes. Hypotonia or atonia indicates that affected limbs are excessively limber or flaccid. Spastic cerebral palsy is more common than hypotonic forms.

B. Incidence

Moderate to severe cerebral palsy occurs in 1.2–2.5 per 1,000 live births, and there are more than 500,000 Americans with the condition.[6,7] Most hemiparetic patients learn to walk. About 50% of diparetic and 33% of quadriparetic patients succeed in walking.[7]

C. Causes

Cerebral palsy (CP) is a descriptive rather than an etiological (causal) diagnosis. Physicians often prefer to use a more specific diagnosis when causal factors are identified. A detailed discussion of causation is beyond the scope of this chapter. Causation issues that are often the focus of litigation include perinatal asphyxia and obstetric trauma.

Perinatal asphyxia (problems with oxygenation and circulation around the time of birth) is a factor in a minority of patients. Other perinatal causes including obstetric trauma account for only 3%–5% of cases. Since multiple risk factors are often present in a single individual, the true contribution of various factors may be difficult to determine. Most risk factors are not under obstetric control. According to Susser et al., "The value of perinatal asphyxia for predicting whether a child will develop CP is quite low . . . only about 12% of surviving children with Apgar scores of 0–3 developed CP. The evidence suggests that cerebral palsy is only very rarely preceded by preventable perinatal asphyxia"[8] Fetal heart monitoring has very limited value in predicting cerebral palsy. Although multiple late decelerations and decreased beat-to-beat variability increase the risk of CP, these findings are not followed by CP in 99.8% of cases.[8]

D. Mental retardation, epilepsy, and cerebral palsy

In about one-third of children who have cerebral palsy, intellect is mildly impaired. In another one-third intellect is moderately or severely impaired, while in the remaining one-third intellect is normal (NINDS). Severe MR occurs in almost all children with quadriplegic CP. Seizures occur in 50% of patients with CP. In some patients, seizures are provoked by fever during early childhood, while in others they occur without obvious triggers and recur over many years.[6,7]

E. Diagnosis

Cerebral palsy is a clinical diagnosis: it is established by history and physical examination. As noted above, etiologies are varied, and there is no specific laboratory test for CP. However, laboratory studies as well as neuroimaging studies (computerized tomographic or magnetic resonance scans) may be helpful in excluding certain progressive disorders. Imaging studies in children with CP may demonstrate cerebral infarction (stroke), atrophy (reduction in the volume of brain tissue), and various malformations of the central nervous system. However, pathology of this type is sometimes encountered in patients who have no apparent neurological deficit. In addition, a normal neuroimaging study does not exclude CP. As a general rule, abnormal scans are more likely to be found in children with severe CP than in those with mild CP.

Tip

The diagnosis of cerebral palsy is established chiefly by the history and physical examination.

F. Management and prognosis

Since the causes of cerebral palsy cannot be modified in an affected individual, treatment is symptomatic. Physical and occupational therapy are often prescribed during the first few years of life. Braces and other supportive devices may be used to facilitate walking in some patients. A variety of orthopedic procedures are available to treat secondary manifestations such as shortening of lower extremity tendons. Oral medications are sometimes used to reduce spasticity but are not very effective in most patients. In mildly affected patients, injection of muscles with botulinum toxin may help to avoid or delay surgery.[9] Selective dorsal rhizotomy is a procedure in which lumbar and sacral sensory nerve roots are partially severed.[10] Decreased sensory input reduces lower extremity spasticity. More recently, a less invasive surgical procedure, implantation of the baclofen pump, has gained favor. The pump is placed in the abdomen and a thin catheter extends from the pump to the lumbar spinal fluid space. When delivered into the spinal fluid in small amounts, the muscle relaxant, baclofen, often reduces spasticity and is generally well tolerated. The pump can be externally programmed for dosage adjustment.[11]

Preschool programs, which usually include physical, occupational, and speech therapy are available to children with cerebral palsy and other developmental disorders under the Individuals with Disabilities Education Act.[12] Special educational needs during the school years are determined by the degree of physical disability, mental ability, and the presence of coexisting problems with vision and hearing. On occasion, epilepsy requires special school provisions.

7.3 Pain and Suffering Associated with Cerebral Palsy

A. Medical issues

Uncomplicated cerebral palsy rarely produces pain. Occasionally patients have spasms (stiffening episodes), which may be uncomfortable. Secondary effects such as dislocation of the hip resulting from spasticity may be painful. Children who receive braces (ankle foot orthoses) may experience minor pain if their orthoses do not fit well. Surgical procedures for the treatment of cerebral palsy are inevitably associated with some degree of postoperative pain. Children confined to wheelchairs or bedridden may develop discomfort and skin breakdown over bony prominences.

Tip

Although pain is not a primary manifestation of cerebral palsy, secondary effects and their treatments may result in pain or discomfort.

As indicated in the introduction, suffering is a broader term than pain and includes the child's emotional response to his or her situation. Anxiety related to medical visits and procedures varies considerably. Parental outlook and support often influence the child's reaction to these situations.

B. Social issues

As a child with cerebral palsy matures, depression and frustration may occur if there is a mismatch between his perceived abilities and desires. "Perceived" is the critical word here since:

1. With the same degree of physical impairment, children may display marked differences in self-image, resourcefulness, and interests.
2. An individual who has always had physical limitations may not experience the same sense of loss as one who is able to remember a time when he was able to participate in all age-appropriate activities.
3. Some schools and parents are more successful than others in helping children assimilate into their peer group.
4. Associated mental impairment may affect insight and analysis of the child's social situation.
5. Coexisting conditions (epilepsy, hip dislocation, scoliosis) may also affect independence and participation in peer activities. A child may be less discouraged if he feels these associated conditions are temporary than if he regards them as permanent and unalterable.

C. School and work

A reasonable goal for children with cerebral palsy or other chronic physical or mental impairments is placement in the least restrictive environment permitted by their condition. This terminology implies an environment where the child is most likely to learn and encounter social success, which includes peer acceptance and meaningful participation in group activities. Depending on the needs of a particular child, these goals may best be achieved by placement in a mainstream classroom throughout the day, part- time placement in the mainstream classroom with remaining time in a special education or adaptive physical education program, or full-time special education. As a general rule, intellectual function and behavior are more critical determinants of class placement than physical abilities. Parental participation, flexibility on the part of school personnel, and financial resources remain critical issues in determining outcome in spite of the existence of laws requiring that an attempt be made to meet the educational needs of all children.

Tip

Family members and school personnel can affect outcome in neurologically impaired children.

In some children with cerebral palsy, intelligence may be underestimated because of unintelligible speech. Inappropriate class placement, lack of opportunity for communication, and peer rejection may occur. These consequences are less frequent in recent years as the result of voice synthesizers and other communication devices.

Many children with physical impairments are capable of financial self-sufficiency. A realistic appraisal of a child's abilities and interest during the high school years facilitates appropriate planning for work or higher education. School counselors and state vocational rehabilitation programs may be helpful.

For children whose physical or mental limitations result in total or partial dependency throughout life, sheltered work programs are available in some communities. Aging parents may need to make difficult decisions about long-term care for their adult offspring with cerebral palsy. These decisions require that parents be well informed about community and family resources.

D. Quality of life for children with cerebral palsy

As indicated previously, cerebral palsy is a descriptive, umbrella diagnosis including a broad range of nonprogressive encephalopathies. For this reasons, QOL studies vary depending on the selection criteria for entry. Although life expectancy for patients with very severe cerebral palsy—those lacking the ability to feed independently or walk even short distances—is significantly reduced, survival of high-functioning adults with cerebral palsy is close to that of the general population.[13] QOL studies may be most useful in this population. Higher functioning patients are more likely to complete questionnaires while our inferences about the feelings and perceptions of the severely impaired are more likely to be based on questionnaires completed by caretakers. In addition, the longer life span generally enjoyed by less severely affected individuals implies greater opportunity to benefit from QOL studies if their findings can be utilized in treatment.

Both generic and condition-specific evaluation tools have been used in CP QOL studies. One recent article commented on the paucity of condition-specific QOL tools for evaluating the CP population.[14]

Hip pain is common in ambulatory adolescents and young adults with cerebral palsy. In one cross-sectional study, the prevalence of hip pain was 47.2% and was judged to be intolerable in about 24% of those affected.[15]

Because of secondary hip disease, weight gain, and a variety of other factors as well, marginally ambulatory CP patients not uncommonly lose the ability to walk during adolescence or early adulthood. In one survey of adults with CP, 35% reported decreased walking ability, and 9% had stopped walking.[16] Although the underlying neuropathology in CP is, by definition, nonprogressive, functional impairment and disability may increase as the result of secondary effects. In addition to loss of locomotor skills, the CP population is at increased risk for a variety of additional health problems, including epilepsy, speech disorders, visual disturbance, hearing impairment, bowel and bladder dysfunction, and various feeding problems.[17] Scoliosis (lateral curvature of the spine) occurs commonly in CP and, depending on severity, may be treated with bracing or surgery. Complications of severe scoliosis include cardiac and respiratory compromise.

Tip

Although "cerebral palsy" implies a disorder that does not worsen with time, complications may result in loss of function as the patient matures.

QOL in families of individuals with CP must also be considered. Practitioners who care for large numbers of children with CP often conclude that emotional stress occurs commonly in their families. However, there appears to be little data to demonstrate that families of children with CP differ from other families. One study noted that there were few differences in family functioning, life satisfaction, or perceived social support in CP families as compared to families without a physically disabled member. Parents of adolescents and young adults with CP demonstrated lower expectations for future independence and success.[18] Children with disabilities require more of their parents' time. For many families, this need leads to one parent giving up employment. Although financial needs may increase as the result of having a disabled child, earning power often diminishes. As summarized in one study, "Care needs of children with severe disabilities are significantly greater than those of non-disabled children and do not decrease with advancing age. Mothers of children with disabilities are unable to work outside the home because of these care needs. Total family income, even when benefits are included, may fall to a level that is less than peer families with non-disabled children."[19]

7.4 Representative Cerebral Palsy Cases

A. Amy: Premature infant

Amy was the one and one-half-pound product of a twenty-four-week, twin gestation of a forty-one-year-old, who had three previous miscarriages. Complications of pregnancy included twin-twin transfusion (crossed circulation). Neurological complications of prematurity included intracranial hemorrhage, which was followed by hydrocephalus (enlarged spinal fluid cavities) and cystic changes in the brain. A ventriculoperitoneal shunt (from brain to abdomen) was performed at three months of age, and additional surgeries were required because of shunt malfunction. Seizures during her nursery stay were treated with medication. Her total stay in the neonatal ICU and extended-care nursery was four months.

Amy's development was globally delayed, and microcephaly (small head circumference indicating deficient brain development) was evident by six months of age. Multiple shunt revisions were required prior to four years of age. She continued to have occasional seizures in spite of medication.

At six years of age, Amy's mother reported that seizures occurred once or twice a month, but they were very brief and had little impact on the patient's daily activities. She continued to receive physical and occupational therapy for spastic quadriparesis. She was able to stand with assistance but could not sit, walk, or feed herself independently. Her speech was limited to a few words, but language comprehension was much more advanced. She enjoyed picture books and music. In addition, she was beginning to use a computer equipped with a voice synthesizer to communicate with teachers and family members. Visual impairment, which occurred as a complication of prematurity, and incoordination limited her use of the computer.

Comment: This patient illustrates neurological problems commonly encountered in very small prematures. Risk factors included advanced maternal age and twin gestation. Cross circulation between the twins was undoubtedly a factor in the surviving twin's cerebral palsy. Common complications of neurological importance included retinopathy of prematurity (leading to visual impairment), intraventricular hemorrhage (producing hydrocephalus), and seizures. Brain injury in this patient was probably due to a combination of prenatal and postnatal factors that are not easily teased apart. At six years of age, the patient's neurological difficulties included mental impairment, quadriparesis, epilepsy, visual impairment and hydrocephalus. She is likely to survive well into adulthood but will remain severely disabled. The extent to which new technologies may increase her independence is difficult to predict, but she has already benefited from a communication device. Although her parents have been intermittently depressed by the challenges of caring for Amy, they have adapted well to their daughter's special needs. In order to provide the attention she requires, they have modified their work schedules and reduced their combined income.

B. Bruce: Diagnosis of CP at eighteen months

Bruce was the seven-pound, seven-ounce product of a term pregnancy complicated only by maternal vertigo. The umbilical cord was wrapped around the neck at delivery, but there was no fetal distress. Nursery course was uneventful, and the patient left the hospital with his mother after the usual stay. A left hand preference was noted in early infancy. At eighteen months of age, neurological examination demonstrated a mild right hemiparesis. A CT scan demonstrated a left cerebral infarction (stroke), which was thought to be of prenatal or perinatal origin. By four years of age, learning difficulties were suspected. Slight growth arrest of the right upper and lower extremities was present. He dragged his right foot slightly when walking and ran awkwardly. By nine years of age, a seizure disorder had developed. His seizures occurred exclusively during sleep and were brief. Re-examination showed no change in the patient's hemiparesis. Superficial sensation was impaired in the right hand. His seizures were fully controlled after several months and trials of multiple medications over several months.

Comment: This patient was found to have cerebral palsy after a largely unremarkable pregnancy and delivery. Although a nuchal cord (umbilical cord wrapped around the neck) was present at delivery, there was no convincing evidence that it affected circulatory function. The diagnosis of cerebral palsy was first established at the time of his initial neurological consultation at eighteen months of age. Although the underlying pathology did not change, neurological manifestations evolved over eleven years. Bruce's hemiparesis was relatively mild and could not be fully appreciated until he began to walk and run. Seizures were first recognized at nine years of age. Because his seizures were brief and initially confined to sleep, it is possible that unwitnessed seizures occurred before that time. Diagnostic studies provided firm evidence that the patient's seizure disorder was due to his longstanding left hemispheric lesion. There was no evidence to suggest a more recent brain injury. Bruce's seizures were not fully controlled with the first drug prescribed, but excellent seizure control was achieved when another anti-epileptic drug was substituted. Overall intellectual potential fell in the normal range, but the patient did have academic difficulty.

Bruce's course was mild by comparison to that of Amy. Although he will always have a neurological deficit and will probably require anti-epileptic drug therapy for the rest of his life, it is likely that he will operate a motor vehicle and be gainfully employed.

C. The legal perspective

For obvious reasons, given the nature of the injury which is inherent in a patient with cerebral palsy, as well as the age of the plaintiff, jury verdicts in this area of medical malpractice are among the highest in the field. Examples abound of jury awards of noneconomic damages which exceed $10 million. This is driven by two distinct factors. First, an infant suffering from the most severe form of cerebral palsy will likely face a lifetime of treatment in a healthcare setting which will generate future economic damages well into the millions of dollars. Those juries which consider the issue of noneconomic damages to be a function of the degree of economic damages which the plaintiff faces will be left with no alternative but to award a staggering figure in order to conform with the jurors' sense of justice and compassion. Second, the allegations of negligence which give rise to a claim of medical malpractice resulting in cerebral palsy are often of a type which have a tendency to inflame the passions of the members of a jury panel, notwithstanding judicial instruction to be objective fact finders. This is especially true in this area of pediatric medical malpractice, where by definition the injured party is the single most vulnerable member of society.

Taken together, these factors often contribute to startling jury awards. Several examples will be described below, including high-end jury awards, significant settlement agreements, and factual scenarios which can result in lower jury verdict awards or even defense verdicts.

Patient D.B. was delivered at a gestational age of thirty-one weeks. D.B.'s mother began to experience signs of labor while she was being evaluated for premature membrane rupture. Allegations of the complaint included assertions that the labor and delivery staff of the hospital failed to respond to these labor signs. Further, the attending obstetrician failed to come to the hospital to manage the labor after these signs were noted. As a result, Patient D.B. was delivered prematurely by a nurse at the hospital. Patient D.B. sued the obstetrician as well as the hospital alleging negligence in failing to timely evaluate, monitor, assess, and manage the labor, as well as the failure to provide an obstetrical physician in order to deliver this high-risk infant. As a result of this complicated delivery, Patient D.B. suffered traumatic, explosive, and hypoxic injury to his brain. He was diagnosed prior to trial with moderate to severe cerebral palsy, a permanent seizure disorder, profound psychomotor retardation including cognitive function, as well as spastic quadriparesis of his extremities. His condition will require specialized medical care and therapeutic care for his injuries for the remainder of his life.

Based on these facts, the jury rendered a verdict of $18,924,000. This amount included a $2 million award for past pain and suffering and an $8 million award for future pain and suffering. This award was likely the product of a combination of factors, not the least of which included the severe nature of Patient D.B.'s injuries, as well as the particular facts of this case, including the failure to provide an obstetrician to supervise a complicated birth. *D.B. v. Albert, Dade County*, Florida case number 92-12140 CA 32; verdict date: September 29, 1997.

Patient G.J. was a two-month-old who underwent open heart surgery. During the course of the procedure, according to the complaint, the perfusionist was negligent in the manner in which he operated the heart lung bypass machine. In general, the perfusionist operates extracorporeal circulation and autotransfusion equipment during any procedure where it is necessary to support or temporarily replace a patient's circulatory or respiratory function. The perfusionist also can be responsible for administering blood products, anesthetic agents, or drugs through the extracorporeal circuit. In addition, the perfusionist is responsible for monitoring blood gases and the adequate anticoagulation of the patient. In this case, the plaintiff alleged that the perfusionist's negligence resulted in anoxic brain injury to Patient G.J., causing severe cerebral palsy, including blindness and spastic quadriplegia. Based on these facts, the jury awarded $10,848,848. *J.G. v. Shands Teaching Hospital and Clinics, Inc.*, Alachua County, Florida case number 98-3199-CA-K; verdict date: January 15, 2002.

Patient T.H. was delivered by cesarean section which was alleged to have been performed too late. The plaintiff also alleged that the defendant hospital had failed to provide proper nursing care during the course of labor and delivery and that hospital staff failed to recognize fetal distress. The hospital argued in its defense that Patient T.H. had suffered from fetal anemia prior to the commencement of labor. Patient T.H. suffered profound mental and physical disability as a result of cerebral palsy alleged to have been caused through the negligent handling of labor and delivery. Patient T.H. will require constant care for all activities of daily living for the remainder of his life, medical, occupational, and other therapies, and in addition will have a reduced life expectancy. Based on these facts, the jury awarded the plaintiff $7,523,000. This award included $2,300,000 in noneconomic damages. *T.H. v. Cape Canaveral Hospital, Inc.*, Brevard County, Florida case number 94-00342 CA D; verdict date: February 28, 2000.

Patient T.H.'s case is typical of the pediatric cerebral palsy case in the manner in which experts play such a significant role during the course of trial. The plaintiffs called seven separate experts to testify at trial, including two gynecologists, one pediatric neurologist, a nursing expert, a vocational rehabilitation expert, an economist, and an expert in the field of maternal fetal medicine. The vocational rehabilitation expert and the economist work hand in hand in an effort to establish the precise nature of the plaintiff's economic damages. The vocational rehabilitation expert is provided information by medical experts in the fields in which the patient will require ongoing therapies for the remainder of his life. The vocational rehabilitation expert then identifies the costs associated with each specific element of therapy which will be required. The economist then evaluates those future expenses which will be incurred over the course of the patient's life expectancy and reduces that number to present value. The result is an economic damages number which can be presented to the jury in an understandable way. This type of expert-driven number is significant to the issue of noneconomic damages as well, for as noted above juries have a tendency to calculate noneconomic damages, and specifically pain and suffering damages, as a function of the value of the economic damages claim.

The defense in the claim brought on behalf of Patient T.H. also called a significant number of experts. The specific fields of expertise included neonatology, pediatric neurology, pediatrics, nursing, and an expert economist.

Patient S.B. was a newborn baby who was left unattended at a hospital's infant nursery. At approximately six hours of age, Patient S.B. began to experience respiratory distress which ultimately led to cardiopulmonary arrest. This episode caused Patient S.B. to experience a partial interruption in the oxygen supply to his brain which lasted anywhere from ten to twenty minutes. It was alleged in the complaint at the hospital's staff was negligent in that the hospital's own policies and procedures mandated that the nursery for newborns had to be under continuous observation. In spite of this policy, Patient S.B. was left unattended, with the allegation that had the nursery been supervised Patient S.B.'s respiratory distress would have been identified and his subsequent severe brain injuries averted. Those injuries include hypoxic ischemic encephalopathy with resulting cerebral palsy. This claim was tried and resulted in a jury verdict of $5,635,000. *S.B. v. University Medical Center, Inc.*, Duval County, Florida case number 85-13974-CA; verdict date: November, 1988.

These exceedingly high verdicts in cerebral palsy medical malpractice cases have had the predictable impact on the manner in which these types of cases are handled. That effect can be seen in exceedingly high settlements being reached. For example, Patient R.S. developed cerebral palsy as a result of an unacceptable rise in his bilirubin level. Bilirubin is a red bile pigment which can be found either as a soluble sodium bilirubinate or as an insoluble calcium salt in the gall stones. It is formed from hemoglobin during both normal and abnormal destruction of erythrocytes by the body. While there is typically bilirubin in the blood, it is usually present in relatively small amounts. However, excessive levels can be harmful. Patient R.S. developed cerebral palsy and deafness as a result of the deposit of bilirubin in the brain. The plaintiff's allegation against the hospital was that the staff failed to intervene appropriately in Patient R.S.'s care by performing a timely blood transfusion. Based on these facts, the defendant hospital settled the claim for $5,950,000. *R.S. v. University of Miami*, Dade County, Florida case number 01-1095 MA; settlement date: September 9, 2001.

Another example of a significant settlement involved Patient A.S., who was delivered by cesarean section with severe perinatal asphyxia, or the deprivation of oxygen during the course of labor and delivery. Patient A.S.'s mother had suffered a significant pelvic fracture in an automobile accident when she was sixteen years old. Orthopaedic surgeons at that time warned the mother that the pelvic fractures may have compromised the shape of her pelvis which might require delivery by cesarean section. The obstetrician who handled the mother's pregnancy agreed that a cesarean section may be indicated in light of her previous pelvic injury, and indicated that he would be present and ready to perform this procedure if necessary. The mother went into labor, and the obstetrician examined her at 12:55 P.M. The obstetrician testified during his deposition that he believed that the mother would be ready to start pushing within thirty to sixty minutes. Based upon this examination, the obstetrician determined that the mother was almost completely dilated, and he ordered Pitocin to stimulate the contractions. At this time, the obstetrician left the medical center in order to attend one of his son's soccer games. The obstetrician told the mother that her labor and delivery would be supervised by a midwife. After the obstetrician left the hospital, the baby's heart rate began to exhibit abnormalities which were not recognized by the midwife or by the nurse. At 3:25 P.M., another obstetrician reviewed the fetal heart monitoring strip and was also apprised of the mother's history of severe pelvic fracture. However, rather than ordering a cesarean section, he directed the midwife to attempt a vacuum extraction delivery. After attempts at this form of delivery failed, the order was given to perform a Cesarean section.

Patient A.S. was delivered at 3:58 P.M. with no heart rate, no respiration, no muscle tone, and bluish color. Her Apgar scores were 1/3/5 at one, five, and ten minutes. Patient A.S. was resuscitated by the neonatal unit, however she continued to experience signs of severe brain injury. The plaintiff's expert testified that Patient A.S.'s signs of fetal distress should have been recognized much earlier than at 3:25 P.M. and that had a timely cesarean delivery been performed. Patient A.S.'s brain injuries would have been prevented. Patient A.S.'s brain injury included a static encephalopathy with cerebral palsy, spastic quadriplegia, severe developmental delays, and other injuries including gastrostomy surgery for the purpose of administering tube feedings. Based upon these facts, a global settlement in the amount of $5,750,000 was reached. This was based on medical bills of approximately $100,000, lost earning capacity of $625,000, and future care needs ranging from $8,500,000 to $25,000,000. *A.S. v. Tallahassee Memorial Regional Medical Center*, Leon County, Florida case number 94-2890; settlement date: September 1, 1995.

Patient A.S.'s case raises another significant issue which confronts those handling a claim for significant brain injury, including cerebral palsy, arising out of medical negligence during the course of labor and delivery. The claim for noneconomic damages, and specifically pain and suffering, is greatly affected by the determination of the economic damages which a plaintiff will suffer throughout the course of his or her life expectancy. Invariably, the largest component of a noneconomic damages claim in a case involving negligently induced cerebral palsy arising out of the delivery of an infant is the future medical care needs of the infant throughout the course of his or her life. This raises a particularly troubling issue with regard to the management of such a lawsuit. The defense must carefully consider what the injured plaintiff's life expectancy is going to be. Obviously, if an individual is going to have a normal life expectancy, with extensive medical treatments ongoing throughout the course of that life expectancy, the damages to be assessed for future medical expenses will invariably be astronomical. In the case of Patient A.S., this figure reached $25 million. However, the defense of Patient A.S.'s claim raised the issue that given the nature of the injuries which Patient A.S. had suffered, it was not reasonable to believe that she would live to a normal life expectancy. This argument is a double-edge sword: on the one hand, it is perfectly logical to expect that an individual with a severe brain injury is not going to live into her seventies; however, there is an inherent difficulty, and a risk of antagonizing the fact finder, in arguing that the damages for which the defendant is arguably responsible should be reduced because the injuries are so significant that the patient will not have a normal life span. In the case of Patient A.S., the defense argued that the present value of the patient's future care needs was actually a figure somewhere between $2–$3 million, far below the plaintiff's stated range of $8.5–$25 million.

The case of Patient J.H. provides another example of the type of acts which can result in the development of severe cerebral palsy. Approximately two hours before delivery, there were signs of fetal distress on the fetal monitoring strip. When the mother was transferred to the delivery room, it was noted that the fetal monitoring machine was not functioning. At delivery, Patient J.H. had Apgar scores of 0 and 0. The delivery was high risk as that term was defined in the hospital's nursing procedure manual in light of the fetal distress noted in the fetal monitoring strips as well as the use of Pitocin to encourage delivery. Contrary to the hospital's procedures, a neonatologist was not in attendance at the time of delivery, and in fact one was not contacted until twenty-five minutes after the delivery. As a result, the neonatologist did not arrive at the hospital until one hour after delivery. A CT scan of Patient J.H.'s skull taken one week postdelivery showed a skull fracture caused by the traumatic delivery. As a result, Patient J.H. suffered from severe cerebral palsy. Based on these facts, the parties settled this claim in the amount of $4,400,000. *J.H. v. Good Samaritan Hospital, Inc.*, Palm Beach County, Florida case number CL 89-1800 AF; settlement date: December, 1990.

As is to be expected, the degree of severity of the condition of cerebral palsy will dictate the damages award obtained in the action for medical negligence. For example, Patient S.G. suffered oxygen deprivation during the course of her delivery. As a result of this oxygen deprivation, a cyst formed on Patient S.G.'s right parietal lobe. This cyst in turn caused Patient S.G. to develop a mild form of cerebral palsy. Based on these facts, the case resolved in a settlement in the amount of $600,000. *S.G. v. St. Mary's Hospital, Inc.*, Palm Beach County, Florida case number 87-2921 AD; settlement date: June, 1991.

Although a negligence-induced cerebral palsy case presents numerous difficulties for the defense, these cases are not impossible to defend, and in fact defense verdicts have been obtained. For example, in the case of Patient B.N., the mother had a history of the delivery of a nonviable fetus. In addition, the mother had undergone a cone biopsy of the cervix for the removal of dysplastic cells. When the mother became pregnant once again, amniocentesis and level-III ultrasounds were normal and essentially ruled out fetal anomaly. The mother was treated as a non-high-risk patient. The mother went into labor at twenty-eight weeks gestational age. Patient B.N. was born and was immediately treated with antibiotics for a suspected beta strep bacterial infection. The mother maintained in her complaint that Patient B.N. was born prematurely because of an incompetent cervix, and that she should have had serial pelvic exams during the course of her pregnancy. In addition, she alleged that the beta strep infection of the mother was preventable. The defendant healthcare providers argued that the mother had a competent cervix, did not require serial pelvic exams, and did not require any stitch across the cervix in order to prevent premature dilation. Further, the defense argued that Patient B.N. sustained an unpreventable inutero infection which caused profound and permanent neurological sequelae. These sequelae included ischemic/hypoxic brain insult resulting in cerebral palsy, spastic quadriplegia, and diminished intellectual capacity. Future care needs included around the clock attendant care, speech and physical therapy, and an inability to live outside of a sheltered environment. However, in spite of the severe nature of Patient B.N.'s injuries, the jury ruled in favor of the defense, finding that the predelivery care was appropriate, and that the severe brain injury was the result of an unpreventable inutero infection. *B.N. v. Newman*, Palm Beach County, Florida case number CL 92-1976 AO; verdict date: September 10, 1994

7.5 Pediatric Head Trauma and Posttraumatic Epilepsy

A. Definitions and incidence

Each year in the United States, traumatic brain injury results in approximately 52,000 deaths, 230,000 hospitalizations, and 80,000 disabilities.[20] In children, the incidence of head injury due to various causes is dependent on age and sex. Head trauma is about twice as frequent in boys as in girls. In addition to motor vehicle accidents, recreational activities, and competitive sports, assaults, firearm accidents, and child abuse are important factors. The term "traumatic brain injury" as used in this chapter refers to a head injury that produces unequivocal brain changes (generally seen on CT or MRI scan) and excludes milder forms of head trauma in which anatomic changes are not demonstrable.

Mild head injuries, which are not accompanied by evidence of anatomic change on CT or MR scan of the head, have been a source of particular interest to attorneys. In general medical parlance, "concussion" refers to a head injury characterized by brief loss of consciousness without evidence of structural brain changes using currently available screening procedures. A more current definition of concussion, which is endorsed by the American Academy of Neurology, is "an alteration of mental status due to biomechanical forces affecting the brain. A concussion may or may not cause loss of consciousness." The American Academy of Neurology recognizes three grades of concussion: grades 1 and 2 require transient confusion without loss of consciousness following a head injury. In grade 1, confusion lasts up to fifteen minutes while in grade 2, confusion lasts longer. Grade 3 concussion is diagnosed when any loss of consciousness occurs.[21,22] These clinical distinctions are often largely dependent on the reports of untrained observers but are useful in formulating management guidelines for sport-related, minor head injuries. Since technology has improved our ability to detect structural changes in the central nervous system over the past thirty years and will undoubtedly continue to advance, the concept of concussion may continue to evolve.

Tip

Concussion refers to transient alteration of mental status resulting from head injury, but not all concussions include loss of consciousness.

Detection of anatomic changes in the brain after head injury depends on the timing of diagnostic studies as well as the study employed. For example, a cerebral contusion (superficial bruise of the brain) is more likely to be detected by MR than CT scan. However, MR scans are not generally performed soon after head injury for several reasons.

1. Traumatic brain injuries requiring neurosurgical intervention are almost always detectable by CT scan.
2. MR scans take longer to perform and require the patient to be motionless throughout the examination.
3. Sedation is often required to perform MR scans in uncooperative, agitated, or claustrophobic patients. As a rule, an attempt is made to avoid sedation in patients who have sustained a recent head injury since changes in mental status may guide clinical management.
4. Metallic equipment used for monitoring or life support cannot be brought into the MR scan suite.

Intracranial hemorrhage from brain injury may occur in multiple compartments. Epidural and subdural hemorrhages occur over the surface of the brain and exert their effects by compression of the brain and its blood supply. Intracerebral hemorrhage refers to bleeding within the cerebral hemispheres and implies destruction of brain tissue.

Penetrating injuries, including those caused by missiles (most often bullets), may also cause laceration of the brain. In addition, such injuries may carry bone fragments and other foreign material into the brain. To prevent infection in these circumstances, neurosurgical debridement (removal of foreign matter and infected tissue) is often required.

Since trauma may produce widespread mechanical forces within the brain, the effects of an injury may be more extensive than initially suspected. Shearing of neural elements is believed to play an important role in this process and may lead to widespread injury of nerve fibers (diffuse axonal injury). Edema (swelling) of the brain may occur after head injury and cause further brain compromise as the result of increased intracranial pressure. In blunt head injury, contusion (bruising) of the brain may occur not only directly adjacent to the site of impact (coup) but also over a surface remote from the point of impact as the result of acceleration of the brain within the skull (contre-coup).

Brain injury often occurs in the setting of multiple trauma. Circulatory or respiratory insufficiency may occur. Hypoxic ischemic encephalopathy (brain injury due to deficient oxygen supply or circulatory insufficiency) may occur in conjunction with traumatic brain injuries, and the effects of the two etiologies may be difficult to disentangle.

B. Diagnosis and management

In large cities, designation of trauma centers at selected hospitals expedites the management of severely injured patients and appears to improve outcome. Level-I trauma centers are tertiary care facilities that provide all major resources required for the treatment of major trauma twenty-four hours a day. Level-II trauma centers are community-based facilities and are not required to have twenty-four-hour resources. Level-III trauma centers are facilities whose primary function is to stabilize and transfer. Such facilities may keep stable, uncomplicated patients. Sophisticated trauma facilities are not available for all head-injured patients.[23]

In patients who have sustained a significant head injury, the possibility of an unrecognized injury to the cervical spinal cord must also be considered. Appropriate precautions depend on the patient's presentation. In a conscious patient, questions concerning neck pain, cautious movement of the neck, and neurological examination may suffice. In unconscious patients, the cervical spine should be stabilized, and a cervical collar may be employed until spine films have been performed to exclude a fracture or dislocation. CT scan of the cervical spine is increasingly performed in conjunction with CT scan of the head in patients whose altered consciousness limits clinical assessment. Newer CT scanners can perform a cervical CT scan rapidly. A CT scan of the cervical spine is more likely than plain cervical spine films to detect a non-displaced fracture or dislocation. In addition, this approach allows more rapid evaluation of the head and neck with less movement of the patient.

Rating scales are commonly employed soon after the head-injured patient arrives in the emergency room in order to quantify neurological function. Such scales do not represent a substitute for careful neurological examination but do facilitate rapid neurological assessment and allow the patient's course to be monitored by nursing personnel. The Glasgow Coma Scale (see Table 7.1) is used primarily for initial assessment of the head-injured patient but may also be useful for monitoring the patient's course after admission to the intensive care unit or hospital floor. Modifications of the Glasgow Coma are utilized for children (see Table 7.2).

C. Surgical management

A number of devices, which may be implanted in the brain or between the brain and skull, are used for monitoring intracranial pressure following head injury if the patient is thought to be at risk for severe intracranial hypertension. Intracranial pressure may be lowered by hyperventilation (in respirator-supported patients), hypothermia, corticosteroids, or diuretics (medications which increase water excretion). Pharmacological coma, usually induced by pentobarbital, may alleviate intracranial hypertension by reducing the brain's metabolic and circulatory requirements. A catheter placed into the cerebral ventricles, which are spinal-fluid filled cavities within the brain, may be used both for monitoring intracranial pressure and drainage of spinal fluid when pressure is elevated. Continuous electroencephalographic (EEG) monitoring for several days may be used in conjunction with pentobarbital therapy since EEG changes may help to optimize the pentobarbital dose. As implied above, surgery may be required for depressed skull fractures, debridement, or removal of intracranial blood (most often epidural or subdural). Craniectomy (removal of a portion of the

Table 7.1
Glasgow Coma Scale*

Eye Opening	**E**
spontaneous	4
to speech	3
to pain	2
no response	1
Best Motor Response	**M**
To Verbal Command:	
obeys	6
To Painful Stimulus:	
localizes pain	5
flexion-withdrawal	4
flexion-abnormal	3
extension	2
no response	1
Best Verbal Response	**V**
oriented and converses	5
disoriented and converses	4
inappropriate words	3
incomprehensible sounds	2
no response	1

$$E + M + V = 3 \text{ to } 15$$

- 90% less than or equal to 8 are in coma
- Greater than or equal to 9 not in coma
- 8 is the critical score
- Less than or equal to 8 at 6 hours—50% die
- 9–11 = moderate severity
- Greater than or equal to 12 = minor injury

Coma is defined as: (1) not opening eyes, (2) not obeying commands, and (3) not uttering understandable words.

*Centre for Neuro Skills: http://www.neuroskills.com/index.html?main=tbi/rancho.html

Table 7.2
Children's Coma Scale*

EYE OPENING		SCORE
Spontaneous		4
Reaction to speech		3
Reaction to pain		2
No response		1
BEST MOTOR RESPONSE		
Spontaneous (Obeys verbal command)		6
Localizes pain		5
Withdraws in response to pain		4
Abnormal flexion in response to pain (Decorticate posture)		3
Abnormal extension in response to pain (Decerebrate posture)		2
No response		1
BEST VERBAL RESPONSE		
Smiles, oriented to sound, follows objects, interacts		5
CRYING	INTERACTS	
Consolable	Inappropriate	4
Inconsistently consolable	Moaning	3
Inconsolable	Restless	2
No response	No response	1

*Hahn Y.S., Chyung C., Barthel M.J., Bailes J., Flannery A.M., McLone D.G., Head injuries in children under 36 months of age. Demography and outcome, *Childs Nerv Syst*, 4: 34–40, 1988.

skull) is occasionally performed to reduce intracranial pressure in patients who do not respond satisfactorily to other measures. In patients with multiple trauma, the initial surgical management may be complex. A team of surgeons may need to operate on multiple sites simultaneously or in rapid sequence.

D. Medical management and rehabilitation

Physicians from multiple disciplines often participate in the management of patients with severe head injury or multiple trauma. In the pediatric intensive care unit, the intensivist may play an important role in coordinating care as well as managing the patient's acute circulatory and respiratory problems. (See Chapter 14, "Pain and Suffering in the Intensive Care Unit," for more information about the role of the intensivist.) As the patient improves, he is likely to be transferred to a different unit where he may be under the care of a pediatric hospitalist or general pediatrician. In some centers, neurologists are actively involved in the management of head-injured patients either acutely or during rehabilitation. A neurologist is often asked to evaluate the patient if seizures occur or if the patient fails to improve as expected. Rehabilitation efforts are usually initiated before the patient leaves the acute facility. Patients with severe head injuries may benefit from referral to an inpatient rehabilitation center where physical, occupational, speech, and cognitive therapies may be offered in a comprehensive program, which is often directed by a physiatrist (rehabilitation specialist). Such programs often accept patients who are comatose or stuporous but no longer require the high-acuity care provided by the admitting hospital. Length of stay in a rehabilitation center may be dictated not only by the severity of the patient's injury but by parental wishes, resources in the home environment, and insurance considerations. Just as a coma scale may be useful in monitoring the acutely head-injured patient, a cognitive scale is often employed in monitoring the recovery of mental function and independence (see Table 7.3).

An important management principle is the avoidance of additional head injury. Lifestyle and behavioral changes are often required to achieve this goal since motorcycles, alcohol consumption, and sports participation are important causative factors in head injury. Although the need to avoid additional head injury is most obvious in patients whose neurological examination or imaging studies indicate persistent neurological dysfunction or anatomic change, this principle also applies to concussion. Second-impact syndrome refers to a second concussion within days or weeks of the first. A second impact, which might have been relatively well tolerated in the absence of previous trauma, is thought to carry a substantial risk of brain swelling, widespread damage, long-term cognitive impairment, and rarely death.[22] Parents may agonize over limiting the activities of a child or teenager who "just wants to get back to normal."

Tip

A second concussion occurring soon after the first may carry much greater risk than would be anticipated from either injury alone.

E. Posttraumatic seizures and epilepsy

Although all patients with epilepsy have seizures, not all seizures constitute epilepsy. Epilepsy implies a chronic tendency to have spontaneous or unprovoked seizures. Seizures occurring soon after head injury may or may not be followed by epilepsy. They imply cortical irritation, are more common in severe than in mild injury, and may complicate management and pose additional risks to head-injured or multiple-trauma patients. In a patient with an apparently minor head injury, a seizure increases the likelihood that imaging studies will demonstrate intracranial pathology.[24] It is not unusual for patients who have had seizures in the first few days after head injury to receive anti-seizure medications for several months and to remain seizure-free after they have been discontinued.

In children admitted to hospital for head injury, seizures are estimated to occur in 3%–6% and the rate rises to 7%–9% for children under five years of age.[24] In about 5% of patients, at least one seizure requiring hospitalization occurs months or years after head injury. Such late seizures do not always predict epilepsy since about 23% of patients having one such episode never have another and others will have no more than two or three.[24] About 50% of patients who have a single seizure occurring months after head injury will demonstrate a persistent tendency to have recurrent seizures. It is important to note that these statistics apply to civilian populations in which most head injuries are closed. The risk of early and late seizures is much greater in penetrating (bullets or other missiles) injury. For this reason, statistics derived from combat and civilian populations are not comparable. For closed head-injury patients who do not experience a seizure in the first two months, the risk of epilepsy is small. Several algorithms exist for predicting the risk that seizures will occur months after head injury ("late seizures"). The risk of late seizures after mild concussion is roughly that of the general population. The incidence of late seizures in a patient with intracerebral or subdu-

Table 7.3
Rancho Los Amigos-Revised

Levels of Cognitive Functioning

Level I—No Response: Total Assistance
- Complete absence of observable change in behavior when presented visual, auditory, tactile, proprioceptive, vestibular or painful stimuli.

Level II—Generalized Response: Total Assistance
- Demonstrates generalized reflex response to painful stimuli.
- Responds to repeated auditory stimuli with increased or decreased activity.
- Responds to external stimuli with physiological changes generalized, gross body movement and/or not purposeful vocalization.
- Responses noted above may be same regardless of type and location of stimulation.
- Responses may be significantly delayed.

Level III—Localized Response: Total Assistance
- Demonstrates withdrawal or vocalization to painful stimuli.
- Turns toward or away from auditory stimuli.
- Blinks when strong light crosses visual field.
- Follows moving object passed within visual field.
- Responds to discomfort by pulling tubes or restraints.
- Responds inconsistently to simple commands.
- Responses directly related to type of stimulus.
- May respond to some persons (especially family and friends) but not to others.

Level IV—Confused/Agitated: Maximal Assistance
- Alert and in heightened state of activity.
- Purposeful attempts to remove restraints or tubes or crawl out of bed.
- May perform motor activities such as sitting, reaching and walking but without any apparent purpose or upon another's request.
- Very brief and usually non-purposeful moments of sustained alternatives and divided attention.
- Absent short-term memory.
- May cry out or scream out of proportion to stimulus even after its removal.
- May exhibit aggressive or flight behavior.
- Mood may swing from euphoric to hostile with no apparent relationship to environmental events.
- Unable to cooperate with treatment efforts.
- Verbalizations are frequently incoherent and/or inappropriate to activity or environment.

Level V—Confused, Inappropriate Non-Agitated: Maximal Assistance
- Alert, not agitated but may wander randomly or with a vague intention of going home.
- May become agitated in response to external stimulation, and/or lack of environmental structure.
- Not oriented to person, place or time.
- Frequent brief periods, non-purposeful sustained attention.
- Severely impaired recent memory, with confusion of past and present in reaction to ongoing activity.
- Absent goal directed, problem solving, self-monitoring behavior.
- Often demonstrates inappropriate use of objects without external direction.
- May be able to perform previously learned tasks when structured and cues provided.
- Unable to learn new information.
- Able to respond appropriately to simple commands fairly consistently with external structures and cues.
- Responses to simple commands without external structure are random and non-purposeful in relation to command.
- Able to converse on a social, automatic level for brief periods of time when provided external structure and cues.
- Verbalizations about present events become inappropriate and confabulatory when external structure and cues are not provided.

Level VI—Confused, Appropriate: Moderate Assistance
- Inconsistently oriented to person, time and place.
- Able to attend to highly familiar tasks in non-distracting environment for 30 minutes with moderate redirection.
- Remote memory has more depth and detail than recent memory.
- Vague recognition of some staff.
- Able to use assistive memory aide with maximum assistance.
- Emerging awareness of appropriate response to self, family and basic needs.
- Moderate assist to problem solve barriers to task completion.
- Supervised for old learning (e.g. self care).
- Shows carry over for relearned familiar tasks (e.g. self care).
- Maximum assistance for new learning with little or nor carry over.
- Unaware of impairments, disabilities and safety risks.
- Consistently follows simple directions.
- Verbal expressions are appropriate in highly familiar and structured situations.

Level VII—Automatic, Appropriate: Minimal Assistance for Daily Living Skills
- Consistently oriented to person and place, within highly familiar environments. Moderate assistance for orientation to time.
- Able to attend to highly familiar tasks in a non-distraction environment for at least 30 minutes with minimal assist to complete tasks.
- Minimal supervision for new learning.
- Demonstrates carry over of new learning.
- Initiates and carries out steps to complete familiar personal and household routine but has shallow recall of what he/she has been doing.
- Able to monitor accuracy and completeness of each step in routine personal and household ADLs and modify plan with minimal assistance.

Table 7.3
Rancho Los Amigos-Revised (continued)

- Superficial awareness of his/her condition but unaware of specific impairments and disabilities and the limits they place on his/her ability to safely, accurately and completely carry out his/her household, community, work and leisure ADLs.
- Minimal supervision for safety in routine home and community activities.
- Unrealistic planning for the future.
- Unable to think about consequences of a decision or action.
- Overestimates abilities.
- Unaware of others' needs and feelings.
- Oppositional/uncooperative.
- Unable to recognize inappropriate social interaction behavior.

Level VIII—Purposeful, Appropriate: Stand-By Assistance

- Consistently oriented to person, place and time.
- Independently attends to and completes familiar tasks for 1 hour in distracting environments.
- Able to recall and integrate past and recent events.
- Uses assistive memory devices to recall daily schedule, "to do" lists and record critical information for later use with stand-by assistance.
- Initiates and carries out steps to complete familiar personal, household, community, work and leisure routines with stand-by assistance and can modify the plan when needed with minimal assistance.
- Requires no assistance once new tasks/activities are learned.
- Aware of and acknowledges impairments and disabilities when they interfere with task completion but requires stand-by assistance to take appropriate corrective action.
- Thinks about consequences of a decision or action with minimal assistance.
- Overestimates or underestimates abilities.
- Acknowledges others' needs and feelings and responds appropriately with minimal assistance.
- Depressed.
- Irritable.
- Low frustration tolerance/easily angered.
- Argumentative.
- Self-centered.
- Uncharacteristically dependent/independent.
- Able to recognize and acknowledge inappropriate social interaction behavior while it is occurring and takes corrective action with minimal assistance.

Level IX—Purposeful, Appropriate: Stand-By Assistance on Request

- Independently shifts back and forth between tasks and completes them accurately for at least two consecutive hours.
- Uses assistive memory devices to recall daily schedule, "to do" lists and record critical information for later use with assistance when requested.
- Initiates and carries out steps to complete familiar personal, household, work and leisure tasks independently and unfamiliar personal, household, work and leisure tasks with assistance when requested.
- Aware of and acknowledges impairments and disabilities when they interfere with task completion and takes appropriate corrective action but requires stand-by assist to anticipate a problem before it occurs and take action to avoid it.
- Able to think about consequences of decisions or actions with assistance when requested.
- Accurately estimates abilities but requires stand-by assistance to adjust to task demands.
- Acknowledges others' needs and feelings and responds appropriately with stand-by assistance.
- Depression may continue.
- May be easily irritable.
- May have low frustration tolerance.
- Able to self monitor appropriateness of social interaction with stand-by assistance.

Level X—Purposeful, Appropriate: Modified Independent

- Able to handle multiple tasks simultaneously in all environments but may require periodic breaks.
- Able to independently procure, create and maintain own assistive memory devices.
- Independently initiates and carries out steps to complete familiar and unfamiliar personal, household, community, work and leisure tasks but may require more than usual amount of time and/or compensatory strategies to complete them.
- Anticipates impact of impairments and disabilities on ability to complete daily living tasks and takes action to avoid problems before they occur but may require more than usual amount of time and/or compensatory strategies.
- Able to independently think about consequences of decisions or actions but may require more than usual amount of time and/or compensatory strategies to select the appropriate decision or action.
- Accurately estimates abilities and independently adjusts to task demands.
- Able to recognize the needs and feelings of others and automatically respond in appropriate manner.
- Periodic periods of depression may occur.
- Irritability and low frustration tolerance when sick, fatigued and/or under emotional stress.

Social interaction behavior is consistently appropriate.

ral hemorrhage is much higher.[23] These statistics are useful for discussions with patients and family members around the time of hospital discharge. Legal issues surrounding head injury are usually resolved one to two years later, and the patient's course during that time allows the neurologist to predict the risk of new or continuing seizures more accurately. The potential impact of epilepsy, which is often an important element when damages resulting from head injury are considered, is reviewed in the following paragraphs.

Tip

The risk of epilepsy after head injury can be predicted with fair accuracy several months after discharge.

Once posttraumatic epilepsy occurs, it may be easily controlled by medication or resistant to therapy. Although a number of new anti-epileptic drugs have been introduced since 1993, seizure control is often unsatisfactory, and medications may be poorly tolerated. Trials of multiple medications are sometimes necessary. Simultaneous use of two or more drugs may be required although the majority of patients are well controlled with a single agent. In children or adults with mental dysfunction following head injury, adult supervision is often necessary to assure compliance. Failure to take medication consistently may result in occasional or frequent seizures in patients who might otherwise experience complete seizure control. Definitions of medically intractable epilepsy vary; seizures resistant to medication occur in 15%–30% patients whose epilepsy may be due to a variety of causes. A recent review of head trauma in children indicates that about 25% of those with late onset seizures will experience ten to fifteen seizures per year.[25]

As is true for epilepsy due to other causes, posttraumatic epilepsy may take different forms. Generalized tonic-clonic (grand mal) seizures describe convulsive episodes that include stiffening and shaking and usually involve both arms and both legs. Focal (sometimes referred to as "partial") seizures are initially confined to one limb or one side of the body. Simple partial seizures (SPS) refer to localized seizures that do not alter consciousness. Complex partial seizures (CPS) differ from (SPS) in that they include alteration of consciousness. A variety of cognitive disturbances or stereotyped movements may occur during a complex partial seizure. The term "aura" is often used to refer to cognitive changes which are the first manifestation of a CPS in some patients. Either a CPS or SPS may evolve into a generalized seizure. When this occurs, consciousness is usually lost. Following a seizure (postictally), common symptoms include sleepiness, confusion, and agitation, which may last for minutes or hours. Prolonged seizures (status epilepticus) or the medications used to control them may lead to respiratory arrest, endotracheal intubation, and admission to an intensive care unit for respirator support.

Seizures may result in recurrent injury and as well as restrictions in driving, school, and work. Death is an uncommon complication of a seizure. It may occur even in patients whose seizures are infrequent if an episode begins when the patient is engaged in an activity that confers additional risk, such as swimming or crossing a busy intersection. In recent years, sudden unexpected death in epilepsy has gained increasing recognition. Incidence varies widely depending on the criteria used and population studied. The typical story is that of a patient who dies unexpectedly in sleep or otherwise unattended. In most cases, the presumed cause is an unwitnessed seizure resulting in respiratory arrest.[26] Seizures may also result in embarrassment and loss of self-esteem. For example, classmates may witness a seizure that includes loss of consciousness, bizarre behavior, and urinary incontinence and later describe it to the affected individual. In the author's experience, children and adolescents are more likely to support than reject a popular classmate who has an occasional seizure at school. However, there is no doubt that seizures sometimes produce fear and confusion in those who witness them and may contribute to social ostracism of some children with epilepsy.

Tip

Posttraumatic epilepsy may profoundly alter the life of a head-injured individual. It is more likely to occur after severe than after mild head injury.

7.6 Pain and Suffering after Head Trauma

Disability following head injury is a function not only of persistent neurological deficit (impairment) but also of age, preexisting skills, social resources, and family support. Risk ratios drawn from large numbers of head-injured patients are often of little value in dealing with individuals. As noted in the previous section, some patients with posttraumatic epilepsy may experience a profound change in their lives even if they are otherwise neurologically intact.

Neurological deficits following severe head injury may be similar, in many respects, to those encountered in cerebral palsy. In both instances, the neurological disorder is static (nonprogressive) and may affect multiple functional domains. The emotional consequences for the patient and family are determined in part by the age at which injury occurs. For example, insight and perception of loss are likely to be greater for a school-aged child than for a toddler. Similarly, parents and siblings may grieve differently for a child who was suddenly deprived of physical and social skills appropriate for age than for one in whom those attributes were never present.

A. Medical issues

Weakness and spasticity (stiffness) due to traumatic brain injury may vary widely in distribution and severity. Less commonly, movement disturbances including ataxia (imbalance and incoordination), athetosis (writhing limb movements), and ballismus (more vigorous or flinging movements of a limb) may occur. Recovery from head injury is usually most rapid in the first few weeks, but some patients show continued improvement for a year or more. In children, maturational processes that are no longer operative in the adult may aid recovery from head injury. The young child's relatively superior ability to recover or acquire various brain functions following injury is often described as "plasticity" of the central nervous system. Recent research has provided insights into the mechanisms underlying plasticity. In particular, synapses (nerve connections) are more abundant in the young child than in the adult, and to some extent their maintenance is dependent on use. Animal and human research suggests that synaptic connections in pathways that are not utilized may be selectively pruned during maturation. In addition, environmental enrichment may maintain synaptic connections that might otherwise be lost. The extent to which early childhood experience alters the physical development of the human brain remains to be fully elucidated, and it is possible that excessive exposure to certain forms of stimulation may be detrimental. However, plasticity of the young central nervous system does offer a rationale for various forms of therapy in children who are brain-injured or environmentally deprived.[27]

In the author's experience, chronic headache related to severe or moderate traumatic brain injury is a relatively uncommon complaint. It is probably reported more frequently after minor head injury.

B. Social issues

A broad range of behavioral and emotional difficulties may interfere with reintegration into a child's family and circle of friends. Diminished anger control, frustration tolerance, attention span, mental agility, or speech-and-language skills may profoundly alter the head-injured child's social interaction. Parents' emotional responses, including anger, depression, and denial, may limit their ability to adapt to the needs of a brain-injured child. Family life may be profoundly altered as the result of personality and intellectual changes. It is not uncommon for parents to report months after the injury that "he's not the same boy he was before."

Tip

Personality and behavioral changes after traumatic brain injury may disrupt family and social relationships.

C. School and work

Varying degrees and types of mental dysfunction may occur as the result of severe head injury. Even when overall intellectual potential is minimally affected, selective deficits in expressive or receptive language may limit school achievement. As noted above in the section on cerebral palsy, children with dysarthria (poorly intelligible speech secondary to traumatic brain injury) or those who are unable to write are frustrated by inability to interact with teachers and classmates and to demonstrate their mastery of academic material. Adaptive physical education may be required and further increase the distance between the head-injured child and former peers. All of these issues may also affect occupational pursuits after the head-injured individual leaves school.

D. Post-concussion syndrome

Persisting or lingering complaints following concussion are notoriously difficult to evaluate from a causal perspective. It is generally acknowledged that, after a grade-2 or 3 concussion, lingering symptoms and subtle cognitive deficits may occur. Assessment may be complicated by preexisting social, emotional, or academic problems, litigation issues, and other forms of secondary gain that may lead to conscious or unconscious embellishment of symptoms. Psychological testing provides data that may be used to infer a causal relationship but may be contaminated by the factors mentioned above. If psychological tests happen to have been carried out prior to injury—as occasionally happens in school-age children—a relationship between the injury and relatively mild abnormalities on subsequent psychological tests may be more readily established. The question of posttraumatic stress disorder is often raised after mild injuries that are followed by fear or anxiety. Symptoms attributed to post-concussion syndrome generally resolve within weeks or months.[25]

E. Quality of life in posttraumatic epilepsy

There have been more QOL studies in epilepsy than in the other conditions discussed in this chapter. Several factors make epilepsy suitable for QOL studies.

1. Epilepsy is a common disorder and accounts for more visits to neurologists than any other single condition.
2. Epilepsy classification schemes allow the identification of relatively homogeneous groups of patients.
3. Practitioners are motivated to carry out QOL studies to show the relative merits of various therapies available for epilepsy (e.g., new drug therapies, epilepsy surgery, and vagal nerve stimulator).
4. QOL studies, often in combination with economic analyses, have gained importance in the managed care environment. Neurologists and neurosurgeons use the results of these studies to influence insurance companies and government agencies to authorize expensive diagnostic and treatment modalities.
5. It is widely recognized that epilepsy has important social consequences and may be associated with other medical conditions that influence outcome. Potential applications of QOL studies in the courtroom are mentioned in Section 7.1.

QOL studies in patients with epilepsy may not separate posttraumatic epilepsy from epilepsy due to other etiologies. Studies on the outcomes of epilepsy surgery have been performed in recent years as surgery for medically intractable epilepsy has become more widely available. Control groups are often lacking in such studies since many epileptologists believe that surgery cannot ethically be denied to patients who are suitable candidates. These studies generally support the view that freedom from seizures offers a broad range of psychological and social benefits. Achieving seizure control rapidly in children is increasingly considered to be an urgent matter. Special issues in children with seizures include

1. effects of repeated seizures and potentially toxic anti-epileptic drugs on the developing nervous system, and
2. inability to participate in critical life experiences during various stages of cognitive and social development.[5]

All chronic diseases affect QOL in children and adults. However, the QOL profile is, to some extent, disease-specific. For example, more disturbances in psychological, social, and school performance were found in a group of children with epilepsy than in a comparison group with asthma.[28]

Adult patients who have had a seizure in the past six months list a variety of concerns, including driving, independence, work, embarrassment, medication dependence, mood, stress, and safety.[29] The incidence of depression is markedly increased. Studies suggest that the negative emotional impact of even occasional complex partial seizures is similar to that of myocardial infarction or congestive heart failure.[29] Discussions with adolescents who have seizures suggest that their concerns are similar to those of adults. Adolescents are particularly upset by the possibility that epilepsy may limit their driving privileges. States laws vary with respect to the seizure-free interval required for operation of a motor vehicle. In addition, most states maintain some degree of flexibility in this determination and consider the opinion of the patient's treating physician.

Tip

Even relatively well controlled epilepsy may have serious consequences.

F. Quality of life after traumatic brain injury without epilepsy

The discussion above assumes that QOL in patients with posttraumatic epilepsy and no other neurological symptoms will be comparable to that of patients with epilepsy due to other causes. The effects of head trauma on QOL in the absence of epilepsy vary according to the extent of impairment and disability. QOL studies related to trauma appear to be less numerous than those related to epilepsy. The most intensive and costly interventions for head trauma occur soon after the injury and are generally covered by insurance; practitioners are less likely to undertake QOL studies in a condition where the results are not expected to have clearly defined therapeutic or economic implications. A major recent text questions the methodology and clinical relevance of QOL studies in head injury.[30]

Quality of life is a central, implicit issue in brain-injured patients whose relatives invoke the right to die. In *Nancy Cruzan*, the United States Supreme Court ruled that the U.S. constitution "does not forbid a state from preserving the life of an incapacitated person unless a surrogate produces clear and convincing proof . . . that the patient would have wanted to die rather than live in a persistent vegetative state." By its specification of "incapacitated" and "vegetative," the Court clearly indicated that it considered QOL.[31] *Cruzan by Cruzan v. Director, Missouri Department of Health*, 497 U.S. 261, 110 S.Ct. 2841, 111 L.Ed.2d 224 (1990).

Direct, subjective responses to questionnaire items may not be available from brain-injured patients with severe cognitive impairment. In patients who are able to participate in QOL studies, there is a strong association between QOL and degree of disability. Patients employed at the time of follow-up were generally more satisfied than those who were unemployed. Various aspects of social integration were clearly related to patients' reports of life satisfaction.[32] Traumatic brain injury takes an extraordinary toll: changes in mental function and independence may lead to social isolation. Ongoing medical care may be time consuming and expensive. Inability to return to a previous occupation or classroom and changes in family dynamics may devastate self-esteem.

G. Quality of life after minor head injury

As noted above, the patient's subjective response is an important component of QOL studies. How does the individual who has sustained a minor head injury assess his health? A prospective study of the effects of minor head injury on general health after one year was carried out in Denmark in 1988–89. Half the patients reported some sequelae from head injury, but only 25% to a degree that resulted in a case score on the questionnaire employed. The incidence of prominent posttraumatic stress symptoms was approximately 20%. The symptoms reported most often included headache, dizziness, memory deficit, concentration deficit, fatigue, irritability, anxiety, sleep disturbance, and sight disturbance. The authors discuss the contribution of psychological and physiological factors to these complaints and note a lack of correlation between indices of injury severity and outcome.[33]

7.7 Representative Head Injury Cases

A. Carl: Motor vehicle accident

Carl, a six-year-old boy, sustained a depressed, left frontal fracture in a motor vehicle accident in which he was an unbelted, front-seat passenger. He was confused when examined soon after admission. Skull surgery was required for elevation of his fracture, and his first CT scan showed swelling of the underlying brain.

Carl's hospital course included a single seizure. Aphasia (a disturbance of language function) and mild right hemiparesis became evident as he became increasingly alert and active. There was a history of language difficulty requiring special education prior to his motor vehicle accident. The patient had been raised in a bilingual environment. Because of his special educational needs, psychological testing had been performed by the public school system one year prior to his accident.

An allergic reaction to anti-seizure medication occurred two weeks after his injury when the patient had already been transferred to a rehabilitation facility. His allergic reaction resolved when medication was changed. Three weeks after admission, a follow-up CT scan of the head demonstrated an area of encephalomalacia (focal atrophy or loss of brain tissue) in the area where edema (swelling) had been reported previously. Psychological testing almost one year after his accident showed a decline in intellectual function by comparison to his pre-accident evaluation. The decline in his verbal abilities was more striking than his decline in other areas. He required modification of his pre-injury class placement. Behavioral difficulties occurred in the classroom and also in the home. The patient was described as restless and inattentive. Behavior and attention span improved after initiation of the psychostimulant methylphenidate (Ritalin). He had a single brief seizure when anti-epileptic medication was omitted but otherwise remained seizure free for three years.

Comment: This youngster, in whom preexisting academic difficulty had been documented, sustained an organic mental syndrome and right hemiparesis as the result of closed head injury resulting from a motor vehicle accident. Comparison of psychological testing carried out after his injury to that performed previously was helpful in establishing causation. His CT scan provided unequivocal evidence of traumatic brain injury. His motor impairment was minimal, but major functional consequences occurred in the intellectual and behavioral spheres. Although Carl's posttraumatic seizure disorder was not severe, he had an allergic reaction to an anti-epileptic drug. Reactions of this type are sometimes severe and occasionally fatal. He will probably require anti-epileptic drug therapy for the rest of his life, and continued freedom from seizures cannot be guaranteed even if he takes his medication faithfully. It is likely that the psychostimulant medication he receives to improve his attention span will be discontinued in a few years.

B. Donna: All terrain vehicle accident

Six-year-old Donna was a passenger in an all-terrain vehicle accident. She was thrown and struck a tree. Loss of consciousness and respiratory insufficiency occurred immediately after injury. Paramedics intubated her airway and provided respiratory support at the accident site. Her Glasgow Coma Scale score on arrival in the emergency room was 5. CT scan of the head showed a linear, left frontal skull fracture and subarachnoid hemorrhage. She required intracranial pressure monitoring via an external ventricular drain. Seizures did not occur. After a one-week hospital stay, Donna was transferred to a rehabilitation unit for several weeks. Subsequently, she received outpatient physical and occupational therapy as well as cognitive rehabilitation services. Her follow-up CT scans of the head showed diffuse, atrophic changes. She was not able to return to school until nine months after her injury, and a modified class placement was required.

Six months after her injury, Donna's mother described her as impulsive, moody, and easily upset. Her speech was slurred, but she was able to communicate effectively. Her most obvious deficit consisted of severe, coarse tremor of the right hand. The patient was right handed prior to her accident but had begun to use her left hand for drawing and writing. Her overall intellectual potential fell in the normal range although she was clearly functioning below her reported pre-morbid level. Her gait was unsteady, and there was a severe tremor of the right upper extremity. There was mild weakness of both legs. She was tried on a variety of medications to reduce her tremor. All of them were ineffective, and her mother felt that most impaired her balance and alertness.

Comment: This girl survived a life-threatening head injury with deficits in cognitive and motor function. Although her overall intellectual potential falls in the normal or near-normal range, she has not returned to her previous level of function, and changes in personality and behavior are evident to family members. Her speech is slurred, but she can be understood with effort. She has a severe movement disorder which required her to abandon use of her right hand for most daily activities. Although she is ambulatory, her gait is precarious, and she cannot run. Longevity will probably not be affected. It is difficult to determine if she will be physically and financially self-sufficient as an adult. Her speech disturbance and prominent tremor, which are likely to be permanent, may have profound social consequences. Surgical procedures for management of tremor may be an option in several years.

C. Eduardo: Abused

Eduardo, a thirteen-month-old boy was hospitalized following sudden loss of consciousness at his daycare center. A seizure was suspected. Physical examination revealed bruising of the ears and back as well as extensive retinal hemorrhages. CT scan of the head showed subdural and subarachnoid hemorrhage. It was determined that he had sustained non-accidental injury, and a police investigation led to the conviction of a worker at the patient's daycare center. Eduardo required respirator support, intracranial pressure monitoring, and drainage of his subdural hemorrhage. Seizures ceased after initiation of anticonvulsant drug therapy. After a two-week hospital stay, he was conscious but functioning below the six-month level. He was transferred to a rehabilitation facility for an additional month. At two years of age, he walked for the first time since his injury. Language milestones were delayed. At five years of age he was active and distractible, and medication was initiated to improve his attention span. A psychologist concluded that overall intellectual potential fell in the normal range. However, his parents observed that the patient functioned at about the same level as his three-year-old brother, who was usually the leader when they played together.

Comment: Ironically, Eduardo's parents had read newspaper accounts of child abuse by babysitters and diligently chose a daycare setting where they expected their son's safety to be assured. After four years, his outcome was better than initially anticipated. However, his "normal" score on a preschool intelligence test is misleading. Both his parents and brother demonstrated superior intelligence. Although the patient achieved a level of function considered to be at the lower end of the normal range, there is little doubt that he would have functioned at a higher level if his injury had not occurred. In addition, psychological testing at a later age is likely to reveal intellectual processing deficits that cannot be readily demonstrated in a five-year-old. Deficient social skills and inattentiveness, as noted in this patient, often occur in children who sustain early brain injury.

D. The legal perspective

Although not as common, cases involving epilepsy can be as significant in terms of monetary value as those involving the negligent onset of cerebral palsy. This is especially true when the seizure disorder is accompanied by a cognitive deficit. For example, Patient W.L. was a six-month-old child who presented to the defendant pediatrician with fever of several days' duration. The pediatrician failed to hospitalize Patient W.L., who had a cough, a fever between 100° and 101°, and a sore throat. The pediatrician diagnosed the infant with adenoiditis for which he prescribed Erythromycin, and ordered a CBC (complete blood count) which reflected signs which were consistent with a virus. The mother brought W.L. back two days later indicating that the child had developed diarrhea and vomiting. The mother brought her child back the following day, at which point the body temperature was 103° and W.L. had lost one pound, five ounces. The child came back the following day, with the pediatrician providing a prescription for Phenobarbital, noting a questionable virus or urinary tract infection. On Christmas Eve, the child suffered a severe seizure, losing consciousness, and suffering hypoxia during the transfer to the hospital. W.L. regained consciousness and was discharged four days later on anti-seizure medication. However, the child, at age fifteen, has been hospitalized four times for a seizure disorder in addition to ten other hospitalizations for unrelated asthma.

The plaintiff argued that the history of fever, vomiting, and diarrhea should have triggered a diagnosis of dehydration. This is further supported by the 9% drop in body weight over a twenty-four-hour period. The plaintiff argued that the continuing dehydration caused the condition of hypernatremia (elevated sodium), in which the loss of fluids resulted in excessive proportion of salt in the cells which causes seizures, leading to hypoxia, which in turn results in permanent brain injury. The plaintiff further argued that if the child had been hospitalized before December 24, the seizure could have been avoided through the infusion of fluid, and that the cause of the child's symptoms could have been ascertained through appropriate testing.

As a result of this episode, Patient W.L. suffers from a permanent seizure disorder, a learning disability, and a borderline normal intelligence quotient. Based on these facts, the jury awarded a verdict of $8 million. Included in this award was a determination of $3 million awarded for pain and suffering damages. The defense, which was rejected by the jury, was that Patient W.L.'s seizure disorder was genetic in nature, in light of the fact that the infant's uncle also has a seizure disorder. However, in light of the timing between the presentation to the pediatrician and the seizure, which caused the hypoxia that ultimately led to brain damage, the jury rejected the defense theory. 1995 W.L. 1933811, Bronx County, New York case number 18363/82; verdict date: June 24, 1995.

7.8 Brachial Palsy

A. Definition

Muscles of the shoulders and upper extremities derive their nerve supply from the cervical spinal cord and first segment of the thoracic spinal cord. After exiting from the spinal cord, nerve roots combine and redistribute fibers in a complex nerve bundle, the brachial plexus, which is located under the muscle of the shoulder and gives rise to the various nerves that supply the upper limb muscles. Many medical students, struggling to master neuroanatomy, have wondered why this complicated nerve arrangement exists. It seems likely that the brachial plexus facilitates simultaneous or coordinated contraction of multiple muscles. It also reduces dependency of any major muscle on a single spinal nerve root and therefore reduces the risk of complete paralysis if a single root is injured.

Neonatal brachial palsy may be divided into three types:

1. Erb palsy, the most common type, refers to brachial plexus lesions resulting in weakness of muscles supplied by cervical nerve roots 5 through 7.
2. Complete brachial palsy involves all muscles of the upper extremity (all muscles deriving their nerve supply from cervical roots 5–8 and the first thoracic root).
3. Klumpke palsy, the least common type, affects the muscles of the hand (which derive their nerve supply from the eighth cervical and first thoracic roots) but largely spares those of the arm.

B. Associated problems

In some infants, fracture of the clavicle accompanies obstetric brachial palsy. This fracture almost always heals uneventfully. Phrenic nerve injury, which results in paralysis of the diaphragm (the major muscle of respiration), occurs in a small minority of brachial palsy patients. This nerve injury may lead to severe breathing difficulties including respiratory arrest.

C. Incidence

Brachial palsy occurs in approximately two per 1,000 live births.[34]

D. Causes

Brachial plexus injuries in the newborn are usually related to delivery but may occur prenatally as the result of intrauterine deformation or compression. Risk factors for obstetric brachial palsy include large birth weight and breech delivery. During delivery of large infants with cephalic (head first) presentation, difficulty in passing the shoulders through the birth canal (shoulder dystocia) may occur. Traction on the head with shoulder resistance results in stretching of the brachial plexus. Nerve elements may be stretched or torn at various levels between the root and plexus. Breech presentation may result in difficulty delivering the shoulders and head. Traction on the shoulders stretches the brachial plexus. Bilateral brachial plexus injuries are more likely to be associated with breech than with cephalic presentation.

Not all cases of obstetric brachial palsy appear preventable. There is a margin of error in estimation of fetal weight near term, and it is not always possible for the obstetrician to know if the mother's pelvis will permit an easy delivery. Mothers sometimes present in advanced labor without warning. In some cases of fetal distress, prompt vaginal delivery may be required even if brachial plexus injury is anticipated.

E. Diagnosis

Brachial palsy is usually recognized in the delivery room or nursery because of the characteristic pattern of weakness. Radiographs of the chest may be done to determine if there is an associated clavicular fracture or diaphragmatic paralysis. Ultrasonography or fluoroscopy may also help to exclude diaphragmatic paralysis. Nerve conduction studies and electromyography one to two months after birth may confirm the diagnosis and offer limited prognostic information. Magnetic resonance scans (MRI) of the cervical spine may demonstrate disruption of the nerve root sleeves, a finding that suggests nerve roots have been torn from the spinal cord. In the author's experience, a computerized tomographic (CT) scan of the cervical spine with intrathecal contrast (contrast in the spinal fluid space) is more useful for this purpose. This study requires a lumbar puncture ("spinal tap") and injection of a contrast material into the cerebrospinal fluid.

F. Prognosis and management

Over the first few months of life, infants with mild injury usually show substantial recovery. Occasionally the first signs of meaningful recovery are slow to occur in infants who ultimately do well. Less fortunate infants are left with permanent, severe weakness. In Erb palsy, common residual findings include weakness of the biceps (used in external rotation and flexion of forearm), deltoid (the major muscle affecting arm movement at the shoulder joint), and shoulder girdle muscles (important for elevating the arm, stabilizing the scapula in order to push the arm forward, and various maneuvers in which the arm is rotated or pushed backward). Wrist or finger extension may be impaired. Contracture (limited range of motion) often occurs at the elbow and shoulder. As the infant matures, the affected arm may be shorter and thinner than the unaffected extremity, and shoulder deformity may be evident.

Physical or occupational therapy is of limited benefit in improving range of motion and strength in infants with brachial palsy. The therapist may play an important role in mobilizing the limb after surgery (see below) and in helping an older child find effective ways to carry out the activities of daily living at home or in school. A few reports indicate that intramuscular injection of botulinum toxin may be useful in reducing contractures caused by brachial palsy.[35]

G. Surgery

Over the past twenty years, evidence has accumulated to suggest that microneurosurgery of the brachial plexus in the first few months of life improves the outcome for appropriately selected infants with obstetric brachial palsy.[36] A combination of microneurosurgery on the brachial plexus and shoulder reconstruction may be required in children over six months of age.[35] In older children, tendon transfers and release of contractures may be performed.

Tip

Surgery may help to restore function in properly selected brachial palsy patients.

7.9 Pain and Suffering in Brachial Palsy

A. Medical issues

Some infants with obstetric brachial palsy appear to experience discomfort during passive movement of the shoulder for a few weeks, but, in the author's experience, pain is not a long-term problem in this condition. Some degree of postoperative discomfort would be anticipated in infants or older children in whom various surgical procedures for brachial palsy are performed.

Depending on the severity of residual weakness, unilateral brachial palsy may interfere with activities of daily living such as dressing and grooming. Sensory impairment is minimal in patients with Erb palsy but may be functionally significant in children with complete brachial palsy. In children genetically programmed to be right-handed, one might speculate that left would be better tolerated than right brachial palsy, but no studies to support this hypothesis were found in a recent Medline search.

B. Social issues

Most children with brachial palsy have no additional physical or mental disability. With maturation, affected children are increasingly likely to become aware of their impairment and its effects on recreational activities. Peers may notice contractures and limb asymmetry, and self-image may suffer. It may not be possible to excel in sports traditionally requiring the use of both arms, but some children are remarkably resourceful in finding alternatives. Brachial palsy has relatively little effect on a child's ability to compete in soccer.

C. School and work

Children with brachial palsy are able to function in a mainstream class. In Erb palsy, the most common form, the hand is functional, although mobility of the arm and sometimes the wrist is limited. Writing with the affected extremity may be possible. Use of a computer with a word processing program is feasible in the later grades if handwriting is poor.

The child's occupational choices should take physical limitations into account. Occupations traditionally requiring bimanual power lifting or rapid, large-amplitude movements of both arms (manual labor, operation of some machinery) are generally poor choices for individuals with brachial palsy. In a motivated and resourceful individual of average intelligence, brachial palsy is compatible with financial self-sufficiency.

Tip

Brachial palsy may limit occupational choices but does not generally prevent financial self-sufficiency.

D. Quality of life in obstetric brachial palsy

QOL studies in persistent obstetric brachial palsy are not abundant. They are likely to increase as surgeons specializing in this condition attempt to evaluate their results. An important distinction between children with obstetric brachial palsy and patients who acquire similar lesions later in life is that the former may become aware of their impairment in a gradual fashion as self-awareness develops during early childhood. Either an acquired or a congenital lesion may adversely affect self-esteem, but for patients with congenital lesions, the sense of loss may be less acute and catastrophic. One study observed that many daily activities of these patients are influenced by the motor deficit, but the authors concluded that "even subjects with relatively serious sequelae apparently enjoy an almost normal life and have a good self-image."[37] A more recent and larger study suggests that the psychosocial outcome in these patients may not be optimal. An increased incidence of developmental and behavioral disorders was noted in children with brachial palsy, and unsatisfactory outcomes in these areas correlated with the severity of the injury.[38]

7.10 Representative Brachial Plexus Cases

A. Fran: Large newborn with difficult delivery

Fran, a nine-pound girl, was delivered to a thirty-seven-year-old woman, whose pregnancy was complicated by diabetes. Shoulder dystocia occurred. Apgar ratings were 3 and 6 at one and five minutes, respectively. She was noted to have bruising over the forehead and left arm, which was limp and motionless. Transient hypoglycemia (low blood sugar) occurred. By three months of age, there was limited improvement: she was able to partially extend the forearm and there was also limited movement at the shoulder joint. There was no function of the biceps (which flexes the forearm), and only minimal function of the muscles responsible for extension of the wrist and fingers was evident. Brachial plexus surgery was performed at three months of age. The surgeon described cervical roots C5–C7 as ruptured (partially torn but not at their origin from the spinal cord) and root C8 as avulsed (torn from the spinal cord). Nine nerve grafts were required: the donor nerve for these grafts was the sural nerve, which transmits sensation from the outer aspect of the fifth toe. At sixteen months of age, she had made an excellent but incomplete recovery. She was able to elevate the arm against resistance. Biceps function had improved, and her surgeon described elbow flexion as "excellent and full."

Comment: Fran was at increased risk for shoulder dystocia because she was large for gestational age as the result of maternal diabetes. Her large size also predisposed her to asphyxia at birth, but in spite of low Apgar scores, her subsequent course showed no evidence of brain dysfunction. Although use of the left arm improved slightly, brachial plexus surgery was suggested because biceps function was not evident at three months of age. Microsurgical repair of the brachial plexus with multiple nerve grafts was performed and appeared to be responsible for the patient's subsequent recovery. Her surgeon reported only a minimal deficit at sixteen months of age, but reassessment will be necessary as the patient matures to determine if her weakness is functionally significant.

B. Geoffrey: Improvement with surgical treatment

Geoffrey was an eight-pound, thirteen-ounce boy. After a term pregnancy, labor was prolonged, and there was shoulder dystocia. Delivery was vacuum assisted. Apgar ratings were depressed. Right arm weakness was evident soon after delivery. At one month of age, his examination was normal except for diminished movement of the right upper extremity. At seven months of age, there was slight improvement in function of the deltoid muscle (arm movement at the shoulder joint), but no biceps function (flexion of the forearm) was evident. Brachial plexus surgery was performed at seven months of age. Partial or total avulsion of the C7 root was demonstrated at surgery. Eight nerve grafts were performed using the sural nerve as the donor. Little improvement was evident six months after surgery, but, by two years of age, biceps and deltoid function had improved considerably. Range of motion was limited by a shoulder contracture ("frozen shoulder"). Surgical release of the shoulder was performed, and improved range of motion was evident in a few weeks.

Comment: Geoffrey's difficult delivery was associated with transient neurological depression (low Apgar ratings) as well as Erb palsy. At brachial plexus surgery, an avulsion of the C7 root was evident although CT scan of the spinal cord with contrast material did not demonstrate it preoperatively. Strength of the right deltoid and biceps improved gradually after surgery, but an additional procedure was required for frozen shoulder at two and one-half years of age.

Fran and Geoffrey are illustrative of patients with severe obstetric brachial palsy. Both had a good outcomes following surgery, but arm function should be reevaluated periodically as they mature. As noted above, the majority of patients with this disorder recover satisfactorily without surgical intervention. Of those patients who are severely affected, not all have a satisfactory outcome even when surgical intervention is offered in a timely fashion.

C. The legal perspective

Although brachial palsy is functionally significant, its neurological impact is focused in the upper extremities and, therefore, does not provide for the same type of jury reaction as does a case involving the brain. The overall ability of the child to function well within society diminishes the noneconomic value of a potential brachial palsy claim.

7.11 Conclusion

Evaluation of chronic neurological impairment in children is often challenging. Function must be evaluated in relation to the repertoire of skills appropriate for the patient's age. Physicians typically address impairment and disability rather than pain and suffering. Careful review of medical records often allows a knowledgeable legal reviewer to draw reasonable inferences regarding these issues. Quality of life studies, which incorporate the subjective responses of the affected individual and family members, may provide insights into pain and suffering beyond those contained in the traditional medical record.

Endnotes

1. Dodrill, S., and Batzel, L., "Issues in Quality of Life Assessment." In Engel, J., and Pedley, T., eds., *Epilepsy: A Comprehensive Textbook*. Philadelphia: Lippincott-Raven, 1998, p. 2228.

2. Devinsky, O., Baker, G., and Cramer J., "Quantitative Measures of Assessment." In Engel J., and Pedley, T., eds., *Epilepsy: A Comprehensive Textbook*, Philadelphia: Lippincott-Raven, 1998, p.1112.

3. Austin, J., and Santilli, N., "Quality of Life in Children with Epilepsy." In Pellock, J., Dodson W., and Bourgeois B., eds., *Pediatric Epilepsy, Diagnosis and Therapy*, Second Edition. New York: Demos, 2001.

4. Jacoby, A., "Age-Related Considerations." In Engel J., and Pedley, T., eds., *Epilepsy: A Comprehensive Textbook*, Philadelphia: Lippincott-Raven, 1998, p. 1125.

5. Berg, A., and Vickrey, B., "Outcome Measures." In Engel J., and Pedley, T., eds. *Epilepsy: A Comprehensive Textbook*, Philadelphia: Lippincott-Raven, 1998, p. 1894.

6. NINDS Cerebral Palsy Information Page, http://www.ninds.nih.gov/health_and_medical/disorders/cerebral_palsy.htm.

7. Swaiman, K., and Russman, B., "Cerebral Palsy." In Swaiman, K., and Ashwal, S., eds., *Pediatric Neurology, Principles and Practice*. St. Louis: Mosby, 1999.

8. Susser, M., et al., "Quantitative Estimates of Prenatal and Perinatal Risk Factors for Perinatal Mortality, Cerebral Palsy, Mental Retardation and Epilepsy." In Freeman, J., editor, *Prenatal and Perinatal Factors Associated with Brain Disorders*, NIH Publication No. 85-1149. Bethesda: U.S. Department of Health and Human Services, 1985, p. 395.

9. Patrick, J., Roberts, A., and Cole, G., "Therapeutic Choices in the Locomotor Management of the Child with Cerebral Palsy—More Luck than Judgment?" *Arch Dis Child*. 85:275–9, 2001.

10. Park, T., "Selective Dorsal Rhizotomy: An Excellent Therapeutic Option for Spastic Cerebral Palsy." *Clin Neurosurg.*, 47:422–39, 2000.

11. Ivanhoe, C., Tilton, A., and Francisco, G., "Intrathecal Baclofen Therapy for Spastic Hypertonia." *Phys Med Rehabil Clin N Am*, 12(4):923–38, 2001.

12. Specialed: Individuals with Disabilities Education Act (IDEA)http://specialed.about.com/cs/idea/.

13. Strauss, D., and Shavelle, R., "Life Expectancy of Adults with Cerebral Palsy." *Developmental Medicine & Child Neurology*, 40:369–375, 1998.

14. Schneider, J., Gurucharri, L., Gutierrez, A., and Gaebler-Spira, D., "Health-Related Quality of Life and Functional Outcome Measures for Children with Cerebral Palsy." *Developmental Medicine & Child Neurology*, 43:601–608, 2001.

15. Hodgkinson, I., Jindrich, M., Duhaut, P., Vadot, J., Metton, G., and Berard, C., "Hip Pain in 234 Nonambulatory Adolescents and Young Adults with Cerebral Palsy: A Cross-Sectional Multicentre Study." *Developmental Medicine & Child Neurology*, 43:806–808, 2001.

16. Andersson, C., and Mattsson, E., "Adults with Cerebral Palsy: A Survey Describing Problems, Needs, and Resources, with Special Emphasis on Locomotion." *Developmental Medicine & Child Neurology*, 43:76–82, 2001.

17. Bottos, M., Sciuto, L., Gericke, C., and Vianello, A., "Functional Status of Adults with Cerebral Palsy and Implications for Treatment of Children." *Developmental Medicine & Child Neurology*, 43:516–528, 2001.

18. Magill-Evans, J., Darrah, J., Pain, K., Adkins, R., and Kratochvil, M., "Are Families with Adolescents and Young Adults with Cerebral Palsy the Same as Other Families?" *Developmental Medicine and Child Neurology*, 43:466–472, 2001.

19. Curran, A., Sharples, P., White, C., and Knapp, M., "Time Costs of Caring for Children with Severe Disabilities Compared with Caring for Children without Disabilities." *Developmental Medicine & Child Neurology*, 43:529–533, 2001.

20. Adekoya, N., "Traumatic Brain Injury Among American Indians/Alaska Native—United States, 1992–1996." *JAMA*, 288:37, 2002.

21. Kelly, J., and Rosenberg, J., "The Diagnosis and Management of Concussion in Sports." *Neurology*, 48:575–580, 1997.

22. AAN Practice Parameter: The Management of Concussions in Sports (Summary Statement). Report of the Quality Standards Subcommittee. *Neurology*, 48:581–585, 1997.

23. Mullens, R., "A Historical Perspective of Trauma System Development in the United States." *J Trauma*, 47(3 Suppl): S8-14, 1999.

24. Temkin, N., Haglund, M., and Winn, H., "Post-Traumatic Seizures." In Narayan, R., Wilberger, J., and Povlishock, J., eds., *Neurotrauma*. New York: McGraw-Hill, 1996.

25. Rosman, N., "Traumatic Brain Injury in Children." In Swaiman, K., and Ashwal, S., eds., *Pediatric Neurology, Principles and Practice*. St. Louis: Mosby, 1999.

26. Ficker, D., "Sudden unexplained death and injury in epilepsy." *Epilepsia*, 41 (Suppl 2):S7–S12, 2000.

27. Committee on Integrating the Science of Early Childhood Development, "The Developing Brain." In Shonkoff, J., and Phillips, D., eds., *From Neurons to Neighborhoods: The Science of Early Childhood Development*. Washington: National Academy Press, 2002.

28. Austin, J., Smith, M., Risinger, M., and McNelis, A., "Childhood Epilepsy and Asthma: Comparison of Quality of Life." *Epilepsia*, 35:608–615, 1994.

29. Gilliam, F., "Optimizing Health Outcomes in Active Epilepsy." *Neurology,* 58 (Suppl 5):S9–S19, 2002.

30. Alves, W., and Eisenberg, H., "Head Injury Trials—Past and Present." In Narayan, R., Wilberger, J., and Povlishock, J., eds., *Neurotrauma.* New York: McGraw-Hill, 1996.

31. Romano, J., "Medicolegal Aspects of Head and Spinal Injury." In Narayan, R., Wilberger, J., and Povlishock, J., eds., *Neutotrauma.* New York: McGraw-Hill, 1996.

32. Corrigan, J., Bogner, J., Mysiw, W., Cinchot, D., and Fugate, L., "Life Satisfaction after Traumatic Brain Injury." *Journal of Head Trauma Rehabilitation,* 16(6): 643–555, 2001.

33. Middelboe, T., Andersen, H., Birket-Smith, M., and Frilis, M., "Minor Head Injury: Impact on General Health after One Year. A Prospective Follow-Up Study." *Acta Neurol Scand,* 85: 5–9, 1992.

34. Strombeck, C., Krumlinde-Sundholm, L., and Forssberg, H., "Functional Outcome at Five Years in Children with Obstetrical Brachial Plexus Palsy with and without Microsurgical Reconstruction." *Developmental Medicine & Child Neurology,* 42:148–157, 2000.

35. Desiato, M., and Risina, B., "The Role of Botulinum Toxin in the Neuro-Rehabilitation of Young Patients with Brachial Plexus Birth Palsy." *Pediatr Rehabil,* 4(1):29–36, 2001.

36. Waters, P., "Comparison of the Natural History, the Outcome of Microsurgical Repair, and the Outcome of Operative Reconstruction in Brachial Plexus Birth Palsy." *J Bone Joint Surg Am,* 81:649–59, 1999.

37. Rossi, L., Vassella, F., and Mumenthaler, M., "Obstetric Lesions of the Brachial Plexus. Natural History in 34 Personal Cases." *Eur Neurol,* 21 (1):1–7, 1982.

38. Bellew, M., Kay, S., Webb, F., and Ward, A., "Developmental and Behavioral Outcome in Obstetric Brachial Plexus Palsy." *J Hand Surg,* (Br), 25(1):49–51, 2000.

Additional Reading

Stern, B., "Representing the Mildly Brain Injured Client." *TRIAL,* 48, September 2000.

Chapter 8

Pain and Suffering in Emergency Care

Reneé Holleran, PhD, RN, CEN, CCRN, CFRN

Synopsis

8.1 Introduction

The emergency department has been designated by many as the "front door" of the hospital. Even though television shows such as *ER*, *Chicago Hope* and *Scrubs* have presented both dramatic and humorous versions of emergency care, emergency departments vary depending on location, staffing, and available resources. Because of this variance, patients may be treated differently as well as require transfer to another institution for further care. Patients are generally cared for based on their level of urgency. However, many studies have shown that most people's perception (including family members of the patient) of their emergency is different from the emergency department personnel treating them, particularly when it comes to pain and pain management.

Pain and suffering are common experiences encountered in emergency care. Pain can be the result of physical injury or disease symptoms, or arise as the result of required diagnostic and critical interventions that are needed to evaluate and treat patient problems. Psychological pain and suffering may result from sexual assault, child maltreatment, or domestic violence. Spiritual pain is felt with the loss both patients and staff members may experience when a sudden death occurs or an incident such as a motor vehicle crash alters a person's life forever.

Generally, people attempt to avoid exposing themselves to sources of pain or suffering. However, when involved in a physical or psychological emergency, pain and suffering may not be avoidable.

In 1990, Selbst and Clark[1] published a landmark study that pointed out how little pain was managed in the emergency department. Their study found that only 40% of the patients who presented with the primary complaint of pain from such illnesses as sickle cell crisis or injury such as a broken bone received any pain medication. However, they did identify significant reasons why pain was not adequately managed. These include

- lack of knowledge about pain management and the pharmacology of medications used to treat pain,
- fear of causing drug addiction,
- fear of causing respiratory depression and hypotension, and
- the need to concentrate more on life-threatening issues such as airway obstruction.

The primary objective of this chapter is to describe emergency care. This chapter will also assist the legal community in understanding how to support plaintiffs and defendants who may have experienced unnecessary pain and suffering in either the prehospital or emergency department environment. It is hoped that this chapter will provide a better understanding of emergency care.

8.2 Location of Emergency Care

Emergency care has grown and expanded over the last thirty years. Initially, patients got into the hospital system by physician or self-referral. Emergency rooms or care areas were designated areas where personnel (generally the nursing supervisor) could decide how sick the patient was and where they needed to be admitted in the hospital. It was not uncommon for the family to drive a gravely ill or injured patient to the hospital and have the patient directly admitted to the intensive care unit. Many of the first ambulance services were run by funeral homes, and patients who required transport were taken in a hearse because it was a vehicle large enough on the inside to allow the patient to lie down.

Tip

Emergency care may be initiated in a number of places depending on how the patient enters the system. Both prehospital emergency care and emergency care are provided in an emergency department.

The location of emergency care will vary depending on where and what has happened to the patient either prehospital or in the emergency department. Federal, state, and some voluntary organizations have developed specific definitions that describe emergency care locations.

8.3 Prehospital Emergency Care

A. Prehospital care providers

In 1973, the Department of Transportation (DOT) passed legislation that attached state transportation funding to the presence of an Emergency Medical System (EMS). The DOT also proposed a framework for the education of those who were to provide care before and during transport. This was the birth of the EMT (emergency medical technician), and the EMT-P (paramedic) and statewide EMS systems. Just as there are fifty states that compose the United States, there are fifty different types of EMS systems. When preparing legal materials related to incidents that occurred in the prehospital environment, the legal counsel must become familiar with the local EMS system in which the incident occurred in addition to the national standards.

The basic curriculum for these providers has undergone multiple revisions, with the most recent one occurring in 1998. The National Highway Transportation and Safety Administration (NHTSA) now administers the National Standard Curriculum. Information about this curriculum can be found at www.nhtsa.dot.gov. It is important to note that even though there is a national standard curriculum for EMT and EMT-P providers, each state, city, and medical director may allow variance in how prehospital care providers may practice.

The primary focus of prehospital emergency care is to provide a medical assessment, perform critical (lifesaving) interventions based on their training, and transport patients. This may vary from BLS (basic life support) to ALS (advanced life support). Figures 8.1 and 8.2 contain examples of each. As previously stated, BLS and ALS interventions may be extended depending on local, state, and a medical director's discretion. For example, Ohio has "emergency medical technicians—epinephrine" (EMT-E). With additional training, an EMT may be allowed to administer epinephrine to a victim who has incurred a life-threatening insect sting.

For the most part, the United States has the best organized and trained prehospital care in the world, although there are still places that EMS care may take a while to get to a patient. This does not always infer that these locations are rural. Traffic congestion in large cities may tax EMS response every day. Because of this, many patients have had some sort of care before they are brought to the emergency department. This is important to remember in determining when and where pain management was initiated. It also points out how important it is to take into account the type of care that the patient has received from the beginning of the event that caused her to require emergency care.

Tip

Pain management is not generally a primary function of prehospital care providers. However, there are many that have pain management protocols developed by their medical directors, that allow the administration of pain medication or the use of nitrous oxide. It is important to find out what the local protocols allow.

B. Prehospital care environment

The prehospital care environment has been described as "controlled chaos." The fact that patient care occurs outside of the hospital contributes to the hectic nature of prehospital care. First, any patient, with any problem at any level of urgency (from life-threatening airway obstruction to those needing a ride to the hospital for a doctor's appointment), may dial 911 and activate the EMS system. The diverse patient population requires that prehospital care provider be prepared for patients who may be suffering from a physical illness such as an acute myocardial infarction, a traumatic injury such a broken pelvis or a behavioral emergency such as an attempted suicide or a drug overdose.

insertion of a nasopharyngeal airway or oral airways. These are devices that are inserted in either the patient's nares or mouth to assist in keeping the airway open.
bag-valve-mask ventilation. Application of a resuscitation mask and bag to assist or manually ventilate a patient in respiratory distress or without any respirations
cardiopulmonary resuscitation (CPR). Chest compressions and artificial ventilation for patients who do not have spontaneous respirations or a heartbeat.
application and use of an automatic external defibrillator (AED). A device that can detect if the patient is in ventricular fibrillation and delivers a shock to correct the chaotic heart rate.
application of a pressure dressing. A dressing that controls bleeding.
application of military antishock garment (MAST). A device that is applied to the lower extremities and abdomen when inflated compress the abdomen and legs to return blood into the general circulation. MAST are used for certain types of shock when there will be a long transport time to the emergency department.
obtaining vital signs. Measurement of the patient's blood pressure, pulse and respirations. Some BLS providers also measure the patient's oxygen saturation (how much oxygen is in the blood) by applying a pulse oximeter.

Figure 8.1 *Examples of basic life support procedures*

endotracheal intubation. Insertion of a tube into the patient's trachea to allow ventilation
needle cricothyrotomy. Placing a needle into the patient's neck so that the patient may have an airway
needle decompression. Insertion of a needle into the patient's chest to allow air to escape and reinflate a collapsed lung
insertion of an intravenous catheter. Placing a plastic tube into the patient's vein for medication and fluid administration
fluid administration. Providing intravenous fluids as dictated by the patient's condition
medication administration. Providing medications as directed and allowed by prehospital care protocols. For example, the administration of epinephrine during a cardiac arrest

Figure 8.2 *Examples of advanced life support procedures*

Tip

In emergency care, it is not just the diversity of the patient's problems that is a challenge. Patient diversity can make pain assessment and management difficult. For example, it is challenging to provide care for the patient whose primary language is not English.

It is difficult if not impossible to list the types of patients that may be seen in the prehospital environment. However, patients whose chief complaint is pain and will require transport may include:

- acute myocardial infarction
- intracerebral hemorrhage (severe headache)
- fractures (extremities, pelvis, vertebral, ribs)
- lacerations
- burns

- cancer
- fever and chills
- active labor
- aneurysms (chest and abdominal)
- infection (abdominal, pneumonia)

Tip

The cause of the emergency alone is a significant source of the patient's pain and suffering and must always be considered when determining whether the patient did or did not receive the appropriate management in the prehospital environment.

The prehospital care environment is influenced by patient location. For example, the patient who is involved in a motor vehicle crash and requires extrication before he can be transported to the emergency department may not be properly dressed for the weather when the crash occurs. The outside temperature may be 10 below zero, which can further add to patient discomfort and risk for further injury such as frostbite. Cold, heat, and trapped extremities are but a few of the causes of pain in the prehospital environment.

Extrication can be very painful and sometimes can put the patient at risk for unavoidable additional injury. We all were witness to the extrication problems encountered by those trying to save patients at both the World Trade Center and the Pentagon on September 11, 2001.

Noise is a given in the prehospital environment. Extrication tools are not quiet. This will require anyone who needs to communicate to shout. Traffic congestion, vehicle movement, lights, and sirens are fundamental components of transport which cannot generally be controlled and may cause further patient discomfort.

C. Patient management in prehospital care

The focus of patient care in the prehospital environment is assessment, intervention, and transport. As previously discussed, the level of assessment and intervention will depend on the level of training of the prehospital care provider. The interventions that may be required to deal with emergencies may cause unavoidable pain and discomfort. Insertion of intravenous lines, the application of a traction splint, or just placing the patient on a backboard to assure spinal immobilization may cause pain. However, the consequences of not performing these interventions could be life threatening.

Even though pain may result from an intervention, continued pain should alert both the prehospital care providers and the patient that what was done may not be meeting the patient's needs or if an intervention has been performed that it is not functioning properly. For example, during transport, an intravenous line may become dislodged, causing pain as fluids or even medication infiltrates into the patient's subcutaneous tissues.

Problems are going to occur in the prehospital environment, but it is important that they are recognized and dealt with as soon as possible. Where prehospital care providers may get into trouble and even cause additional patient problems is when they do not heed a patient's complaint. Even when a patient is not able to respond, a continuous assessment of interventions should occur throughout the transport process.

Tip

When obtaining information about a patient or family's complaint about pain and suffering, always identify how the patient got into the emergency care system.

8.4 The Emergency Department

Similar to the critical care unit, emergency departments (ED) became more common in the late '60s and '70s paralleling the development of EMS systems in the United States. Initially, many emergency departments were only one or two beds or a designated room where a nurse (usually the supervisor) could evaluate the patients and determine where they belonged in the hospital. Emergency rooms became emergency departments as more and more patients presented to the hospital for care that did not require hospital admission but could not be delayed and was not easy to obtain elsewhere. MacPhail[2] notes that emergency departments became emergency centers, which incorporated

- prehospital care (includes the education, training and direction of prehospital providers);

- transport programs (air medical, critical care, basic and advanced life support teams that provide patient transport);
- fast-track and urgent care centers (an area within the emergency department with personnel who treat patients with nonurgent problems such as lacerations, sore throats, venereal diseases, or broken bones and who do not require urgent care and are generally not admitted to the hospital; these areas were developed to decrease patient waiting time and enhance patient flow through the emergency department);
- observation units (a designated area in the ED where a patient can be observed for a period of time without having to be admitted to the hospital; an example of a patient who may be placed in an observation area is a patient with a minor head injury); and
- specialty evaluation areas (such as a chest pain units where patients with specific diagnoses are monitored and sometimes ruled out; these units were begun to decrease the need for admission to limited critical care beds).

In 1970, the Emergency Nurses Association was formed to develop nursing standards that described the preparation for and the practice of emergency nursing. In the early '70s, emergency medicine residencies were started with the first one in Cincinnati, Ohio. These residencies specifically trained physicians to provide care in emergency departments. In 1979, the American Medical Association recognized emergency medicine as a specialty. Today, emergency departments may also be designated as trauma or pediatric centers.

Tip

The practice of emergency nursing and emergency medicine is based on standards. The emergency nursing standards are available from the Emergency Nurses Association (ENA) (ena.org) and the physician's standards from the American College of Emergency Physicians (ACEP) (acep.org).

Each year, millions of people come to emergency departments for care. The level of care provided by an emergency department will depend on the personnel who staff it as well as the resources available to it. For example, an emergency department may be a part of a level-I trauma center which means that it is capable of providing the initial care for a severely injured patient because the institution that the emergency department is a part of can continue the care required by that patient. In other words, the nurses, physicians, specialists, diagnostic tests, and definitive care (such as a twenty-four-hour staffed operating room) are available to that severely injured patient.

The level of care provided by an emergency department varies all over the United States. There has been a push over the last several years to staff emergency departments with board-certified emergency medicine physicians as well as specially trained emergency nurses. However, there is not any federal mandate to do so, and depending on what part of the country one becomes ill or injured in, care may be rendered by a variety of nurses and physicians.

In the 1990s emergency departments began facing even greater challenges. Many factors have contributed to ED overcrowding, long wait times, and even serious mistakes being made. These include: an increase in ED patient volumes; dramatic increase in uninsured or underinsured patients; increased complexity of diseases and the evaluation required to make a diagnosis; reduced primary care services; managed care barriers; inadequate funding; hospital closings; and, probably one of the most serious, the nursing shortage.[3] This has lead to the admission of critically and injured patients to the emergency department, patients leaving without being seen (many times to return later sicker than when they presented); and diversion (closing the emergency department to patients).

Tip

Not all emergency departments are the same. Each must be evaluated based on what personnel and resources are available. However, ED personnel need to recognize when they cannot provide the services and care the patient needs and either refer or transfer the patient to an appropriate ED or hospital for care.

Most emergency departments have a "triage" area. This is where the patient will be evaluated and the acuity of their injury or illness will be determined. Patient acuity is generally based on a three-level system:

emergent. The patient must be treated immediately or he may suffer damage, injury or death; for example, a patient with an airway obstruction is an emergent patient.

urgent. The patient has an acute illness or injury, but there is not an immediate threat of damage, injury or death, yet a timely intervention must occur; for example, a patient with a fracture dislocation, who needs timely reduction is urgent.

nonurgent. The patient may be ill or injured, but treatment may be given for their problem in a non-emergency setting; for example, the patient who is requesting a pregnancy test is nonurgent.

Once the level of acuity is determined, the patient is assigned an area for treatment. As previously discussed, there may be many areas where the patient may be treated in the emergency department. For example, the patient with an airway obstruction would be taken to an area where there are personnel and equipment available to manage the airway problem.

The emergency department environment is usually very busy, bright, and noisy. There is limited privacy because most nurses are assigned to specific patient care areas. Some departments have doors to patient rooms, but most use curtains. Even though it may cause some patient and family discomfort, it is much safer for the patient because they can be watched easier.

Once the patient has received treatment and does not require hospital admission, she will be discharged. The patient discharge process should include instructions on how to care for the problem that brought her to the ED, follow-up care and any prescriptions that the patient may need. Some emergency departments are able to give the patient a limited number of prescribed medications so that she can get started on her medications or even fill the entire prescription.

Patients who require admission may be taken quickly to a critical care unit, the operating room, or a regular floor bed. However, some patients may have to be admitted to the emergency department because of a lack of beds or staff to care for them.

There are many types of patients seeking treatment in the ED. A patient with gastrointestinal bleeding may be placed next to a patient experiencing a stroke. Patients requesting treatment for minor problems such as gonorrhea may be treated in the same area as a patient who requires sutures for a head wound incurred in a fight with the police. In other words, the nature of the ED produces a diverse, challenging environment. However, the majority of ED providers are there because they love this type of work and are capable of providing some of the best, compassionate, and competent care the patient may ever receive.

8.5 Pain and Pain Management in the Emergency Department

That pain management has not always been of primary importance in emergency care was pointed out by Selbst and Clark.[1] In 1992, the Agency for Health Care Policy and Research released *Acute Pain Management: Operative or Medical Procedures and Trauma. Clinical Practice Guidelines*.[5] These guidelines have shed light on the problem of pain and pain management in emergency care. No matter where the emergency care is being provided (prehospital, transport or emergency department), the patient's pain must be recognized and managed.

A. Sources of pain and suffering in emergency care

The nature of emergency care many times necessitates that the patient suffer some pain. The illness or injury that caused the patient to seek care can produce pain and suffering. For example, a patient diagnosed with meningitis may suffer a severe headache, photophobia, and generalized discomfort from a fever. A spinal tap is generally performed to diagnose the cause of the infection so that the appropriate treatment can be started. Unfortunately, this will be uncomfortable and sometimes painful, but it is necessary.

The laboratory tests, radiographic studies, and diagnostic procedures such as insertion of a gastric tube for lavage will cause pain. Figure 8.3 provides a list of some of the common procedures performed in emergency care that may cause pain.[4]

The emergency environment can also contribute to pain and suffering. Light, noise, and temperature changes can accentuate pain. For example, a patient with a migraine headache who cannot be placed in a quiet, dark environment because most emergency departments do not have any quiet dark places may have difficulty obtaining pain relief despite receiving medication. Because of the number of patients that must be monitored and cared for, most patient care is given out in the open. Unfortunately, the emergency care environment does not lend itself to being easily controlled.

Patients must be moved, and transport itself can be a source of pain and suffering both physically and emotionally. Physical pain can result from movement from one stretcher to another. Emotional pain can occur when patients and families must be separated due to the critical care that may be required to save the patient's life.

In summary, the nature of emergency care can contribute to a patient's pain and suffering in the course of trying to manage it. This is an unavoidable and frequently a non-manageable component of emergency care.

B. Resuscitation

Just as previously discussed, emergency care can cause pain and suffering even though care providers are attempting to save a life. The components of resuscitation can potentially cause pain and suffering in emergency care.

The resuscitation of an ill or injured patient begins with the primary assessment and performing needed critical interventions. If a patient does not have a pulse, defibrillation and manual compressions to reestablish a perfusing rhythm are necessary. Cardiopulmonary resuscitation has resulted in broken ribs and sternum, punctured lungs, and internal bleeding.[6] Defibrillation, even when properly done, can cause burns to the chest. Yet, without these procedures, death is inevitable.

Figure 8.4 contains a summary of some of the other sources of pain and suffering that may result from resuscitation.

C. Emotional pain and suffering

Pain has more than a physical component. Emotional and spiritual suffering can also occur in emergency

Application of oxygen therapy can cause patient discomfort because the prongs inserted in the nose can dry out the mucous membranes and a facial mask can make the patient feel as if she is suffocating

Suctioning can cause discomfort because it can stimulate the gag reflex and cause coughing

Administration of a breathing treatment can cause discomfort because the side effects of the medication administered can cause an increased heart rate, anxiety and shaking

Venipuncture for laboratory studies can cause discomfort from the needle stick and the formation of a hematoma or bruising

Obtaining venous access can cause pain or discomfort related to insertion of the needle necessary to insert the intravenous catheter into the vein

Medication administration can cause pain or discomfort, for example phenytoin, a drug given for seizures, can cause severe pain

Spinal immobilization can cause pain or discomfort because of an ill-fitting collar or lying on a hard board

Insertion of a gastric tube can cause pain or discomfort because it needs to be placed in the stomach either through the nose or mouth

Insertion of a urinary catheter can cause pain or discomfort because it is a tube that is inserted into the patient's bladder. It can be very painful when a urinary specimen needs to be collected from a patient with a urinary tract infection

Splinting and cast application can cause pain because the fracture needs to be manipulated

Wound care can cause pain depending on the size, depth and location of the wound. Wound care involves cleansing, irrigation; sometimes wound closure (stitches, staples or glue) as well as application of a dressing.

Figure 8.3 *Examples of common procedures performed in the emergency department that may cause pain and discomfort*

care. Separation and loss are two common occurrences faced by both patients and family. Something as simple as the loss of one's clothes or a favorite piece of jewelry can cause intense discomfort.

Separation from loved ones because of the illness or injury can also cause pain and suffering. Once again, the location and nature of emergency care can present difficult challenges in allowing significant others to be with their family members. Barriers to allowing family members to be with a patient in the prehospital, transport, or emergency department environments include [7]

- lack of space for additional personnel,
- availability of personnel to provide support for the family,
- timing of arrival of the family during the emergency,
- number of family members (weight and size of the family member will also influence whether they can accompany the patient during transport),
- coping mechanisms of the family,
- potential for the family to interfere with needed procedures or the resuscitation, and
- type of procedure being performed.

Tip

Many emergency departments have policies and protocols that allow family members to stay with their loved ones during treatments, even invasive procedures and resuscitation.

8.6 Management of Pain and Suffering in Emergency Care

As the previous discussion has indicated, emergency care may cause pain and suffering intentionally or unintentionally in the pursuit of providing much needed care. However, care can be directed at providing comfort.

Care begins by recognizing that the patient is experiencing pain. When the patient is able to speak and express, pain assessment should begin with the patient's description of the pain. Remember, pain is what the patient says it is.

endotracheal intubation without adequate sedation. Placement of a tube in the patient's trachea to allow ventilation. If the patient is not adequately sedated, it can be a very painful experience, particularly if neuromuscular blocking (paralysis) is required.

chest tube insertion. Insertion of a plastic tube to allow drainage of air or blood or both so that the patient's lung can reinflate

insertion of a central line for intravenous access. Insertion of a catheter for fluid, blood, medication administration into a large vein usually in the chest area near the clavicle.

insertion of the arterial line. Insertion of a catheter into an artery, which is then hooked to a monitor to directly measure the patient's blood pressure.

fluid resuscitation. Administration of fluids for blood pressure management. Rapid fluid resuscitation with unwarmed fluids can cause the patient to become hypothermic (cold).

blood and blood product administration. Can cause hypothermia (cold).

administration of a vasoactive agent. Cause peripheral vessel constriction and loss of blood flow to the extremities causing pain

administration of fibrinolytic agents. Cause bleeding

insertion of intracranial monitor. Insertion of a catheter into the patient's brain to allow measurement of the patient's intracranial (inside the head) pressure

Figure 8.4 *Causes of pain and suffering from resuscitation*

Tip

Unfortunately, many patients with substance abuse problems or inadequate pain management come to the emergency department seeking pain medications. It can be difficult to identify drug-seeking behavior versus inadequate pain management

If the patient is not verbal or is unconscious, there are behavioral and physiological changes that may indicate pain. Behavioral indications of pain include crying, restlessness, agitation, and guarding. Physiological indications of pain include tachycardia, hypertension, hypotension, tachypnea, and sweating.

McCaffery and Pasero[8] suggest some specific questions that may help elicit a description of the patient's pain. For example:

- Do you have any ongoing pain problems (i.e., low back pain)?
- Where is the location of the pain? Does it move anywhere?
- How does the pain interfere with your ability to do your work, sleep, or live your life?
- What does the pain feel like? For example is sharp, dull, throbbing, cramping, heavy, or burning?
- When did the pain begin? Is there anything that makes it better or worse?
- What relieves the pain?
- Have you been given any treatment for the pain?

Pain assessment can also be accomplished with the use of selected pain scales such as the FACES Scale. This scale uses selected facial expressions such as a smile or frown to help the patient describe a level of pain or whether a particular treatment was helpful in providing comfort or relief. These scales can be useful for nonverbal or non-English speaking patient. However, the most common type of pain assessment tools used in the emergency department is numbering the pain from 0–10 (from the least to the greatest).

Pain is managed in emergency care with pharmacological and nonpharmacologic methods. Examples of medications that may be used in the management of pain in emergency care are summarized in Figure 8.5.

The amount and method of medication administration will influence their effectiveness. For example, most pain medications such as opioids and fentanyl need to be administered intravenously. However, some medications can only be given orally and other, such as nitrous oxide, are inhaled.

Some pain can be managed with acupuncture, acupressure, massage, therapeutic touch, and music therapy. Distraction has also been shown to be an effective method of decreasing patient discomfort. Application of heat or cold (warm blankets), changes in position, and elevation are other examples of some simple interventions that can provide comfort. Research continues to demonstrate that the emergency management of pain is multifaceted and sometimes both pharmacological and nonpharmacologic methods are required for effective care.[4,9]

Comfort can also be provided to patients and families by allowing family members to be present as much as possible. Research continues to demonstrate that family presence can provide emotional support, make invasive procedures go much smoother, allow families to witness that everything possible has been done for the patient, and give them an opportunity to say goodbye to the dying patient.[10]

Family presence is not always an option in some emergency care situations. However, when possible, it should be considered as another way of providing comfort in some very painful care situations. Some suggested questions to be used by attorneys in eliciting descriptions of pain and suffering in the emergency room are shown in Figure 8.6.

Medication	Examples
Opioids	Morphine Fentanyl
Nonopiods	Acetaminophen Ibuprofen Ketorolac
Benzodiazepines	Midazolam Lorazepam
Sedation agents	Etomidate Propofol
Local anesthetics	EMLA Cream Lidocaine
Dissociative agents (drugs that cause a dissociation between the cortex (understanding) of the brain and the pain signal. In other words, it hurts, but the patient does not care.	Ketamine Nitrous oxide

Figure 8.5 *Examples of medications used in the management of pain in emergency care*

Questions for the patient (family may be able to answer some)

- Why did you call 911?
- Why did you go to the emergency department?
- How did you get to the emergency department?
- What do you remember about the accident?
- What did you see or hear after the accident occurred?
- If you were involved in a motor vehicle accident, were you stuck (entrapped) in the car?
- Do you remember anything about the rescue process?
- What thoughts went through your head after the accident?
- What is the first thing you remember after the accident?
- Do you remember anything about your ride to the hospital? If so, what do you remember?
- If you were in an ambulance, did you see red lights or hear a siren?
- What kind of EMS providers took care of you?
- What did the EMS providers do to you?
- Did they ask you if you were having pain?
- What medications did you receive at the scene or during the trip, if you know?
- When you got to the hospital, who was the first person to talk to you?
- Did you go to the triage area?
- Were you taken directly to a bed?
- Was there anyone else in the room or area with you?
- What treatments did you receive while in the emergency department? Were they painful?
- Did the nurses or doctors tell you that what they were doing may cause you pain or discomfort?
- Did someone ask you if you were having pain?
- Did they ask you where it was or where it went?
- Did they ask you if you have ever had similar pain before?
- Did they ask you to "rate" your pain by numbering it from 1–10?
- Were you asked if you use street drugs?
- Were you asked what kind of pain medication you usually take?
- Did you receive something for your pain? If so, how long did you have to wait before it was given to you?
- Were the effects of the medicine explained to you?
- Did the medicine make you sick (nauseated or cause vomiting)?
- Did someone check to see if the pain medicine changed the level of your pain?
- Were any of your clothes or valuables lost?
- Were your clothes cut off?
- Was your family allowed to come with you in the ambulance?
- Was your family allowed to stay with you while you were in the emergency department?
- When you were discharged, were you given instructions about your illness or injury?
- Were you told when to return to the emergency department? For what signs and symptoms?
- Given the choice, would you return to that emergency department again?

Questions for the families

- How long did it take for the life squad to come?
- Did they explain to you what was happening?
- Did they let you go with your family member?
- Who was the first person you talked to when you arrived at the emergency department?
- Did you feel that the emergency department staff managed your family member's pain?
- Were you allowed to remain with your family member while in the emergency department?
- Did they allow you to witness your family member's care?
- If you were not allowed to be with your family member, how did that make you feel?
- Who gave you information about your family member?
- Did you receive sufficient information when the patient was discharged from the emergency department?
- Did you feel supported by the nurses, physicians, social workers or pastoral care service?
- Given the choice, would you bring your family member to this emergency department again?

Figure 8.6 *Questions for attorneys to ask clients about emergency care*

8.7 Summary

In 2001, the Joint Commission on Accreditation of Health Care Organizations (JCAHO) (www.jcaho.org/standard) released pain standards that pertained to pain management in the emergency department. These standards require that the care of patients in the emergency department should include

- assessing pain in all patients,
- educating staff about using analgesia,
- monitoring the patient is closely while he or she is receiving pain management, and
- educating patients about pain and managing their pain as a part of their treatment as appropriate.

Pain and suffering are an unavoidable part of emergency care. Illness, injury, and critical interventions are only a few of the sources of pain and discomfort in emergency care. However, pain can be managed and comfort provided in emergency care. It is imperative that emergency care providers be familiar with how to recognize pain as well as the interventions that can be provided to decrease any pain and suffering a patient may experience when receiving emergency care.

Endnotes

1. Selbst, M., and Pasero, C., "Analgesic Use in the Emergency Department." *Annals of Emergency Medicine*, 1990;19: 1010–1013.

2. MacPhail, E., "Overview of Emergency Nursing." In Newberry, L., editor, *Sheehy's Emergency Nursing*, Fifth Edition. St. Louis: Mosby,s 2003, pp. 1–5.

3. Franaszek, J., *Responding to Emergency Department Crowding: A Guidebook for Chapters.* Dallas: American College of Emergency Physicians, 2002.

4. Semonin Holleran, R., "The Problem of Pain in Emergency Care." *Nursing Clinics of North America,* 2002, 37:67–78.

5. *Acute Pain Management: Operative or Medical Procedures and Trauma, Clinical Practice Guidelines*, Rockville, MD: Agency for Health Care Policy and Research, 1992.

6. Baubin, M., Rabl, W., Pfeiffer, K.P., Benzer, A., and Gilly, H., "Chest Injuries after Compression-Decompression Cardiopulmonary Resuscitation in Cadavers." 1999, *Resuscitation*, 1999, 1: 9–15.

7. Williams, J., "Family Presence during Resuscitation." *Nursing Clinics of North America,* 2002, 37:211–220.

8. McCaffery, M., and Pasero, C., *Pain: Clinical Manual for Nursing Practice*. St. Louis: Mosby, 1999.

9. Hageness, S., Kreitzer, M.J., and Kinney, E., "Complementary, Integrative and Holistic Care in Emergency Nursing." *Nursing Clinics of North America*, 2002, 37:123–134.

10. Cummins, R.O., and Hazinski, M.F., "The Most Important Changes in International ECC and CPR Guidelines." *Resuscitation*, 2000, 46:431–437.

Chapter 9

Spinal Cord Injury

Guy William Fried, MD and Karen Mandzak Fried, MSN, RN, CRRN, CCM

Synopsis

9.1 Introduction

Spinal cord injury is one of the most devastating conditions that can affect the body. The changes that take place often have a permanent impact on all aspects of the patient's life; physiologically, psychologically, vocationally, socially, and emotionally. Although technology and advances in medical treatment have had a tremendous impact on the care and long-term survival of these patients, the pain and suffering that is endured usually persists for the rest of their lives. In addition to this, dual diagnoses and concurrent complications are not uncommon. Persons who become spinal cord injured may also experience extensive burns, traumatic brain injury, multiple fractures, and pain, just to name a few. Attorneys handling spinal cord injury cases are well aware of the huge damages and long-term care involved in these injuries.

The reason that there is such a great impact on a patient's life is because of the spinal cord's key functions. The spinal cord carries all the messages between the brain and the body. These messages involve all voluntary motion, breathing, sensation, tone, pain perception, bowel and bladder control, and sexual functioning. Spinal cord injury leads to a major disruption of this message system, and although the person may survive the injury itself, his body no longer functions the way it did before the injury.

A. Incidence and etiology

The estimated incidence of spinal cord injury in the U.S. is thirty to forty new cases per million people per year.[1] The prevalence of spinal cord injury in the population is 250,000–300,000 with the addition of 10,000 new injuries each year. The most common causes of spinal cord injury are motor vehicle accidents (44%), falls (18%), violence (16%), and sports injuries (12.7%). Falls are more commonly found in individuals greater than forty-five years old; violence is more common among those who are younger.

B. Classification of injuries

Spinal cord injury that affects both the motor and sensory function in the arms, neck, trunk, and legs is called tetraplegia (this replaces the older term quadriplegia). In tetraplegia, the bony injury to the spinal column usually occurs in the cervical area. Paraplegia refers to an injury that does not affect the arms and neck. Typically, this spinal cord injury occurs within the thoracic, lumbar, or sacral areas of the spinal column. When healthcare providers are involved in the care of patients with spinal cord injury, it is important to have a clear idea of the type and level of the injury in order to anticipate the care that will be required for the rest of the patient's life. Attorneys and lifecare planners need to understand the types of paralysis, as this will have an effect on the expected needs of the paralyzed plaintiff.

There are multiple methods of classifying spinal cord injury. The American Spinal Injury Association (ASIA) Impairment scale[2] is one of the most widely accepted methods among professionals who treat patients in designated Spinal Cord Injury Centers. This classification is based entirely on an in-depth physical, neurological, and musculoskeletal examination. The ASIA scale helps to standardize the classification of spinal cord injury for consistent data collection and communication. The radiographics, imaging, and electrodiagnostic studies do not contribute to these scores; however, they do assist in further refining the type and level of injury for initial neurosurgical and orthopedic intervention.

The ASIA scale (Figure 9.1) looks at five key muscles in each arm and five key muscles in each leg. Each of these key muscles is innervated by a different spinal cord root level which correlates with muscle contraction or function. Each muscle is graded individually from 0–5, with 0 representing total paralysis of the muscle and 5 being normal strength and power. A grade of 1 indicates a muscle flicker only. A grade of 2 indicates that the muscle can move the limb with gravity eliminated. A grade of 3 indicates that the muscle has the strength necessary to contract and lift the limb against gravity. A grade of 4 indicates that the limb muscle can move against gravity and additionally accept some resistance.

Sensation is rated according to a standard dermatomal distribution that consists of twenty-eight sequentially layered, bilateral dermatomes innervated by pairs of nerves which exit the spinal cord at each bony vertebral level. Every part of the body is represented by a dermatome. These sections represent each sensory root, nerve level, and where it enters the spinal cord. The sensory evaluation is rated separately for light touch and pinprick since each sensation is carried within a different tract in the spinal cord. The rating system for each level is 0 for absent, 1 for impaired, and 2 for normal.

Spinal cord injuries are also labeled "complete" or "incomplete" based on whether there is any preservation of sensation or motor function in the lowest sacral area.[3] Whether a person's injury is called a complete or an incomplete injury is based solely on the physical examination and not the operative, radiographic, or electrophysiologic finding. If there is any evidence of sensation or voluntary muscle action in the perianal sacral segments, this represents that a message was able to travel unencumbered from the brain down the entire spinal cord to the sacral area. The preservation of this sensory or motor function would then be called incomplete. An incomplete spinal cord injury carries a better prognosis for recovering some function compared with a complete lesion. After a spinal cord injury, it can take up to two years for the neurological recovery phase to end.

9.2 Immediate Care

In the initial management of spinal cord injury it is essential to minimize the neurological deficit while simultaneously addressing any associated injuries to the body.[4]

A. Spinal stabilization

The vertebral column enables us to be mobile while simultaneously encasing and protecting the spinal cord. Damage to the spinal cord may not be evident at the time of an injury, because in some cases there is no bone damage to the vertebral column.

Tip

It has been estimated that up to 5% of patients who have suffered trauma may have an injured or unstable spine.

In addition, the spinal cord injury may not be obvious in any case involving decreased awareness because of head injury or intoxication. Life-threatening coexisting injuries or dramatic appearing injuries can distract the treating personnel from the occult (not easily detected) spinal cord injury. In any accident where a spinal cord injury is conceivable, immediate spine immobilization should occur. Because the spinal cord injury may be occult, steps must be taken to immobilize

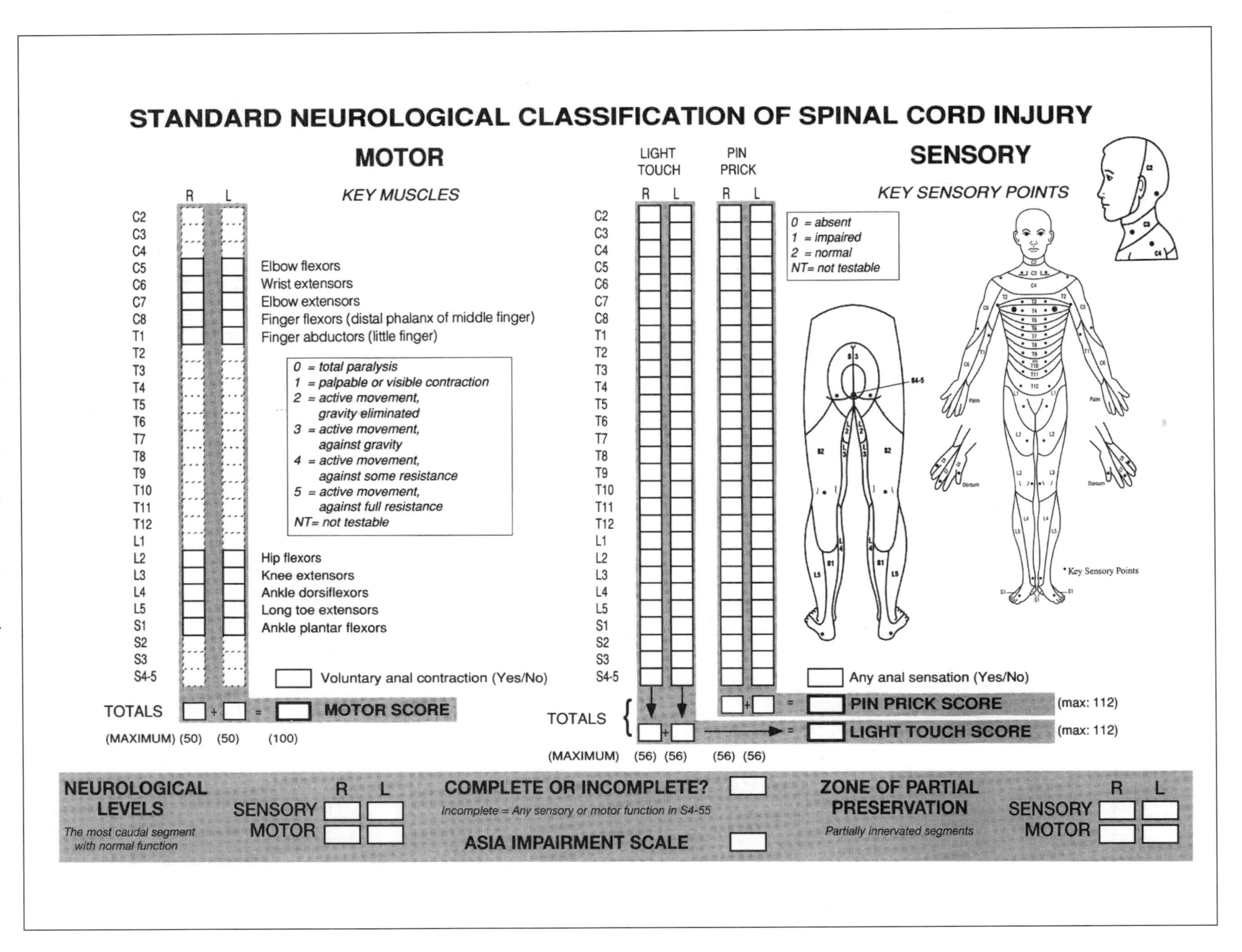

STANDARD NEUROLOGICAL CLASSIFICATION OF SPINAL CORD INJURY

MOTOR

KEY MUSCLES

	R	L	
C2			
C3			
C4			
C5			Elbow flexors
C6			Wrist extensors
C7			Elbow extensors
C8			Finger flexors (distal phalanx of middle finger)
T1			Finger abductors (little finger)
T2			
T3			
T4			
T5			
T6			
T7			
T8			
T9			
T10			
T11			
T12			
L1			
L2			Hip flexors
L3			Knee extensors
L4			Ankle dorsiflexors
L5			Long toe extensors
S1			Ankle plantar flexors
S2			
S3			
S4-5			

0 = total paralysis
1 = palpable or visible contraction
2 = active movement, gravity eliminated
3 = active movement, against gravity
4 = active movement, against some resistance
5 = active movement, against full resistance
NT = not testable

☐ Voluntary anal contraction (Yes/No)

TOTALS ☐ + ☐ = ☐ MOTOR SCORE

(MAXIMUM) (50) (50) (100)

SENSORY

KEY SENSORY POINTS

	LIGHT TOUCH R	LIGHT TOUCH L	PIN PRICK R	PIN PRICK L
C2				
C3				
C4				
C5				
C6				
C7				
C8				
T1				
T2				
T3				
T4				
T5				
T6				
T7				
T8				
T9				
T10				
T11				
T12				
L1				
L2				
L3				
L4				
L5				
S1				
S2				
S3				
S4-5				

0 = absent
1 = impaired
2 = normal
NT = not testable

☐ Any anal sensation (Yes/No)

TOTALS ☐ + ☐ = ☐ PIN PRICK SCORE (max: 112)

☐ + ☐ = ☐ LIGHT TOUCH SCORE (max: 112)

(MAXIMUM) (56) (56) (56) (56)

Palm

Dorsum

* Key Sensory Points

NEUROLOGICAL LEVELS — The most caudal segment with normal function: SENSORY R ☐ L ☐; MOTOR R ☐ L ☐

COMPLETE OR INCOMPLETE? ☐ — Incomplete = Any sensory or motor function in S4-S5

ASIA IMPAIRMENT SCALE ☐

ZONE OF PARTIAL PRESERVATION — Partially innervated segments: SENSORY R ☐ L ☐; MOTOR R ☐ L ☐

Figure 9.1 *The Standard Neurological Scale of Spinal Cord Injury/ASIA Scale*

the spine to prevent further damage from inadvertently occurring. Although this is accomplished easily in principle, 10% of the patients with cervical spine injuries are still transported without adequate spine immobilization.[5]

In the acute phase, it is imperative for the orthopaedic, neurosurgical, and rehabilitation teams to perform accurate neurological evaluations and ensure proper alignment and stabilization of the spinal column. This may be accomplished with either surgical intervention with or without spinal immobilization or non-surgically with spinal immobilization alone. Among all patients admitted into the Model Spinal Cord Injury System, 45% did not undergo any spine procedure, 49% underwent one spinal procedure, and 5% underwent two spinal procedures. In 18% of the cases an immobilization device was used to stabilize the spine without surgery. In tetraplegic patients, cervical vertebral internal fixation with fusion was the most common surgical procedure accounting for 30% of the cases.[6]

Spinal orthosis (an immobilization device such as a brace or neck support) and advanced surgical techniques help stabilize the spine, which will allow earlier mobilization of the patient. There are still some controversy and practice variations over which patient needs surgical stabilization. From a long-term rehabilitative perspective, it is clear that early mobilization of the patient helps to minimize a variety of emotionally and physically draining side effects, including deconditioning, pressure ulcers, and heterotopic ossification (abnormal bone growth).

Surgery itself has inherent risks. Of patients who underwent at least one surgical procedure, 0.9% needed a repair of the internal fixation and an additional 0.9% had the fixation hardware removed. At least 4.4% of the patients developed postoperative infection because the acutely injured spinal cord patient is at a greater risk of infection.[6]

In the acute phase of management, high-dose administration of intravenous steroids (methylprednisolone) is usually initiated within eight hours of a traumatic spinal cord injury according to a specific protocol. This has been shown to improve ultimate recovery. Currently, research studies are focusing on using different chemical agents to limit the damage of the initial trauma and assist with neurological recovery.

B. Spinal shock

Acute spinal cord injury brings about catastrophic changes to all of the body's major systems. Clearly the patient is at the highest risk for morbidity (illness) and mortality (death) during the first days after the injury. Initially the body is in a temporary state of spinal shock, in which the muscles may be paralyzed and flaccid. Blood tends to pool in the lower extremity veins, which then leads to orthostasis (a drop in blood pressure) and deep venous thrombosis (blood clots).

After spinal cord injury, the autonomic nervous system does not act properly to support the patient's blood pressure. Those with cervical injuries resulting in tetraplegia lose their ability to control blood pressure. The spinal cord injury brings about a collapse of the body's fine balance. Over time a new equilibrium is found, but unfortunately, the patient may remain emotionally and physically fragile for a lifetime.

9.3 Long-Term Effects of Spinal Cord Injury

A. Respiratory changes

The diaphragm is the major muscle of respiration, originating from the spinal cord at C3-4-5. The intercostals (muscles between the ribs) and abdominal muscles controlled by T1-12 also assist with respiratory functioning. In an uninjured body, the diaphragm and the chest muscles greatly expand the thoracic cavity when breathing in. The chest and diaphragm recoil passively to exhale. A cough can generate high sudden pressures to clear the lungs of excess secretions or foreign bodies. The filling of the lungs with oxygen keeps the microscopic breathing apparatus, the alveoli, fully inflated and helps to minimize secretions. Injuries to the thoracic or cervical spinal cord limit the ability to breathe, cough, and clear secretions effectively. Initially, many patients with tetraplegia may require tracheostomies (breathing tubes inserted into the neck) and ventilators. Those with injuries at C3 or above usually require lifetime ventilator support. Below that level, patients can usually be weaned from the ventilator for some period of time.[7]

Spinal cord injury significantly changes the balance and functioning of the lungs. Immediately after the injury, the patient will find it difficult to inhale and exhale fully. Secretions that previously could clear easily now tend to pool in the base of the lungs, inhibiting the lungs from expanding fully. This is defined as atelectasis. As secretions and bacteria mount, pneumonia develops. As the lung partially collapses due to the atelectasis, and fills with the secretions and bacteria causing pneumonia, the energy required to breathe increases. Unfortunately, paralysis limits the body's ability to compensate for this stress, often leading to respiratory failure or arrest. During the initial hospitalization, atelectasis, pneumonia, and ventilatory failure are among the most common problems encountered by spinal cord injured patients.[8]

Tip

Respiratory problems are the first threats to survival after spinal cord injury due to the nerve damage in the muscles of respiration.

Pneumonia and respiratory disorders also remain the highest cause of death in the spinal cord injured population.[9] Up to the first year after the acute spinal cord injury remains the most precarious time. As the first year after the injury passes, the patient starts to reach a new equilibrium; however, she will always remain a respiratory risk. The higher the spinal cord injury, the higher the associated risk. For example, three-quarters of the ventilator-dependent high tetraplegics admitted to a spinal cord injury model system die within the first year of injury. For those patients who do survive the first year, 61% continue to survive for the next fourteen years.[10]

The object of rehabilitation is to anticipate the problems with acute paralysis and respiratory compromise and aggressively treat the patients to maintain their lung expansion and handle their secretions. This is often done with aggressive pulmonary care that is performed initially by nursing or respiratory therapists and continued by the family or caregivers for the rest of the patient's life. These techniques include clapping on the chest to loosen secretions and assistive ("quad") coughing to force the secretions up toward the mouth. This also includes aggressively treating the affected accumulation of bacteria with appropriate antibiotics.

Because spinal cord injury can so massively affect the ability to breathe, it can create deep anxiety and fear. The treatment that is needed for patients to survive also contributes to their pain and suffering. Families and caregivers also experience this stress. Early in the injury, the vigilance of the treatment team must be nonstop to ensure the survival of the patient. As time goes on this never-ending vigilance must be continued by the family and caregivers.

B. Cardiovascular changes

Initially after a spinal cord injury the paralysis and spinal shock leads to a decrease in muscle tone and movement. This results in vasodilatation, or pooling of blood in the abdomen and lower extremities, and it becomes difficult to get the blood back to the heart. This makes it harder to maintain the normal equilibrium of blood pressure so that any rapid movements or changes in position may cause orthostatic hypotension in which the blood pressure drops rapidly, leading to loss of consciousness. Over time, the hypotension can be counteracted with binders, elastic stockings, and certain medications and it may stabilize. Also, because of the inability to sweat or shiver below the level of the injury, patients can no longer maintain normal temperature regulation, which is also known as poikilothermia. The higher the level of injury, the more likely this is to occur. Hypothermia and hyperthermia can also contribute to cardiac dysrhythmias (irregular heart beat). For this reason spinal cord injured patients, especially tetraplegic patients, usually require a consistent ambient temperature range, which may necessitate the use of air conditioning for adequate survival.[11]

C. Skin changes

The spinal cord injured population is at a very high risk for pressure ulcers. They are common, with a 25% incidence per year.[12] They are also expensive in terms of the thousands of dollars of care that is needed. They add to the person's dependence and persistent hospitalization.

Pressure ulcers are so frequent due to the combination of features of spinal cord injury.[13] The most significant factor is the immobility. Patients frequently are in one position for a prolonged time period. They may not have the strength to shift positions. The blood supply, which carries oxygen and nutrients to the skin, is hampered by the immobility. If the patient is lying on his back in one position the bony sacrum pushes against the bed surface and squeezes the tissues in between, which creates pressures that exceed the capillary pressure. The tissue therefore does not receive adequate blood supply and begins to die. Any incontinence may macerate (moisten and irritate) the skin and lead to further breakdown. Additionally, the skin is exposed to bacteria and any disruption of the skin surface can easily become infected. The spinal cord injury also leads to inadequate nutrients in the blood, which makes skin and muscles more likely to break down and impedes their reparative process.

Tip

The spinal cord injured population is at a very high risk for pressure ulcers, therefore expenses associated with mobilization and skin care are almost always cost effective.

Pressure ulcers are graded by a four-point classification system. Stage I is limited to the skin and appears as a defined area of redness. Stage II consists of partial thickness skin loss presenting as an abrasion, blister, or shallow crater. Stage III is full thickness skin loss involving damage or necrosis of subcutaneous tissue that may extend down to, but not through, underlying fascia. Stage IV consists of full thickness skin loss with extensive destruction, tissue necrosis, or damage to underlying muscle, bone, or supporting structures. Stage I and II pressure ulcers may heal with topical treatments, pressure relief and equipment. Stage III or IV pressure sores very often can only heal with surgery.

D. Bowel, bladder, and sexual changes

For a person's bowel, bladder, and sexual organs to function properly, there is a blending of physiologic, metabolic, and hormonal influences that are controlled by the nervous system. As a result of the neurological changes that occur after a spinal cord injury, bowel, bladder, and sexual functioning are impaired. The type of neurogenic bowel and bladder dysfunction usually depends on the level of injury. Patients with an injury at or above the T12 to L1 level have an automatic or reflex bowel and bladder. Those with an injury at or below T12 to L1 have an areflexic (without reflexes) bowel and bladder. In both types, the patient typically has lost all sensation related to bowel and bladder fullness as well as the ability to initiate or inhibit bowel and bladder activity. For these reasons individuals must maintain a fairly involved bowel and bladder program that will require not only medications—but catheterizations, suppositories, manual techniques, and specific equipment—for the rest of their lives. A once extremely private and intimate activity may now become fairly time consuming and require the assistance of others, not to mention the constant fear and embarrassment of incontinence.

Sexual activity, which may return in some capacity depending on the level of the injury, also remains forever altered as a result of the neurological changes. This too, may require specific medications, injections, surgical interventions, or equipment for it to occur.

E. Bone changes

Heterotopic ossification is the body's production of excessive bone in and around a joint or connective tissue where it does not belong. This also occurs after traumatic brain injury and burns. Unfortunately the etiology of heterotopic ossification is unknown. Heterotopic ossification has been reported in 16%–53% of patients with spinal cord injury.[14] It is most common below the level of injury, although not below the knees or elbows. Heterotopic ossification will present with the clinical signs of pain, loss of range of motion, and swelling. Medical treatment may include the use of the medications disodium etidronate and Indocin. Surgical resection is reserved for those patients with severe loss of range of motion causing functional loss. Surgery carries significant risks, including excessive bleeding, fractures, infection, and a significant risk of recurrent heterotopic ossification.

F. Neurological changes

1. Autonomic dysreflexia

Spinal cord injuries above the T6 level cause problems associated with disruption in the autonomic nervous system that regulates many of our involuntary body functions such as breathing, sweating, shivering, and blood pressure. A serious, life-threatening complication that can occur after a spinal cord injury is known as autonomic dysreflexia, or hyperreflexia.

Autonomic dysreflexia occurs when the body is no longer able to restore equilibrium after being presented with noxious stimuli from below the level of the injury. Autonomic dysreflexia occurs after the patient is out of the phase of spinal shock in which reflexes return. A noxious stimulus starts the process. Bladder distention, bowel impaction, kidney stones or appendicitis are examples of noxious stimuli. Ironically, the stimuli cannot be felt by the patient. The uninjured individual can respond to any stimulus that the nervous system picks such as pain, trapped abdominal gas, or having to go to the bathroom. In a spinal cord injured patient, such stimuli lead to a precipitous elevation of blood pressure, causing a pounding headache, blurred vision, nasal congestion, and sweating above the injury level. In addition, the patient also experiences intense anxiety, a profound sense of doom, and subsequent bradycardia (slow heart rate) in an attempt to bring the blood pressure down. These events cause a life-threatening situation requiring immediate medical intervention directed at finding the source and alleviating the cause. Treatment includes sitting the patient up and checking for bladder distention, as this is the most common cause of the dysreflexia.[15] If the blood pressure is still high, the next step is checking for fecal impaction, as this is the second most common cause for the dysreflexia.[16] If this does not solve the problem, any other noxious stimulus may need to be evaluated. If the blood pressure persists, a rapid onset antihypertensive agent may be required, but the patient must be monitored carefully for overtreatment leading to hypotension. Patients that experience dysreflexia frequently will be very anxious as this is occurring. Not only is the dysreflexia painful, the sense of severe impending danger cannot be forgotten. Unfortunately it plays directly into the patient and family's sense of helplessness as a result of the spinal cord injury itself. Autonomic dysreflexia is something that patients, families, and caregivers must be on alert for and respond to immediately for the rest of the patient's life.

Tip

Autonomic dysreflexia is a serious, life-threatening complication that requires immediate medical intervention.

2. Spasticity

Spasticity is the most common neurological change associated with spinal cord injury. Immediately after the injury the patient is usually in a flaccid state of spinal shock. Over several weeks or months the flaccid state evolves into a state of spasticity, which is an abnormal increase in muscle tension. Spasticity is an upper motor neuron disorder that causes increased tightness and resistance to passive movement. There may also be involuntary jerky movements. Spasticity is both a blessing and a curse. It is helpful when it assists with functional activities such as transferring but harmful when it interferes with proper positioning, hygiene, or activities of daily living, which could lead to skin breakdown and contractures.

One year after an injury, 78% of spinal cord injury patients demonstrate spasticity. Up to 91% of tetraplegics demonstrate spasticity,[17] with almost half (49%) requiring treatment with antispasticity medications. Spasticity is uncomfortable for the patient. The involuntary muscle jumping can embarrass patients and counteract any voluntary muscle movement that they might have. Common medications used to treat spasticity include oral medications such as Baclofen, Zanaflex, Dantrium, and Valium. A common complaint among patients however is that they feel drugged or fatigued on these oral medications. However, untreated spasticity can be fatiguing as well, because in some patients the legs continue to spasm constantly, causing fatigue. There are newer agents such as intramuscular injectables or botulinum toxin (Myobloc and Botox) that have helped address specific spastic muscles without the negative side effects as noted above. Intramuscular botulinum injections are able to slow the course of spasms for three months after injection without the fatigue or cognitive effects. Surgical implantation of an intrathecal baclofen pump may also be useful for severe muscle spasticity. For recalcitrant spasticity, permanently destructive surgical techniques that may be considered include tendonotomy (cutting the attachments of the muscles to the bones) or cordectomy (cutting part of the spinal cord).

3. Syrinx

A syrinx is a fluid-filled cyst within the spinal cord. The patients commonly present with new onset of pain and numbness. The cysts grow and push against the spinal cord nerve tissues, causing new loss of strength and sensation or changes in spasticity. These changes in neurological status may occur above or below the level of injury. Surgical drainage of these cysts and placement of a shunt can limit the damage of the expanding cyst. Although there may be a reversal of recent neurological loss, the procedures are considered successful if they prevent future functional loss.

Before MRI (magnetic resonance imaging) scans were available, the incidence of syrinx was estimated to be between 1%–3% of spinal cord injured patients.[18] With the advent of MRI, syrinxes have been found to be much more common, occurring in up to 67% of the spinal cord injured patients.[19] Conservative treatment is directed to avoiding Valsalva maneuvers (bearing-down) as these can indirectly change the spinal fluid pressures and potentially enlarge the syrinx. Many activities after spinal cord injury may involve the Valsalva (such as transfers, strengthening muscles, moving the bowels, and voiding) unless the patient is trained to breathe deeply, relax, and keep her mouth open to avoid consciously bearing down during these activities. The development of a syrinx and the precautions associated with it bring another painful recognition that the body has drastically changed and now has new rules and fragility. Unfortunately, these realities fuel the patient's fears, anxieties, depression, and mental suffering.

G. Pain

Pain is extremely common after spinal cord injury. Initially, there is acute pain at the site of the spinal trauma. Fusion sites can cause a great deal of pain and stiffness that usually diminishes with the healing of the bone and soft tissue. Patients commonly complain about neck pain and stiffness associated with the surgery and immobilization device. Iliac bone graft sites are frequently painful if they are in regions of the body with sensation. It is also common to have complaints of pain associated with positioning in order to protect the skin. Shoulder pain occurs from the side lying position in patients with both complete and incomplete injuries. Hip pain also occurs in this position for those with an incomplete injury. The pain of being in one position for a prolonged period of time adds to the emotional pain and suffering of not being able to do anything about it.[20]

1. Neuropathic pain

Neuropathic pain consists of varieties of chronic pain that arise following injury to the nervous system (the brain, spinal cord, spinal nerve roots, and cauda equina). Several studies indicate that up to one-third to one-half of all spinal cord injury patients experience chronic unpleasant sensation.[10,21] Bonica concluded that 69% of the patients with spinal cord injury experienced pain, and in one-third the pain was severe.[22] Mariano[23] found that the estimated prevalence of disabling pain ranged from 18%–63% in the spinal cord injured population. Nepomuceno[24] surveyed 200 people with spinal cord injuries. Eighty percent of the patients reported pain and discomfort. In this study, 23% (high thoracic/cervical injuries) to 37% (low thoracic/lumbosacral injuries) of those surveyed stated that they would be willing to trade the loss of sexual or bowel function, as well as the hypothetical possibility for a cure, to obtain pain relief.

Pain can occur after damage in the spinal cord, brain, or peripheral nerves. This pain may occur when there is damage to the somatosensory pathways, especially the spinothalamic tract in the spinal cord, which carries pain and temperature sensation. There are two types of central nervous system pain, spontaneous and hyperesthesia. Spontaneous pain is constantly present but varies in intensity over time. It may be exacerbated by generalized phenomena such as minor activity, emotional state, and weather changes. It can vary by internal feedback to the spinal cord injured patient such as noxious stimulation below the level of injury, bowel impaction, or urinary retention. It is frequently described as a numb, burning, twisting, and annoying electrical shooting sensation. Although this pain is found in both complete and incomplete injuries, it may occur more frequently in patients with complete spinal cord injuries.

The second type of central pain is hyperesthesia. This occurs frequently at the zone of injury where normal sensation meets abnormal in the complete spinal cord injured patient. It may also occur in any area with a partially damaged sensory deficit in incomplete injuries. There are two types of hyperesthesia, hyperpathia and allodynia. Hyperpathia is a condition where intense pain is experienced as a result of mildly painful stimuli. Patients with hyperpathia may experience the scratching of their limbs as a sense of being deeply cut or burned.[25] Allodynia is where a patient experiences an unpleasant sensation as a result of normally non-painful stimuli. In these patients the nerves are overly sensitive and misinterpret the information. Just being touched or having a blanket on top of a limb is experienced as being extremely painful.

Neuropathic pain is idiosyncratic. Two patients with identical lesions may experience different qualities and quantities of pain. Research shows that certain strains of rats and species of monkeys are more prone to develop neuropathic pain.[26,27] Genetic predisposition may account for some of the variability in pain type and intensity in patients with similar classifications of spinal cord injury.

Tip

Conclusions should not be drawn about the presence or absence of pain based on the complete versus incomplete SCI model. Even the patient with a complete injury can experience pain.

Central pain of spinal origin may occur immediately or after an extended period of time. Tasker[28] reviewed seventy-two cases and found an immediate pain onset in 17% of the cases. Thirteen percent of the patients experienced pain within the first month of injury. From one to six months, 19% of the patients experienced the onset of pain and 8% experienced the onset from six to twelve months after injury. An additional 13% of the patients experienced their pain onset from one to five years after injury, and after five years only 2% experienced the onset of pain. In some cases, the pain intensifies over time, and in others it improves. Spinal cord patients have described this pain as burning, shooting, numb, tingling, aching, and visceral. As the pain lingers on it can lead to further frustration and depression as the patient experiences this unrelenting internal distraction.

Phantom limb sensation, which is known to be experienced by patients with an amputation, may also develop in spinal cord injured patients. Phantom limb sensation is best described as the brain's perception that a limb is still present despite its amputation. Wall[29] found that phantom sensation for the spinal cord injured had an onset that was more likely delayed, whereas for the amputee pain was immediate. The phantom sensation of the limb tended to be more vivid for the amputee than for the spinal cord injured, where it was more diffuse. The phantom sensation of the amputee tended to "telescope," where the limb length shortened over time, as opposed to the spinal cord injury where the limb length remained the same.

Tip

The experience of pain after a spinal cord injury that continues long term has been cited as the single most important factor responsible for lower ratings of quality of life.

---

2. Upper extremity pain and overuse

Upper extremity pain and overuse is another extremely common long-term consequence after spinal cord injury. Upper extremity musculoskeletal issues also become more prevalent when the patient ages. It makes sense that a tetraplegic or a paraplegic patient's arms are overused. In a follow-up clinic for chronic paraplegia, Gellman[31] found that 68% of the patients had upper limb pain and 34.5% had shoulder pain after their initial injury. Bayley[32] also noted that in a group of ninety-four patients, one-third noted the presence of shoulder pain during transfers. Further evaluation detected that 16% had aseptic necrosis (bone destruction without infection) of the humeral head and 74% had a chronic impingement of the subacromial area. The patients with chronic impingement were given an arthrogram that revealed a rotator cuff tear in up to 65% of these cases. After a spinal cord injury there is also a high incidence of entrapment of the medial and ulnar nerves in the lower half of the arm.

Stover found that shoulder pain among the spinal cord injured patients was due to the dependence upon the upper extremity for activities of daily living (ADLs), wheelchair transfers, and dressing.[33] Weakness of the shoulder muscles can cause an imbalance of the muscles within the rotator cuff (the deltoid, biceps, and trapezius muscles) that keep the humeral head depressed in the glenoid fossa.

An approach to treatment for these problems in uninjured people would be to change their body mechanics, strengthen the weak muscles, or limit the activity. Unfortunately, these interventions are difficult to abide by due to the paralysis and resulting increased demands on the upper body. Frequently, the arms are being overused because they must be overused in order to accomplish a task. The weakness of some muscles caused by the paralysis leads to muscle imbalances that then cause shoulder, elbow, and wrist problems. Medications that are often used include oral anti-inflammatories and steroid injections. Unfortunately, because of the underlying paralysis, the mechanics of wheeling a wheelchair or transferring as independently as possible cannot significantly change. Although technological advances have developed power chairs and mechanical lifts, frequently there is no getting around the need for the persistent use of arms.

Surgery may be an option to repair a torn rotator cuff or release the carpal tunnel. After surgery there is an expected immediate decline in function due to the postoperative weight-bearing and lifting restrictions. These restrictions would exclude transfers and activities of daily living, rendering the patient completely dependent during the postoperative healing phase. Any utilization of the operated arm may lead to severe pain and threaten the integrity of the surgery. After the patient remobilizes and regains any lost strength and functioning, there is always the possibility that future upper extremity pain and damage may recur, continuing the cycle of treatment.

See Figure 9.2 for a summary of the functional capabilities according to the level of spinal cord injury.

H. Psychosocial and emotional changes

After a spinal cord injury it is common for patients to have an extended grief reaction. Many patients also experience depression. A diagnosis of major depression should be considered if the grief lasts for longer than two months.[34] A major depressive episode includes five of the following symptoms every day during the same two-week period:

- depressed mood most of the day,
- marked diminished interest in almost all activities
- appetite disturbance or significant weight gain,
- insomnia (inability to sleep) or hypersomnia (constant sleeping),
- psychomotor agitation or retardation,
- fatigue, and
- feelings of worthlessness or excessive guilt, trouble thinking or concentrating, and recurrent thoughts of death.

Many spinal cord injured patients may experience one or more of these symptoms for greater than two months, requiring the use of antidepressant medications.

Tip

There is a huge amount of emotional pain and social devastation that accompanies a spinal cord injury and its massive devastation of the body.

After spinal cord injury a number of patients also consider suicide. As Dijkers[35] describes: "Some persons continue to find the gap between what had been (or could have been) and the present unacceptable, and either commit suicide or bring about death through systematic and prolonged self-neglect (e.g., inattention to skin care) or refusals of necessary care (e.g., operational rehabilitation interventions)." The frequency of death due to prolonged self-neglect is difficult to estimate. Suicide rates after spinal cord injury have ranged from 5%–10% as compared to a rate of 1.4% for the United States population as a whole. The incidence of suicide is most common in the first years after the spinal cord injury.

There also is a terrific amount of social devastation for the patient. Spinal cord injury brings about multiple stressors to a marriage or any long-term relationship. These stressors result in an increased divorce rate in marriages that occurred either before or after the spinal cord injury. Up to 88.5% of the patients who were single at the time of injury remain single, as opposed to the uninjured population where approximately 65.4% would have remained single. If the injury occurs to an adolescent or young adult there may be a regression

TABLE 51-7. *Typical functional outcomes for patients with complete SCIs*

Location of injury	Pressure relief	Wheelchair transfers	Wheelchair propulsion	Ambulation	Orthotic devices	Transportation	Communication
C3–C4	Independent in power recliner wheelchair; dependent in bed or manual wheelchair	Total dependence	Independent in pneumatic or chin control–driven power wheelchair with power recliner	Not applicable	Upper extremity externally powered orthosis, dorsal cock-up splint, BFOs	Dependent on others in accessible van with lift; unable to drive	Independent with adapted equipment for phone or typing
C5	Most require assistance	Assistance of one person with or without transfer board	Independent in powered wheelchair indoors and outdoors; short distances in manual wheelchair with adapted handrims indoors	Not applicable	As above	Independent driving in specially adapted van	As above
C6	Independent	Potentially independent with transfer board	Independent moderate distances with manual wheelchair with plastic rims or lugs indoors; assistance needed outdoors; independent in hand-driven wheelchair	Not applicable	Wrist-driven orthosis, universal cuff, writing devices, built-up handles	Independent in driving specially adapted van	Independent with adapted equipment for phone, typing, and writing; independent in turning pages
C7	Independent	Independent with or without transfer board including car, except to or from floor with assistance	Independent in manual wheelchair indoors and outdoors, except stairs	Not applicable	None	Independent driving car with hand controls or specially adapted van; independent placement of wheelchair into car	Independent with adapted equipment for phone, typing, and writing; independent in turning pages
C8–T1	Independent	Independent, including to and from floor and car	Independent in manual wheelchair indoors and outdoors; with curbs, escalators; assistance on stairs	Exercise only (not functional with orthoses); requires physical assistance or guarding	None	As above	Independent
T2–T10	Independent	Independent	Independent	Exercise only (not functional with orthoses); may not require assistance	Knee–ankle–foot orthoses with forearm crutches or walker	As above	Independent
T11–L2	Independent	Independent	Independent	Functional ambulation indoors with orthoses; stairs using railing	Knee–ankle–foot orthoses or ankle–foot orthoses with forearm crutches	As above	Independent
L3–S3	Independent	Independent	Independent	Community ambulation; independent indoors and outdoors with orthoses	Ankle–foot orthoses with forearm crutches or canes	As above	Independent

Figure 9.2 *Functional levels, reprinted with permission of Lippincott Williams & Wilkins* *(continued on next page)*

TABLE 51-7. *Continued*

Location of injury	Pulmonary hygiene	Feeding	Grooming	Dressing	Bathing	Bowel and bladder routine	Bed mobility
C3–C4	Totally assisted cough	May be unable to feed self; use of BFOs with universal cuff and adapted utensils indicated; drinks with long straw after set-up	Total dependence	Total dependence	Total dependence	Total dependence	Total dependence
C5	Assisted cough	Independent with specially adapted equipment for feeding after set-up	Independent with adapted equipment	Assistance with upper extremity dressing; dependent for lower extremity dressing	Total dependence	Total dependence	Assisted by others and by equipment
C6	Some assistance required in supine position; independent in sitting postion	Independent with equipment; drinks from glass	Independent with equipment	Independent with upper extremity dressing; assistance needed for lower extremity dressing	Independent in upper and lower extremity bathing with equipment	Independent for bowel routine; assistance needed with bladder routing	Independent with equipment
C7	As above	Independent	Independent	Potential for independence in upper and lower extremity dressing with equipment	Independent with equipment	Independent	Independent
C8–T1	As above	Independent	Independent	Independent	Independent	Independent	Independent
T2–T10	T2–T6 as above; T6–T10 independent	Independent	Independent	Independent	Independent	Independent	Independent
T11–L2	Not applicable	Independent	Independent	Independent	Independent	Independent	Independent
L3–S3	Not applicable	Independent	Independent	Independent	Independent	Independent	Independent

BFO, balanced forearm orthosis.

Figure 9.2 *(continued)*

and prolonged dependence upon the parents to remain the primary caretakers for the rest of the patient's life. In these situations some type of respite care may be necessary. In addition, intense fear, anxiety, and feelings of helplessness may occur for both the patient and the family. What if there is a fire in the home? What if there is a power failure in the home of a ventilator dependent tetraplegic? Plans must be established for how to deal with these and other situations.

9.4 Survival and Prognosis

Patients who have been spinal cord injured need a scientific prediction of what the future holds. What the patient wants to hear is that she will be "normal" rather than she will never walk again. Unfortunately few patients will ever be close to the way they were. Every injury creates a major physical and emotional challenge for the patients and their families, requiring that every ounce of energy be summoned. Being told what the future brings is usually a psychological devastation to the patient and family. The grief and prolonged suffering that a family goes through are often worse than if the person had died. As the patient struggles to survive he has to also hold himself together to survive emotionally. This will prove to be the struggle of his life. The suffering that many patients go through is unending and results in permanent changes in personality. Ongoing psychological counseling can help both patients and caregivers to process the grief. However, many patients and families refuse psychological support. It is sometimes easier for them to go into denial, shut down and try to stay numb. Denial as a coping mechanism can become a very strong method of reacting after a spinal cord injury.

Tip

Patients and their families do survive and adjust; however, they may never accept the fact that they must live with a spinal cord injury.

Most patients and families want to know if the patient will ever walk again. Extensive research has been done to identify early predictors for ultimate walking ability. Penrod noted that in patients with symmetrical incomplete tetraplegia with some motor return the majority of the patients under fifty years old will ambulate, whereas the majority of patients over fifty years old will not be able to ambulate.[36] It becomes quite clear that age is a major factor in a "good" prognosis. Maximal recovery after a spinal cord injury is enhanced by the responsiveness of a young, healthy body and the motivation and determination displayed with the blood, sweat, and tears of hard therapy.

Additional research by Crozier[37] noted that the majority of patients who had an accurate sense of pinprick below the level of injury would ultimately ambulate. The majority of patients who could not accurately appreciate pinprick sensation below the level of injury would not be able to ambulate. The rationale behind the pinprick appreciation being predictive of motor recovery and ambulation is based on spinal cord anatomy. The spinal cord has distinct nerve tracts that are message pathways traveling from one area to another. The corticospinal tract is a specific pathway that carries messages to allow voluntary movement. Pathways begin in the brain, go through the spinal cord and ultimately end up at the specific muscles. The brain will send a message via the corticospinal tract to a leg to step forward. Right next to the corticospinal tract in the spinal cord is the spinothalamic tract. The corticospinal tract and the spinothalamic tract run closely together through the length of the spinal cord. The spinothalamic tract is the only tract that carries any pinprick sensation messages. When there is damage to one tract, there is likely damage to the other tract due to proximity. If pinprick is preserved below the level of injury, it indicates that the damage to the spinothalamic tract is limited. If the damage to this tract is limited, it is likely that the damage to the corticospinal tract is also limited. This is why pinprick sensation may be predictive of future motor return. Light touch sensation does not have the same specific predictive value because multiple tracts throughout the spinal cord carry the sensation of light touch.

Over the last fifty years the acute and long-term survival rates for patients with spinal cord injury have dramatically improved. In the past, it has often been cited that the ancient Egyptian physicians referred to spinal cord injury as "an ailment not to be treated."

With modern technological advances, the survival rates have significantly improved.

The leading cause of death in patients with spinal cord injury is usually due to respiratory changes. Death from pneumonia is more evident for patients with high tetraplegia, especially during the first year postinjury. With the advent of aggressive pulmonary care and newer antibiotics the death rate has significantly dropped and is expected to improve in the future.

In the past, deep vein thromboses (DVT) and pulmonary emboli (PE) contributed substantially to the mortality in the spinal cord injury population, especially in the first year postinjury. Medical advances in detecting and treating DVT and PE have significantly reduced the mortality rates, and these rates are expected to improve in the future. Septicemia, which is an infection that has spread to the blood stream, was also a major contributor to death; its risk is highest within the first two years after injury.

"Many of the deaths (of spinal cord injured patients) might be preventable with appropriate skin care, proper supplies and equipment, routine long-term follow-up and improved compliance with therapeutic regimens."[38] After a spinal cord injury, it is paramount that the patient has adequate access to ongoing appropriate medical care. Most regional spinal cord injury centers are committed to providing lifetime follow-up care for patients and their caregivers. Because spinal cord injury so severely affects every aspect of a patient's body, it is necessary to remain vigilant with regards to postinjury care. The past few years have brought about major advances in the care of the spinal cord injured patient that is only expected to continue in the future. Access to the technological advances in equipment and supplies as well as adequate caregiver support maximizes the patient's quantity and quality of life. Today, as long as the spinal cord injured patient has access to ongoing, advanced medical care in order to prevent and treat potential complications, his longevity can and often does approach a normal life span.

Endnotes

1. Go, B., Devivo, M., and Richard, J., "The Epidemiology of Spinal Cord Injury." In Stover, S., Delisa, J., and Whiteneck, G., eds., *Spinal Cord Injury: Clinical Outcomes from the Model Systems*. Gaithersburg, MD: Aspen, 1995, 21–55.

2. *American Spinal Injury Association International Standards for Neurological and Functional Classification of Spinal Cord Injury.* Chicago: American Spinal Injury Association, 1996.

3. Waters, F., Adkins, R., and Yakura, J., "Definition of Complete Spinal Cord Injury." *Paraplegia* 1991; 9:573–581.

4. Chiles, B. III, and Cooper, P., "Acute Spinal Injury." *New England Journal of Medicine*, 1996, 334:514–520.

5. Garfin, S., Marshall, L., Eisenberg, H., et al., "Spinal Cord Injury in Three Regions in the United States." *Paraplegia* 1988; 26:113. Abstract.

6. Waters, R., Apple, D., Mayer, P., et al., "Emergency and Acute Management of Spine Trauma." In Stover, S., Delisa, J., and Whiteneck, G., eds., *Spinal Cord Injury: Clinical Outcomes from the Model Systems*. Gaithersburg, MD: Aspen, 1995: 56–78.

7. Staas, W., Formal, C., Freedman, M., et al., "Spinal Cord Injury and Spinal Cord Injury Medicine." In Delisa, J., Gans, B., Bockenek, W. et al., eds., *Rehabilitation Medicine Principles and Practice*, Third Edition. Philadelphia: Lippincott-Raven, 1998, 1259–1287.

8. Jackson, A., and Groames, T., "Incidence of Respiratory Complications following Spinal Cord Injury." *Arch Phys Med Rehabil* 1994; 75:270–275.

9. Devivo, M., and Stover, S., "Long-Term Survival and Causes of Death." In Stover, S., Delisa, J., and Whiteneck, G., eds., *Spinal Cord Injury*. Gaithersburg, MD: Aspen, 1995, 289–316.

10. Devivo, M., and Ivie, C. "Life Expectancy of Ventilator-Dependent Persons with Spinal Cord Injuries." *Chest* 1995; 108:226–232

11. Cardenas, D., Burns, S., and Chan, L., "Rehabilitation of Spinal Cord Injury." In Grabois, M., Garrison, S., Hart, K., et al., eds., *Physical Medicine and Rehabilitation the Complete Approach.* Malden, MA: Blackwell Science, 2000, 1305–1321.

12. Whiteneck, G., Charlifue, S., Frankel, H., et al., "Mortality, Morbidity, and Psychosocial Outcomes of Persons Spinal Cord Injured More than 20 Years Ago." *Paraplegia* 1992; 30:617–630.

13. Byrne, D., and Salzberg, C., "Major Risk Factors for Pressure Ulcers in the Spinal Cord Disabled: A Literature Review." *Spinal Cord* 1996; 34:255–263.

14. Finerman, G., and Stover, S., "Heterotopic Ossification Following Hip Replacement on Spinal Cord Injury: Two Clinical Studies with EHDP." *Metab Bove Dis Relat Res* 1981; 3:337–342.

15. Guttman, F., and Whitteridge D., "Effects of Bladder Distention on Autonomic Mechanisms after Spinal Cord Injury." *Brain* 70 (1947): 361–404.

16. Calachis, S. III, "Autonomic Hyperreflexia with Spinal Cord Injury." *J Am Paraplegia Soc,* 15, 1992 171–86.

17. Maynard, F., Karunas, R., and Waring, W., "Epidemiology Spasticity Following Traumatic Spinal Cord Injury." *Arch Phys Med Rehabil* 1990; 71:566–569.

18. Barnett, H., and Jousse, A., "Post-Traumatic Syringomyelia (Cystic Myelopathy)." In Vinken, P., and Bruyn, E., eds., *Handbook of Clinical Neurology*. Amsterdam: North Holland; 1976, 26:113–157.

19. Backe, H., Betz, R., Mesgarzade, H., et al. "Post-Traumatic Spinal Cord Syrinx: An Evaluation by MRI." In *Abstracts Digest*. Chicago: American Spinal Injury Association, 1990, 85.

20. Lundquist, C., Siosteen, A., Blomstrand, C,. et.al. "Spinal Cord Injuries: Clinical, Functional and Emotional Status." *Spine* 1991; 16:78–83.

21. Tunks, E., "Pain in Spinal Cord Injured Patients." In Bloch, R., and Basbaum, eds. *Management of Spinal Cord Injuries*. Baltimore: Williams and Wilkins, 1986: 180–211.

22. Bonica, J., "Introductions: Semantic, Epidemiological and Educational Issues." In Casey, K., editor, *Pain and Central Nervous System Disease: The Central Pain Syndromes*. New York: Raven Press, 1991, 12–28.

23. Mariano, A., "Chronic Pain and Spinal Cord Injury." *Clin J Pain* 1992; 8:87–92.

24. Nepomuceno, C., Fine, P., Richards, J., et al., "Pain in Patients with Spinal Cord Injury." *Arch Phys Med Rehab* 1979; 60:604–608.

25. Prithvi, P. Raj., "Pain Mechanisms." In *Pain Medicine: A Comprehensive Review.* St. Louis: Mosby 1996, 12–43.

26. Levitt, M., and Levitt, J., "The Deafferation Syndrome in Monkeys: Dysesthesias of Spinal Origin." *Pain* 1981; 10:129–147.

27. Inbal, R., Devor, M., Tuchhendler, O., et al,." Autotomy Following Nerve Injury: Genetic Factors in the Development of Chronic Pain." *Pain* 1980; 9:327–337.

28. Tasker, R., "Pain Resulting from Central Nervous System Pathology (Central Pain)." In Bonica, J., editor, *The Management of Pain*, Second Edition. Philadelphia: Lea and Febiger, 1990, 264–280.

29. Wall, D., "On the Origin of Pain Associated with Amputation." In Siegfried, J., and Zimmerman, M., eds., *Phantom and Stump Pain*. Berlin: Springer-Verlag, 1981, 2–14.

30. Lundquist, C., Siosteen, A., Bloomstrand, C., et al. Spinal Cord Injuries: Clinical, Functional and Emotional Status. *Spine*. 1991; 16:78–83.

31. Gellman, H., Sie, I., and Waters, R., "Late Complications of the Weight-Bearing Upper Extremity in the Paraplegic Patient." *Clin Orthop.* 1987; 233:132–135.

32. Bayley, J., Cochran, T., and Sledge, C., "The Weight-Bearing Shoulder." *J Bone Joint Surg.* 1987; 69A(5): 676–678.

33. Maynard, F., Karunas, R., Adkins, R., et al., "Management of the Neuromusculoskeletal Systems." In Stover, S., Delisa, J., and Whiteneck, G., eds,. *Spinal Cord Injury: Clinical Outcomes from the Model Systems*. Gaithersburg, MD: Aspen, 1995, 145–170.

34. *Clinical Practice Guideline: Spinal Cord Medicine. Depression Following Spinal Cord Injury: A Clinical Practice Guideline for Primary Care Physicians*. Paralyzed Veterans of America, 1998, 1–30.

35. Dijkers, M., Abela, M., Gans, B., and Gordon, W., "The Aftermath of Spinal Cord Injury." In Stover, S., Delisa J., and Whitneck, G., eds. *Spinal Cord Injury: Clinical Outcomes from the Model Systems*. Gaithersburg, MD: Aspen, 1995, 185–212.

36. Penrod L., Hegde, S., and Ditunno, J. Jr., "Age Effect on Prognosis for Functional Recovery in Acute, Traumatic Central Cord Syndrome." *Arch Phys Med Rehabil* 1990; 71:963–968.

37. Crozier, K., Graziani, V., Ditunno, J., et al., "Spinal Cord Injury: Prognosis for Ambulation Based on Sensory Ex-

amination in Patients Who Are Initially Motor Complete." *Arch Phys Med Rehabil* 1991; 72:119–121.

38. Devivo, M., and Stover, S., "Long-Term Survival and Causes of Death." In: Stover, S., Delisa J., and Whiteneck, G., eds., *Spinal Cord Injury: Clinical Outcomes from the Model Systems*. Gaithersburg, MD: Aspen, 1995, 289–317.

Chapter 10

Pain and Suffering in Orthopaedics

Nancy E. Mooney, MA, RN, ONC

Synopsis

10.1 Introduction

Orthopaedics is the specialty that cares for individuals with musculoskeletal injuries and disorders across the life span. From the neonate with congenital disorders, through the frail elderly person suffering a hip fracture, orthopaedic caregivers restore motion and function and help an individual get back to an optimal level of functioning.

Salmond reports that the burden of musculoskeletal disease to the United States is profound. Musculoskeletal injuries are a major cause of morbidity and have a substantial effect on health and quality of life. They are the number one category of reported chronic impairment and the number one reason for visits to physicians accounting for more than 131 million visits to healthcare providers and 7.3 million musculoskeletal procedures performed annually.[1] Orthopaedic injuries commonly occur in a variety of personal injury accidents, from falls to motor vehicle accidents.

Chronic pain from orthopaedic injuries causes suffering on many levels to patients and their families—physical, financial, spiritual, emotional and psychological. It is difficult to imagine or measure the amount of hopelessness and loss some patients feel. While many orthopaedic patients are able to return to their optimal ability (we tend to not use the term normal in orthopaedics, as it is relative to individuals with physical challenges), many suffer over long periods of time and have life-changing sequelae from accidents or failed surgeries.

Walid Aref's car was broken down in the left lane of a highway at night. The tail lights and emergency flashers were on. The car was hit by another driver, pushing the car and Aref, who was standing behind it, twenty feet. Aref's left leg was cut off at the knee by the impact. His right leg was crushed, requiring amputation above the knee. He also suffered a broken neck and back injuries. Aref, age forty, suffers from back and neck pain, depression, and phantom pain. A man with a Ph.D. in computer science who owned a consulting company before the accident, he has since taken a lower-paying but less physically demanding job teaching at a university. The settlement has a present value of $11 million.[2]

Musculoskeletal conditions, including back disorders, arthritis, and orthopaedic impairments, rank in the top five of the reported causes of activity limitation and work disability in the United States. The direct and indirect costs (mortality and morbidity) of musculoskeletal disease are estimated to be $215 billion per year.[1]

The World Health Organization is promoting bone and joint health in an international initiative, the Bone and Joint Decade 2000–2010. There are four goals of this initiative:

- Reduce the social and financial burden of musculoskeletal conditions to society.
- Improve prevention, diagnosis, and treatment for all clients.
- Advance research on prevention and treatment.
- Empower clients to make decisions about their care.

Musculoskeletal disorders are the most common causes of severe long-term pain and physical disability, affecting hundreds of millions of people across the world. The extent of the problem and its burden on patients and society can be understood from some examples:

- Joint diseases account for half of all chronic conditions in persons aged 65 and over.
- Back pain is the second leading cause of sick leave.
- Fractures related to osteoporosis have almost doubled in number in the last decade; it is estimated that 40% of all women over fifty years in age will suffer from an osteoporotic fracture.
- The severe injuries caused by traffic accidents and war produce a tremendous demand for preventive and restorative help. It is anticipated that 25% of health expenditures of developing countries will be spent on trauma-related care by the year 2010.
- Crippling diseases and deformities continue to deprive many children of their normal development.

The effects of such bone and joint disorders on the individual, society, and healthcare and social systems led to an initiative beginning with an inaugural Consensus Meeting held in Lund, Sweden, in April, 1998 and culminating in a proposal for the Decade of the Bone and Joint from 2000–2010.[3]

The Decade of the Bone and Joint will raise awareness of the suffering and cost to society associated with musculoskeletal disorders such as joint diseases, osteoporosis, spinal disorders, severe trauma to the extremities, and crippling diseases and deformities in children; the means to reduce this presently available, and the need to advance this through research.

No one single organization can accomplish the desired benefits for the patient. The Bone and Joint Decade is a multidisciplinary initiative involving everyone concerned, including communities, patients, healthcare providers, and researchers.

The goals of the Decade will be achieved by

1. raising awareness of the growing burden of musculoskeletal disorders on society,
2. empowering patients to participate in their own care,
3. promoting cost-effective prevention and treatment, and
4. advancing understanding of musculoskeletal disorders through research to improve prevention and treatment.

10.2 Causes of Orthopaedic Pain

Rothley and Therrien propose seven causes of orthopaedic pain. They are:

1. Distortion of tissue, vessels, and periarticular nerve plexus (nerves surrounding the joints) creates immediate sharp nociceptive pain. Nociception is defined as the actual sensation resulting from the activation of specific nerve pathways as a consequence of tissue damage.
2. Pain may result from distention of joint capsule or fascial compartment by fluid and blood accumulation following an injury.
3. Pressure may increase within a compartment and result in irreversible death to the tissue if not relieved.
4. Pain results from tissue damage that releases bradykinin, serotonin, prostaglandin, and histamine. These are all compounds that are released locally when the tissue is damaged, to alert the body that something is wrong.
5. Prostaglandin, produced through a series of events related to traumatized tissue, is thought to be the precursor to the painful perception.
6. There is evidence of swelling, redness and heat.

7. Musculoskeletal pain is brought on by use or weight bearing and relieved with rest. Chronic recurrence of pain indicates instability of the structure.[4]

10.3 Assessment of Neurovascular Status

The hallmark of musculoskeletal care is the neurovascular assessment. This assessment includes evaluating how much the person can move the extremity, as well as what sensations could be felt. When a healthcare professional is performing a neurovascular assessment, it is important to have a baseline assessment documented prior to surgery or a procedure. It is also important compare the affected side with the unaffected side and to document the results.

Tip

Changes in baseline assessment of how fingers or toes move or feel can indicate to the healthcare professional that something is wrong.

Most healthcare facilities have a policy and procedure which spell out who can perform this assessment, where to document it, and how often it should be done. This policy may be of importance in a medical malpractice case when a critical series of assessments was not performed when warranted, such as after orthopaedic surgery or an orthopaedic injury. Both sensation and motion are measured in assessing the nerves. Generally, three nerves in the upper extremity and two in the lower are assessed. Figure 10.1 summarizes the important assessment criteria for each of these nerves.

Neurovascular assessment is a key principle in the management of orthopaedic patients. If a patient has a normal neurovascular assessment preoperatively, or before a procedure is done (such as cast application), care must be taken to avoid the many complications that could happen. Some of these complications include foot drop, which can change a person's life forever. Foot drop happens when the patient loses the integrity of his motor and sensory neurovascular status. Delays in reporting changes in the neurovascular status (which can be subtle) can lead to not only foot drop but also other catastrophic diagnoses such as compartment syndrome, paralysis, and so forth. Documentation of neurovascular status is key, and the nurse should document a clear assessment of both the motor (can the patient move the body part in question?) and sensory (can the patient feel touch to the body part?) parts being tested. Generally, the standard of practice is a baseline assessment and an ongoing assessment according to the institution's policy.

In the case of *Richard Henry v. Balkrisha Jagdale, M.D., and Heritage Hospital* in Michigan, the forty-six-year-old plaintiff suffered a fall at home, fracturing his fibula (one of the smaller bones in the leg). The plaintiff developed foot drop and alleged that prior to his surgery his foot was neurologically intact. He alleged that the tourniquet (used in surgery to control bleeding)

Hand

Nerve	Sensation	Motion
Radial nerve	Prick the web space between the thumb and the index finger.	Have patient hyperextend ("high five" motion) thumb then wrist
Ulnar nerve	Prick the fat pad at the end of the small finger.	Have patient open fingers, separating fingers.
Median nerve	Prick the fat pad at the end of the index finger.	Have patient touch thumb to small finger; see if he can flex his wrist.

Leg

Nerve	Sensation	Motion
Peroneal nerve	Prick the web space between the big toe and the second toe.	Have patient dorsiflex ankle ("step on the gas" motion)
Tibial nerve	Prick the middle and side of the sole of the foot.	Have the patient plantarflex ankle and toes (motion is to bring foot toward patient)

Figure 10.1 *Neurovascular assessment*

was placed on his leg too long during surgery and inflated too high. The defendants contended that the tourniquet was placed properly but the patient had a preexisting condition of his leg, a motor neuron disease (like Lou Gehrig's disease) which led to the foot drop. The jury returned a defense verdict.[5]

Tip

Neurovascular assessment is critical, and it is important that the physicians and nurses document findings in the medical record. Since the nurses are with the patient twenty-four hours a day, it is an important nursing function to advocate for the patient and report abnormal findings to the physician. Communication is key in preventing serious complications, such as compartment syndrome and foot drop.

10.4 Fractures

Simply stated, a fracture is a disruption, complete or incomplete, in the continuity of a bone. Trauma is the number one cause of death in Americans ages one to forty-four and the third leading cause of death in Americans in general. Fractures can occur in all age groups, at any point of the skeletal system, and may negatively affect the quality of an individual's life. There are basically two types of fractures, open and closed. Open fractures (formerly known as compound fractures) are those in which there is a loss of the continuity of the bone internally and there is an external wound communicating directly with the fracture site, or there is a fracture fragment protruding through the skin. In closed fractures (formerly known as simple fractures, a misleading term as it can be very complicated) there is no break in the skin.

There are many types of fractures, classified by their severity. Figure 10.2 summarizes the types of open fractures based on wound and severity.

As is evident from the list, fractures cause a lot of pain. The words "disruption in the continuity of a bone" are a sanitized way of saying "this hurts!" Depending on the age of the person, and where the fracture occurs, the pain differs. For example, some children experience greenstick fractures that are picked up healed on x-rays (often putting parents and caregivers under suspicion of child abuse). A careful history must be obtained to ascertain how and why injuries occur.

Tip

Parents of children with healed fractures visible on x-ray may not even know that the child had a fracture and are sometimes accused falsely of abuse.

Along with the fracture, the person experiences swelling (edema) which can increase the pain. Consider a fracture of the ankle. There is not much space

Type	Soft Tissue Damage	Contamination	Other Characteristics
I	Minimal	Minimal	Small wound (< 1cm) Simple transverse fracture, transverse or oblique with skin pierced by bone spike
II	Moderate	Moderate	Wound > 1 cm. in size Comminution (> 2 fragments)/crush injuries
III	Extensive, including muscle, skin and neurovascular structures	High	Severe comminution and instability Traumatic amputations See below for subgroups of Type III
III A	Soft tissue coverage of fracture is adequate	High	Segmental or severely comminuted fractures.
III B	Extensive injury to or loss of soft tissue, periostial stripping, and exposure of bone	Massive	Severe comminuted fractures.
III C			Any open fracture associated with arterial injury that must be repaired regardless of the degree of soft tissue injury.

Figure 10.2 *Classification of fractures*

there, so when it does swell (and all fractures do) there is nowhere for the edema to go, which increases the pressure and, ultimately, the person's pain.

Fractures can also be characterized by the type of fracture line. The type of fracture dictates the kind of pain the person will have, although it is safe to say that most fractures are painful and require immediate medical attention. Figure 10.3 summarizes the types of fracture by what they look like on an x-ray.[6]

Given that the human skeleton has 206 bones, there are a multitude of descriptions of fractures related to anatomical part. For example, in the forearm and wrist there are twelve separate fractures, each named for a distinct part of the forearm and wrist. Some are common (Colles' fracture, which is a distal radial head fracture, resulting from a fall on an outstretched hand), and some very rare (Essex-Lopresti, which is another radial head fracture, with a distal radioulnar dislocation, resulting from perhaps a similar fall but landing in a different direction).

A. Why does a fracture hurt?

Many fractures are caused by extrinsic factors, such as accidents, high-risk activities such as skateboarding, and penetrating factors, such as gunshot wounds. Some are caused by intrinsic factors, such as energy-absorbing capacity, elasticity, fatigue strength, size, and density.

Tip

It is easy to see that fractures cause pain when the mechanism of injury is considered. They are caused by direct force, such as a motor vehicle accident, crush injuries, and so forth.

Rarely do fractures occur alone. For example, a person who has been involved in a motor vehicle acci-

Name	Definition	Type of Injury Causing this Fracture
Angulated	Fractures not in alignment	Any trauma
Avulsion	Bone fragments and tissue are pulled away from bone at the insertion site	Shoulder injuries
Burst	Multiple fracture fragment, usually at the end of the bone	Spine injury
Butterfly	Segmental or comminuted fracture, with a center fragment shaped like a triangle	Trauma
Chip	Tiny fragment, usually near a joint	Elbow trauma
Comminuted	Fracture is in more than 2 pieces	Forceful trauma
Complete	Fracture line goes completely through the bone, through the entire thickness of the bone including the cortex	Forceful trauma
Compression	Force to long axis of bone and usually result in tubular bone changing in size and shape	Vertebral fractures
Depressed	Fracture fragment is displaced below the level surface of the bone	Skull fracture
Displaced	Ends of fracture fragments are separated	Forceful trauma
Impacted	Direct force causes a telescoping of bone (smaller fragment goes into larger diameter of bone)	Some hip fractures – when knee hits dashboard in a MVA
Salter Harris	Classification of epiphyseal growth plate	Children's fractures
Spiral	Twisting force resulting in an oblique fracture coiling around the bone	Femur fracture – skiing injuries, where foot is in one plane, and the thigh rotates forcefully, can also occur is an extremity such as an arm is grabbed while the person is trying to pull away, as in abuse.
Transverse	Crosses the shaft of the bone involved at a 90 degree angle	Angulation force.

Figure 10.3 *Classification of fractures by appearance*

dent could easily have a fracture, which affects soft tissue, nerves, muscle, vessels, and tendons. Movement causes further pain, which is why patients with suspected fractures are kept in one place until the extremity can be immobilized with a splint. Fractures themselves are painful, but the concomitant soft tissue damage is also quite painful.

A thirty-seven-year-old man was injured when he slipped on ice in a parking lot of a shopping center. He alleged that the icy patch was the result of overnight hosing in the loading dock area and that the parking lot was improperly maintained. He suffered multiple fractures to his right ankle and a torn meniscus. After undergoing four operations, he is now suffering from traumatic arthritis and likely will need ankle fusion surgery. He is no longer able to work as a delivery person but is employed in light construction. He had to give up his work as a volunteer firefighter and his position as a drummer in a garage band. This suit was settled for $425,000.[7]

Tip

A thorough neurovascular assessment can inform the clinician of the degree to which soft tissue and nerves are damaged. Depending on where the fracture is located, the bone shards can cause other damage to the body—nerves can be severed in the mechanism of injury, clots can form from a fracture, causing pulmonary emboli, and unless bleeding is controlled internal hemorrhage is a possibility if, for example, a fracture happens near an organ such as the spleen.

B. Fracture healing

The amazing and in some ways unique characteristic of bone is that healing does occur through regeneration of tissue rather than scar tissue formation. For example, if a person has a heart attack, there is death to the tissue that does not regenerate. Given the appropriate circulation to the fracture site, as well as adequate immobilization, bone can heal. Bone is dynamic tissue, and can be classified as either cancellous (spongy) or cortical (compact). Bone forms and remodels itself in response to the force applied to it. This is known as Wolff's law, which postulates that osteogenesis (bone formation) is stimulated by the direction of loading forces. Bone strength is greatest where maximal stress is applied from any area with a bony structure.[6] There are several reasons why fractures heal—the location of the fracture (and whether the bone had a good blood supply at the end of the bones), immobilization, the extent of the soft tissue damage, and the weight-bearing status of the bone.

Bone heals over time, and there are five stages of fracture healing. They are:

I. Hematoma formation. The blood clot forms at the fracture site.
II. Fibrocartilage formation. Granulation tissue (tissue that contains blood vessels as well as the beginning of the bone regrowth) forms around the hematoma.
III. Callus formation. The granulation tissue begins to mature.
IV. Ossification. Bone gradually replaces the callus.
V. Consolidation and remodeling. Bone is reshaped.

X-rays are the hallmark of diagnosing fractures, although not all are appreciated in the early stages of the injury. When there is a lot of soft tissue injury, and a lot of swelling, it may mask the actual fracture. Early intervention can lead to correct management of a fracture.

Tip

The goal in fracture management is for the bone to heal and for function to be restored.

When not healed properly, fractures can lead to deformity and post traumatic arthritis. Post traumatic arthritis is a sequela of complicated fractures, generally occurring in the shoulder in the upper extremity and the knees in the lower. This complication leads to difficulties in managing one's day-to-day activities. Simple activities, such as brushing one's hair and walking, are painful. If the arthritis is severe enough, joint replacement surgery is required. This puts the patient through a surgical procedure, the risk of anesthesia, a recovery period with physical therapy, and the potential of rejection of the prostheses. Much pain can result from not having the fracture treated properly, which may result in another procedure to correct the deformity.

An example of this improperly treated fracture is illustrated in the case of *George Gleason v. Anant Ram, M.D.* The plaintiff sustained severe fractures to his right ankle and right wrist when he slipped and fell at home. The defendant did not treat the right wrist surgically, but put the plaintiff in a cast. (The right ankle was treated surgically, with a positive outcome.) The wrist fracture did not heal in the cast, which led to deformity and severe pain. The defendant underwent four surgeries on his wrist before he obtained a pain-free wrist. The jury awarded the plaintiff $105,000 in noneconomic damages.[8]

10.5 Modalities of Immobilization

A. Casts

Once a fracture has occurred, the principle involved is to immobilize the fracture in a manner which will promote healing, minimize pain, and keep the patient as mobile as possible. In general, a fracture is immobilized above and below the fracture. For example, for a tibia (lower leg) fracture, the cast would incorporate the ankle and the knee to prevent motion in the fracture. One mechanism of immobilization is casting. A cast is an immobilizing device made up of layers of plaster or fiberglass (water activated polyurethane resin) bandages molded to the body part that it encases. There are five purposes of casts:

- to immobilize and hold bone fragments in reduction,
- to apply uniform compression of soft tissues,
- to promote early mobilization,
- to correct and prevent deformities, and
- to support and stabilize weak joints.

Casts are categorized as short arm, short leg, long arm, and long leg, depending on the fracture. While they are heavy, they do provide comfort to individuals while the fracture heals. The healthcare provider can monitor the fracture healing through an x-ray of the extremity—bone can be seen through a plaster cast. Depending on the healing process of the individual and the degree of the injury, casts are worn for four to eight weeks.

There are complications with casts if they are not monitored closely. Pressure on the cast by neurovascular and bony structures can cause nerve palsies or weakness, pressure sores, and necrosis (tissue death). These complications imply that the extremity is either numb, has the feeling of "pins and needles" and is not only painful, but not functional. This might happen when something is put into the cast. For example, a well-meaning adult might want to scratch an itch in the cast and put a wire hanger in the cast that cannot come out. Children are notorious for inserting small toys, pencils, or whatever will fit into a cast. If not found, the item can cause pressure and pain to the patient. It is part of the routine care of a patient with a cast to educate the patient not to put anything down the cast.

B. Cast brace

Cast braces are based on the concept that some weight bearing will assist the fracture in healing. These devices are a combination of a cast and a hinged brace which promotes the formation of bone and provides a distribution of forces across the fracture site, promoting healing. They are usually applied once the initial edema and pain have subsided and there is evidence of fracture stability. The principle of cast braces is to promote early motion of joints and ambulation.

C. Traction

There are essentially three kinds of traction—skin, skeletal, and manual, as defined below. Traction is a force applied in a specific direction. There are six purposes of traction. They are

- to reduce and immobilize a fracture,
- to regain normal length and alignment of an injured extremity,
- to lessen or eliminate muscle spasm,
- to prevent deformity,
- to allow patients freedom to do some activities in bed, and
- to reduce pain.

Manual traction is used to reduce fractures prior to treatment or immobilization. An example of manual traction is for a dislocated shoulder—the healthcare provider pulls on the individual's arm, using traction to return the shoulder to its normal position. This happens with pitching injuries, where the shoulder becomes separated in the thrusting motion.

Skin traction is used for short-term traction, to exert a small amount of traction on a fractured extremity. Patients who have hip fractures often have skin traction (called Buck's traction) while they await going to the operating room. Skin traction provides temporary comfort to patients and can be removed and reapplied periodically. No more than five to eight pounds of traction is generally used with skin traction (less for children). This type of traction is also used on children. Complications of skin traction can be skin blisters and necrosis. The skin in the traction needs to be inspected periodically for any untoward reaction.

Skeletal traction is a force applied to a body part through fixation directly into or through bone by means of a metal pin or screw. This is rarely used, as technology has shown us that taking patients to the operating room and fixating their fracture gets them up earlier, preventing many of the complications that go along with prolonged bed rest. (Pneumonia, pressure sores, renal calculi, foot drop, and so forth.) If the soft tissue damage is profound, a patient may be in skeletal traction for some time until the tissue heals.

D. External fixation

External fixation is a method of fracture immobilization in which a system of percutaneous pins or wires is connected to a rigid external frame. It can be constructed in many different configurations and permits three-plane corrections of deformities. It might be used in an open fracture where there is a high risk for infection. The places where external fixation is generally used are pelvic fractures, fingers, and the limbs.

Tip

Pin tract infections may be complications of an external fixator. The risk of infection increases the longer the fixator is in place. Generally, the longer the fixator is in place, the higher the probability is that the pins can loosen. Loose pins need to be reported to the physician and in some cases, removed so that the pin tract infection does not lead to osteomyelitis, a serious bone infection.

The fixator is applied under general anesthesia, and there is pain associated with the surgery. In the first few weeks of having the fixator, the patient experiences pain and needs to be medicated, but in time (these are worn for up to a year) the pain subsides.

10.6 Complications

Prevention of complications is another hallmark of orthopaedic care. The team caring for the orthopaedic patient works hard to get these patients mobile, ambulating, and generally moving to prevent some of the sequelae of orthopaedic injuries. The hazards of immobility are fairly clear: staying in bed leads to pneumonia, pressure sores, weakness, urinary retention, increased heart rate, and so forth. Just about every system has increased stress, leading often to pain, when one is immobile. For example, pressure sores from staying in one position too long are painful and often preventable for immobile patients. Prevention of these complications is the major goal of the orthopaedic community. Some of the complications related to orthopaedic conditions are the following:

A. Bone union problems

For the most part, fractures heal. Complications may arise that prevent that healing. They are:

- **delayed union**. The bone takes longer to heal than average for the type of fracture. This occurs most commonly in the tibia and fibula, and the scaphoid.
- **nonunion**. The fractured bone fails to unite, causing both pain at the fracture site and the inability for the patient to heal; nonunion relates to healing that has not taken place in four to six months.
- **malunion**. The fracture heals, but not in alignment, causing a deformity of the bone.

B. Cast syndrome

Cast syndrome (superior mesenteric artery syndrome) is a rare sequela of body cast application, yet it is a potentially fatal condition. It is thought to be caused by a hyperextension of the spine, causing a lumbar lordosis, leading to compression of the third portion of the duodenum between the superior mesenteric artery and the aorta, posteriorly. Symptoms include abdominal pain, distention, and vomiting. While a rare complication, it happens in children following body cast application—following Harrington rod insertion for scoliosis. The treatment includes decompressing the abdomen and bowel with a nasogastric tube, and feeding the patient intravenously for three to four days. Vigilant assessment of the patient's intake (fluid and food) and listening with a stethoscope to the stomach—listening for the presence of bowel sounds—will prevent any further progression of cast syndrome.

C. Limb length discrepancies

This is a difference in length between the two upper extremities or the two lower ones. In general, it is the lower extremities that are more problematic, as a change in the angle of the pelvis causes pain to the hips and knees from constant limping. The etiology of the discrepancy can be congenital, vascular, or neurological or due to a tumor, infection, or fracture.[9]

D. Osteomyelitis

This is a severe pyogenic infection of the bone and surrounding tissues that requires immediate treatment. Pyogenic means it is infected, or septic, and pus producing. It is transmitted in one of three ways:

- through the bloodstream
- through an adjacent soft tissue injury
- direct introduction of the causative microorganism into the bone

Osteomyelitis occurs in neonates, children, and adults, for different reasons. These patients undergo surgical intervention, and long-term intravenous antibiotics (four to eight weeks), and have wounds that are painful, non-healing, often draining. There may also be tenderness to the area, as well as muscle spasm. The key here is prevention, and all healthcare workers, as well as the patient and family, are encouraged to use good hand washing techniques as well as infection control principles to prevent infection when working with any patient who has an orthopaedic injury.

E. Foot drop

Foot drop is a disorder of the distal aspect of a lower extremity. This impairment is a malfunction of either a peripheral nerve or a part of the central nervous system. It is also known as peroneal nerve disorder or palsy. The peroneal nerve is a section of the sciatic nerve, and pressure on the peroneal nerve can cause foot drop. Since the peroneal nerve is located superficially near the side of the knee, it can be injured in surgery (for example, total hip arthroplasty, disc injuries), or with prolonged bed rest.

Foot drop results in lifestyle changes. Simple things like driving become challenging, as the patient no longer has the ability to move the foot up and down—it is generally in a drooping position. Patients can wear a brace to bring the foot into a normal position, but this is a serious, life-changing event. Foot drop, the main component of a peroneal nerve lesion, is a condition that is difficult to disregard.

10.7 Hip Fractures

Hip fractures are one of the most costly and devastating injuries suffered by Americans. The Agency for Health Care Policy and Research (now called the Agency for Healthcare Research and Quality) has estimated that over 350,000 incidents of hip fracture occur each year, accounting for approximately 30% of all fracture related hospitalizations. More than 4% of these patients, generally frail elderly people with other preexisting health problems, die during their hospitalization. Within a year of the injury, 5%–10% will die.[10]

Patients with hip fracture undergo the pain of surgery, and the agonizing rehabilitation period, which is uncomfortable because ambulation is hard work for these patients, many of whom are deconditioned and sometimes anemic or malnourished. Typically, the patients are women, over sixty-five years old, who might have osteoporosis which leads her to be at risk to fall due to brittle bones. In addition, if the hip fracture is a result of a fall (which is often the case) the person is very hesitant to "get back on the horse."

As the population of the United States ages, there will be an increase of hip fractures. By the year 2040 the number of individuals over sixty-five is expected to almost double.[11] The costs of treating patients with hip fractures will rise significantly as well. The National

Consensus Conference on Improving the Continuum of Care for Patients with Hip Fracture estimates that the cost could increase three- to eightfold by the year 2040. As an unappreciated public health issue, hip fractures are serious business, and there is really no way to estimate the cost emotionally to individuals and their families. The recommendation of the Consensus Conference is to return the patients to their preferred living situation, ideally home with affordable services. The goal of returning patients home cannot be overemphasized because of its effect on the medical, psychosocial, financial, and cultural needs of each patient.[12]

A. Risks

Orthopaedic surgery, like all surgery, brings with it some level of risk to the patient. All patients give informed consent prior to having surgery and should have an opportunity to speak with the surgeon about the possibilities of complications. Orthopaedic nurses and physicians work hard to prevent these complications. For the most part, early ambulation is encouraged so that many of these complications do not happen.

B. Fat embolism syndrome (FIS)

Fat embolism occurs after trauma or long bone fractures and is a major cause of morbidity and mortality. Fat emboli are small collections of fat globules which travel from the marrow of the bone through the bloodstream and wind up in the patient's lungs.

Restlessness, confusion, irritability, and disorientation may be the first signs of fat embolism syndrome.

Tip

Young adults (ages twenty to thirty) and older adults (ages sixty to seventy) with multiple fractures, long bone fractures or pelvic fractures are particularly susceptible to development of fat emboli.

The exact mechanism of how this occurs is not well understood, and the mortality rate ranges from 5%–15%.[13] The patient is acutely ill, has difficulty breathing, and depending on the amount of fat globules deposited in the lungs, can go into shock and die very quickly.

C. Pulmonary embolism (PE)

Pulmonary embolism refers to the obstruction of one or more pulmonary arteries by a thrombus (clot) originating usually in the deep veins of the legs or the right side of the heart. There are many risk factors associated with pulmonary emboli, including

- immobilization,
- obesity,
- varicose veins,
- trauma,
- pelvic fractures,
- lower extremity (especially hip fractures),
- a history of thromboembolic disease,
- pregnancy,
- postoperative patients, and
- being elderly.

These patients suffer chest pain, difficulty in breathing, and a tremendous amount of apprehension. This, too is considered an orthopaedic emergency and requires critical intervention. Sculco (2002) and colleagues[14] report that fatal pulmonary embolus is lowered to <0.1% by three things:

- collective use of predeposited autologous blood,
- expeditious operative technique (getting patients to the operating room more quickly) so clots don't have time to form from prolonged immobility, and
- early mobilization.

D. Deep vein thrombosis (DVT)

Patients who have orthopaedic surgery, or have any kind of trauma are at risk for deep vein thrombosis (DVT). A thrombosis is a blood clot, and much like the fat emboli it goes through the bloodstream to the lungs, causing a pulmonary embolus. This is a great concern of all patients having hip and knee surgery and is of concern to all orthopaedic caregivers. Early ambulation and mobility are the keys to preventing DVT. There are several modalities to prevent DVT. The medications used are aspirin, coumadin or low-molecular heparin. Prescribing these medications is specific to the surgeon. Several issues contribute to the preference—what the surgeon is used to using, what has worked for him or her, patient selection and compliance, and the home care situation of the patient. For example, if the patient takes coumadin, he has to have his blood drawn daily to see what his blood level is. This may be impractical for some patients. Other patients are taught to do self injection (of low molecular heparin) and need to have their blood drawn weekly. Coordination of this is important in the discharge plan for the patient.

Mechanical devices, such as antiembolic stockings (elastic bandages), sequential compression devices which assist the pumping of the blood back up to the heart, and foot pumps which do the same thing are used while the patient is in bed. Once they are up and walking, the foot pumps and sequential compression devices are generally discontinued. The antiembolic stockings may still be worn, but their efficacy in returning blood to the heart is limited.

A deep vein thrombosis is a painful process, because the patient has a clot in a vein. Warm, moist heat is generally prescribed, as well as elevation of the extremity, and an analgesic.

10.8 Revised Total Arthroplasty

Total hip replacement is a common surgery the United States. The hip is a ball and socket joint, with the ball being the head of the femur and the socket the acetabulum. The surgery involves resecting the femoral head and neck and then preparing the acetabulum for the new hip, which generally comes in three pieces which are fitted to the patient's anatomy: a femoral neck and stem, a femoral head, and an acetabulum. This is done in the most sterile of conditions, as infection is possible at every part of the surgery.

Tip

The number one reason a patient has a total hip replacement is to reduce pain. When the pain keeps the patient up at night and is not relieved by medications, exercise, and so forth, the patient will opt to have the surgery.

Surgeons should discuss all possibilities of complications with patients having any kind of surgery. Specific to total hip replacement is a loosening of the prosthesis. Loosening of the prosthesis might lead to a

- Which is your dominant hand?
- Can you dress and feed yourself?
- Does this injury interfere with your daily activity?
- Does this injury interfere with your family activity – for example, if you have small children, can you lift them up?
- What kind of work did you do prior to this injury?
- Can you do it now?
- How are you limited in your activity now?
- Do you feel weak in your arms or hands?
- While in the hospital, did you have a lot of pain?
- Did you get pain medication when you asked for it?
- Was it enough to make the pain better?
- Did you have any side effects from the medication?
- Were your doctors and nurses attentive to your pain?
- Can you still wear rings on your fingers?
- Do you ever experience numbness or tingling in your hands?
- Does your pain keep you from sleeping at night?
- Do you think about the pain all the time?
- Did you receive any physical or occupational therapy while in the hospital?
- Did anyone discuss goals with you concerning your injury?
- How would you describe your quality of life now?
- Can you wear shoes you wore prior to your injury?
- Do you have difficulty walking?
- Do you have difficulty with your balance?
- Do you have pain or tingling in your feet?
- Do your hands or feet ever go numb?
- Do you have a limp you didn't have before?
- If you had pins in your legs or hands, did someone clean them routinely?
- Were you taught how to care for these pins?

Figure 10.4 *Questions for attorneys to ask clients about orthopaedic injuries*

revision surgery. The following are indications for revision:

- fracture of the femoral shaft
- repeated dislocation
- infection
- incorrect placement of the prosthesis
- acetabular protrusion
- heterotopic bone formation
- loosening

With the individualization of the components, loosening occurs less commonly following total hip replacement. Pain related to loosening is relieved by rest, while pain experienced in the groin is probably due to a loose socket.

10.9 Summary

Figure 10.4 lists some questions an attorney might ask clients about their orthopaedic injuries. The specialty of orthopaedics provides the patient with clear goals to restoration of function and mobility. Meeting those goals cause much pain, and a large part of the orthopaedic patient's day is trying to manage that pain while continuing the mobility. Bone has the capacity to heal, and with the right conditions, it does.

Endnotes

1. Salmond, S., "Orthopaedic Wellness." In Maher, A., Salmond, S., and Pellino, T., eds., *Orthopaedic Nursing*, Third Edition. Philadelphia: W.B. Saunders, 2002.

2. Suits and Deals, *New Jersey Law Journal*, March 11, 2002.

3. Bone and Joint Decade 2000–2010. For prevention and treatment of musculoskeletal disorders. Executive summary. [Online] http://www.boneandjointdecade.org.

4. Rothley, B., and Therrien, S., "Acute Pain Management." In St. Marie, B., editor, *Core Curriculum for Pain Management Nurses.* Philadelphia: W.B. Saunders, 2002.

5. Suits and Deals, *New Jersey Law Journal*, April 11, 2002.

6. Kunkler, C., "Fractures." In Maher, A., Salmond, S., and Pellino, T., eds., *Orthopaedic Nursing*, Third Edition. Philadelphia: W.B. Saunders, 2002.

7. Suits and Deals, *New Jersey Law Journal*, April 29, 2002.

8. Suits and Deals, *New Jersey Law Journal*, May 4, 2002.

9. Alexander, M., "Congenital and Developmental Disorders." In Maher, A., Salmond, S., and Pellino, T., eds., *Orthopaedic Nursing*, Third Edition. Philadelphia: W.B. Saunders, 2002.

10. Agency for Health Care Policy and Research, Department of Health and Human Services, *Hospital Inpatient Statistics.* AHCPR Pub. No 99-00341999, 1996.

11. Melton, L. III, "Hip Fractures: A Worldwide Problem Today and Tomorrow." *Bone,* 14, S1–S8, 1993.

12. "Conference Report, National Consensus Conference on Improving the Continuum of Care for Patients with Hip Fracture." *Orthopaedic Nursing* 21 (1), 16–22, 2002.

13. Bulger, E., Smith, D., Maier, R., and Jurkovich, G.J., "Fat Embolism Syndrome: A Ten-Year Review." *Archives of Surgery* (132), 435-439, 1997.

14. Sculco, T., Colwell, Jr. C., Pellegrini, Jr. V., Westrich, G.H., and Bottner, F., "Prophylaxis Against Venous Thromboembolic Disease in Patients Having a Total Hip or Knee Arthroplasty." *Journal of Bone and Joint Surgery* (84-A), 3, 466–475, 2002.

Internet Resources
Orthopaedic Websites

American Academy of Orthopaedic Surgeons
www.aaos.org
Arthritis Foundation
www.arthritis.org
National Association of Orthopaedic Nurses
http://www.orthonurse.org
Wheeless' Textbook of Orthopaedics (full text)
www.medmedia.com/Welcome.html
National Osteoporosis Foundation
www.nof.org
Spine Universe
www.spineuniverse.com
OrthoSeek.com
www.orthoseek.com
Orthopaedics.com
www.orthopaedics.com
About Orthopaedics
http://orthoguide.com/ortho/
MEDLINEplus
http://www.nlm.nih.gov/medlineplus
Healthfinder
http://healthfinder.gov

Chapter 11

Cancer Pain and Suffering

Carol Bales, MSN, RN, AOCN, CCRP

Synopsis

11.1 Introduction

Pain and suffering are companion terms that are often used as a legal descriptor of harm experienced by plaintiffs and their family members. These terms may seem inseparable when used to describe the oncology patient. However, pain is defined differently than suffering, leading one to believe that one can be experienced independently of the other. Both experiences are complex and multidimensional. The dimensions of pain and suffering both include the physiological, the psychological, the spiritual, and the cultural. These dimensions are experienced in different planes as well, such as the temporal, the geographical, the etiological, the quantitative, and the qualitative. In this chapter, a matrix will be defined, explored, and analyzed for legal and advocacy implications.

Although the dimensions of pain and suffering overlap as illustrated in Figure 11.1, this chapter will address each separately, followed by a discussion of legal considerations and resources for attorneys.

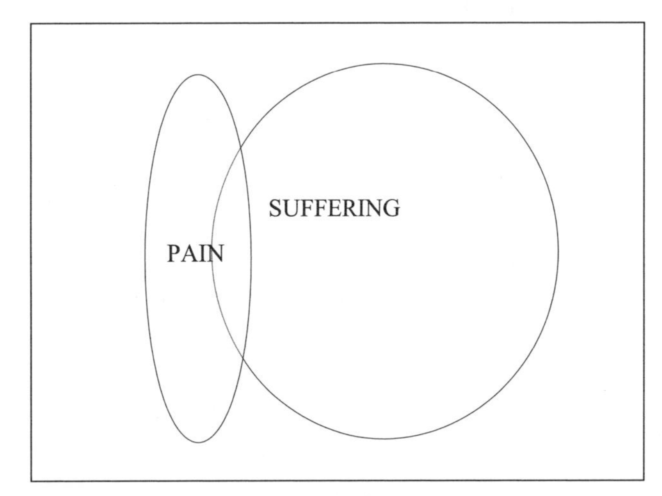

Figure 11.1 *Overlapping spheres of pain and suffering of the cancer patient*

Throughout the chapter, there will be many questions that healthcare providers use to explore the dimensions of pain and suffering. Attorneys may use these questions to interview patients, their families, and their acquaintances to obtain insights into the lives of the plaintiffs or defendants. The goal of this chapter is to provide an in-depth overview to help put into perspective complaints of inadequate pain management or incompetent medical or nursing care relative to the cancer patient's experience with pain and suffering.

11.2 Cancer Defined

Attorneys should understand the medical terminology related to cancer in order to understand medical records, testimony, and documents related to cancer cases. Commonly used terms are therefore defined in this chapter. Medical literature helpful in understanding oncology is cited in the additional reading.

Tip

The word cancer describes more than 100 diseases, all of which involve a disorderly, abnormal, uncontrolled growth of cells. Normally, the division and multiplication of cells is a response to a physiological stimulus such as the need for tissue repair or replacement.

Medical terms that describe early changes in cells are: hyperplasia (excessive number of cells in one location), hypoplasia (too few cells in a specific body system), and dysplasia or dysplastic cells (abnormal appearance of cells). Dysplasia is a precancerous condition that, untreated, can develop into cancer. The diagnostic period is one in which many tests are conducted to determine the characteristics of the disease condition.

11.3 Pain Defined

The ultimate definition of pain is that which the patient herself describes.[1] The International Association for the Study of Pain defines pain as, "An unpleasant sensory and emotional experience associated with actual or potential tissue damage, or described in terms of such damage."[2] This definition precludes that pain which is experienced through unconscious dreams, the pain that is exclusive of tissue damage, and psychological pain. A more comprehensive definition needs to include those types of pain. A functional and operational definition of pain in terms of tissue damage is offered by Chapman and Stillman, who defined pathological pain as "severe persisting pain or moderate pain of long duration that disrupts sleep and normal living, ceases to serve a protective function, and instead degrades health and functional capability."[3] This definition describes pain experienced by many cancer patients, especially at the end of their lives.

11.4 Oncological Terminology

It is important to understand certain medical terms used to describe cancer in order to make sense of the pain associated with cancer. A tumor is a mass of dense tissue formed when there is a massive proliferation of cells in one anatomical site. Tumors can be benign (noncancerous) or malignant (cancerous). Tumors can be solid or liquid (leukemia). Cancer tumors usually are named for the type of tissue in which they originate, such as lymphoma (cancer of the lymphatic system). As tumors grow, they stimulate the growth of new blood vessels designed to feed the rapidly dividing cells. When the tumor grows to be large enough for the new blood vessels and lymph vessels to feed and drain it, cells may migrate through these vessels to other parts of the body.

If the migrating cancer cells encounter a physiological environment that is optimal for their growth, they begin growing into new tumors. These sites are described as metastatic tumors, or metastases, commonly called "mets." The process is known as metastasis. Metastases always retain cellular characteristics of the parent tumor. Pathologists can determine whether or not a tumor is a metastatic growth by comparing the microscopic and genetic characteristics of the primary and secondary tumor specimens. If the secondary tumor characteristics are different from the primary, the tumor is known as a second primary tumor. If the pathology report reveals similar cells, it is a metastatic tumor. An example of a metastatic tumor is a melanoma of the face that spreads to the liver. An example of a second primary tumor is an infiltrating ductal carcinoma of the left breast when the patient has already developed an invasive lobular carcinoma in her right breast. Metastases can be located just adjacent to the first or primary tumor, in which case it is described as local. Local metastases are usually found in the lymph nodes that drain the site in which the primary tumor is located. Distant metastases are located in an anatomical site or system distinct from the primary tumor location and its drainage system. Distant metastases are an indication of the aggressiveness of the tumor, and using this characteristic along with other factors such as the stage and pathology of the tumor, physicians predict the patient's outcome (prognosis) in terms of response to treatment, survival time, and the chances of recovery. The patient's physical condition, age, general health and past health all play a part in the prediction of how well a patient will fare with his or her cancer and its treatment.

11.5 Cancer Diagnosis and Prognosis

A patient's primary physician usually conducts the initial evaluation of the patient with an abnormal mass or abnormal blood values suspected to be cancer. The primary physician makes a referral to an appropriate specialist for a definitive diagnosis. The specialist can be a surgeon, pulmonologist, hematologist, medical oncologist, gynecologist, ontolaryngologist, ophthalmologist, or other subspecialist. The diagnosis of cancer and treatment planning usually involves the physicians who performed diagnostic examinations and tests for the patient, as well as the radiation oncologist, medical oncologist, and surgeon. Medical specialists have specific knowledge of the type of pain and suffering associated with the different types of cancer with which they are concerned. All these physicians are aware of the risks of missing a cancer diagnosis and also of making a false diagnosis of cancer when in fact none exists. If a patient fails to contact the specialist to whom he or she is referred, it becomes partially his referring physician's responsibility to pursue that referral and make it clear to the patient that although symptoms may subside he should be evaluated for possible signs of serious illness, specifically, cancer.

Most hospitals in which cancer treatment is available hold regular cancer conferences, tumor boards, or oncology grand rounds attended by an entire spectrum of health professionals in which cancer cases are presented proactively and treatment plans are discussed. The identity of the patients is protected during this process. These meetings are forums in which a patient's physicians and healthcare providers are able to confer with each other, affording each the benefit of a multidisciplinary approach to treatment planning. Attorneys can gain information from a patient's oncologist by asking if the patient's case was presented at a tumor conference and if so what the discussion entailed.

Tip

Attorneys are especially attuned to misdiagnosis because of the prevalence of such cases. Physicians may be at fault for failing to evaluate pain as an early sign of lung, breast, prostate, or other cancer. Physicians may also fail to follow up on referrals to specialists for evaluation of such symptoms.

Barring any life-threatening interventions, the cancer treatment planning process begins with addressing the comfort needs of the patient, including the need for acute or chronic pain management and respiratory support (if these needs are present), psychosocial intervention, and immediate spiritual support. These interventions are usually begun well before the diagnostic process is completed. The cancer patient's need for management of pain and suffering thus starts prior to the medical treatment of his or her disease. Questions that healthcare professionals ask while taking a medical history are:

- What was your initial treatment when your cancer was first diagnosed?
- Were you referred to any specialists?
- Did you have any pain or distressing symptoms when you first went to the doctor about your cancer?
- Was the pain or were the symptoms treated at that time?
- If so, did the treatment relieve your symptoms?
- If not, how much were your symptoms bothering you in spite of treatment?
- How did you cope with your symptoms on your own?
- Who is helping you to cope with your pain or symptoms?

11.6 Survival Rates and Other Epidemiological Terminology

Epidemiology is the study of disease in populations. Health professionals use epidemiological terms, or statistics, to help them develop a prognosis for cancer patients. Using the most recent statistics is important in predicting survival. Cancer diagnosis and treatment trends are rapidly improving, and with earlier detection and treatment, more cancer patients are experiencing symptom-free survival than in years past.

Some statistical terms used in reports published in peer-reviewed journals are commonly quoted by physicians as they discuss prognosis with their patients. Incidence measures the development of a certain type of condition in a specific population, usually in 100,000 people.[4] The American Cancer Society publishes these rates annually.[5]

Physicians also refer to the response rate. Response rates (percentages) are categorized into complete response (CR), partial response (PR), no response, and progression. Response rates are related to a specific type of treatment regimen in a specific type of patient with a specific stage of cancer. For example: "Of the 62 patients who could be evaluated after induction chemotherapy, 17 (27%) patients achieved a CR and 31 (50%) a PR, yielding a 77% response rate."[6] Response rates can be applied to any treatment, whether it is chemotherapy, surgery, radiation therapy, or pain management. The one statistic that seems to have the greatest implication for the cancer patient is survival rate. Although one would think that the fatality rates would be the statistic most frequently cited, health care professionals most often use survival rates, as this is a more psychologically acceptable statistic. Survival rate is expressed in terms of percentages for overall survival, symptom-free survival, and disease-free survival. Survival rates are quoted for one-year, five-year and ten-year periods of time following diagnosis (e.g., overall five-year survival rate of 78%). "Time to progression" is the amount of time in terms of months or years from the time a patient is diagnosed and treatment is begun until the cancer relapses (begins to grow again).

Tip

Health professionals use epidemiological terms, or statistics, to help them develop a prognosis for cancer patients. Using the most recent statistics is important in predicting survival. Cancer diagnosis and treatment trends are rapidly improving, and with earlier detection and treatment, more cancer patients are experiencing symptom-free survival than in years past.

11.7 Breaking the News

The physician or the nurse who is in a position of informing a cancer patient of his or her diagnosis ascertains his or her information needs, receptiveness, educational level, psychological state, and social support system prior to consulting with the patient. The general stress level of patients will affect their ability to hear and assimilate critical information, and subsequently make choices about treatment options, however careful caregivers are in delivering the news.[7]

Since attorneys will be handling cases of delayed diagnosis, they will want to find out how their client felt when she found out that she has cancer that is so advanced that treatment would probably not be curative. This situation often develops when either breast or lung cancer progresses to the point where it is evident to any radiologist that a suspicious mass is present on x-ray or CT scans. Retrospective review of previous mammographic or x-ray films might reveal a subtle finding that was overlooked as insignificant months before. It can also be the case when a cancer lesion is misdiagnosed as a different medical problem such as an infection, a benign cyst, or a benign inflammation.

In the case of a cervical cancer patient versus her obstetrician-gynecologist,[8] the plaintiff alleged that the physician misread pap smears as normal for two years prior to the plaintiff's diagnosis, when in fact the tests revealed cervical cancer. The patient's treatment was delayed, which resulted in metastasis and eventual death. The action was settled for $1.2 million.

In questioning clients, attorneys might want to inquire about how their clients received the news of their diagnosis. It is interesting to compare what physicians and nurses say about how the news was delivered with how the person with cancer perceives he was told the news. It seems to the author after thirty years of oncology nursing, that as time elapses the more divergent the opinions of patients and healthcare givers become. When a patient finds out that her cancer diagnosis was delayed or misdiagnosed previously, she typically reacts with heightened anger, frustration, resentment, and a loss of faith in the medical system that has failed her. Healthcare providers can help to alleviate this suffering by going through a process of value assessment with patients. Attorneys may find these questions useful in the direct examination of the cancer client. Questions that help in understanding how patients feel and cope with delayed diagnosis are:

- How do you feel about the delayed diagnosis or misdiagnosis?
- What do you think could have been done differently?
- How would your situation be different if your diagnosis had been made earlier?
- Who and what do you understand contributed to your misdiagnosis?
- Have you discussed your feelings about the misdiagnosis with the doctor who is responsible for your situation?
- Were your cancer symptoms dismissed or disregarded by your physician?
- Could you have done anything that would have changed the outcome?
- Who or what do you blame for this misdiagnosis?
- How are you coping with your feelings about the misdiagnosis?
- What do you think would make a difference for you in coping with this situation?
- What legal outcome do you desire as a result of your action?
- What will make a difference for your spouse or family as far as an outcome is concerned?

Since most cancers are slow growing, a delayed diagnosis may take two years or more before it is evident that the diagnosis has been missed.

In the case of an anonymous plaintiff versus a hospital in Ohio, though, the patient's penile cancer diagnosis was delayed by thirteen years![9] The plaintiff first complained of painful erections and curvature of the penis when he was twenty-four years old. His physician performed a biopsy on a penile lesion that was diagnosed as Peyronie's disease, a benign condition that is treated with vitamin E and sometimes surgery. Seven years later the patient went to his doctor complaining of the same problem. Again a penile lesion was biopsied and misdiagnosed as progressive Peyronie's disease. The patient was given treatment and did not seek medical intervention again until six years later, at which time a biopsy of his penile lesion, done at a second hospital, revealed cancer. The patient ended up with an amputation of his penis, lung disease, and a shortened life expectancy. The patient was told by the second hospital that his cancer had been present at least seven years prior. The first hospital failed to find the original pathology slides. The patient was awarded a settlement of $6.5 million for his pain and suffering.

11.8 Diagnostic Period Anxiety

Completing a thorough diagnostic evaluation of a patient suspected of having cancer takes several days, and often weeks. Delays due to scheduling difficulty, heavy workloads of pathology departments, the patient's work schedule, and physicians' crowded schedules are frequently encountered. Patients' anxiety may be accentuated by their frustration, fears, and stress and by their pain, metabolic dysfunction, and fatigue. This waiting period has been described as emotionally painful by many patients who feel that it is unbearable to have to wait for all the test results upon which their doctor bases his staging of their cancer, his treatment plan, and most important, the patient's prognosis.

As anxiety increases, the threshold for pain usually decreases, creating the potential for anxiety attacks accompanied by surges of pain. Fortunately, most patients now have their cancer diagnosed at an early stage when it is not causing any physical pain. However, the suffering that is caused by the anxiety is enough to make most people extremely stressed.

Questions that help to evaluate the patient's pain and anxiety during this diagnostic period are:

- Is pain or anxiety keeping you from your normal activities?
- Is it affecting your sleep?

- Can you function normally at work or with your coworkers and family?
- If you take medication for pain or anxiety, does it help you to function normally?
- Have you had any anxiety or panic attacks?
- Is pain or anxiety causing you to have fatigue?
- How is your doctor helping you cope with your pain or anxiety?
- If you are not getting any relief from your pain or anxiety with medication, what are you doing to cope?

11.9 Dealing with the Diagnosis

Healthcare providers and attorneys recognize that dealing with the diagnosis of cancer differs greatly among individuals. The shock and disbelief that one's body is not sound, supportive, and cancer-free can jolt a person into a profound grief or depressive reaction.[10] Cancer patients often react by searching for an answer to their question of why they developed cancer. This search may take the form of an internal or external spiritual or philosophical examination, manifested by a social withdrawal or an extroverted questioning of many sources of cancer information. If a person has good coping ability, a supportive family and circle of friends, an optimistic attitude, and a positive approach to problem solving, he will be able to deal with his diagnosis much better than a person without these resources. These individuals might respond with normal feelings of emotional shock, followed by a brief period of denial, then anger, and finally a resolve to face the challenge of dealing with their conditions. The amount of suffering a person bears seems to be directly related to his or her coping ability and social support system, rather than some external cause such as a particular physician or other healthcare professional's lack of competent care.

11.10 Cancer Care Team Support of Newly Diagnosed Patients

Some hospitals and healthcare networks have developed specialized cancer care teams designed to fill in gaps in health care for cancer patients. These teams are usually comprised of a registered nurse, social worker, pastoral care counselor, nutritionist, and occupational therapist. Much information can be gleaned from these teams and their records. They help to fill in the gaps in cancer care that are often missed by the patient's healthcare team. These professionals assess the complex needs of the newly diagnosed cancer patient and his or her family, develop a plan of care to meet those needs, and provide information, counseling, nursing support, social services, and pastoral care as appropriate, and in collaboration with the patient's primary physician and oncologist.[11]

Patients who are from minority, low-income environments whose social and financial needs are high can experience more suffering as a result of a fragmentation of their cancer care than other patients from more affluent, mainstream environments.[12] In one study, elderly, poor, single, black women with chronic diseases were the most likely to suffer with symptoms of distress aggravated by a lack of attention to their social needs.[13]

During the diagnostic period and early treatment planning, the focus on medical tests and treatment is often so intense that a patient's physician or medical team inadvertently neglects psychological, spiritual, and social support. A lack of attention to these needs during the early part of cancer care might result in unnecessary suffering or distress both at the beginning of cancer care and in the future.

11.11 Framing the Cancer Patient's Experience of Pain and Suffering

Figures 11.2 and 11.3 provide a framework of descriptors and questions that can help attorneys to frame the cancer patient's experience of pain and suffering within his physical, social, psychological, and spiritual context. Patients benefit from the values clarification that results from a frank discussion of how they view their experiences. In describing the plaintiff's cancer and the problems it causes, the attorney can gain valuable insight into the impact of a missed diagnosis, delayed diagnosis, incompetent care, or injury due to cancer treatment.

11.12 Pain: A Subjective Symptom versus an Objective Clinical Sign

Patients describe cancer pain in different ways. There are hundreds of words that are used to describe cancer pain. Many pain assessment tools are available that

DESCRIPTORS OF PAIN EXPERIENCE	Physiological	Psychological	Spiritual	Cultural
Temporal	Pain intensity before or after eating, sleeping, or physical activity	Pain induced stress response; meaning of pain to individual	Acuity before or after prayer, meditation, yoga, balancing, grounding; Associations with belief system	Onset relative to sentinel social/cultural event; Association of action/inaction and pain.
Geographical	Physiological location of pain	Physical manifestations of pain relative to past experience	Acuity or presence of pain during spiritual practice(s)	Cultural associations of pain with bodily functions and/or location
Historical	Length of time pain has been experienced	Current versus past pain experiences relative to emotions	Onset of pain relative to spiritual experiences/insights	Cultural history relative to cancer pain; non-cancer pain
Etiological	Physical cause of pain	Psychological cause of pain	Spiritual association with pain	Cultural associations with causes of pain
Qualitative	Type of pain sensations	Emotions associated with pain	Judgments about pain and spiritual meaning of pain	Importance of pain in patient's culture
Quantitative	Intensity of pain	Level of distress caused by pain	Scope of pain experience relative to spiritual belief system	Degree of cultural impact of pain experience

Figure 11.2 *Pain and suffering matrix—Part A: Multidimensional descriptors of pain experience*

QUESTIONS RE: PAIN/SUFFERING EXPERIENCE	Physiological	Psychological	Spiritual	Cultural
Temporal	Where is your cancer? Where did it start growing? When did it begin?	Do you associate the pain with any event or experience?	Has the pain affected spiritual or religious aspects of your life?	Is your cancer experience the same as others in your community or culture?
Geographical	Where in your body the cancer is located? Where has it spread?	Do you associate the part of your body where the cancer is with a certain emotion?	Does your pain and suffering change when you are involved in spiritual activities?	Do your family and friends think they know why you developed this kind of cancer?
Historical	Have any of your family members had cancer?	How have your emotions been associated with physical symptoms in the past?	How are pain and suffering described historically by your church or religion?	How do people from your community or culture cope with pain & suffering?
Etiological	What is the physical cause for your pain and/or suffering?	Do you associate any emotional distress with your pain or cancer?	What does your pain or cancer mean to you in spiritual terms?	What is thought to cause pain and suffering in your community or culture?
Qualitative	What does your pain feel like? Can you describe it in terms that others would understand?	How do you feel emotionally and psychologically when you have pain and/or suffering?	How do you use spirituality to help you cope with your pain/suffering/ cancer?	In what ways do people from your community or culture usually cope with or treat pain?
Quantitative	How severe do you feel your pain/suffering are at this time?	How much does your pain/cancer affect you psychologically?	To what degree does this pain/cancer affect your spiritual life?	How much does your pain/suffering restrict you socially?

Figure 11.3 *Pain and suffering matrix—Part B: Questions used to explore dimensions of pain and suffering*

guide the health professional in evaluating pain. Most address the following: severity, location, time and duration of occurrence, type, and associated activities. Assessment is addressed in Chapter 2; however, it is interesting to know which types of cancer are associated with the worse pain. Overall, bone cancer and pancreatic cancer are associated with pain that is the most difficult to treat. Cancers that have advanced to the stage that they are invading major nerve pathways cause intractable (unrelieved) pain that needs to be treated with surgical nerve blocks. Brain cancer can cause intolerable pain that can only be treated by heavy sedation and medically induced coma.

Attorneys can evaluate pain experiences by using the matrix of questions provided in Figure 11.3, or they can use pain assessment questionnaires readily available on the Internet or in the literature. The information about the clinical dimensions of pain may not be as useful as information about the effect of pain on the lives of the patients and their family.

11.13 Individual and Cultural Perceptions Related to Cancer

Patients differ widely in their individual perceptions of pain, depending on personal and demographic factors such as sex, age, educational level, psychological status, economic status, and cultural setting. Whereas a middle-aged male physician with advanced lung cancer may interpret his neck and shoulder pain as understandable and acceptable given adequate pain medication, an indigent black female senior citizen of Trinidad, living in the United States, who has been through much physical and psychological trauma, may find the same type of pain excruciating and unbearable in spite of adequate pain medication.

A. Sex differences

The American Pain Society conducted a study completed in 2001 that included data collected from 967 females and 680 males who had chronic pain.[13] They found differences in that the women reported more fear and frustration related to pain than men. Men reported more anxiety and frustration with intense pain, whereas women reported only frustration to intense pain. On the other hand, men reported only frustration to the highest pain intensities, whereas women reported depression with frustration. The researchers found that, surprisingly, pain-related emotions were reported by men to be more strongly related to pain than those reported by women. They found that emotions were most closely related to the unpleasantness of pain rather than to the intensity of pain.

The implications of these findings from a legal perspective are that cancer pain affects the psychological and social aspects of a person's life and that men and women's experiences differ considerably and should be examined from a sex-specific perspective. Attorneys might ask clients to describe how they feel pain affected them from a man's or a woman's perspective.

B. Inadequate pain management

1. Communication barriers

Some patients receive inadequate pain management due to communication barriers. Patients may feel guilty about broaching the subject with their physicians. There are many psychological reasons that patients are reluctant to ask for pain treatment. The educational level of the patient with cancer pain affects the patient's ability to understand and communicate the origin, nature, and treatment of his or her pain. Since pain is a dynamic rather than a static symptom, and since pain varies in intensity, pain assessment is a continual process that is ongoing throughout the patient's cancer experience. It is not an assessment that takes place only once at the beginning of treatment. The complete assessment of pain may take days or weeks and should be constantly reassessed. If the patient is able adequately to articulate the occurrence, site, history, possible origin, nature, and amount of his or her pain, the physician can more easily understand and treat them. Conversely, if the patient is unable adequately to describe his or her pain or cannot remember much about its occurrence and history, it makes it very difficult to address his or her needs. When determining whether the physician has adequately addressed the pain needs of his or her patient, the ability of the patient to describe his or her needs must be taken into consideration.

2. Nonphysical factors

Clients who complain that they experienced intolerable pain may associate their pain with nonphysical factors. These factors may not be able to be addressed by the oncologist and may require the help of a psychologist, counselor, or spiritual counselor. Attorneys can question the client about whether he asked for or received referrals to support services other than medical personnel to help him cope with his pain. The psychological status and spiritual orientation of the patient in pain can increase or decrease the patient's individual perception of the amount and intensity of pain as well as the suffering he experiences. Stress increases levels of adrenalin and decreases pain tolerance. Patients with high levels of stress, or who are distressed about spiritual or psychological matters and issues can have very high levels of pain. If the psychological problems are addressed and resolved, patients may be able to decrease their dose of pain medication. Addressing spiritual needs may put a patient's mind and heart at rest, allowing his or her body's natural endorphins to rise, thus decreasing levels of pain. From a legal perspective, it is important to understand how a client best copes with her pain and what resources were withheld or inaccessible to help her cope.

3. Importance of social support

Living within one's own community or in a community of one's own culture helps a patient to have access to the social support of family, friends, clergy, and neighbors. Empathy and good will toward the cancer patient can help to soften the psychological trauma of cancer and cancer pain. Health professionals often face challenges of treating pain of patients from foreign countries, whose perceptions and understanding of pain, as well as the associations with cultural beliefs and practices, may be confusing and challenging to understand. In these situations, it is imperative that the physicians use an interpreter who can describe cultural associations with pain. To understand a patient from a different culture's experience of pain, one must use a cultural interpreter who can explain the meaning of the pain in terms of that culture. This is important not only from a medical standpoint, but from a legal standpoint as well. Attorneys should not only seek to understand the situation from their client's perspective, but also from the perspective of the patient's healthcare provider.

4. Finances

The financial status of patients must also be considered in the overall pain management plan. Some indigent patients struggle to obtain enough food or clothing to provide for their families or themselves. When presented with the opportunity to sell their pain medications on the street, they are sometimes led to do so out of need to provide for their families or out of hunger or need to pay rent or bills. They might go without pain medication and not inform their healthcare providers out of fear of recrimination. Therefore, it is wise for the attorney to understand how the financial needs of cancer patients may have affected their ability to obtain effective pain treatment.

The difficulty of assessing, understanding, and addressing the pain needs of patients with multiple social, psychological, spiritual, and physical needs is a daunting challenge even for the most skilled medical and legal professionals.

5. Neurogenic and psychosomatic pain

Neurogenic and psychosomatic pain are other challenging symptoms for the healthcare provider, and difficult to understand from a lay perspective. Neurogenic pain tends to be chronic in nature and resistant to standard methods of pain management because of the damage to nerves that occurs. It is sometimes necessary for the physician to try different combinations of narcotic and nonnarcotic pain medication and medications for anxiety, depression, and agitation. The use of non-pharmacological pain management strategies such as chemical and surgical nerve blocks, surgery, or radiation therapy to reduce the pressure of tumors on nerves and complementary therapies such as biofeedback, acupuncture, massage, and psychotherapy are also needed for certain patients.

Psychosomatic pain is not another term for imaginary pain. This type of pain requires accurate assessment and careful treatment planning to manage. Physicians have been known to use this term when the cause of the pain cannot be detected or explained by traditional standard diagnostic methods or medical knowledge. When patients with this type of pain undergo certain diagnostic tests that are not usually performed, such as spiral or 3-D CT scans, many of the tests reveal tumor growth or pathology that was not evident before.

It is not necessary to go to great lengths to diagnose the cause of a cancer patient's pain before the pain is addressed by prescribing a pain management plan.

11.14 Psychoneuroimmunology and Pain

The study of the interrelationships between the emotions and learning, the nervous system, and the body's immune system is called psychoneuroimmunology (PNI). The Oncology Nursing Society, an international organization of more than 6,000 oncology nurses, has developed a special interest group called the PNI and Alternative Therapies SIG (special interest group) that is concerned with this particular science. This organization publishes position statements on PNI and alternative therapies from an oncology nursing perspective that may be valuable for the attorney. The position statement includes directives about the attitudes, practices and beliefs of oncology nurses, setting the pace for nursing practice worldwide. Among these directives are those that describe acknowledgment and acceptance of the widespread use of traditional medicine, alternative and complementary healthcare practices, and integrative medicine by persons with cancer.

Studies reveal that a large percentage of patients use these remedies, most of which they pay for out of pocket. The studies also show that most of the patients do not divulge the use of these remedies to their primary physicians.[14] Many patients express a hesitancy to discuss their use of home or folk remedies or alternative therapies for fear of ridicule or criticism from their healthcare providers. Nonetheless, many cancer patients find these therapies very useful for pain management. See Figure 11.4 for resources related to these areas.

11.15 Suffering

The first part of the chapter has dealt specifically with pain. The second part of this content covers suffering.

A. General stress related to cancer diagnosis

The diagnostic period is a time full of dread, shock, denial, fear, not knowing enough or knowing too much, and going through painful and uncomfortable procedures. It is the most stressful period during the course of cancer that patients go through. Attorneys should note that although the following stories portray

The National Center for Complementary and Alternative Medicine provides administration and oversight for federally funded research in this area. The agency can be contacted by mail at NCCM Clearinghouse, P.O. Box 7923, Gaithersburg, MD 20898, by e-mail at info@nccam.nih.gov, by phone toll-free at 1-888-644-6226, or by fax at 1-866-464-3616.

Publications and resources about pain and pain management

The following list is not exhaustive, but contains names and contact information for organizations that provide information on cancer pain and its management to the public upon request. Many of these organizations have literature that provides a comprehensive perspective on pain and suffering that may be of value as references for attorneys.

American Cancer Society, 800-ACS-2345

American Society of Clinical Oncology, 1900 Duke Street, Suite 200, Alexandria, VA 22314, 703-299-0150, fax: 703-299-1044, asco@asco.org

Cancer Information Service, National Cancer Institute (NCI), 800-4-CANCER

American Institute for Cancer Research, 800-843-8114

The Association of Community Cancer Centers, 301-984-9496

Cancer Care, 800-813-HOPE

Cancer News on the Net, http://www.cancernews.com/

National Coalition for Cancer Survivorship, 1010 Wayne Ave., Fifth Floor Silver Spring, Maryland, http://www.cansearch.org/

National Cancer Institute's cancer fax line, 301-496-7403. Patient Advocates for Advanced Cancer Treatment, 616-453-1477, 1143 Parmelee NW, Grand Rapids, MI 49504. Mail to: P.O. Box 141695, Grand Rapids, MI 49514, fax: 616-453-1846.

Figure 11.4 Sources of information about alternative treatment and pain management

patients who suffered throughout their diagnostic period, suffering because of stress is common and routine. It is the patients who are misdiagnosed, or whose cases take too long to diagnose, who may experience unjustifiable suffering. If an indefensible delay or misdiagnosis results in untimely death, an escalation of painful or uncomfortable treatment, or a loss of confidence in the medical system, the patients affected may indeed have a right to recover from their caregivers.

Patients whom the author has helped through this stressful period often express doubt that they have cancer. It should be noted that physicians also dread the diagnosis of cancer and find it difficult to tell their patients of their diagnosis. This denial on the part of patients and aversion on the part of physicians and nurses should not prevent a thorough and timely diagnostic workup or a straightforward discussion of the diagnosis with the patient.

Two nurse colleagues who went through tests to determine if their breast lumps were malignant expressed strong doubt that they would ultimately be diagnosed with cancer. Eve and Joan both quoted statistics in their favor. They described a lack of symptoms usually found in cancer patients, such as fatigue, pain, and swollen lymph nodes. As if the act of hoping that their lumps would be benign was going to ensure the desired outcome, they stoically and bravely underwent numerous mammograms and CT scans, biopsies, and examinations, verbally affirming their absence of fear. They spent day after day waiting for the results of their tests because they immersed themselves in their professional lives, working many hours overtime, fiercely focusing on whatever would distract them from their clinical situations. Even though they had not received their diagnoses, it was obvious that they were going through a process of reassessing and reevaluating their interpersonal relationships. They confided only in those people whom they trusted that they were going through the diagnostic workup. They drew closer to their dearest family members. They lost sleep and came to work groggy with black circles under their eyes. When it became possible for them to access their biopsy results on the hospital's computer system, instead of looking up the reports themselves, they asked the author to do it for them. There was a conscious distancing from what could be devastating news, while at the same time there was a strong need to know what the results were. In the end, Joan received a diagnosis of cancer, and Eve the diagnosis of a benign cyst. The author was with both women when they received the news. They both dissolved in tears, Eve from a sense of profound relief and Joan from profound grief. Their reactions were immediate and seemed to dissolve all of their resolve and fortitude. It was as if the dam had broken, and all of their stress came pouring through.

No matter how gentle or considerate the messenger, the diagnosis of cancer is still heard as a death sentence by many cancer patients. Common reactions to the diagnosis are, "The doctor says I have cancer, but the diagnosis must be wrong" or "It can't be true. I don't feel as if I have cancer." There is a period of time during which it is natural and common for patients to go through this denial and finally adjust to the diagnosis. Should a patient present her case to an attorney, claiming undue pain and suffering because her physician was not compassionate or caring enough in delivering her diagnosis, both the defense and plaintiff counsel should interview the nurses who were present for that clinic or office visit to determine whether they have the same perception. Patients can perceive the news as shocking and, by extension, perceive the messenger as rude or unfeeling. The process of assimilating the news of a cancer diagnosis is easy for only a few patients. For some patients, it takes a few days. For others, the process takes several months.

Danny, a patient who suffers from mesothelioma, a form of lung cancer, stoically went through all his initial evaluations and examinations, laughing and joking with the nurses in the oncology clinic. At home, his response was very different. There, in the privacy of his home with his wife, he wept many hours from sorrow over the loss of hope. He waited until he had completed his first few cycles of chemotherapy before he told any of his family about his illness, hoping to spare them the pain of knowing he had cancer. Danny eloquently described the stress of feeling that he needed to put on a "happy face" for his healthcare team, while he felt devastated and wounded by his diagnosis.

An excerpt from Danny's letter describes the acute suffering he felt during his diagnosis:

> The worst day of my life was November 1, 1999. I was told two things: 1) I had terminal lung cancer, Stage IIIb; and, 2) the Chemo I was going to receive on a weekly basis cost $6,000 per treatment. Between bouts of tears I remember telling my wife: "Not only am I going to die, but it's going to cost us six grand a week for me to do so!" (That's an attempt at Cancer humor). To rub salt in the wound I was then told this treatment was palliative, not curative. In other words, the doctor guesstimated my life could be extended 15–18 months with chemo . . . without chemo I had 6–8 months.

Danny eventually was told that he had been misdiagnosed as having a particular kind of lung cancer, different from his actual diagnosis of mesothelioma. Although the treatment for both types of lung cancer is the same, the misdiagnosis destroyed his confidence in his oncologist. He felt that it was necessary to seek help not only by a different doctor, but also in another state, in a hospital that is world-renowned for its lung cancer care. The misdiagnosis was the result of the lack of local access to an electron microscope with which pathologists can make the distinction between the two types of lung cancer cells. He chose not to pursue the matter legally since he could not claim that he was physically harmed or injured by the misdiagnosis. He chose instead to focus on finding a cure for his disease in a positive way.

B. Impact of the diagnosis on family

Another common type of suffering that occurs is the impact of the diagnosis on interpersonal family relationships and the family's hopes for the future.

A friend of the author, a psychologist and specialist in cancer, reacted to his wife's diagnosis of ocular melanoma by saying that, "In one day everything changed." All of their promises, hopes, dreams, plans, premises, and belief systems were indelibly marred by her cancer diagnosis. He responded by immediately adopting an attitude of faith that she would survive and be okay in the end. She was gripped by fear, paralyzed and terrified of the prospects of losing her sight, her job, her eye, her beauty, and her faith. The stress of their divergent responses on their relationship eventually took its toll, and they are now separated.

Stress can often strain interpersonal relationships. Friendships sometimes dissolve when the cancer patient discovers that his friends cannot support him through the ordeal. Marriages suffer from the stress of losing the vision of "living happily ever after." Cancer patients often find that their tolerance of insincerity, shallowness, flippant behavior, and "fair weather" friendship is reduced to zero. Cancer brings what is important in one's life into very sharp focus. That sharp focus can leave not only acquaintances, friends, and family out of the picture but can make otherwise enjoyable pastimes and interests part of one's "life before cancer." Many cancer patients recognize the diagnosis of cancer as an event that sharply divides their life into two distinct phases—before and after the diagnosis.

Danny, the mesothelioma patient quoted earlier, described this impact on his life:

> As you might expect I found prayer and worship a great consolation. When you have this disease, you and your family spend a lot of time in "limbo." You want answers now and you're told you need another test. Nothing happens fast. (Someone wrote a book appropriately entitled: *Living Between Office Visits*). So the "in between" time, the waiting, the not knowing when, not being in control . . . this is what I found difficult.

Tip

Since attorneys want to know how a patient suffered during the diagnostic period, and since many cancer patients have poor memory of that period during the course of the treatment, it would be helpful if the patient could produce letters, diaries, or journals in which she described what she went through at the time of diagnosis. Friends and family members can be very helpful in this regard, since they might not have forgotten how much the cancer patient suffered. They might also be able to share verbal or written communications from the patient during that period of time.

The author has spoken with one of her friends a year after her breast cancer was diagnosed about how much she suffered during her diagnosis. Frequent e-mails were sent during her diagnostic workup. She is an emergency room nurse and familiar with treating and caring for patients. However, when the roles were reversed and she was a patient instead of a nurse, she expressed much apprehension, self-doubt, frustration, difficulty making decisions about treatment options, and trouble sleeping and concentrating. A year later, after going through surgery, radiation treatment, and chemotherapy, she had forgotten about any distress she had felt during her diagnosis. When told how brave and courageous she was, she asked the author what she was talking about. The author then shared with her some of her e-mails. She then remembered what she had been feeling at the time and said that she was glad that the author had saved those e-mails so that she could remember and perhaps help someone else who was going through cancer diagnosis. Having access to such correspondence during the course of a patient's disease would provide an attorney insight into how a patient felt and reacted to her treatment.

C. Fear of stigmatization

Along with the shock, denial, and stress that cancer patients experience comes the fear of stigmatization. Healthcare providers can unwittingly adopt negative attitudes about cancer and cancer patients that may surface in statements to cancer patients and their families. Patients without strong self-esteem and assertiveness may suffer much distress as a result of such negativity. Although the vast majority of oncologists and oncology surgeons are very positive in their approach to their patients, there are a few who have caused irreparable harm to their patients by being negative.

One of the author's patients who since died of his disease was a forty-year-old surveyor who first was diagnosed as having genital cancer two years prior to his death. During the course of his disease, the author cared for him during several hospitalizations during which he received chemotherapy and supportive care. His physician convinced him early on in his treatment that there was no hope that his disease might be cured. Bobby choked up as he told the author several times that his physician had told him, "Bobby, no matter what you do, this cancer is going to get you!" The physician had allowed his knowledge of grim statistics to destroy any hope that the patient had at a time when there was a slim chance that a cure could be achieved.

Susan Sontag, in her classic book *Illness as a Metaphor,*[15] explains how historically society has viewed cancer as an enemy and something that people bring upon themselves by taking on too much stress or by manifesting the disease as a response to a traumatic situation. She sees this as an unfortunate circumstance and thinks that attributing the cause of cancer to the patient is victimizing and stigmatizing. Susan Sontag herself was angered when she was diagnosed with cancer and she encountered the suffering that the reputation of cancer caused in the lives of fellow cancer patients. In addition to the fear she felt after hearing the dreaded prognosis, she felt stigmatized as a victim of cancer, somehow being characterized as one who brought the disease on herself through a defeatist attitude. She found that during her treatment, many authors, physicians, and others whom she encountered used military terminology to describe cancer and its treatment. Words such as enemy, fighting, blasting the cancer cells, waging war on cancer, the arsenal of cancer drugs, and targeting the cancer tumor were commonly used. Sontag says that using such terminology makes cancer patients feel stigmatized, as if the enemy had marked them with the social disgrace of having cancer. Cancer has historically been associated with disfigurement, unbearable pain, debilitating symptoms, and a death devoid of dignity and grace. Because of the relationship of lifestyle to the risk of developing cancer, especially with smoking as it relates to lung cancer, and sexual activity as it relates to genital cancer, patients feel as if they have been marked with a stigma of having cancer. It might help attorneys to ask patients how they think their caregivers, friends, and family describe their disease, and whether they accept their perception of the disease.

Tip

Stigma: **noun** (PL. **stigmas** or especially in sense 2 **stigmata**) **1** a mark of disgrace associated with a particular circumstance, quality, or person: *the stigma of mental disorder | to be a non-reader carries a social stigma.* describe or regard as worthy of disgrace or great disapproval: *the institution* ***was stigmatized as*** *a last resort for the destitute.* Copyright © Oxford University Press 2002.

Modern medical scientists know the causes of cancer are carcinogens, genetic predisposition, and a compromised immune system. However, there is a new age philosophy that cancer is a manifestation of discord within the cancer patient's life. Karl Menninger, the founder of the world famous Menninger Clinic in Topeka, Kansas, said, "Illness is in part what the world has done to a victim, but in a larger part it is what the victim has done with his world, and with himself . . ."[15] In her book, Susan Sontag describes numerous examples of the stigmatization of the cancer patient. She describes how cancer treatment is often called "the fight against cancer" and the characterization of cancer as an enemy, invading the human body of a "victim."[15] These words imply that cancer is a deplorable enemy and that the person that has cancer is harboring this enemy. It was this stigmatization of cancer patients that led her to write her book, a classic in medical literature.

More recent autobiographies and biographies of prominent cancer patients portray cancer in a more positive light, describing it in terms of a serious medical problem, an illness, and a breakdown of the body's immune system. Cancer treatment is described as a race for the cure, radiation treatment, surgical removal of the tumor, and chemotherapy. Authors such as Ronnie Kay in her book, *Spinning Straw into Gold*,[16] emphasize that knowledge about treatment options enables patients to choose which options they want to use and thus help formulate their treatment plan instead of giving complete control of their treatment to their physicians. Spiritual and medical authors Rachel Naomi Remen, M.D.[17] and Jeanne Achterberg, Ph.D.[18] reinforce this concept. They both emphasize that cancer patients should not feel victimized by a death sentence, but encouraged to take part in deciding on their treatment as an active and primary planner of their treatment.

D. Misdiagnosis and delayed diagnosis

Misdiagnosis and delayed diagnosis are two events that frequently result in pain and suffering. Many such cases have resulted in juries awarding large verdicts to the affected patients and families.

In *David Francisco and Maria Francisco v. United Healthcare of Florida and Jorge De Cardenas, M.D.*, Dade County (FL) Circuit Court,[19] a tongue cancer diagnosis was delayed. Dr. De Cardenas missed the diagnosis and treatment of Mr. Francisco's squamous cell carcinoma of the tongue in spite of receiving a referral from the patient's original physician that requested that a biopsy be performed of the patient's tongue lesion. Dr. De Cardenas delayed performing a biopsy for eight months, instead treating the lesion with cauterization. By the time the eventual diagnosis was made, the cancer had progressed to stage 2, and even radiation therapy could not prevent the loss of 75% of his tongue. The patient eventually had recurrence of the cancer and was not expected to survive at the time of the trial. He ended up with a severe speech impediment, a reconstructed tongue made from a part of his forearm that grew hair and was very unpalatable, and a shortened lifespan. The jury awarded Mr. Francisco $1 million for past pain and suffering, $1 million for future pain and suffering, and $252,000 for medical expenses. In addition Mrs. Francisco was awarded $500,000 for pain and suffering.

An example of a New Jersey verdict that resulted in an award of $767,000 to the plaintiff was *Taormina v. Murry*, Monmouth County (NJ) Superior Court[20]. His doctor misdiagnosed Mr. Taormina's nasopharyngeal cancer in June 1993 as tonsillitis. Two months later, his doctor's partner, Dr. Weinstein, also misdiagnosed the condition as pharyngitis. Four months after that when Mr. Taormina's neck was still swollen the doctors ordered a CT scan and a biopsy by an ontolaryngologist which revealed cancer. The patient needed to undergo chemotherapy that resulted in weakness, pain, and a buzzing sensation in his legs. He was unable to resume his work as a salesman. The attorney argued that if the patient had been given the correct diagnosis in June 1993, he could have been treated with radiation alone, sparing him the pain and suffering he eventually experienced. The jury found both Dr. Murry and Dr. Weinstein liable.

E. Anxiety as a manifestation of suffering

Anxiety is the persistent feeling of restlessness, nervousness, and apprehension; a feeling that one is out of control or having a loss of autonomy over life situations. Many situations may stimulate the development of anxiety in cancer patients, such as waiting for a diagnosis, receiving chemotherapy or radiation treatments, the fear of pain, helplessness, or death, or the fear of being shunned by society. It is important to realize that in America general levels of anxiety have risen significantly in the past forty years.[21] Given that this is true, it is not surprising that cancer patients feel especially anxious and suffer from anxiety when trying to cope with a life-threatening illness. Fortunately, there are many potent anti-anxiety medications that can be used to relieve this suffering, the potency of which ranges from very mild to extremely strong. Physicians and nurses can and should assess the anxiety level of the cancer patient and prescribe medication and nonpharmacologic treatment as appropriate.

Tip

In a study of 390 cancer patients conducted at the Sepulveda VA Medical Center in California, 44% of the patients reported that they had some anxiety in medical situations, and 23% reported significant levels of anxiety.[22]

Three oncology cases in which the author was involved as a nurse illustrate the extreme anxiety that can result from inappropriate monitoring of hospitalized patients. One is the case of a woman with advanced liver cancer who was hospitalized She was actively dying, supported by oxygen, IV fluids, IV pain medication, respiratory therapy, and nursing care. She was on a potent anti-anxiety sedative called Ativan, which intentionally kept her in a comatose state. To achieve that level of sedation, she needed IV injections of the drug every four hours. One of her doses was given late, and she came out of her coma, and became so alarmed and anxious about her situation that she started screaming and thrashing about uncontrollably. It took four nurses to restrain her from injuring herself and to administer the Ativan she needed to render her unconscious again.

Another patient was a nineteen-year-old girl with advanced pancreatic cancer. She was fiercely independent and was also actively dying. Although she was receiving continuous morphine and Ativan through an IV pump and was strongly sedated, she managed to arouse herself enough to get out of her hospital bed, walk into her bathroom, and pull out her IV tubes, disconnecting herself from the medication that made her situation bearable. Before the nurses could restart her IV and administer enough medication to calm her, she started feeling unbearable pain and became so anxious that she started screaming uncontrollably. Both patients died peacefully within twenty-four hours of these incidents. However, the incidents serve to remind us how very anxiety provoking it can be to be dying in intractable pain.

The third example of anxiety associated with cancer is that of a sixty-year-old woman with advanced breast cancer. The woman was a highly educated, articulate, and self-reliant university professor. In spite of the failure of medical treatment of her disease, she told the author that she could manage her anxiety as long as she had "options" for treating her symptoms. She meticulously and methodically went through all her options with the author each time she was admitted to the hospital for pain management, treatment of anemia, or treatment of jaundice. Knowing that she had treatment options gave her a sense of security and control over her situation. During her final hospitalization, just hours before she died, she reluctantly sighed that she needed some medication to cope with overwhelming anxiety. She said that she realized that she had run out of options.

Family and patient education about anxiety and its treatment is best accomplished prior to the final stages of cancer when anxiety is difficult to control. Patients should be encouraged to report anxiety to their physicians just as they would pain or shortness of breath. Anxiety assessments should be done on a regular schedule during office or clinic visits so that anxiety levels do not rise to intolerable levels causing patients to lose sleep or withdraw from social situations. Attorneys should question patients or their families about whether such assessments were performed on a regular basis during visits to their physicians. Medical records should contain documentation of such assessments and interventions to address anxiety.

F. Depression and depression assessment

Ronnie Kaye, a psychotherapist in private practice in Los Angeles and a breast cancer survivor, explains in her book, *Spinning Straw into Gold*,[16] that after counseling many cancer survivors she made two lists of topics that arise time after time. One is a list of life and social issues. The other is a list of the most common feelings that women cancer patients describe. The issues include some of the following: death, body image, sexuality, self-worth, isolation, fatigue, and relationship problems. The feelings include fear, grief, depression, anxiety, anger, loneliness, and powerlessness. In the author's nursing practice, many cancer patients have described how these issues and feelings change their lives. Most often they will want to talk about such topics when they are depressed and need someone to listen.

Depression affects many cancer patients at some time during the course of their disease. The depression may be situational and brief in duration, or it may become chronic, lasting for a lifetime. Healthcare providers should always provide intervention when a patient mentions suicidal thoughts, but thorough assessment and treatment of mild or transient depression is not part of standard cancer care.

Tip

There are brief questionnaires that are available to help doctors and nurses to evaluate depression in cancer patients, but these are not as widely used as pain or fatigue assessment questionnaires. Attorneys may find documentation of such evaluations or assessments in a patient's medical record.

When nurses or doctors interview patients during the course of their treatment, they often ask open-ended questions to solicit reports of any psychological or mental problems. A typical question would be, "How are you feeling about your condition and its effect on your relationships? Life? Work? Finances?" Another statement that often results in an outpouring of information from the cancer patient is, "You are going through so much and I wonder how you cope with it all." The responses provide insight into whether or not the patient is depressed or coping well with his or her illness. Other questions that might give insights into suffering due to depression are:

- Do you feel sad and blue even when good things happen to you?
- Is your sleep affected?
- Do you have difficulty doing even minor tasks?
- Do you just want to sit and not socialize with anyone often?
- Do you ever feel like life is not worthwhile?
- Do you still enjoy hobbies and pastimes?
- Do you find yourself crying or getting angry or frustrated easily?

Medicating patients for depression and anxiety is complex and often takes several attempts before the right drug or combination of drugs is found. Consultations with psychologists or psychiatrists can guide the oncologist in selecting the correct antidepressants. Patients suffering from depression should also be referred to a source of clinical support and to a support group, if available, for treatment of the depression. Drugs alone cannot resolve a moderate or severe depression.

G. Isolation and loneliness

Depression, deterioration of self-image, fatigue, social anxiety, and fear of infection can collectively and individually cause cancer patients to withdraw from social interactions. Family events can be exhausting, even for the patients who are not outwardly ill. Shopping can turn into an ordeal. Exposure to everyday colds, flu, and germs can easily infect patients whose immune systems are compromised.

Patients can suffer miserably without support of their family members, friends, and peers. The isolation can result in patients not being able to do any reality testing with others. The result is that they can develop the perception that they are worthy of being shunned and abandoned. In gathering information about suffering of patients, attorneys should not overlook this particular social aspect of cancer.

Tip

Patients who withdraw from social contacts begin to feel isolated and abandoned by their friends and family. This leads to further depression and loss of self-esteem, a dangerous downward spiral and vicious cycle of depression and withdrawal.

Danny said that when he started feeling down and blue because he did not feel that anyone understood or empathized with what he was facing, he turned to spirituality as a solace. Many patients express finding comfort in prayer, going to church, seeking spiritual guidance, and meditation to relieve the deep sense of loneliness and isolation.

H. Aggravation of existing psychological symptoms and conditions

Cancer and its treatment can make pre-existing emotional and mental problems and conditions much worse. Anxiety disorders, depression, paranoia, aggressiveness, borderline personality, and neuroses all get worse as stress increases. Patients who have these conditions under control and stabilized with counseling and medication at the onset of their disease may need close supervision and intervention by their psychologist or psychiatrist during treatment. Attorneys faced with evaluating and investigating claims of mental distress and disorder caused by cancer treatment should seek access to the patient's behavioral health records. Special permission must be obtained in writing from the patient or legal representative to obtain access to or copies of such records.

I. Helplessness

Emotional issues that create a great deal of suffering of cancer patients and their families are the loss of control, loss of power, and feelings of helplessness. Even physicians are subject to these feelings. The result is an accumulation of frustration, anger, resentment, and a strong desire to control and direct whatever is amenable to that behavior. The author has known patients to compulsively keep track of every single prescription, x-ray report, lab test result, CT scan report, and doctor's assessment because it is only when they have all the information about their disease and its status that they feel in control. This is a heavy burden and can cause stress on the medical staff, the patient, and the family.

A conversation with the patient or his or her family members can be helpful in determining whether they have experienced feelings of helplessness. Questions that nurses ask patients are:

- Do you feel that you have gained or lost a sense of control over your life and health since you were diagnosed?
- How are you coping with knowing that you have cancer?
- Who makes decisions about your treatment or diagnostic tests or health care?
- What are you doing that gives you a sense of control over your health?
- Do you ever feel helpless in the face of your cancer?
- If so, how do you manage with that feeling?
- How have you managed to regain some control over your life and health?

Caregivers can also feel very powerless in the face of progressive cancer. They can feel intense guilt or anger at either the patient for putting them in that situation or at God for allowing the situation to develop in the first place. Unexpressed feelings can burden the patient and family with negativity, tension, stress, and anger. This can manifest itself in physical signs of high blood pressure, headache, sore muscles, irritability, and chemical imbalances. Most people lack the skills or grace it takes to have an open, honest conversation with anyone about this type of situation. Attorneys might broach the subject by asking the patient or family the following questions:

- Have you felt that your cancer has caused you or your family to have any emotional stress?
- If so, how is this stress expressed?
- What is the result of the stress on your health, your family's health, your relationships, and your ability to communicate with each other?

It is normal to have feelings of fear of loss or fear of death.[22,23] These feelings are accentuated when a person is diagnosed with cancer. Exploring these feelings with the patient requires much sensitivity and tact. Any conversation with the patient should be prefaced with the caveat that if the patient feels uncomfortable he or she can terminate the conversation.

J. Suffering of and caused by family and significant others

Family members sometimes unintentionally cause additional suffering for the cancer patient. Out of protectiveness, they occasionally request that the patient not be given the diagnosis of cancer. If this request is honored, the physician and family succeed in setting up a relationship that will most likely lead to misunderstanding, confusion, and mistrust on the part of the patient for his or her healthcare providers. It is the author's experience that even when cancer patients do not have the mental ability to understand their diagnosis, they sense that they have a life-threatening condition. If energy is spent on sheltering them from the truth, less energy is available to help them through their therapy. When lawyers interview patients, physicians, nurses, and the families of patients, they should tactfully ask if this has been the case. If so, the family is partially at fault for whatever misunderstandings have occurred.

The grieving process is as hard for the family and friends as it is for the cancer patient. Not only does the patient usually practice denial, anger, and blaming when told of the cancer, but family and friends do also. The additional stress that this can place on interpersonal relationships is sometimes very destructive and leads to alienation, detachment, and the splitting of families. Many patients end up feeling abandoned by their spouses or families. They face loneliness and isolation and suffer from the loss of contact with their loved ones. If a spouse or close friend perceives that the patient's cancer was caused by the lifestyle the patient leads, they may blame the patient for bringing the cancer personally. When the patient is unable to change his or her habits, the family or friends may outwardly blame the patient for hastening his or her own death.

A small-cell lung cancer patient the author cared for during the last year of her life had a chain-smoking habit. There was no doubt that the smoking had played a large part in causing her cancer. Mary had two young teenagers and was a single mother. Her ex-husband was her main source of support and transportation. During the course of her chemotherapy, Mary's ex-husband continually berated her for not giving up her smoking habit. He told her that when she died he would tell her children that it was her fault and that she loved smoking more than she loved them. Mary made the decision to stop smoking several times during that year but was never successful. Her ex-husband's blaming behavior was a cause for much of the stress in her life. When her lung cancer was first diagnosed, however, it was so advanced that she had a very slim chance of cure. Her smoking habit, although aggravating her shortness of breath, probably did little to hasten her death. She would have been a much happier person had her ex-husband not criticized her so severely.

Mary suffered a great deal from pain, shortness of breath, fatigue, nausea and vomiting, and insomnia during the last year of her life. Her lung cancer diagnosis had been delayed by several years, although her chest x-rays showed evidence of the disease in years past. Her physician thought that the dense areas in her lungs were pneumonia or scarring from previous lung infections. Although the delayed diagnosis resulted in delay of life-saving therapy early in her disease, the suffering that she experienced because of her physical symptoms was less than the psychological suffering she experienced because of her ex-husband.

Attorneys need to explore the family relationships, the family members' responses to the patient, and the emotional and spiritual distress that a patient suffers at the hands of the family.

11.16 Suffering Caused by Symptoms of Cancer or its Treatment

Other sources of suffering include physical and psychological limitations caused by cancer. The disease limits those aspects of life and freedoms that we so often equate with life: breathing, eating, drinking, ambulating, autonomy, ability to form interpersonal relationships and help others, and the ability to take care of ourselves and our needs. Let us explore some of these limitations that commonly occur in oncology patients. Attorneys might find these descriptions helpful in understanding the source of pain and suffering of cancer patients.

A. Shortness of breath

Dyspnea, the medical term for shortness of breath, causes significant problems for some cancer patients, especially for those with advanced stages of cancer or in the terminal stages of their disease. Lung cancer patients, in particular, often suffer from this problem. Patients describe this condition as air hunger instead of pain. They say they feel as if they just cannot get enough air into their lungs. Dyspnea can be worse if accompanied by anxiety. Pre-existing anxiety can be a factor in creating a reactive airway and dyspnea.

Helen, a patient with lung cancer for whom the author provided care during the nine month course of her illness, had asthma and chronic anxiety prior to her diagnosis of cancer. Although she felt psychologically ready to undergo her first chemotherapy treatment, as soon as the chemotherapy drug started to infuse into her veins she had an immediate and severe episode of dyspnea. She had been appropriately premedicated with an antihistamine, an antiemetic, and antacid. She had forgotten to take her anxiety medication before she came to clinic. She was treated for the dyspnea with oxygen, antihistamines, and sedatives and recovered almost immediately. She was able to undergo subsequent treatments without shortness of breath as long as she took her anxiety medication prior to arriving in the clinic. Helen never forgot the episode and always mentioned her fear of not being able to get enough air. She asked the chemotherapy nurse if there was extra oxygen available whenever she came to the clinic. She became preoccupied with having oxygen available in the clinic and at home, and her anxiety increased as she became sicker with her illness. As we discussed her fears at length, Helen said that she associated shortness of breath with death and that she felt that when she was short of breath death was imminent. At the end of her life, she told the author that she did not care whether she had control over her legs, her bladder, her bowels, or her speech as long as she maintained control over her breathing.

Danny, the lung cancer patient who has mesothelioma, recently called the author when he was having shortness of breath. He had gone to the emergency room where a doctor who was unfamiliar with lung cancer and his case evaluated him. He had a chest x-ray that did not reveal any reason for his dyspnea. He was alarmed and anxious. Six months prior, he had gone out of state and had investigational surgery in which his cancerous lung, several lymph nodes, and the covering around his heart were removed. He was optimistic that the operation had removed all of his cancer and that he was cured. He had found out about a week before he called that his cancer had recurred and formed another tumor in his chest. Now he felt anxious because the emergency room physician had sent him home without any treatment. He was not feeling well enough to travel out of state to be cared for by his out of state doctor, and he had no confidence in the doctor who saw him in the emergency room. Although a prominent oncologist had seen him in his community, he was not sure that his situation warranted a call to him about his dyspnea. The initial misdiagnosis and resultant loss of confidence in his hometown doctor was now causing him anxiety on top of the acute dyspnea. In fact, the anxiety was making his shortness of breath worse. The author tried to reassure him that he was justified in calling the oncologist since he was having trouble breathing. He followed this advice and was appropriately evaluated and treated.

Shortness of breath can have several causes. Mechanical restriction of lung expansion by a growing tumor is one cause. The tumor can be in the lung, the chest cavity outside of the lung, or around the heart, trachea, or esophagus. Treatment can include surgery to reduce the size of the tumor or remove it or chemotherapy and radiation treatment to shrink the tumor. Dyspnea can be caused by an accumulation of fluid in the chest cavity, restricting the expansion of the lungs. This condition can be relieved by removal of the fluid by insertion of a needle and suctioning of the chest cavity, a procedure called thoracentesis. Laryngeal (voice box) spasms can make it difficult or impossible to breathe. Medication can be prescribed that can alleviate that problem. Blockage of the passages in the lungs can cause shortness of breath and can be due to a blood clot that formed elsewhere in the body and was carried to the lungs through the bloodstream. Anticoagulants (blood thinners) can help to dissolve clots and prevent them from forming again. Finally, a low concentration of oxygen in the bloodstream can trigger a feeling of shortness of breath. Oxygen-poor blood can be caused by anemia (low red blood cell count), by ineffective heart function, or an inability of the lungs to absorb oxygen because of scarring due to cancer or treatment effects.

Anything that reduces anxiety, helps to relax the patient, and enables her to breathe easier will help to ease her suffering. Positioning the patient in a semi-upright sitting position with a fan to provide sufficient fresh air circulation is often helpful. The alleviation of suffering due to shortness of breath is an important consideration in the care of most cancer patients at some time in the course of the disease.[25]

B. Suffering related to oncological emergencies

Acute suffering can occur when cancer causes conditions that constitute medical emergencies. Without immediate treatment these conditions can be fatal or result in permanent injury. After a brief overview of these conditions, information will be provided about how attorneys might solicit some reflections on how the suffering related to them. In describing the conditions, this material is extracted from the American Cancer Society's 1991 edition of *Clinical Oncology*.[25]

> A. Pericardial Effusion And Cardiac Tamponade: Constriction of the heart by accumulation of fluid between the heart and the membranous sack covering the heart (the pericardium). This condition can develop gradually over several days, but it becomes symptomatic with the patient complaining of chest pain, cough, dyspnea, swelling of the upper body and palpitations. Surgical draining of the fluid is necessary for immediate treatment, with more permanent therapy such as chemotherapy or radiation therapy following. Sometimes the surgeon will create a surgical opening in the pericardium called a pericardial window to allow for continuous draining of the fluid.
>
> B. Spinal Cord Compression: Constriction of the spinal cord by growing tumor or swelling of surrounding tissue. This condition can develop rapidly, causing numbness or paralysis of the extremities, back pain, difficulty with elimination or with breathing, depending on where the compression is located on the spinal cord. If blood circulation is blocked the extremities can feel cold. Prompt treatment with steroids to reduce swelling, and radiation therapy with or without decompression surgery can relieve symptoms. Without prompt treatment, permanent damage to the spinal nerves can occur. Rapid diagnosis and swift treatment is necessary, often within an hour or two of the development of the condition.
>
> C. Superior Vena Cava Syndrome: Swelling of the head, neck, chest and arms caused by compression of the vein that drains blood from those areas. Lung and non-Hodgkin's lymphoma patients can develop SVCS. This condition develops when cancer tumors impinge upon the blood vessels in the neck and upper chest, causing blood to back up and congest the head, neck, and upper chest area. Treatment is to reduce the size of the tumor through non-surgical means as quickly as possible. Treatments may include spot radiation therapy or high-dose chemotherapy. Surgery will be used as a last resort if the swelling becomes unbearable.
>
> D. Obstructive Uropathy: This condition is the result of a physical blockage of the urethra, ureters or bladder outlet. Symptoms include rapid onset of retention of urine, flank pain, blood in the urine, or bladder infections. The causes of this condition can be uric acid deposits blocking the ureter, blood clots anywhere in the kidney or urinary pathway, scar tissue that forms after radiation therapy and blocks the urinary pathway, or tumors that obstruct the urinary tract. Treatment depends on the cause of this condition. Surgery to remove the blockage can be performed after a urinary indwelling catheter is placed either through the abdomen or through the urethra. Radiation therapy can reduce the size of tumors if they are causing the blockage. If prompt treatment is not provided, permanent kidney damage can occur.
>
> E. Airway Obstruction: Constriction of the windpipe or the bronchial tree by tumor or swelling of surrounding tissues. This occurs gradually, but once 75% of the airway is blocked, patients will seek emergency care. Most lung cancer patients have airway obstruction to some extent. Immediate treatment is necessary to prevent lung failure and a fatal outcome. Surgical treatment involves creation of an artificial opening in the trachea called a tracheostomy. After surgery, radiation therapy or chemotherapy can reduce the size of the obstructing tumor.
>
> F. Increased Intracranial Pressure: Caused by swelling of the brain due to hemorrhage or tumor

growth. Patients will complain of headache, nausea, vomiting, blurred vision and decreased mental status. This condition can also cause seizures. Treatment consists of high-dose steroids and immediate radiation therapy. Neurosurgery is necessary if less invasive therapy is not effective.

G. Hypercalcemia: Abnormally high levels of calcium in the bloodstream, usually caused by leaching of calcium from the bones due to tumor metastasis to the bones. Patients complain of fatigue, loss of appetite, nausea, excessive thirst and urination and constipation. Without immediate treatment, this condition can lead to neurological damage causing muscle weakness, apathy, loss of reflexes, coma and eventually death. Treatment again depends on the cause, but giving large amounts of intravenous fluids can dilute the calcium salts in the bloodstream. Giving specific medications that reduce the leaching of calcium from the skeleton can rapidly reverse this condition.

H. Hyperuricemia and Tumor Lysis Syndrome: Abnormally high levels of uric acid in the bloodstream usually caused by rapid destruction of a large number of cancer cells. This condition occurs when a patient with a large tumor or advanced lymphoma or leukemia is treated with high-dose chemotherapy. Patients will complain of lethargy, nausea, vomiting, and urinary retention. Giving a drug called allopurinol and adequate IV fluid prior to chemotherapy treatments usually prevents this condition. Prompt treatment with intravenous fluid replacement, sodium bicarbonate to make the urine alkaline thus dissolving the uric acid, and close management of electrolyte balance can prevent kidney damage.

I. Hyponatremia: This condition occurs along with a rare but dangerous condition called syndrome of inappropriate antidiuretic hormone secretion (SIADH). This is a hormonal condition that originates in the pituitary gland and results in an abnormally low level of sodium in the bloodstream. It is seen most often with small-cell lung cancer patients, who will complain of lethargy, nausea, muscle aches and pains, and mild neurological symptoms. Treatment consists of eliminating the cause of the condition, which is the cancer tumor. Chemotherapy can accomplish a reduction in the size of the tumor. If the condition is severe, patients will be placed on a water restriction that normalizes the sodium level in 7 to 10 days. If patients develop severe hyponatremia and seizures or coma, they can be given sodium intravenously. Delaying therapy can result in permanent kidney or brain damage.

J. Hypoglycemia: Abnormally low blood glucose level found in patients with tumors in the abdomen or pancreatic cancer. Patients will complain of feeling very tired, weak, dizzy and confused. They may break out in a cold sweat and become comatose or have seizures if the blood glucose level is extremely low. Treatment consists of giving IV glucose. Treatment consists of monitoring blood glucose levels, eating frequently and once or twice during the night, and treating the underlying cancer that is causing the condition with radiation or chemotherapy.

When patients report that they have experienced any of these oncological emergencies, nurses may ask them some of the questions found in Figure 11.5. The attorney may find these questions to be useful in deposition or at trial.

C. Central nervous system conditions caused by cancer metastasis or treatment

Many types of cancer will progress by spreading to the brain or spinal cord. For patients who are at risk of central nervous system metastasis, close monitoring of cognitive and neurological status is required. Few chemotherapy drugs will reach cancer cells in the brain or spinal cord, and the drugs that will are very potent, cause many side effects, and carry a high risk of causing tissue damage. For this reason, oncologists do not routinely use these drugs to prevent central nervous system metastasis. Early detection and prompt treatment of cancer provide the best prevention for this and other types of cancer metastasis. Plaintiffs may rightly claim that delayed or incorrect diagnosis of their cancer lead to central nervous system damage.

D. Cancer fatigue

Fatigue is the most common symptom of cancer patients. Practically every cancer patient suffers from this

- When did this condition happen?
- Has it occurred more than once, and if so how many times?
- What precipitated the event?
- How did you feel when it started?
- Did your symptoms get worse?
- What made you seek medical treatment?
- How long after it started did you go see the doctor?
- How was the condition diagnosed?
- How long did it take to obtain the test results?
- How long was it between the time you first saw the doctor for the condition and the time treatment started?
- What did the doctor explain or discuss with your family about the event?
- Did the doctor explain what caused the condition and how to prevent it from reoccurring?
- Did the condition cause you to have any lasting symptoms or permanent injury?
- (If the patient has a poor prognosis and is in hospice care:) If the condition reoccurs, do you want to receive curative treatment or do you want to just be made comfortable and let the condition run its course?
- How do you feel living with this condition (if it is not treatable) and how do you cope with its effects?

Figure 11.5 *Questions attorneys can ask clients about events of pain and suffering*

debilitating exhaustion at some point during the course of his or her illness. It affects 76% of cancer patients during their treatment.[25] Patients' self-esteem can fall, and frustration can result in a sense of helplessness or despair.

In the 1970s through the 1990s the focus of cancer research organizations was standardizing and improving pain management. Fatigue is now the focus for much interest and research. In 1998, the Fatigue Coalition published results of "Fatigue I" that examined the incidence and impact of cancer fatigue. "Fatigue I", the follow-up survey began in 1998.[26] It examined the emotional, social, physical, and economic impact of fatigue on patients with cancer and their caregivers. The Fatigue Coalition is a multidisciplinary group of health professionals who develop and conduct research on fatigue and its effects on patients, their families, and their healthcare providers.

The suffering that is caused by fatigue is sometimes overlooked or perceived as unimportant or insignificant by both patients and attorneys. It might be the symptom of cancer that has the strongest effect on the quality of life of the cancer patient and his or her family. Questions that solicit information about this effect are:

- Has fatigue or unusual exhaustion kept you from taking part in activities you normally enjoy?
- Are you unable to join your family events and celebrations because of fatigue or exhaustion?
- How do you cope with fatigue and exhaustion?
- Has your doctor given you any advice on how to manage or cope with fatigue?
- Has your fatigue ever caused you to miss your chemotherapy or radiation therapy sessions?
- Has your treatment been delayed because of fatigue?

Fatigue can result from chemotherapy or radiation therapy induced anemia (low red blood cell count). There are several injectable drugs available that can be prescribed for patients to help maintain or achieve a normal red blood cell count during cancer therapy. These drugs are expensive, costing from $500 to $1,000 a month. Although insurance companies cover the cost of the drugs, physicians are not yet prescribing them on a regular basis for prevention of anemia. "It's not acceptable to tell patients that fatigue is just something they must live with . . . . We need to create greater awareness about cancer-related fatigue and develop approaches for assessing and treating it. For some patients, treating fatigue may be as important."[27]

E. Suffering caused by chemotherapy, radiation therapy, and surgery

There is no doubt that cancer therapy causes a vast amount of discomfort, pain, and suffering. Even as humane as it has become with the advent of potent drugs to combat pain, nausea, fatigue, infection, and gastrointestinal complaints, patients suffer from side effects that are unavoidable such as hair loss, loss of appetite, peripheral nerve and central nervous system damage, skin damage, and damage to major critical organs (heart, liver, lungs, kidneys, brain, skeleton).

When evaluating the side effects and suffering experienced by a cancer patient, attorneys should ask healthcare providers the following questions:

- Was the patient informed about the risk of these side effects?
- What were the potential benefits or risks of using the therapy given to this patient?
- Did you think that the potential benefit of this therapy to this patient outweighed the risks of developing side effects?
- When was this problem detected or brought to your attention?
- Was there an intervention available that would help to resolve the problem?
- Was this intervention provided as soon as the problem was brought to your attention?

These questions, phrased slightly differently, could be addressed to the patient or family to obtain a different perspective.

11.17 Fragmentation of Support Services

Specialization of healthcare providers and services leads to fragmentation of medical care and support services. Not only are healthcare providers and their patients confused by the maze of referrals, pre-approvals from insurance companies, specialists, healthcare systems, and HMO and PPO policies, but attorneys must find it very difficult to track down information available from all the different sources of healthcare of which their clients have availed themselves. One way to obtain an overall perspective of the scope of healthcare systems and providers that have provided services for clients is to contact the client's healthcare case manager. The patient should have the name and contact information for that individual. If the client has only been to outpatient providers, he may not have a case manager. In that case, the office nurse of the oncology provider who manages the cancer treatment plan would be the individual who can provide this information. If the client has been hospitalized, chances are that there would be a risk manager or case manager who would be willing to provide the attorney with information as long as the patient or patient's legal representative has given permission for them to do so.

Tip

Specialization of healthcare providers and services leads to fragmentation of medical care and support services. Not only are healthcare providers and their patients confused by the maze of referrals, pre-approvals from insurance companies, specialists, healthcare systems, and HMO and PPO policies, but attorneys must find it very difficult to track down information available from all the different sources of healthcare of which their clients have availed themselves.

Patients, as a general rule, have been advised of their rights as patients, but they are not aware of their legal rights and when those rights have been violated. The attorney can provide that information to the client and may be able to clarify the legitimate complaints that the plaintiff has that constitute a compensable injury. There is precious little information available in public libraries or on the Internet about the legal rights of cancer patients or where to seek legal help in deciding whether harm has been done or whether the complaint constitutes a good case. There is nothing fair about cancer, or the pain and suffering it causes, but it would be very helpful to cancer patients to have such guidance readily available in deciding whether the medical treatment they have received is legally just and fair.

A. Need for advocacy

When patients feel that the medical system or providers have wronged them, they need to find a person who will help them present their complaint to the powers that be. They might not have the energy or perseverance to pursue resolution of their complaint. Patient representatives cannot provide legal advice, however, they can help the patients find an attorney. Such personnel might be able to provide additional information to attorneys about clients who feel that their rights were violated. Patients and their families usually do not have very much information about their legal rights as patients or legal representatives of cancer patients. It would be very helpful if attorneys could present public presentations, workshops, and seminars on the legal rights, power of attorney, end of life decisions, and living wills of cancer patients and their families.

B. Need for support groups

Cancer patients are commonly referred to support groups for their particular type of cancer or the problems caused by cancer treatment. These groups may from time to time invite guest speakers who inform the members of resources, give tips for coping with their disease or the problems it causes, or offer a tutorial of the disease or a particular problem area often encountered by patients with that condition. Attorneys could be very helpful as guest speakers at such support groups. Social service departments at healthcare facilities or hospitals have resource guides that list support groups in their geographical areas.

11.18 Legal Considerations

To summarize the legal considerations related to pain and suffering of the cancer patient, it is important to stress that the attorney needs accurate, up-to-date information about cancer diagnosis, treatment, and palliation of cancer symptoms. Expert nurse and physician witnesses, nurse paralegals, case managers, and social workers with experience and expertise in oncology practice can be very helpful in understanding the clinical and social context of the client's case. The texts that are included in the "Additional Readings" section of this chapter contain current information regarding oncology practice and would be authoritative and respected references to cite as sources of oncology information.

The care of the cancer patient is complex, requiring the services of many physicians, healthcare providers, social workers, support personnel, and clergy. In researching a case, attorneys should take the same multidisciplinary approach to their interviews and investigation, even if the case is focused on one particular healthcare provider. Evidence should be gathered from many different perspectives, including the client, family members, friends, and diaries, journals, and correspondence. The multiple dimensions of pain and suffering need to be explored, using a methodical approach so as not to miss their impact on a particular aspect of the client's life. After the facts are gathered and the evidence is as complete as possible, it may be necessary to ask the patient or the family members to focus on the most important aspects of the patient's life that were affected by pain and suffering. This values clarification process is as important to the client as it is to the attorney in understanding and addressing the issues most crucial to the case.

11.19 Summary

This chapter was written from my perspective of thirty years of caring for oncology patients. I have watched many patients go through untold suffering from physical and psychological pain. Most have chosen not to pursue legal action as a remedy for delayed diagnosis, missed diagnosis, or injury sustained during cancer therapy. In my opinion, the reason for this is that they are so trusting and dependent on their healthcare providers that they forgive them. It might be that they feel that there are more important issues they face rather than obtaining justice for perceived or actual harm at the hands of their healthcare providers. The experience of cancer causes patients to reevaluate and reorder their personal priorities, and finding peace and spiritual comfort is sometimes much more of a priority than ensuring that justice has been served. For some cancer patients, however, that peace will never be found if they do not bring those that have caused them harm to a court of law and have a jury find them guilty of harming them. Some patients will not be satisfied until a court has awarded them a large monetary judgment to help them and their families cope with the damage that has been done. It is in the interest of helping those patients that this chapter is dedicated.

Endnotes

1. McCaffery, M., and Beebe, A., *Pain: Clinical Manual for Nursing Practice*. St. Louis: Mosby, 1989.

2. Merskey, H., and Bogduk, N., eds., *Classification of Chronic Pain,* Second Edition. Seattle: IASP Press, 1994, 209–214.

3. Chapman, C., and Stillman, M., "Pathological Pain." *In* Krueger, L., editor, *Handbook of Perception: Pain and Touch.* New York: Academic Press, 1996, 315–340.

4. Roht, L., Selwyn, B., Holguin, A., and Christensen, B., *Principles of Epidemiology.* San Diego: Academic Press, 1982.

5. *Cancer Facts and Figures*. Atlanta: American Cancer Society, 2002.

6. Fountzilas, M., et al., "Induction Chemotherapy with a New Regimen Alternating Cisplatin, Fluorouracil with Mitomycin, Hydroxyurea and Bleomycin in Carcinomas of Nasopharynx or Other Sites of the Head and Neck Region." *Cancer*, 66(7): 1453–1460, 1990.

7. Brock, D., and Wartman, S., "When Competent Patients Make Irrational Choices." *New England Journal of Medicine*, 322: 1595–1599, 1990.

8. Laska, L., editor, "Failure to Diagnose Cervical Cancer." *Anonymous Decedent v. Anonymous Obstetrician-gynecologist*, Prince George County (MD) Circuit Court, case no. _____, *Medical Malpractice Verdicts, Settlements and Experts,* May, 2002, 51.

9. Laska, L., editor, "Penile Cancer Misdiagnosed as Peyronie's Disease." *Anonymous Male v. Anonymous Hospital,* _____ County (OH) Court of Common Pleas, case no. _____, *Medical Malpractice Verdicts, Settlements and Experts*, May, 2002, 51.

10. Block, S., "ACP-ASIM End-of-Life Care Consensus Panel, Assessing and Managing Depression in the Terminally Ill Patient." *Annals of Internal Medicine,* 132(3): 209–218, 2000.

11. Wolfe, L., "A Model System: Integration of Services for Cancer Treatment." *Cancer,* 72 (11, Supplement) 3525–3530, 1993.

12. O'Hare, P., Malone, D., Lusk, E., and McCorkle, R, "Unmet Needs of Black Patients with Cancer Post-Hospitalization: A Descriptive Study." *Oncology Nursing Forum*; 20(4): 659–64. 1993.

13. Riley, J., Robinson, M., Wade, J., Myers C., and Price D., "Sex Differences in Negative Emotional Responses to Chronic Pain." *The Journal of Pain,* 2(6). Dec. 2001.

14. Eisenberg, D., et al., "Unconventional Medicine in the United States: Prevalence, Costs, and Patterns of Use" *New England Journal of Medicine*, 32, 246–52, 1993.

15. Sontag, S., *Illness as Metaphor and Aids and its Metaphors*. New York: Anchor Books, 1990.

16. Kay, R. *Spinning Straw into Gold*. New York: Simon & Schuster, 1991.

17. Remen, R., *Kitchen Table Wisdom.* New York: Penguin-Putnam, 1996.

18. Achterberg, J., *Lightning at the Gate.* Boston: Shambhala Publications, 2002.

19. Laska, L., editor, "Man Loses Front Portion of Tongue Due to Lack of Timely Diagnosis and Treatment for Cancer—$2.65 Million Verdict in Florida." *David Francisco and Maria Francisco v. United Healthcare of Florida and Jorge De Cardenas, M.D.*, Dade County (FL) Circuit Court, case no. _____, *Medical Malpractice Verdicts, Settlements and Experts,* February 2002, 14.

20. Laska, L., editor, "Nasopharyngeal Cancer Diagnosed as Tonsillitis and Pharyngitis—Progression of Cancer Requiring Chemotherapy—$767,000 Gross New Jersey Verdict." *Taormina v. Murray*, Monmouth County (NJ) Superior Court, case no. _____, *Medical Malpractice Verdicts, Settlements and Experts*, January 2002, 11.

21. Twenge, J., "The Age of Anxiety? Birth Cohort Change in Anxiety and Neuroticism, 1952–1993." *Journal of Personality and Social Psychology*, 79(6): 1007–1021, December 2000.

22. Schag, C., and Heinrich, R., "Anxiety in Medical Situations: Adult Cancer Patients." *Journal of Clinical Psychology*, 45(1): 20–27, 1989.

23. Mickleson, K., "One Way to Make Sense of Depression with Thoughts on How It Touches Those Dealing with Cancer." http://www.jasper-web.com/texascanceronline/depression. htm, 2000.

24. American College of Physicians, 1996–2002, American College of Physicians-American Society of Internal Medicine. http://www.acponline.org/vas2000/sessions/anxiety.htm

25. Holleb, A.I., Fink, D., and Murphy, G., eds., *Clinical Oncology*. Atlanta: American Cancer Society, 1991.

26. CancerFatigue.org. Learn about cancer treatment-related fatigue. Oncology Nursing Society, 1999–2001. http://www.cancerfatigue.org/learn/article.php?article_num=1&list=articles.

27. Lamb, K., Cox News Service. 1999. "Severe Fatigue Strikes Most Cancer Victims." *The Standard Times*, The South Coast Today online newspaper. http://www.s-t.com/daily/02-99/02-16-99/b02he041.htm.

Additional Reading

Berge, A., Portenoy, R., and Weissman, D., *Principles and Practice of Palliative Care and Supportive Oncology.* New York: Lippincott Williams & Wilkins, 2002.

DeVita, V., Hellman, S., and Rosenberg, S., *Cancer Principles and Practice of Oncology,* Hardbound/Single-Volume Edition Plus CD-ROM. New York: Lippincott Williams & Wilkins, 2001.

National Cancer Institutes, Cancer Statistics Branch, *1973 to 1999 SEER Overview.*

Perry, M., *The Chemotherapy Source Book.* New York: Lippincott Williams & Wilkins, 2001.

Rosenberg, S., *Principles and Practice of the Biologic Therapy of Cancer.* New York: Lippincott Williams & Wilkins, 2001.

Sykes, N., Fallon, M., and Patt, R., eds., *Cancer Pain.* London: Arnold Publishers, 2002.

Chapter 12

Wounds and Burns

Kelly Jaszarowski, MSN, RN, CNS, ANP, CWOCN

Synopsis

12.1 Introduction

Many of the injuries and their consequences that give rise to personal injury litigation are hidden. The effect of a head injury, for example, is difficult to explain to a jury. They cannot "see" the injury. Changes in roles, depression, chronic pain, and other consequences of injuries are likewise not particularly visible. However, scars are injuries that are visible and easy for the jury to understand. This particular chapter focuses on the effects a wound and burn may have on one's life. The events that could lead to the development of one of either phenomena are explored. The available treatment modalities as well as the physiological rationale for pain are described. This information is provided so that the attorney litigating a case involving a wound or burn has a better understanding of the development, healing, and effects of these injuries.

12.2 Wound Characteristics

A wound may be defined as any break in the integrity of the skin. Skin integrity may be interrupted as the result of trauma or surgery. A wound may be something as minor as a superficial abrasion or as extreme as involvement of multiple skin layers and body components. The sections that follow provide a limited overview of the etiology, physiology, and management of wounds.

A. Etiology

Mechanical, chemical, allergic, and infectious factors can contribute to an alteration in skin integrity. For example, a puncture as a result of a knife stabbing is a wound. Wounds are produced as a result of a surgical procedure. The skin may be injured by chemicals. The skin may break down as a result of incontinence, drainage from around a tube or drain, improper use of products, and harsh solutions. A rash or open area may be the result of an infection.

1. Mechanical injuries

External forces such as shear, friction, and pressure may create mechanical damage to the skin. Mechanical injuries may occur individually or in combination with each other. A shear injury is created when there is a resistance to skin movement. The classic example is a person who sits up in bed in a semi-fowler's position (with the head of the bed elevated 30 degrees) for extended periods of time. The torso slides to the bottom of the bed (gravity) while the sacral skin remains in the same location (resistance). Thus, shear injuries are predominately identified in the sacral and coccyx areas. The injury may present as a shallow insult or a deep one.

Injuries commonly located on the elbows and heels are friction injuries. Friction occurs when the skin rubs against another surface. Tissue injury is typically shallow involving the epidermis. Another type of mechanical injury is skin stripping or skin tears. Skin stripping occurs when the epidermis is inadvertently removed, such as during tape removal. The dermis may or may not be involved.

Pressure injuries result when a force applies pressure to the skin and compromises blood flow to that area of the body. Pressure injuries typically occur over a bony prominence of the body. For example, a person who is paralyzed from the waist down may spend most of the day sitting in a wheelchair. Pressure occurs between the wheelchair sitting surface and the bones of the legs. Thus, the blood flow is compromised to the back of the legs. If there are no attempts to relieve the compromise, a pressure ulcer will result. More information on pressure ulcers is provided in Chapter 9, "Spinal Cord Injury," and Chapter 15, "Pain and Suffering in the Elderly Population."

2. Chemical injuries

Chemical injuries are also typically shallow in nature. A chemical injury may present itself within a few hours or after several days of repeated exposure. The development of the injury depends on the strength of the irritant. The stronger the irritant, the sooner the injury is evident. For example, exposure to small bowel drainage will produce a visible injury within a few hours.

Tip

Injuries noted in an area of exposure to drainage and chemicals help to distinguish chemical injuries from allergic reactions.

---

3. Allergic reactions

Allergic reactions are immunologic responses to an allergen. They may present locally or systemically. Local reactions are commonly referred to as allergic contact dermatitis. Obvious allergic reactions are those where the allergen is present, such as in the case of adhesives or solutions. Less obvious reactions are those whose allergen is not visible or whose response is obscured by other concurrent processes. For example, poison ivy reactions manifest themselves after exposure. The poison ivy plant's substance is not visibly present on the skin.

4. Infectious reactions

Infectious reactions may present as a skin rash or wound. Some of the common classifications of infections are fungal, bacterial, and viral. Allergic reactions are typically referred to as contact dermatitis. Fungal infections, such as Candidiasis, present as a pustule. Folliculitis also presents as a pustule. The common bacteria responsible for this type of infection is *Staphylococcus aureus*. Types of bacterial infections include impetigo, toxic shock syndrome, and necrotizing fasciitis. Necrotizing fasciitis is a superficial tissue infection that spreads along the superficial plane. It is often referred to as a flesh eating disease. A delay in diagnosis of this condition can, therefore, cause devastating injuries. Viruses are an additional source of infectious related injuries. The more common viruses include herpes simplex and varicella-zoster.

In *Egbert v. Unnamed Physician*, the plaintiff had a red welt under her left eye which was diagnosed as dermatitis. Twenty-four hours later the red welt, however, progressed to swelling down to her neck. She developed a feeling of achiness, vomiting, and a fever of 102 degrees. The swelling continued to spread to her neck, and her cheek was grayish in color. In another twenty-four hours, the swelling extended to her clavicle. She had pus oozing from her face, and the gray area had spread. A month later after multiple procedures including debridement (removal of dead tissue) and skin grafts, the plaintiff has muscle and nerve damage resulting in the loss of the use of her right eye, the ability to blink the eye, the ability to open her mouth fully, and to smile. The plaintiff's face is disfigured. She requires regular use of narcotics for pain.[1] The suit settled in favor of the plaintiff for $2 million.

B. Physiology of wound healing

Whatever the etiology of the wound, the mechanism of repair is determined by the number of tissue layers involved in the alteration and the ability of the involved tissue to regenerate. Partial-thickness wounds, or those which involve the epidermal and superficial dermal layers, heal by regeneration. Epithelial, endothelial, and connective tissue can all reproduce. However, full-thickness wounds extend through the dermis. Full-thickness wounds heal by scar tissue formation. See Figure 12.1.

Wound healing may be categorized as primary, secondary, or tertiary. Hence, these terms are frequently found in medical records. In primary wound healing, the wound is closed such as with sutures or staples. The epithelial barrier is restored. These types of wounds tend to heal quickly with minimal scar formation.

Unfortunately, conditions do not always exist allowing for primary closure. These types of wounds are left open and are allowed to heal by secondary intention. Secondary intention refers to allowing the body to fill in the open area with scar tissue. This is typically true in contaminated or infected wounds and wounds with severe edema (swelling). Healing is achieved through scar tissue formation.

Tertiary wounds are those wounds managed by delayed closure. The open wound may be protected with heavy dressings. These wounds can be complicated, and the individual may be critically ill.

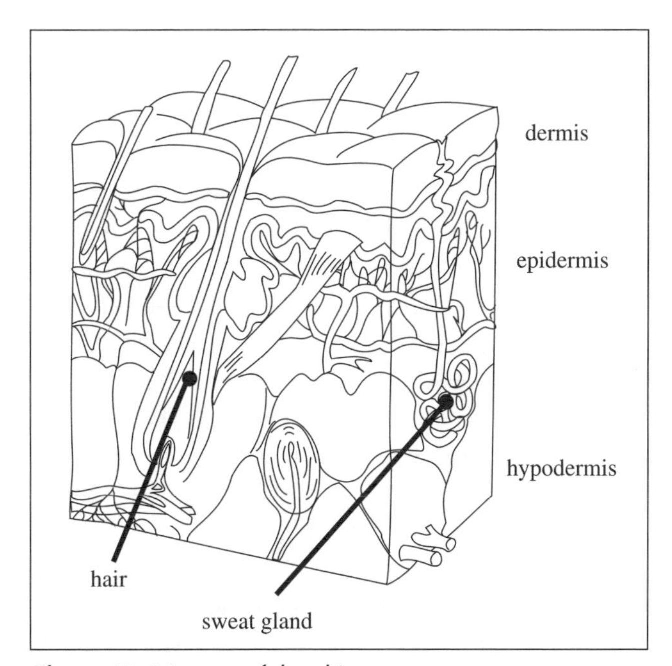

Figure 12.1 *Layers of the skin*

Wounds that proceed through the healing cascade uneventfully and reach wound closure are referred to as acute wounds. Acute wounds heal in a timely manner. The cause is typically known. An acute wound may be the result of a surgical incision or trauma injury.

Not all wounds heal in a timely manner or proceed uneventfully through the healing cascade. These wounds are referred to as chronic wounds. The cause of chronic wounds, however, are more challenging to identify. An underlying pathologic process that produces repeated and prolonged insults to the tissues usually causes chronic wounds. Typically present is local tissue ischemia, necrotic (dead) tissue, heavy bacterial contamination, and tissue breakdown. All these factors impede wound healing. Thus, it is imperative for the healthcare provider to assess for the cause of the chronic wound.

The healing process itself is a series of events. There is a cascade of physiological responses to the alteration in skin integrity. An insult to the tissue triggers an acute inflammatory response resulting in erythema (redness) and edema in the injured area. Injured cells release clotting factors, resulting in the activation of clotting. Exudate (drainage) is produced which contains leukocytes. The goal of the inflammatory phase is control of cellular injury and minimization of blood loss. A clean wound bed is established. This particular phase lasts approximately three days in an acute, clean wound. See Figure 12.2 for a diagram of the healing process.

The second phase of wound healing is referred to as the proliferative phase. New capillary networks are established to restore wound bed perfusion. Connective tissue is produced. In open wounds, forces of the new connective tissue mobilize the skin and tissue around the wound. This mobilization creates wound contraction. The wound is resurfaced through a process known as epithelialization. Epithelial cells migrate from the wound edges. The cells proliferate and differentiate to resurface the wound bed. Epithelial cells require a moist, vascular wound bed to migrate.

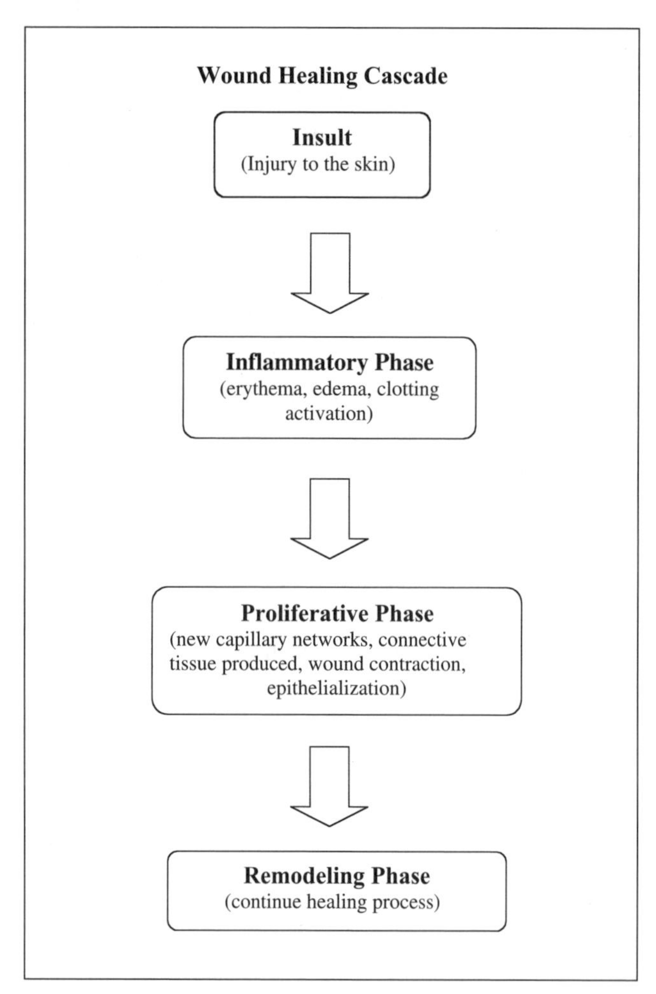

Figure 12.2 *Wound healing cascade*

Tip

For up to one year or longer, the wound continues to mature. This phase of wound healing is referred to as the remodeling phase.

C. Management principles

The viability of the affected tissue determines the healing course. The ability to heal is related to one's vascular and nutritional status. Wound management must be a holistic approach. First one needs to eliminate or, at the very least, control any causative factors. Pressure, shear, friction, moisture, and circulatory impairments require attention before healing will begin. Additionally, nutritional support must be provided. Any other systemic conditions impeding wound healing must be controlled. Pulmonary and cardiovascular conditions, immunosuppression (depressed immune system), and diabetes are just a few such conditions requiring evaluation. Finally, an optimal physiological wound environment needs to be provided. The wound must be cleansed, and nonviable tissue removed. Exudate needs to be managed, and dead space eliminated. The wound has to be protected.

Wound location and characteristics may provide some insight into the cause or cofactors affecting wound healing. Characteristic assessment should include examination of the distribution, arrangement, and configuration of the injury. When lesions or rashes are present, the characteristics of the primary lesion should be assessed. For example, there is a separation of dermal and epidermal layers of tissue exposed to a bed or chair surface in the case of shear wounds. Thus, one will see a shallow or deep wound in the coccyx area. In the case of chemical causes, drainage or solutions have contact with the skin. The epidermis is eroded in the area of contact. It is imperative, therefore, to eliminate the cause and any cofactors to avoid impeding wound healing. This is especially true in the presence of a chronic wound.

Tip

Eliminating causative factors alone will not produce wound healing. Adequate oxygen, growth factors, and nutrients must all be present.

Assessment requires the evaluation of the individual's nutritional status as well as cardiopulmonary status. Chronic conditions should also be evaluated. For example, assessment should include the oxygenation status in the presence of chronic obstructive pulmonary disease. In the presence of cardiovascular disease, the circulatory status should be evaluated. This is especially true where injuries involve the extremities. Diabetes is another condition necessitating a circulatory assessment whenever extremities are involved.

Concurrently, an optimal physiological wound environment must be provided. Tissue hydration, body temperature, wound pH, blood perfusion, and microorganism control are all imperative for wound healing. These factors are essential in assisting with the identification of the appropriate wound treatment. First, the wound itself must be assessed. Assessment includes location, size, tissue involvement, presence of undermining, presence of tunneling or sinus tracts (channel), presence of exudate, and presence of nonviable tissue. The condition of the wound edges as well as the condition of the surrounding skin should also be assessed. The presence of infection and odor contribute to local wound dressing selection as well.

Location of the wound affects dressing choice in that some body areas are more difficult to cover than others. Additionally, some dressing products are manufactured for use on specific areas of the body. For example, contoured dressings with smooth backings and thin adhesives have been developed for use on coccyx and sacral wounds in the presence of shear and friction.

Manufacturers have also developed various dressing sizes. Primary dressings have been developed to cover various wound sizes and to provide at least one inch of adhesive surface to intact skin. Additionally, dressings have been developed to provide enough material to fill in a wound. Various sizes of secondary dressings have also been developed. Secondary dressings are those dressings which cover wound fillers or primary dressings.

Dressing selection is influenced by the extent of involved tissue. In the presence of extensive tissue loss, wound fillers and packing dressings will need to be used to eliminate dead space. Eliminating dead space is also of concern in the presence of undermining, tunneling, and sinus tracts. In the presence of these characteristics, the ideal dressing should not only eliminate dead space but also be retrievable in one piece at time of removal. Dead space should be loosely filled to allow for wound closure without cellular destruction. In some instances, an antimicrobial product may be necessary to control bacteria.

The amount of wound exudate affects the hydration of the wound. Dry wounds require hydration. Thus, dressings have been developed which hydrate the wound bed. Conversely, absorption dressings have been developed to absorb excessive exudate.

Tip

Exudate control is not only important in terms of overhydration. Exudate control is an important factor in odor control and protection of periwound skin. The presence of a foul odor may add to the individual's distress.

Healing is also affected by the presence of nonviable tissue. Nonviable tissue supports the growth of bacteria, therefore, placing one at risk for infection. Thus, nonviable tissue must be removed from the wound bed. Debridement is the process used to remove nonviable tissue and is discussed in detail later in this chapter. Nonviable tissue that is yellow in color is referred to as slough. Slough is typically loose and stringy. Black tissue is necrotic, dead tissue. Products have been developed which target each of these types of tissues collectively or individually. Nonviable tissue may also be debrided using instruments instead of dressings, such as in the case of surgical debridement and conservative sharp debridement, as described below.

Wound edges (tissue at the perimeter of the wound) ideally should be attached to the wound. However, wound edges may be unattached or rolled down. Unattached and rolled down edges inhibit wound healing and, thereby, extend wound-healing times. In the presence of unattached wound edges, a dressing should be used to eliminate the dead space created by the unattachment. Loose, gentle packing is required to facilitate wound closure. Some individuals experience pain when packing is inserted into the wound.

Periwound skin condition requires assessment as its condition affects wound dressing selection. In the presence of macerated (excessively moist) periwound skin, the periwound skin requires protection from excessive moisture. The source of the moisture may be related to excessive wound exudate or the application technique of the wound dressing. The cause of the maceration needs to be identified and eliminated. Additionally, the injured skin requires treatment to facilitate healing. Periwound skin should also be assessed by the healthcare provider for dryness, cracking, erythema, and infection. Treatment choices for the wound are affected by the periwound assessment findings.

The presence of infection limits wound treatment choices. Only those dressings specifically indicated for use in the presence of infection should be used. A complete systemic assessment should be conducted whenever infection is present. While the presence of an odor frequently triggers the idea of an infection, minimal odor may be present in a wound. This is especially true in the presence of nonviable tissue. Odor has also been linked to certain types of dressings. For example, an odor may be noted on the removal of an occlusive dressing. Dressing strike through (drainage visible on the exterior of the dressing) and inappropriate dressing use may contribute to the presence of odors.

Tip

A dressing permitted to remain in place for an extended period of time will emit an odor. Poor hygiene will contribute to the presence of an odor as well.

D. Methods of treatment

The attorney should note that a variety of treatment options is available to promote wound healing. Hyperbaric oxygenation, negative pressure wound therapy, surgical closure, debridement, and topical dressings are all treatment options for wounds. A combination of these modalities may be used to treat a wound. Virtually all wound treatment regimens incorporate a topical dressing.

1. Hyperbaric oxygenation

Hyperbaric oxygenation therapy delivers oxygen under pressure, systemically and intermittently. Oxygen carrying and oxygen delivery capabilities of the blood are enhanced. Circulation to compromised areas and cellular function may be restored. In wound healing, the result is increased wound site oxygen. Hyperbaric oxygenation is not appropriate for everyone. Treatment is contraindicated in individuals with conditions that may trap oxygen or pose a risk for oxygen toxicity. Individuals with a history of emphysema or other pulmonary diseases are at risk for oxygen trapping. An individual who has a history of receiving bleomycin is not a candidate for hyperbaric oxygenation therapy related to the increased risk for oxygen toxicity. Hyperbaric oxygen therapy is not a primary wound treatment modality.

2. Negative pressure wound therapy

Another wound treatment option is negative pressure wound therapy. This treatment option is believed to reduce localized edema, to reduce bacteria, and to help the wound to close while providing a moist wound environment. Reducing localized edema increases localized blood flow and promotes the formation of granulation tissue. Negative pressure wound therapy helps the body to heal itself. A candidate for negative pressure therapy must have the physiological capacity to heal. Contraindications for this type of therapy are those patients whose wounds contain nonviable tissue, who have untreated osteomyelitis (bone infection), and whose wound margins have malignancy. As a result, the use of negative pressure therapy is limited.

3. Surgical wound closure

Surgical wound closure is also a limited wound treatment modality. The ideal candidate is nutritionally sound, free of wound infections, and possesses granulation tissue at the wound base along with new epithelialization (skin formation) at the wound margins. Surgical closure is typically a treatment modality for wounds caused by pressure.

4. Debridement

Debridement is the removal of nonviable tissue and foreign matter from the wound. This process may occur naturally. Debridement occurring naturally as a result of the wound repair process is referred to as autolysis (body digests its own tissue). Other mechanisms of debridement include chemical, mechanical, and sharp.

Chemical debridement removes tissue through the use of chemicals or enzymes. One form of enzyme debridement is maggot therapy. Maggot therapy debridement is primarily reserved for those instances when other treatments have failed. Multiresistant strains of bacteria, however, have sparked a new interest in this therapy. Maggot therapy involves placing sterile larvae into the wound bed. It is believed maggots secrete enzymes that liquefy dead tissue. Maggots actually ingest the tissue. The end result is a clean wound that has been disinfected and has been stimulated to heal.[2] The larvae need to be restricted to the wound bed. This can be accomplished by using dressings devised for maggot therapy, such as a hydrocolloid dressing, a mesh net, and an absorbent pad.[3] While maggot therapy may be effective, the therapy may create a sense of revulsion in the individual to who the maggots are applied.

Mechanical debridement removes tissue by means of dressings, irrigation, and whirlpool. Debridement, in general, may be classified as selective or nonselective. Selective debridement involves the removal of only nonviable tissue. Mechanical debridement is considered nonselective as both viable and nonviable tissue is removed.

Tip

Sharp debridement is the use of a surgical instrument to remove tissue.

Sharp debridement can be categorized as conservative or surgical. Conservative sharp debridement involves the removal of loosely adherent, nonviable tissue. On the other hand, surgical debridement may be an aggressive form of debridement. Typically, large amounts of tissue are removed. Conservative sharp debridement is considered selective debridement in that only nonviable tissue is removed. As a result of this selectiveness, conservative sharp debridement is also considered to be painless. This particular type of debridement is frequently performed at the bedside and in outpatient wound care clinics. Surgical debridement may also be performed at the bedside and in outpatient wound care clinics under a local anesthetic. Because surgical debridement may be painful, a local anesthetic is administered. In most instances, however, surgical debridement is performed in the operating room under general or spinal anesthesia.

5. Topical dressings

Topical dressings are the treatment of choice for most wounds. Correct dressing choice and use will facilitate wound healing. Dressings must be selected based on the principles of wound management mentioned previously in this chapter. Algorithms, flow charts, clinical pathways, and decision trees have been developed to assist clinicians in the appropriate dressing identification process. Generic dressing categories exist with design and performance variations present in each generic category. One such generic category possessing variations is hydrocolloid wound dressings. Variations within this particular category include the ability to absorb exudate, the absorbance capacity, the adhesive strength, and the thickness of the dressing. Thus, it is imperative for the clinician to choose a dressing whose performance parameters are tailored to meet the specific wound characteristics. Nurses specializing in wound care management are the ideal resource for dressing selection.

E. Physiological rationale for pain

Pain assessment must be incorporated into wound management principles. Wound pain should be quantified in terms of procedural pain versus nonprocedural pain. Pain duration, pain intensity, and specific pain characteristics should all be components of pain assessment. Partial-thickness wounds are painful. The epidermal covering of the skin is lost, resulting in the exposure of the nerve endings. Likewise, chemical wounds may be shallow in nature exposing the nerve endings. Negative pressure therapy pain is associated with the application of the suction and removal of the dressing. Debridement can be painful as well. Thus once pain has been identified, interventions should be incorporated into the wound treatment plan to eradicate or, at the very least, minimize pain. Pharmaceutical as well as non-pharmaceutical interventions should be explored.

Traditionally, pain has been quantified as acute pain or chronic pain. Another pain model is the Chronic Wound Pain Experience Model developed by Diane Krasner.[4] Three distinct categories are identified: noncyclic acute wound pain, cyclic acute wound pain, and chronic wound pain. All individuals may not experience all categories.

Pain occurring as a result of a single episode is classified as noncyclic acute pain. Pain associated with sharp debridement would be an example of noncyclic acute wound pain. Pain associated with dressing changes would be categorized as cyclic acute pain. That is, the pain is a periodic acute pain recurring as a result of repeated treatments or interventions. Conversely, chronic wound pain is a persistent pain occurring without manipulation. A complaint of a throbbing pain from a leg ulcer while sitting in a chair would be an example of chronic pain.

Pain management in the Chronic Wound Experience Model consists of interventions targeted to each category. The attorney may see a physician's order in the medical record for premedication with an analgesic before the nurse changes the wound dressing. The physician may administer an anesthetic prior to debridement. In the event of a chronic wound, pain alleviation interventions would consist of measures providing constant relief. Regularly scheduled analgesics or relaxation strategies would be examples of such interventions.

Strategies for approaching pain management include eliminating the cause, protecting wound edges, controlling inflammation and edema, stabilizing the wound, and addressing the aches and anguish.[5] These strategies reflect best practices. Additional research is required to provide evidenced-based practice.

12.3 Life with a Wound

There are several consequences of having a wound. The next section describes the effect on an individual. Wound pain may exacerbate the psychological effects of living with a wound.

Tip

Uncontrolled wound pain results in sleep deprivation and fatigue.

An individual's self-image and self-concept along with activities of daily living are all affected by the existence of a wound. Self-image and self-concept are affected by the existence of a wound related to the individual having an alteration in the physical body. The individual is struggling with a change in physical appearance. This change may or may not be visible to others. Additionally, an individual's mental image of himself is altered. He may no longer perceive his body as perfect.

Individuals with chronic wounds suffer with feelings of embarrassment, or frustration, and from social isolation.[6] Embarrassment results in the individual isolating himself from others. Embarrassment is exhibited when the wound is visible or wound dressings interfere with clothing. Depending on the wound location and treatment modality, different types or styles of clothing may need to be worn. For example, a foot wound may result in the inability to wear one's shoe. A special shoe may need to be purchased for the individual to remain mobile. Another potential source of embarrassment is a healing complication known as keloids. Keloids are irregularly shaped, elevated scars that grow beyond the wound boundaries.

Frustration may be exhibited as a result of the wound's mere existence. All efforts to accomplish wound healing may have failed. Perhaps, the wound has healed and, then, reoccurs. Hence, there is a feeling of powerlessness. Infectious wounds may require the individual to be isolated from others to prevent the spread of the underlying pathology. These individuals can experience feelings of shame.

Wound odor contributes to social isolation and embarrassment. Noticeable wound odor attracts the attention of others. Thus, the individual is embarrassed. The individual prefers to remain alone at home and avoid the public exposure and attraction, thus, socially isolating himself from the world. The social isolation and embarrassment may even lower self-esteem.

The social isolation and frustration may impede the individual's ability to work.[7] Frequent therapy treatments and healthcare provider visits may also intrude on the ability to work. The location of the wound may affect the individual's mobility. The individual may not be able to go to work because of the immobility or limited mobility imposed by the wound.

Tip

A wound can effect an individual's sexuality.

Feelings of imperfection related to the physical existence of a wound contribute to the viewpoint of being less than a whole person. Hence, an individual may consider himself to be undesirable and unattractive. Additionally, the cause of the wound can result in a functional loss. For example, a trauma or surgical wound may have disrupted nerves and vascular supply to the genitals.

Tip
Wound care dressings and wound management can be costly.

Financially, the wound may affect an individual's income. Healthcare coverage that does not cover the costs results in out of pocket expenses. An individual with a limited income may experience even more limitations. In the instance of inability to work, finances are affected even more. In the following case, the plaintiff claimed loss of job advancements as an element of damages resulting from scarring.

In a New Jersey case, a woman was disfigured when her car hit the rear of a garbage truck. The truck had no lights to warn drivers that it was stopping. The woman suffered multiple facial fractures and fractures to her right hand, kneecap, and femur. Her speech is slurred since the accident and her face is seriously disfigured. Although the plaintiff earned several promotions in the years before the accident, she had not been promoted since then. The jury found the defendants liable and assessed $15 million in damages for pain and suffering and loss of quality of life.[8]

Individuals may need to abstain from recreational activities permanently or temporarily. For example, infectious wounds need to be contained. Additionally, facial lesions and reactions of others can result in embarrassment.

Wound care management can affect an individual's ability to travel. Travel may need to be postponed until after the wound heals. The need to return to a healthcare provider for frequent treatments and evaluation is not conducive to travel. Frequent dressing changes and the need to have supplies readily available and accessible also hamper traveling.

Dietary intake may require altering during wound treatment. More calories and substrates are required for healing. Protein needs are increased. Nutrient deficiencies may hinder healing. Thus, dietary habits require assessment with modifications indicated based on findings and the demands for wound healing.

Tip
Special attention needs to be focused on each individual's perception of the wound and the effect the wound may have on his or her life.

Obviously, a wound affects every facet of an individual's life. Support, both physical and emotional, as well as resources is an integral component of wound management. The questions in Figure 12.3 will provide a starting point for determining the effects of a wound on an individual and the family.

12.4 Burns

Burn injuries affect the structural and functional capabilities of the skin. Extensive burns, or those involving a large body area, affect all bodily systems. Burns are classified as chemical, thermal, and electrical injuries. In addition to identifying the cause, burn assessment includes quantifying the amount of the body involved as well as the depth and the severity of the burn. Assessment findings help to guide treatment. Treatment must include both the physical and psychological needs of the individual.

A. Etiology

Swimming pool chemicals, drain cleaners, fertilizers, oven cleaners, paint removers, and acids may all cause chemical injuries. Chemical burns are more likely to be full thickness burns with the depth of tissue involvement being evident several days after the initial insult. Therefore, photographs may be useful in documenting the severity of the burn as the tissue damage progresses. Tissue damage will continue until the chemical is inactivated. The skin splashed with chemicals should be irrigated with water as soon after the initial insult as possible to inactivate the irritant. The depth and severity of the insult depends on how the injury occurred, the manner and duration of skin contact, the area of the body involved, and the chemical's concentration.

Exposure or contact with a flame, hot liquids, or radiation can result in thermal injury. Thermal injuries are the most common cause of burns. Their severity is related to the amount of time exposed and the temperature of the irritant. Cooler temperatures require longer contact to produce an injury, while hotter temperatures require less contact. Thermal injuries may occur during cooking. Individuals may be scalded by boiling water or oil. Children may experience a scalding injury when placed in a hot bath. Other vulnerable individuals may be similarly burned.

A nursing home resident was to have a sitz bath for a cyst on her labia. The nurses thought they were to steam the woman's vaginal area as opposed to placing

The following is a list of questions an interviewer might ask to assist in identifying the pain and suffering experienced by the client with a wound as well as that of their significant others. The list, while extensive, is not an exhaustive one and is only meant to be a guide for interviewing.

Wound Patient

Pre-operatively
- Did anyone explain to you the possibility of waking up with an open wound?
- Did anyone discuss with you what an open wound is?
- Do you feel your questions were answered regarding your surgery and possible open wound?
- Did anyone come to talk with you who said she was specially trained to take care of people with an open wound?

Post-operatively or post-hospitalization
- Did anyone come to talk with you who said she was specially trained to take care of people with an open wound?
- Did anyone explain to you the care involved with your open wound?
- Did anyone explain to you how to care for your open wound, change your dressing?
- Does someone else take care of your open wound?
- Did anyone explain to you where to buy supplies?
- Did anyone discuss with you any changes you might need to make in your diet, clothing, or work habits?
- Did anyone talk to you about disclosing to others you have an open wound?
- Did anyone discuss with you about having intimate relationships with others?
- How often do you need to change your dressing?
- Has your dressing ever fallen off in public?
- Is the skin around your wound irritated?
- Have your clothes ever been soiled as a result of your wound?
- Do you think you have an odor that others can smell?
- How do you think others feel about you now that you have an open wound?
- How do you feel about yourself?
- Do you have difficulties with intimate relationships?
- Did you have to change your clothing style, eating habits, or work as a result of your wound?
- What do you fear the most as a result of having the open wound?
- Has the care of the wound been a burden on you financially?
- Have you had to make a change in your employment as a result of the open wound?
- Do people stare at you when you go out in public? How does that make you feel?

Figure 12.3 *Questions for attorneys to ask clients about their wounds*

her in lukewarm water. The nurses obtained the water for the bath from the industrial coffee urn in the kitchen. The water temperature was 185 degrees. The resident suffered second and third degree burns. Her buttocks were burned in the area of the anus and outward covering approximately half of each buttock as well as a portion of her perineum. The plaintiffs alleged that it took the resident four months to recover. The decedent died from congestive heart failure seven months after the accident. The estate also alleged that the decedent's death was related to the burning incident. The case settled for $1.5 million.[9]

A youth scalded by cooking oil while working at a food stand agreed to accept a $500,000 settlement. Rafael Duran, age seventeen, was collecting cash at a food stand owned and operated by Freddy Dellano. Dellano fried dough treats, zeppole, in a set of heated oil pans behind Duran. Supplies were stacked behind

Significant Others

Pre-operatively

- Did anyone explain to you the possibility your loved one would wake up with an open wound?
- Did anyone discuss with you what an open wound is?
- Do you feel your questions were answered regarding the surgery and possible open wound?
- Did anyone come to talk with you who said he was specially trained to take care of people with an open wound?

Post-operatively or post-hospitalization

- Did anyone come to talk with you who said he was specially trained to take care of people with an open wound?
- Did anyone explain to you the care involved with an open wound?
- Did anyone explain to you how to care for the open wound, change the dressing?
- Did anyone explain to you where to buy supplies?
- Did anyone discuss with you any changes that might need to be made in the diet, clothing, work habits?
- Did anyone talk to you about the disclosure of having an open wound?
- Did anyone discuss with you about having intimate relationships with a person with an open wound?
- How often does the dressing need to be changed?
- Has the dressing ever fallen off in public?
- Is the skin around the open wound irritated?
- Has clothing ever been soiled as a result of the open wound?
- Do you think there is an odor that others can smell?
- How do you think others feel about your loved one having an open wound?
- How do you feel about your loved one?
- Do you have difficulties with intimate relationships with your loved one as a result of the open wound?
- Did your loved one have to change clothing styles, eating habits, or work habits as a result of the open wound?
- What do you fear the most as a result of your loved one having the open wound?
- Has the care of the wound been a burden on you financially?
- Have you had to make a change in your employment as a result of the open wound?
- Have you ever had to hide your feelings when you look at your loved one's wound?
- Do you dread having to do wound care?

Figure 12.3 *(continued)*

and above the oil pans. The pile of supplies collapsed, falling into the pans and splashing oil on Duran. He was burned on the shoulder, lower back, and left thigh. According to his attorney, Duran also developed some bad keloid (hard, lumpy, raised) scars.[10]

Other individuals may be burned by flames. Burning leaves and timber may also result in a thermal injury.

Electrical injuries can result in a burn. Electrical insults commonly occur from alternating current. Alternating current flow may produce cardiac arrhythmias, seizures, respiratory arrest, and loss of consciousness. Tetany (spasm) of the skeletal muscles may also result from an electrical insult making releasing the wire difficult. Electrical injury severity is related to the voltage and strength of the current. Electrical injuries have an entrance and exit wound. Low voltage shocks produce edematous areas surrounded by shriveled, depressed skin, whereas high voltage shocks produce dry, shriveled, scarred skin and sometimes death.

B. Treatment modalities

Burn management focuses on fluid resuscitation, ventilation stability, and hemodynamic (bodily fluid and blood pressure) stability. Injury care focuses on controlling microorganism growth, reducing the potential for an infection, and preparing the area for closure. Topical agents, such as the cream Silvadene, are used to delay infection and to keep wound bacteria to a minimum.

Surgical procedures may be necessary to relieve pressure and edema. A fasciotomy, as explained below, may be performed to relieve edema. In injuries extending into the muscle, edema may develop beneath the fascia and muscle compartment. The fascia is cut to prevent further tissue ischemia and nerve damage. An escharotomy is a linear incision through full-thickness wounds to divide the eschar. Full-thickness eschar is fixed. Edema may form under the eschar in the tissues. Ischemia may result as pressure, from the fluid leaking into the tissues, exceeds capillary closing pressure. Neurological and vascular deficits may also occur as a result of the tight muscle compartments. An escharotomy incision is performed as deeply as necessary to split the eschar. In other words, the person is sliced open.

Another surgical technique is burn excision. Burn excisions are performed to remove the nonviable tissue and to expose healthy tissue. Thin layers of nonviable tissue are removed until a viable wound bed is reached. This technique is used in deep, full-thickness injuries which may reach into the subcutaneous fat. Fascial excisions are used to remove burned tissue down to the muscle fascia. Burn excisions aid in reducing the chance of infection and in decreasing the body's response to the burn injury.

Burn wound closure reduces complications and fluid loss. Skin grafts and skin replacements are techniques used for burn wound closure. Skin graft options include autologous skin grafts, allografts, and xenografts. Skin replacement options include biologic, synthetic, and biosynthetic.

1. Autologous grafts

Autologous skin grafts involve grafting the individual's own skin. Epidermal sheets containing a thin layer of dermis are removed from an area of healthy tissue, resulting in a partial thickness wound. The areas most often used as donor sites are the thighs, back, and buttocks. The graft is then placed in the burned wound bed. The graft is laid flat and does not overlap onto intact skin. Adherence of the wound margin is not jeopardized.[11] Partial thickness wounds expose nerve endings and, therefore, may be painful. The donor site is painful and often itchy.

Sheet grafts are generally used on the face, hands, feet, and neck. Grafts may also be meshed to allow for more coverage while minimizing donor sites. Mesh grafts are typically used on larger burn wounds. The strip of skin is placed through a device that creates a mesh appearance. Epidermal cells then migrate in between the mesh. Staples or sutures secure the mesh graft.

2. Allografts

Allografts are cadaver-procured tissue which are typically used as temporary coverage of excised burn wounds. They may be purchased fresh or preserved. Because a foreign tissue is being introduced to the body, rejection of allografts frequently occurs. Other concerns that interfere with the successful use of allografts are the limited supply, the variable quality, and the transmission of disease.[12]

3. Xenografts

Skin grafts involving the transferring of skin from another species, such as pigs, are referred to as xenografts. Xenografts augment re-epithelialization, or the formation of new skin. They have demonstrated effectiveness on partial-thickness burns, especially those that will eventually heal on their own. However, a xenograft that has been left in place for too long will become a component of the wound, resulting in a difficult removal. Replacement of a xenograft should occur every three to seven days.

4. Skin replacements

Skin replacement dressings, such as biosynthetic dressings, are another option for partial-thickness wounds. Biosynthetic dressings are secured to the burn wound bed by compression dressings. They remain in the wound bed until epithelialization occurs. As epithelialization occurs, dressing edges loosen and require trimming. Biologic skin replacements include cultured epithelial sheets and cultured epidermis. Cells are harvested from donor skin or donor sites and expanded. Once placed in the burn wound, epithelialization is induced by the graft's release of growth factors. Synthetic skin replacements are used when replacement of the dermis and epidermis is warranted, such as in full-thickness wounds. Synthetic skin replacements have a dermal matrix. They are placed in burn wounds to provide protection. Many synthetic skin replacements are undergoing clinical trials.

5. Complications

An individual afflicted with a burn may suffer from complications such as infection, excessive scarring, skin changes, and contractures. Infection risk is twofold. The nonviable tissue provides a medium for bacterial growth. In addition, grafts allow for the opportunity to transmit infection. Wound and burn care are also sources of microorganism transmission. Scarring results from an imbalance in skin protein and is related to an individual's age, pigmentation, family history, and scar location. Scarring, skin changes, and contractures are discussed later in this chapter.

C. Physiological rationale for pain

Burn pain is related to the extent of tissue damage, the tissue surface involved, and the treatment modalities. Pain is further exacerbated by anxiety and fear. Burn pain can also be affected by an individual's psychological perception of life with a burn.

Tissue damage refers to the extent of tissue loss or the depth of the burn. Superficial burns or those burns resulting in partial thickness tissue loss are painful because of the involvement of nerve endings. Deep tissue loss or full-thickness burns tend to be less painful. Edema and pressure resulting from the injury to the tissue, as previously described, result in pain.

An off-duty police officer was delivering a propane tank to a township picnic. The hardware store negligently used a propane tank that was past its expiration date and should have been taken out of service. The gas began to leak and then ignited. The plaintiff suffered second and third degree burns to his arms, hands, and legs. The plaintiff's burn specialist related that second degree burns are actually more painful than third degree burns because the nerves are not deadened as is the case with third degree burns. The physician related that the several month recuperation period was extremely painful and that the plaintiff required excruciating debridements. The case settled prior to trial for $532,000.[13]

The extent of bodily surface involved contributes to both the psychological and physical phenomenon of pain. The larger the surface area, the more nerve endings that are involved. In addition, extensive surface burns can contribute to difficulties with bodily functions. For example, breathing can be compromised by chest and facial burns. The individual's perception of self as a result of the burn and treatment pain contributes to the psychological pain. Prompt and effective pain relief is necessary to reduce suffering. In the following case, pain management was delayed, resulting in needless suffering.

The decedent was an elderly woman with Alzheimer's disease. A nurse's aide followed an order for a soap suds enema. Subsequently, the patient was found to have blistering first and second degree burns on her thighs, legs, buttocks, and perianal area. During the course of discovery, the hospital produced a written statement by a nurse's aide who was in training and who had observed the administration of the enema. The witness documented that when the patient began receiving the enema, she cried out. "Oh! That's hot!" The nurse's aide then stated, "Well, they all say that," and continued administering the enema. The patient began shaking, sat up in bed, and with her hands over her face exclaimed, "You're burning me up!" The aide continued the enema. Because the patient was lying on a rubberized sheet, the hot water formed puddles. The woman sustained extensive first and second degree burns. The physicians delayed writing an order for morphine for approximately nine hours after the incident. Nursing personnel did not administer any pain medication until approximately eleven hours after the order was written. Thus, the patient went for approximately twenty hours without pain medication. The patient died a few weeks after the burns. The plaintiff's complaint alleged a wrongful death cause of action and, alternatively, a pre-death pain and suffering claim. The defendant contended that the medical records established that the decedent was not in significant pain prior to the administration of pain medication. A settlement of $1.65 million was paid. The hospital agreed to revise its policy on the administration of enemas to prevent reoccurrences and to disseminate a public apology for the incident.[14]

Treatment modalities themselves can inflict pain. For example, multiple treatments with debridement can be required with a full-thickness burn. The purpose of debridement is to remove nonviable tissue. Thus, one could suspect the procedure will not create pain. However, debridement may interfere with or disrupt nerve endings. This is especially true when aggressive, nonselective (both dead and living) tissue debridement is performed. In this situation, debridement is painful.

Debridement may involve "tanking"—that is, the individual is submersed in a tank of water or a whirlpool. Whirlpool is used to soften and loosen adherent necrotic (dead) tissue. This therapy will also cleanse and remove wound exudates. Whirlpool can be performed on any body part that can be immersed in a tank, such as the trunk and extremities. Once the whirlpool session is complete, conservative sharp or surgical debridement is performed. Both conservative sharp and surgical debridement are discussed in the wound section of this chapter.

Additionally, each burn treatment is a reminder of both the etiology of the injury and the effect the injury has on the individual's life. Every effort, then, should be undertaken by the healthcare professional to eliminate or to reduce anxiety and pain beginning with the very first treatment. The theory here is subsequent treatments will then produce less anxiety and pain. Thus, burn treatment affects psychological pain.

12.5 Life with a Burn

Burn patients are scarred physically and emotionally. The adaptation to life with a burn is influenced by the presence and extent of a physical scar, support of others, reaction by others, and period of life development when the scar occurred. Burn management affects the individual's daily life, socialization, and economics.

Tip

Body-image adaptation is influenced by sex, societal support, burn severity, and stage of development.[15]

Visible scars and skin pigmentation changes can result in adverse reactions by societal members. This is especially true in cultures where great emphasis is placed on appearances. The notion of appearing different can result in feelings of embarrassment and shame. Reactions by others and by peers influence an individual's sense of self. This sense of self becomes internalized as his self-image.[16] Prolonged stress and shame can also result in a decreased self-image.

An explosion in a recycling plant resulted in severe second and third degree burns of the scalp and top portion of the face of one of the workers. His eyelids literally were burned off. A $3 million dollar verdict resulted.[17]

Tip

An individual's stage of development at the time of injury affects her self-image and reaction to the injury.

Burn injuries occurring before school age are incorporated into the individual's sense of self.[18] This concept is related to the injury occurring at a point when the individual's body image is still developing. Conversely, school age children generally have developed their sense of self. A school age child's reaction can be one of a lower self-esteem and depression.

An individual's mental image of self may not be in congruence with the physical image. The physical scar is visible. Mentally, the scar is not present. This incongruence can lead to further feelings of shame. For example, an individual may have a mental image of having muscular, attractive legs. However when the individual looks at his legs, burn scars are present and occupy most of the skin surface below the knee. His legs are physically unattractive. The physical scar is also a reminder of how the burn injury occurred. This memory in and of itself may create pain. The individual may feel mutilated.

Tip

Special care is needed because hair follicles and sweat and oil glands are frequently not a part of the skin graft.

Burn management affects every facet of an individual's life. Special care must be taken with the burn injury and grafts. The individual with extensive grafting needs to avoid extreme temperatures. In addition, the individual needs to avoid exposure to the sun. Sun exposure may be minimized with sunscreens and clothing, such as large brim hats. To help reduce the itching that occurs as a result of dryness, lanolin-based skin lotion is suggested to provide moisture.

Burn management may necessitate frequent visits to a healthcare provider for dressing care or treatments, such as debridement. Healthcare professionals may even need to visit the individual's home. Thus, burn management can restrict an individual's ability to attend school or to work.

Social contact may be limited. While in the hospital, social contact may be limited related to the need for the individual to be isolated from others. Feelings of embarrassment and shame result in the individual isolating himself. Limited school, work, and social contacts affect an individual psychologically.[19]

In addition to work and school, recreational activities can be affected both temporarily and permanently by the burn-management program. However, long-term effects of the burn scar and its psychological effect may contribute to permanent changes. In recreational activities, for example, an athlete who sustains a severe burn to an extremity may lose significant extremity function. This loss of function results in the individual being unable to continue to participate in the sport. There is, basically, a loss of bodily function.

This loss of bodily function can lead to feelings of being less than whole. The perception of being less than whole can lead to feelings of undesirability and unattractiveness. Thus, an individual's sexuality is affected. The skin is an organ of life related to its sense of touch. Touching is a component of sexual contact. Therefore, patients who do not feel they can be touched because of their burn injuries may possess feelings of being different and unworthy of love.[20] These individuals often have difficulty with contact with others. As a result, their lives are well-organized and structured so as enable them to avoid conflict and to avoid facing rejection.

Diet and clothing may require modifications. Diet may be modified to include those elements necessary to promote healing. Injury wound healing dietary requirements were discussed in the previous section on wounds. Clothing styles may need to be altered to cover the burn injury and prevent its exposure to others. Clothing style may also need to be altered to cover the components of burn management, such as a dressing or donor site, or to provide access for care. Long-sleeve shirts might be chosen to cover arm burn injuries. A top with buttons might be worn to permit access to a chest injury. In addition, pressure garments are worn to prevent excessive scarring and to allow the graft to heal flatter and more uniformly. Pressure garments do not resemble regular clothing in appearance. As a result, these garments can contribute to feelings of embarrassment. Feelings of embarrassment may be intensified when the need arises to wear these garments in areas where clothes are typically not worn, such as on the face and hands.

Burn management affects finances. There are expenses for the initial management and treatment. Expenses are incurred for subsequent treatments, such as grafts and burn injury care products. Burn management may also include physical or occupational therapy. Occupational therapy helps to restore normalcy to the activities performed by the individual. Physical therapy helps to prevent contractures and helps to maintain range of motion.

Contractures result from excessive scar tissue formation and normal tissue being pulled or stretched. To prevent contractures pressure garments and splints are employed. Splints prohibit the skin from pulling. Different types of splints are used at various intervals during the healing process. Range of motion exercises are also performed by the therapist and the individual to prevent contractures. The necessity of pressure garments, splints, and range of motion exercises may extend over a period of years. Splints can cause friction on the skin and result in pressures and skin irritation.

Thus, physical and occupational therapy can be extensive and expensive. Furthermore, additional surgeries and grafting may need to be performed when there is a lack of healing. The inability or limited ability to work further compounds the financial issues of the individual. In addition, health insurance may not provide reimbursement to cover the expenses of treatment and management.

Figure 12.4 outlines some questions that may be used to determine the effect of a burn on an individual and the family. The questions serve as a stimulus for the process needed to determine how the burn affected the individual.

This chapter has provided a limited overview of life with a burn injury. One can see the multifaceted effects a burn injury can have on an individual's life. As with wounds, it affects virtually every aspect of life temporarily or permanently.

Endnotes

1. Suits and Deals, *New Jersey Law Journal*, April 15, 2002, p.8.

2. Sherman, R., "What is Maggot Therapy." Maggot Therapy (Larvae Therapy) Project, located at www.ucihs.uci.edu./com/pathology/sherman/home_pg.htm, 7/9/2002.

3. Sherman, R., "A New Dressing Design for Use with Maggot Therapy." *Plastic & Reconstructive Surgery,* 1997, 100(2).

4. Krasner, D., "The Chronic Wound Experience: A Conceptual Model." *Ostomy Wound Management,* 1995a; 41(3).

5. Krasner, D., and Kane, D., "Chronic Wound Pain." In *Chronic Wound Care: A Clinical Source Book for Healthcare Professionals.* Health Management Publications, 1998.

6. Neil, J., and Munjas, B., "Living with a Chronic Wound: The Voices of Sufferers." *Ostomy Wound Management,* 2000; 46(5).

7. Krasner, D., "Painful Venous Ulcers: Themes and Stories about Their Impact on Quality of Life." *Ostomy Wound Management,* 1998, 44(9).

8. Suits and Deals, *New Jersey Law Journal,* December 17, 2001.

9. Laska. L., editor, "185-Degree Water Used for Sitz Bath for Vaginal Cyst Treatment." *Marilyn Pease, As Special Administrator of the Estate of Elizabeth Jawor, Deceased v. Brentwood North Nursing and Rehabilitation Center, Inc., Riverwood Associates, and John D. Galbraith, Jr.*, Cook County (IL) Circuit Court, case no. 00 L 10804, *Medical Malpractice Verdicts, Settlements and Experts*, July 2002, 32.

10. Suits and Deals, *New Jersey Law Journal*, December 17, 2001.

11. Gallico, G., et al, "Permanent Coverage of Large Burn Wounds with Autologous Cultured Human Epithelium." *New England Journal of Medicine,* 1984; 311(7).

12. Kealy, G., "Disease Transmission by Means of Allograft." *Journal Burn Care Rehabilitation,* 1997, 18 (1) Part 2.

13. Zarin, I., editor, "$532,000 Recovery." *Plt. v. Deft.* docket no. L-9521-00, *New Jersey Jury Verdict Review and Analysis,* 23(3), August 11, 2002.

14. Laska. L., editor, "Negligent Administration of Enema Containing Scalding-Hot Water." *Anonymous Deceased Alzheimer's Patient v. Anonymous Hospital*, Robeson County (NC) Superior Court, case no. _____, *Medical Malpractice Verdicts, Settlements and Experts*, June 2002, 23–24.

15. McQuaid, D., Barton, J., and Campbell, E., "Body Image Issues for Children and Adolescents with Burns." *Journal of Burn Care and Rehabilitation,* May–June 2000, 21(3).

Burn Patient

Pre-procedure or treatment

- What were you told to expect with your burn treatment, procedure?
- What was discussed with you in terms of what a burn is?
- Do you feel your questions were answered regarding your burn and possible treatment?
- Did anyone come to talk with you who was specially trained to take care of people with burns?

Post-hospitalization

- Did anyone come to talk with you who said they specially trained to take care of people with burns?
- What was explained to you about burns and the care of your burn?
- What was explained to you about pressure garments?
- What was explained to you about skin grafts?
- What was explained to you about the need to wear splints?
- What was explained to you about the need to do range of motion exercises?
- What was explained to you about the need for physical or occupational therapy?
- What was explained to you about where to buy supplies?
- What was explained to you about hygiene measures to avoid dryness?
- What was explained to you about the need to avoid exposing the burned area to the sun?
- What was explained to you about the possible need to avoid extremes in temperatures?
- What was discussed with you about changes you might need to make in your diet, clothing choices?
- What was discussed with you about disclosing to others that you were burned?
- What was discussed with you about having intimate relationships with others?
- How often do you need to go to physical or occupational therapy?
- How often do you need to go for burn treatments (such as whirlpool)?
- Please describe the debridements you underwent.
- What was the pain like?
- What is the pain like now?
- What clothing changes have you made because of your burn?
- Do you think you have an odor that others can smell?
- How do you think others feel about you now that you have been burned?
- How do you feel about yourself?
- What do you miss about your life before you were burned?
- How do you feel about your appearance?
- What kind of, if any, difficulties with intimate relationships do you have since you were burned?
- What changes have you made to your clothing style, eating habits, or work as a result of your being burned?
- What do you fear the most as a result of being burned?
- How has the care of your burn been a burden on you financially?
- What changes in your employment have you made as a result of being burned?
- Have you lost the use of your _________ (hand, arm, leg, etc.) as a result of being burned?

Figure 12.4 *Questions for attorneys to ask clients about burns (continued on next page)*

Significant Others

Pre-procedure or treatment

- What was explained to you about what to expect with the burn treatment, procedure?
- What was discussed with you about what a burn is?
- Do you feel your questions were answered regarding the burn and possible treatment?
- Did anyone come to talk with you who was specially trained to take care of people with burns?

Post-hospitalization

- Did anyone come to talk with you who said they were specially trained to take care of people with burns?
- What was explained to you about burn treatment?
- What was explained to you about pressure garments?
- What was explained to you about skin grafts?
- What was explained to you about the need for your loved one to wear splints?
- What was explained to you about the need for your loved one to do range of motion exercises?
- What was explained to you about where to buy supplies?
- What was explained to you about the need for physical or occupational therapy?
- What was explained to you about hygiene measures to avoid dryness?
- What was explained to you about the need to avoid exposing the burned area to the sun?
- What was explained to you about the possible need to avoid extremes in temperatures?
- What was discussed with you about any changes that might need to be made in diet, clothing, or work habits?
- What was discussed with you about the disclosure of your loved one being burned?
- What was discussed with you about having intimate relationships with a person with a burn?
- How often does your loved one need to go to physical or occupational therapy?
- How often does your loved one need to go for burn treatments (such as whirlpool)?
- What kind of clothing choices have been changed because of the burn?
- What kind of odor, if any, have you noticed that others can smell?
- How do you think others feel about your loved one now that he has been burned?
- How do you feel about your loved one?
- What kind of, if any, difficulties with intimate relationships do you have since your loved one has been burned?
- What kind of change has been made in clothing style, eating habits, or work as a result of your loved one being burned?
- What do you fear the most as a result of your loved one being burned?
- Has the care of your loved one's burn been a burden on you financially?
- What kind of changes have you made in your employment as a result of your loved one being burned?
- Has your loved one lost the use of her _________ (hand, arm, leg, etc.) as a result of being burned?

Figure 12.4 *(continued)*

16. Jesse, P., Strickland, M., Leeper, J., and Wales, P., "Perception of Body Image in Children with Burns, Five Years after Burn Injury." *Journal of Burn Care and Rehabilitation,* Jan–Feb 1992, 13(1).

17. Zarin, I., editor, "$3,000,000 Verdict to Surviving Plaintiff Suffering Severe Burn Injuries." *Lopez et al. v. Joseph D'Amato Paperstock, Inc., et al.*, docket no. L-3783-98, *New Jersey Jury Verdict Review and Analysis,* 23(2), July 25, 2002.

18. Stoddard, F., "Body Image Development in the Burned Child." *Journal of The American Academy of Children & Adolescent Psychiatry* 1982, 21.

19. Rivlin, E., "The Psychological Trauma and Management of Severe Burns in Children and Adolescents." *British Journal of Hospital Medicine*, Sept 1988, 40(3).

20. Bogaerts, F., and Boeckx, W., "Burns and Sexuality." *Journal of Burn Care and Rehabilitation,* Jan–Feb 1992, 13(1).

Chapter 13

Ostomies and Incontinence

Kelly Jaszarowski, MSN, RN, CNS, ANP, CWOCN

Synopsis

13.1 Introduction

Bowel and bladder continence are two bodily functions most people take for granted. A change in either bodily function, however, forces people to focus on these processes and how often they need to urinate or defecate. In addition, more attention is paid to the newly required hygiene regimen. The change can take over one's life. Over time, one realizes the stigma placed by society on incontinence. Ostomies also carry a societal stigma.

In the following sections, ostomies and incontinence will be explored. An examination of possible etiologies and treatment, associated pain, and life with these types of alterations are discussed. The intent is to help the trial attorney and healthcare professionals understand the consequences of ostomies and incontinence. Terms that may be unfamiliar appear in italics and are defined in the glossary at the end of the chapter.

13.2 Ostomies

The term ostomy refers to an opening. This section will focus on ostomies created in the gastrointestinal and genitourinary tracts. Ostomies are created as both a palliative treatment and a cure for the underlying pathology. Implications for the surgical creation of an ostomy will be discussed along with management modalities and life with an ostomy.

A. Gastrointestinal ostomies

Disorders and diseases of the gastrointestinal tract may necessitate the need to create an opening in the small or large intestine. The most common type of ostomy involves cutting the intestine into two pieces, suturing one piece closed, and bringing the other piece out onto the skin through a surgically created opening. Fecal contents, then, drain through the stoma (or opening) on the skin. Gastrointestinal ostomies may be permanent or temporary. The following are some possible etiologies:

- congenital disorders
- diverticular disease (disease involving the lining and the wall of the colon)
- extrahepatic biliary atresia (destructive disease of the bile ducts starting outside the liver)
- gastrointestinal polyposis (numerous polyps in the intestine)

- inflammatory bowel disease
- ischemic disorders (damage caused by lack of circulation to the bowel)
- malignancies
- necrotizing enterocolitis (death of the intestinal mucosa)
- obstructive disorders
- radiation enteritis (inflammation of the bowel caused by radiation)
- surgical errors, such as perforation
- trauma

1. Draining diversions

Gastrointestinal ostomies can be broadly categorized into draining diversions and continent diversions. Draining diversions are those with an external opening (stoma). Continent diversions may or may not have an externally visible stoma. With an external stoma, the stoma is typically visible on the individual's abdomen. The stoma is surgically created using a segment of the intestine. Basically, the intestinal segment is brought out through the abdomen. The intestinal segment is then the point of drainage for stool contents.

2. Continent diversions

Continent diversions may or may not have an externally visible stoma. A continent diversion without a stoma results from an anastomosis procedure or a reservoir creation procedure performed to facilitate stool drainage. Anastomosis procedures involve suturing one segment of the gastrointestinal tract to another. For example, an ileoanal anastomosis involves suturing the ileum (the end of the small intestine) to the anal canal. Fecal contents drain through the anus. With reservoir procedures, fecal contents can also drain through the anus. Reservoirs involve the creation of a storage compartment for fecal contents. An ileoanal reservoir involves the surgical creation of a reservoir using the terminal ileum. One end of the pouch is connected to the remaining proximal segment of the gastrointestinal tract while the other end of the reservoir is anastomosed to the rectum. Not all reservoirs, however, drain through the anus. A Kock continent ileostomy is one such reservoir. This particular reservoir involves the creation of an ileal pouch within the abdominal cavity. A portion of the ileum is also used to create a continent nipple valve and outflow tract under the skin. This particular reservoir is then accessed to facilitate fecal drainage. Access is obtained by inserting a catheter into the tract and through the valve.

3. Ostomy locations

The location of the ostomy is reflected in the name or type of the ostomy. The drainage from an ostomy also reflects the ostomy location. A colostomy is an opening created in the colon (large intestine). A colostomy can be an ascending colostomy, transverse colostomy, descending colostomy, or sigmoid colostomy. See Figure 13.1. Drainage from a sigmoid colostomy should be soft, formed stool as the sigmoid colon is the most distal segment of the large intestine. Likewise, a toothpaste consistency stool would be expected from an ascending colostomy. An ostomy created in the small intestine is an ileostomy. Ileostomies produce liquid to toothpaste consistency stool.

4. Causes of intestinal ostomies

Obstructive disorders of the intestine can be diagnosed in any age person from the neonate to the elderly. Obstructive disorders have been broadly categorized as

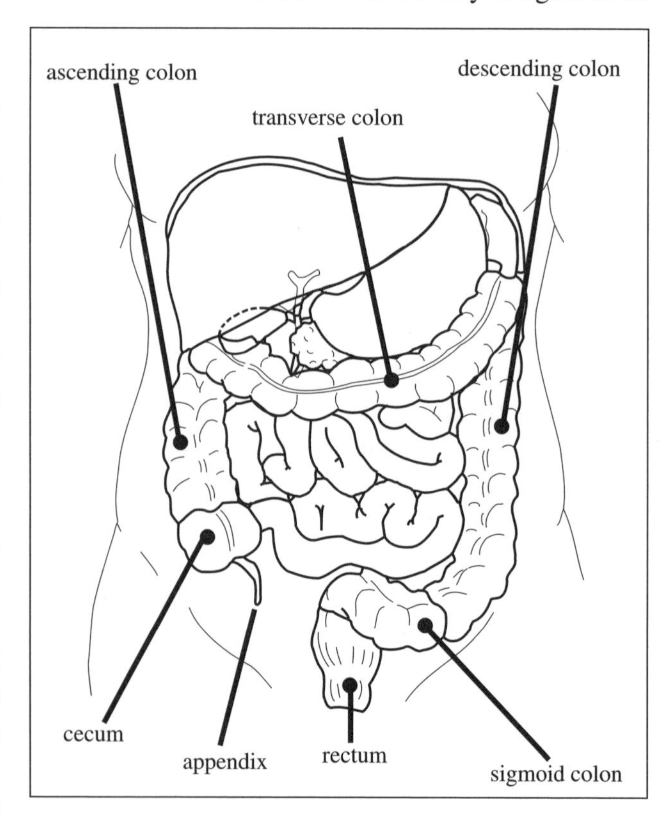

Figure 13.1 *Anatomy of the bowel*

adynamic and dynamic.[1] Adynamic disorders result from the absence of peristalsis in various parts of the gastrointestinal tract. Paralytic ileus (paralysis of the bowel) is the most familiar type of adynamic obstruction. Adynamic obstruction is a complication that can result from abdominal surgery, retroperitoneal surgery, narcotic medications, spinal disease, and retroperitoneal injuries. Dynamic intestinal obstructions can be located within the bowel lumen, within the bowel wall, or be external to the bowel. Intestinal obstructions can occur both in the large and small intestine with the small intestine being the more common site. Intense abdominal pain along with the vomiting of fecal contents can occur, resulting in a very distressed individual. Vomiting feces puts the individual at risk for aspirating or inhaling the feces, which can be fatal. Underlying etiologies associated with dynamic intestinal obstructions include abdominal adhesions, strangulated hernia, malignancy, volvulus (twisted bowel), intussusception (bowel telescoped into itself), and meconium ileus (newborn intestinal obstruction with thick meconium).

Attorneys may be involved in a case involving an alleged delay in diagnosis of a bowel cancer. Obstructions resulting from malignancies can result in the need to create an ostomy. These are particularly devastating injuries, as the individual is simultaneously confronted with the diagnosis of cancer and the adjustment to an ostomy. Malignancies of the colon and rectum can be classified as primary or metastatic. Primary colorectal malignancies are those malignancies originating from the bowel wall. Conversely, metastatic malignancies are those that have spread from adjacent or distant sites. Adenocarcinomas and epidermoid or squamous malignancies are primary colorectal malignancies. Metastatic malignancies can develop from cancer of the breast, ovary, prostate, and lung. Lymphoma, leimyosacroma (sarcoma with smooth muscle cells), and malignant melanoma can all result in metastatic colorectal cancer as well.

Neonatal necrotizing enterocolitis is an acute necrosis of the intestine. The distal terminal ileum is always involved. The outcomes of deviations from the standard of care which can contribute to the development of this condition include asphyxia at birth and arterial hypoxemia (insufficient oxygen in the blood). Necrotizing enterocolitis can also result from damage to the epithelial cells in the bowel mucosa. Feeding solutions can contribute to epithelial cell damage. Epithelial cells can be damaged by the osmolarity, volume, or composition of the feeding solution.

Intestinal damage can also occur as a result of radiation, especially when used to treat pelvic malignancies. This is especially true in the presence of gynecologic tumors, prostate tumors, and bladder tumors.

Tip

Miscalculated radiation dosages and injurious radiation delivered in higher than usual doses may result in a medical malpractice suit.

Catastrophic vascular accidents, such as may occur in the operating room, resulting in various degrees of colonic infarction (tissue death as a result of a loss of blood supply). Colonic infarction can result in colonic ischemia. Colonic ischemic disorders may be classified according to the severity of the injury. Some disorders may be reversible, while others result in colonic gangrene with perforation and peritonitis.

Trauma injuries can also result in the necessity for ostomy creation. This is especially true in abdominal and pelvic injuries. Shearing forces, such as seatbelt injuries, cause extensive damage, including mesenteric disruption and loss of blood supply to the intestine. Penetrating trauma, such as a stab wound, can contribute to the need for the creation of an ostomy.

The presence of multiple benign polyps in the gastrointestinal tract characterizes gastrointestinal polyposis syndromes. Some of these syndromes are Peutz-Jeghers syndrome, juvenile polyposis syndrome, Turcot syndrome, and familial adenomatous polyposis. Peutz-Jeghers syndrome consists of polyps in the stomach, small intestine, and colon. Mucocutaneous pigmentation, or melanin spots, is noticeable around the mouth. Juvenile polyposis syndrome is characterized by polyps located in the rectum. Polyps can also be found in the colon, stomach, and small intestine. A coexistence of a central nervous system tumor along with polyps in the colon indicates Turcot syndrome. The polyps are often tubular and premalignant. Polyps in familial adenomatous polyposis do become malignant. This particular syndrome is characterized by adenomas occurring early and growing faster and abundantly.

Tip

A delay in diagnosis and removal of polyps can necessitate the need for an ostomy.

B. Genitourinary ostomies

Like gastrointestinal disorders, disorders of the genitourinary tract can result in the need to create a temporary or permanent ostomy. Genitourinary ostomies may be caused by congenital disorders, malignancies, traumatic injuries, and inflammatory disorders. This section will focus on the types of urinary diversion and explore the associated disorders.

1. Types of diversions

Urinary ostomies drain urine. They may be broadly categorized as continent diversions and draining diversions. Continent diversions are those diversions with an internal bladder. An internal bladder is surgically created for the storage of urine. Externally, a stoma is created to facilitate access to the internal bladder. As in gastrointestinal reservoirs, a catheter is used to gain access to the continent urinary diversion bladder. An external stoma is also created with draining diversion. Draining diversions do not require access. Urinary drainage seeps through the stoma whenever it reaches that end.

2. Associated disorders

Several disorders contribute to the necessity for the creation of a urinary diversion. Congenital disorders, inflammatory disorders, neoplasms, and traumatic injuries can all precipitate the need to create a genitourinary ostomy. Urinary diversions may be permanent or temporary.

A breakdown in any part of the genitourinary system can result in a backward flow of urine from the bladder into the ureter. See Figure 13.2. Prevention of urinary reflux involves a complex valve system. Ureters enter the posterior bladder wall at an oblique angle traveling through the bladder wall until exiting at the ureteral orifice. Reflux results when the ureter does not pass through the bladder wall obliquely or with enough distance. Most commonly, the cause of vesicoureteral reflux is an abnormality in the trigone muscle in the bladder.

Urinary tract infections, pyelonephritis, renal abscess, cystitis, ureteral stones, retroperitoneal fibrosis, urethral strictures, and pelvic masses are all inflammatory disorders that can necessitate the need for a urinary diversion. Pyelonephritis can be categorized as acute or chronic. Acute pyelonephritis affects the renal parenchyma and the renal pelvis. As a result of the inflammation, the kidney enlarges. Micro abscesses may be present throughout the kidney. Chronic pyelonephritis is the result of vesicoureteral reflux. Cortical thinning of the kidney can occur along with dilated renal calices. Damage from pyelonephritis can progress. Prompt diagnosis and treatment of urinary infections, therefore, is essential to prevent this type of damage. Persistent infections and reflux can produce a thin hydronephrotic kidney with minimal function.

Cystitis can result in the need for a genitourinary diversion. It may be acute cystitis or radiation cystitis.

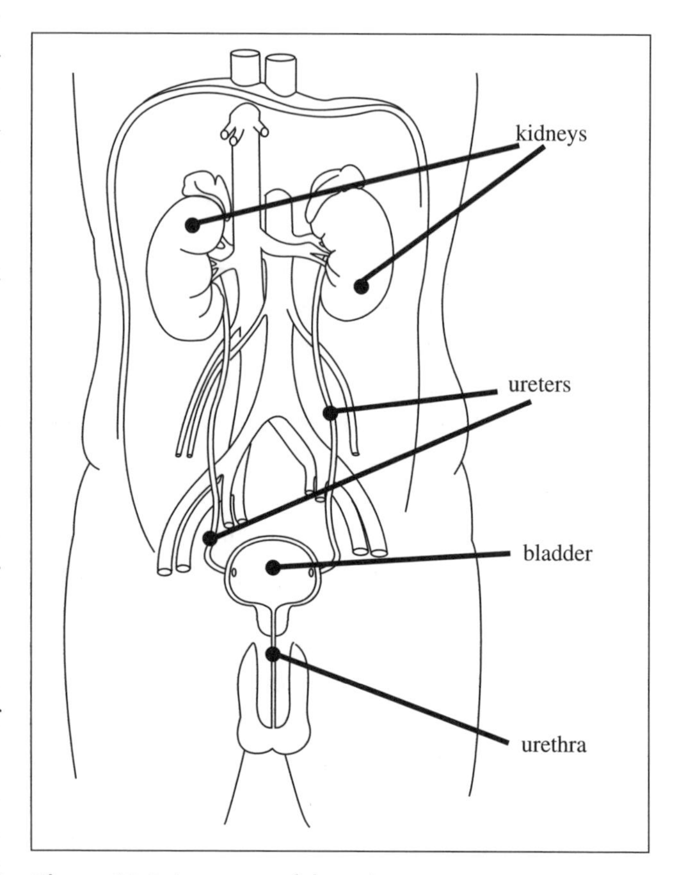

Figure 13.2 Anatomy of the urinary system

Acute cystitis results from an ascending infection from the urethra. Radiation cystitis can develop in individuals who have received radiation. It may present immediately or months after the radiation. Bladder complications include bladder instability and reduced bladder capacity. In some instances, ulcerations develop. These ulcerations can also precipitate fistula development.

Fistulas are abnormal passages in body tissue. The tubelike passage may connect two internal organs or connect an internal organ to the body surface. The passage allows contents to travel to other areas where they would not have previously been able to travel. For example, a woman may develop a vesicovaginal fistula as a result of a difficult labor during childbirth. That is, a passageway between the bladder and vagina may occur. This particular fistula permits urine to leak into the vagina. In the event a rectovaginal fistula occurs, stool escapes into the vagina as a result of the passageway between the rectum and the vagina. Fistulas can persist for months, thereby, creating much need for medical attention.

Tip

Fistulas are devastating injuries associated with much suffering.

A disease involving the tissue over the lumbar vertebrae in the retroperitoneal space is retroperitoneal fibrosis. In retroperitoneal fibrosis, ureter obstruction can occur. Hodgkin's disease, metastatic breast cancer, and colon cancer can result in retroperitoneal fibrosis.

Trauma and infections can result in urethral strictures. Urethral strictures commonly present as a decrease in urinary stream. Urinary retention as a result of urethral strictures increases the risk for infection and sepsis. Long-term use of indwelling bladder catheters can result in urethral strictures.

Obstruction can result in the pelvis from purulent (pus) material from a variety of diseases. The purulent material obstructs the ureters, resulting in the need for a genitourinary ostomy. Diverticular disease can result in pelvic obstruction, especially when an enterovesicular fistula (tunnel between the bowel and bladder) exists. Pelvic abscesses can also occur as a result of urinary leakage from surgical injury, trauma, and other causes.

Bladder, prostate, and urethral cancers can also precipitate the need for a urinary diversion. Of the three malignancies, urethral cancers are the least common. Extensive pelvic malignancy can require the removal of all organs in the pelvis. Total pelvic exenteration is the procedure whereby all pelvic contents are removed, including the bladder, rectum, and gynecologic organs. These are devastating injuries.

Trauma to the renal pelvis, urethral, ureters, and bladder can result in the necessity for a genitourinary ostomy. Renal pelvic trauma can occur as a result of flexion extension of the torso, as may occur during an accident. This extensive flexion extension can injure the renal collecting system. In children, the trauma can result in disruption of the ureteropelvic junction. Penetrating and blunt trauma can result in urethral and ureter injury. Penetrating trauma includes such things as a gunshot wound or a knife stabbing. Blunt trauma can result in bladder rupture. That is, the dome of the bladder ruptures as a result of a compression injury. Perforation from bone fragments as a result of a pelvic fracture can also rupture the bladder.

The bladder may be lacerated during surgery on the prostate or uterus.

A woman who underwent a laparoscopic assisted hysterectomy had her right ureter resected during the procedure. Once the error was diagnosed, the woman had to wear a drainage pouch for three months to collect the urine. This particular woman sued her physician for the surgical error and the failure to timely recognize the error. According to the *New York Verdict Reporter*, there was a settlement of $490,000 in favor of the woman.[2]

Neurogenic bladder dysfunction can be created by nerve injuries. The sacral area of the spinal cord contains nerves that are a component of the neurological transmission between the brain and the bladder. These nerves are referred to as the sacral micturition center. Thus, injury to the sacral micturition center interrupts the normal urinary process. Lesions above the sacral micturition center create a spastic bladder. A flaccid bladder is created by injuries at or below the sacral micturition center.

C. Methods of treatment

Treatment modalities for both gastrointestinal and genitourinary ostomies involve management of the ostomy. Both the peristomal skin and the stoma must be protected from complications.

Tip

Ostomy management involves containment of the output, protection of the stoma, and prevention of complications. This complex care is a prime source of suffering.

The goal of output containment is the collection of the diversion's output in an odor-proof device that inhibits leakage. The leakage of drainage contributes to odor and peristomal skin irritation. Thus, the device requires a secure seal. Pouching systems are used to contain the drainage. Pouching systems are commonly referred to as one-piece or two-piece and disposable or reusable. Pouching devices may or may not have adhesive backings.

Pouches incorporating both the drainage pouch and an attached skin barrier are referred to as one-piece systems. Systems with a skin barrier (faceplate) separate from the drainage pouch are referred to as two-piece systems. Urinary pouching systems differ from fecal pouching systems in that they have a spout attached. The spout facilitates draining of the pouch. Fecal pouches are drainable or closed-end. Drainable pouches have an opening in the bottom of the pouch to facilitate emptying of the pouch. Closed-end pouches do not.

A properly fitting appliance prevents both odor and peristomal skin irritation. Factors that healthcare professionals consider when selecting a pouching system include stoma type, stoma construction, stoma height, and abdominal contours. The individual's visual acuity, manual dexterity, activities of daily living, preferences, and financial resources are additional factors for consideration. Identification of an appropriate pouching system requires the healthcare professional to have special knowledge. Wound, ostomy, and continence nurses specialize in ostomy management. Nurses who specialize in ostomy care are also excellent resources. The Wound, Ostomy, and Continence Nurses Society is the organization to contact for further information regarding this nursing specialty and to assist with the identification of a specialty nurse. This society's Internet website address is www.wocn.org.

Another management option for containment is colostomy irrigation. Individuals with a descending or sigmoid colostomy are candidates for irrigation to establish bowel continence. The principle behind stoma irrigation is bowel retraining. The bowel is trained to expel its contents in response to a larger volume of pressure than would normally be established by fecal contents alone. The result is the expulsion of fecal contents at the time of irrigation, thereby, reestablishing a form of continence. However, colostomy irrigation is not successful or appropriate for all individuals.

The stoma itself requires protection from trauma because it lacks nerve endings. Thus, the stoma is insensitive and damage could occur without the individual's knowledge. The attorney or legal nurse consultant who is reviewing medical records may see documentation referring to irritation, bleeding, or ulcers on the stoma. Stomal damage can result from an improperly fitting appliance. Thus, care must be taken to properly size the appliance opening to accommodate the characteristics of the stoma. A nurse specializing in ostomy care would be a resource for the task of fitting an appliance.

Tip

The peristomal skin requires protection from mechanical trauma, product-related trauma, and effluence (waste).

Mechanical peristomal trauma results from inappropriate adhesive removal and inappropriate cleansing.

Inappropriate adhesive removal causes epidermal stripping, resulting in painful ripping of the skin. Inappropriate peristomal skin cleansing causes epidermal abrasions. Skin sealants assist with preventing mechanical damage by providing a protective layer over the epidermis. Solvents may also be beneficial in adhesive removal, especially in individuals with sensitive skin.

Product-related trauma results from the incorrect use of products used for pouching and peristomal skin protection. Pouching products may contain allergens. Thus, healthcare providers need to be cognizant of any sensitivity that develops and institute measures to remove the irritant. Adhesives may be applied to the skin to increase the adhesion of an adhesive appliance. Adhesives need to be dry before applying the appliance to prevent chemical damage to the peristomal skin. Additionally, an improperly fitting appliance can result in stomal damage during peristaltic movement.

An improperly fitting appliance can also result in effluence contacting the skin. Continuous skin contact with effluence results in peristomal skin irritation. This particular peristomal complication is known as irritant dermatitis. Peristomal skin can also develop an allergic dermatitis where the allergen is a component of the pouching system.

Folliculitis is a peristomal skin complication where there is an inflammation within a hair follicle as a result of traumatic hair removal. Traumatic hair removal can occur from shaving the peristomal hair too frequently, indiscriminate shaving or drying techniques, or careless pouch removal.

Hyperplasia is another peristomal skin complication that is characterized by wartlike papules or nodules. These papules or nodules have a white-gray or reddish brown discoloration. These lesions are extremely painful, and bleeding from the lesions is common. Hyperplasia is commonly seen in urinary stomas. It develops as a result of chronic exposure to stoma effluence.

Peristomal hernia is a complication that is common in individuals with end colostomies. Herniation may occur months or years after stoma formation. Loops of intestine protrude through a fascial defect around the stoma and into the subcutaneous tissue creating a bulge around the stoma.

Tip

Causative factors associated with hernia formation include stomal placement outside the rectus muscle, an excessively large fascial defect, stomal placement in a midline incision, increase in intra-abdominal pressure, loss of muscle tone, and wound infection.

Bacterial and *Candida* (yeast) infections are two additional peristomal complications. Bacterial infections may appear as large, patchy, red, crusty areas with plaque. Leaking pouch and body perspiration provide an optimal environment for *Candida* infections. These infections begin as pustules. With irritation, the pustules become papules with erythema. Satellite lesions are often noted.

Tip

Stomal complications include bleeding, laceration, prolapse, mucutaneous separation, retraction, stenosis, and necrosis.

Stomal bleeding can result from hemorrhage, trauma, and diseases. Hemorrhage typically occurs postoperatively as a result of an inadequate homeostasis (maintenance of stability) during stoma construction. Hemorrhage can also be caused by portal (liver) hypertension and by trauma to the stoma. Trauma injuries result from improper fitting appliances, improper peristomal skin shaving technique, and sports-related injuries. Lacerations can also be a result of improperly fitting pouches and trauma.

Prolapse stoma complications occur as a result of an excessively large abdominal wall opening, inadequate fixation of the bowel to the abdominal wall, poorly developed fascial support, and increased abdominal pressure. Prolapse involves a telescoping of the bowel out through the stoma.

Mucutaneous separation involves the separation of the stoma from the skin. The separation creates a defect. Mucutaneous separation often occurs in individuals with compromised healing abilities, such as in malnourished individuals. Another cause of mucutaneous separation is the creation of an oversized opening. The opening through which the bowel is brought externally is too large.

Retraction can be described as a stoma that is below skin level. Retraction frequently occurs as a result of excessive scar tissue formation, premature removal of the loop ostomy's support device, and weight gain.

Retraction has also been associated with surgical technique where there is an insufficient mobilization of the mesentery or excessive tension is created on the suture line at the fascial layer.

Inadequate suturing at the fascial line can also result in stenosis. Stenosis is the narrowing of the stomal lumen. Other factors associated with stenosis include edema, serositis, inadequate skin excision during stomal construction, or a mucocutaneous separation. Still additional causes of stenosis include disease, excessive scar tissue formation, trauma, hyperplasia, and chronic irritant dermatitis.

Necrosis is a stomal complication that can occur as a result of ischemic damage to the stoma. Excessive tension on the mesentery can compromise arterial flow as well as venous flow resulting in necrosis. Additionally, interruption of the blood supply to the stoma can be caused by an embolus or blood clot, excessive devascularization or reduction in blood supply, and suture technique. The extent of necrosal damage and depth can vary.

D. Physiology of pain

Pain is associated with the surgical procedure, underlying pathology, and complications. As discussed, the stoma itself does not contain nerve endings. Thus, physical pain is not related to the stoma. However, injury to the skin surrounding the stoma exposes nerve endings, resulting in physical pain. Surgical pain is related to the traumatic injury to the nerve endings.

Tip

The creation of an ostomy causes both physical and psychological pain and suffering. This type of alteration to the gastrointestinal and the urological system has far-reaching consequences on an individual's life.

Psychological pain is related to life with an ostomy. The effect an ostomy has on one's self-image, activities of daily living, sexuality, and finances correlate with psychological pain. Life with an ostomy is explored in the next section.

13.3 Life with an Ostomy

Individuals with an ostomy are affected both physically and psychologically. There is a physical change in their appearance, the presence of a stoma. This physical change affects their self-image. There is a change in their elimination routine which affects the activities of daily living. Plus, individuals are confronted with the very reason the stoma was created along with the financial costs of ostomy management.

Body image change for an individual is multifaceted. The individual is struggling with a change in physical appearance, a loss or change in body functioning, the loss of bodily parts, and loss of the mental self-image. Physically, the individual is different from others related to a component of the internal body now being visible externally. Society views the elimination of stool and urine as a personal, dirty process. Thus, any bodily component associated with the process is also dirty. Additionally, urine and stool have now become more visible. This is related to the relocation of the elimination process to the abdomen.

Containment of elimination products requires special attention. Individuals are faced with the changing and care of an appliance containing their urine or stool. The individual is no longer continent of bowel or bladder. Other individuals are faced with catheterizing themselves to expel urine or stool to maintain their continence. No longer does the individual go to a restroom and eliminate directly into a toilet. The time involved with the elimination process has increased related to the need to perform a procedure. It takes time to care and change a pouch, to perform a catheterization, and to irrigate a stoma. Colostomy irrigations can take up to an hour or more to perform and allow for fecal expulsion. For individuals with a urinary diversion, a night drainage system is used to prevent overdistention of the appliance. The night drainage system requires care and maintenance. Additionally, time is required to care for the stoma itself.

Appliances can fall off, resulting in clothing and bedding being soiled by urine or stool. Embarrassment can also result from gas emitted through the stoma. The stoma does not contain a sphincter, resulting in no way to control gas emission. Additionally, excessive gas can cause the appliance to enlarge, much like blowing up a balloon. The result is a visible bulge in the individual's clothing.

Sexual function may be lost because pelvic surgery can physically disrupt nerve and vascular supply to the genitals. In men, an arousal depends on the parasympathetic nerve plexus. The parasympathetic nerve plexus lies behind and alongside the prostate. Any pelvic surgery that removes the bladder, rectum, or prostate has the potential for damaging the plexus. The discharge of semen can be disrupted if sympathetic nerves in the presacral area are damaged. Abdominoperineal resection procedures can result in sympathetic nerve damage. Thus whenever possible, nerve-sparing procedures are performed.

The creation of an ostomy as well as the underlying condition necessitating ostomy surgery results in a loss of bodily parts. Sigmoid colon cancer surgery involves the removal of part of the intestine along with the tumor. Surgical findings may necessitate the removal of the rectum. While the exterior physical appearance of the individual does not change, the anus no longer functions. Individuals can be affected by the loss of their bodily parts. Psychologically, an individual may not consider herself to be a whole person. Others may consider themselves to be less of a person related to the loss of their bodily parts.

In addition to the loss of a bodily part, an individual's mental self-image can also be affected as a result of the surgical scar, stoma, and external pouching system. The surgical scar, stoma, and external pouching system are visible externally. Thus when an individual looks into the mirror, the physical image may not coincide with the mental image of self. This incongruence can result in depression and social isolation. This incongruence can also affect the person's view of his sexuality. The individual may now consider himself to be unattractive and undesirable.

Tip

Everyday activities of life are affected by an ostomy. Elimination process, clothing, diet, medications, work, recreation, and sexual activities all may require some altering.

The change in elimination process has previously been explored. With urinary diversions, an individual needs to adapt to sleeping with a night drainage system. This adaptation is not limited to just the ostomate, significant others must adapt too. An independent person may become partially or totally dependent on another for ostomy care and management.

Clothing choices and styles may need to be altered. Stomas in the waistline may require individuals to change their waistline location. Others may need to wear suspenders instead of a belt. Appliance access issues may necessitate a change in clothing style. The belief that the appliance is noticeable may require the individual to begin wearing clothing with patterns instead of solid color clothing. Concealment of stomas high in the abdomen may necessitate the need to begin wearing a layer of knit clothing to keep the pouch secure and smooth. Other individuals may choose to wear loose fitting clothing.

Diet is of special concern for those with an ostomy. An ileostomy causes the loss of 500 to 750 milliliters of fluid a day through the stool. Ileostomates (those with an ileostomy), then, must be sure to compensate for this fluid loss by increasing their daily fluid intake. For urostomates (individuals with a urinary diversion), fluid loss can be 1,800 to 2,400 milliliters per day. Thus, it is extremely important for these individuals to increase their fluid intake. Additionally, fluid intake and diet modifications can help prevent the development of urinary tract infections and stone formation. Individuals with a transverse colostomy also need to increase their fluid intake.

The opening of the ileum is relatively narrow. This narrowed lumen can be further narrowed by scar tissue development in the fascia layer. Undigested fibrous food can produce a partial or complete obstruction. Thus, ileostomates must be conscious of the potential for obstruction. The individual, then, must evaluate high-fiber foods for tolerance. Foods must be chewed well. Constipation is a concern for individuals with a descending or sigmoid colostomy. Routine prevention measures may necessitate an increase in fluid and fiber intake.

Gas and odor control can be facilitated through the diet. Swallowed air contributes to gas. Chewing gum, consumption of carbonated beverages, talking while eating, drinking through a straw, and smoking all contribute to an increase in swallowed air. Thus, eliminating or modifying these habits can reduce gas. Intestinal bacteria can form gas. Intestinal bacteria are primarily located in the colon. Thus, colostomates can be especially concerned about gas and odor. Additionally, it takes approximately six hours from ingestion of a gas-forming food for a colostomate to produce gas. These individuals may, therefore, choose to eliminate gas-forming foods from their diet or selectively eat the foods.

Medications differ in their absorption rate and location. Some forms of medications are designed to be absorbed gradually along the full length of the bowel. For individuals with a fecal ostomy, then, consideration must be given to the type of ostomy and medication absorption. This is especially true for those individuals with a short or reduced amount of bowel, like an ileostomy. Administration of enteric-coated, large tablet, time-released capsules, and spansule medications can result in these medications not being completely absorbed.

Tip

The ability to work or attend school is a concern for ostomates. Ostomates are concerned with the ability to remain private, to care for their ostomy, and to perform their work.

Supplies for ostomy care and appliance maintenance need to be readily available in times of need. Supply storage and ease of access, therefore, become a challenge. The ability to change an appliance related to restroom facilities is also a challenge. This is especially true when the restroom facility permits use by more than one person simultaneously. Privacy becomes dependent on the individual's ability to change the appliance in a restroom stall while his or her feet face the same direction as anyone else's feet. Work performance can be an issue when the environment does not provide for adequate fluid intake or for adequate breaks. Heavy lifting or rigorous activity may be contraindicated for some ostomates. Thus if these are components of an individual's job, the individual may need to seek other employment.[3] At the very least, a position change may be required. For some individuals, work or school may be too overwhelming to handle in conjunction with their ostomy.

Recreational activities, including travel, are affected by the existence of an ostomy. Modifications may be required for those who exercise regularly. For example, a support belt or binder might be necessary for securing the appliance during vigorous exercise. Swimmers may need to reinforce the adhesive edges with waterproof tape. During physical sports, the stoma requires protection from injury.

Traveling with an ostomy necessitates the need to carry sufficient supplies for the trip itself and, possibly, for the extent of the time at their destination. Again, ostomy supplies need to be readily accessible and protected from extremes in temperature. Individuals may desire to locate ostomy suppliers near their destination. In doing so, ostomates have the peace of mind of knowing supplies can be obtained should they be required. This task, however, may not be as easy as it sounds. Traveling to another country also poses the question of restroom facilities and dietary considerations. While travel may not be as spontaneous as previously, travel is still possible for the ostomate.

Social and sexual activities are a concern of the ostomate. Socially, individuals want to appear and to be perceived to be "normal." This is especially true throughout childhood and adolescence.[4] Individuals are concerned about disclosure and are confronted with the issues of whom to disclose to and when. An individual's lack of confidence and insecurities related to the ostomy can result in social isolation.[5] Sexual activity is another concern. Concealing, emptying, and securing the appliance are all changes facing the ostomate. For individuals with a continent diversion, concern also focuses on concealment. Sexual spontaneity may be affected. Sexual desire may be reduced.[6] Individuals, thus, fear rejection by their loved ones.[7]

An individual's inability to adjust to an ostomy can result in a desire to commit suicide. A forty-year-old male colostomy patient of this author considered himself to be less than a man. Despite the ostomy being a temporary one, the ostomy symbolized his inadequacies. He felt like damaged goods. No longer could he and his wife be intimate. He had a piece of his intestine visible on his abdomen. Thus, he was repulsive. He believed his life was no longer worth living. He preferred death over life and attempted suicide.

Financially, an ostomy represents additional expenses for supplies. Expenses are now being incurred for supplies. Ostomy care and management can be a financial hardship, especially if health insurance does not adequately offset the cost of supplies. The financial hardship is compounded if the ostomy resulted in a change in income.

Tip

The very reason for stoma creation needs to be addressed. Emotionally, the individual may need to face an illness, disease, or trauma. For some, ostomy surgery may be a cure for a life-threatening disease, such as in the case of colon cancer. For others, the ostomy may represent a fight with a knife. Still others who required an ostomy due to a surgical malpractice may be extremely angry.

As is evident, ostomy surgery affects every aspect of an individual's life. Special attention needs to be given to recognizing the effect of an ostomy. Individuals need to be provided the counseling, resources, and support to assist them in living with an ostomy. The attorney's questioning of the plaintiff during deposition or at trial helps the jury understand the consequences of having an ostomy. Figure 13.3 provides questions that the defense attorney may wish to use during deposition or the plaintiff attorney may use during direct examination at trial.

13.4 Continence

Continence of bowel and bladder is a societal expectation. Children generally are accepted into school programs with the expectation of some form of continence. Conversely, incontinence has been accepted by society as a consequence of aging and child bearing. As an individual ages, there is a reduction of sensory awareness of bladder filling and of the ability to empty the bladder effectively.

This section explores incontinence. Etiologies for both bowel and bladder incontinence will be discussed. Treatment modalities for each type or classification of incontinence will be explored. Finally, life with incontinence will be described.

A. Urinary incontinence

Urinary incontinence may occur as a result of factors both intrinsic and extrinsic to the urinary tract. Incontinence may be quantified as acute or chronic in duration. Acute incontinence generally refers to a new onset or sudden worsening of urinary leakage. Acute urinary incontinence is sometimes classified as transient incontinence. The theory is that the incontinence is reversible. Urinary incontinence is neither age nor gender-specific.

Urinary incontinence is best understood by classifying the incontinence as problems with storage, problems with emptying, or mixed problems with storage and emptying. Problems with storage include bladder dysfunction and sphincter dysfunction. Problems with emptying involve urinary retention.

1. Problems with storage

Urge incontinence is a bladder dysfunction. There is an involuntary loss of urine associated with a sudden strong urge to urinate. Detrusor overactivity is a result of detrusor hyperreflexia or detrusor instability. In other words, the bladder is overactive as a result of involuntary bladder contractions, reduced bladder capacity, or urinary urgency. Sphincter dysfunction results in an involuntary loss of urine during physical exertion, such as in the occurrence of sneezing or coughing. Thus, this dysfunction is commonly referred to as stress incontinence. Urinary leakage may also occur as a result of urinary volume exceeding bladder capacity. Urine may leak as a result of a source other than the urethra. This type of incontinence is typically classified as extraurethral incontinence.

2. Problems with emptying

Problems with emptying the bladder involve retention. That is, there is an inability of the bladder to empty. Overflow incontinence is the term used to describe incontinence associated with an incomplete emptying of the bladder. Causes of overflow incontinence include detrusor instability and bladder outlet obstruction.

Sample ostomy questions

The following is a list of questions an attorney might ask to assist in identifying the pain and suffering experienced by the client with an ostomy as well as that of the significant others. The list, while extensive, is not an exhaustive one and is only meant to be a guide for questioning.

When questioning the ostomy client and spouse or loved one, the attorney may find it easier and clearer to utilize the correct name for the ostomy (colostomy, ileostomy, urostomy, etc.). In the questions following, however, the word ostomy will be used.

Pre-operatively

- What did you know about the possibility of waking up with an ostomy after surgery?
- What did you know about an ostomy?
- Did anyone mark a site on your abdomen where the ostomy might be located?
- Do you feel your questions were answered regarding your surgery and possible ostomy?
- Who talked with you about the ostomy?
- Did anyone come to talk with you who was specially trained to take care of people with an ostomy?

Post-operatively

- Who talked with you about the ostomy after surgery?
- Did anyone come to talk with you who was specially trained to take care of people with an ostomy?
- What were you told about how your ostomy works?
- Did anyone explain to you how to empty your appliance, change your appliance?
- Did anyone explain to you where to buy supplies?
- What did you know, if anything, about any changes you might need to make in your diet, clothing choices?
- Did anyone talk to you about disclosing to others you have an ostomy?
- Since your ostomy was created, what did you know, if anything, about having intimate relationships with others?
- How often do you need to change your pouch?
- Has your pouch ever fallen off?
- Has your pouch ever fallen off in public?
- How did you feel when your pouch fell off?
- Is the skin under your appliance irritated?
- Have your clothes ever been soiled as a result of your ostomy?
- Do you think you have an odor that others can smell?
- How do you think others feel about you now that you have an ostomy?
- What emotional effect has the ostomy had on you?
- How do you feel about yourself now as opposed to before your surgery?
- Do you have difficulties with intimate relationships since your ostomy was created?
- How did you have to change your clothing style or eating habits as a result of your ostomy?
- How has your relationship changed with your loved ones?
- What, if anything, can you no longer do as a result of your ostomy?
- What do you fear the most as a result of having the ostomy?
- Has the care of the ostomy been a burden on you financially?
- What effect, if any, has your ostomy had on your employment?

Figure 13.3 *Questions for attorneys to ask clients about their ostomies*

3. Mixed problems

Incontinence involving mixed problems, problems with storage and emptying, are commonly associated with neurological lesions above the sacral spinal cord. Mixed problems may also occur in individuals with spinal stenosis, disc disease, and cervical spondylosis. The term "reflex incontinence" refers to problems with storage and emptying. Reflex incontinence involves the involuntary loss of urine as a result of detrusor hyperreflexive contractions along with diminished or absent sensory awareness of the urge to void.

Cauda equina syndrome involves weakness in the legs, gait disturbance, severe back and leg pain as a result of nerve root compression in the lumbar spinal canal. Some individuals also have problems with bowel and bladder continence. Cauda equina syndrome due to surgical trauma or undiagnosed epidural hematoma is one of the biggest causes of malpractice cases.

A steel factory worker who sustained a back injury while working suffers from permanent bladder and sexual dysfunction and requires an enema to stimulate his bowels as a result of a failure to diagnose cauda equina syndrome.[8]

Tip

Cauda equina syndrome due to surgical trauma or undiagnosed epidural hematoma is a major source of damages in medical malpractice.

---

4. Extrinsic factors

Extrinsic urinary tract factors commonly include delirium, restricted mobility, excessive urine production, stool impaction, and pharmaceuticals. Assessment of incontinence should include an exploration of these factors. Additionally, interventions to alleviate these factors will contribute to restoring continence.

a. Delirium. Delirium is an extrinsic factor of incontinence related to the individual being in a confused state. The individual is unable to recognize and respond to a full bladder. Some of the common causes of delirium are alcohol use, drug use, medications, and sleep deprivation. Metabolic conditions, such as hepatic or renal failure, may also result in delirium. A sudden onset of confusion in an elderly individual may be a clinical indicator of a urinary tract infection. Assessment focuses on ruling out this diagnosis. An elderly individual may also become confused as a result of other illnesses and hospitalization.

Mobility has a role in incontinence. Restricted mobility may occur as a result of hospitalizations due to injury, illness, or surgery. Mobility and the ability to respond to the urge to void is restricted, resulting in incontinence.

b. Stool impaction. Stool impaction is a contributing cause to urinary incontinence. Pressure is exerted by the hard stool mass on the soft tissue of the perineum. The exerted pressure creates an obstruction at the bladder neck resulting in urinary retention and overflow incontinence. Increased bladder contractility may also occur resulting in urge incontinence. Impacted stool may occur due to insufficient attention to elimination patterns and failure to have a bowel movement on a regular basis.

5. Intrinsic factors

Intrinsic factors, or those conditions within the urinary tract itself, will also result in urinary incontinence. Conditions resulting in bladder outlet obstruction and altered bladder position or innervation are examples of intrinsic factors. Inflammatory conditions reducing bladder wall compliance are another potential intrinsic factor resulting in urinary incontinence.

Bladder outlet obstruction is associated with two types of voiding symptoms. An individual may experience obstructive symptoms as a result of the urethra being mechanically obstructed. The individual will present with a reduced urinary stream force, intermittent or interrupted urinary flow patterns, postvoid dribbling, hesitancy, and feelings of incomplete bladder emptying. Prolonged outlet obstruction produces irritative symptoms. These symptoms include frequency, urgency, and nocturia. All these symptoms can produce suffering. Prolonged obstruction results in detrusor muscle hypertrophy (weakened, enlarged muscle) and decompensation (reduction in function). The end result is involuntary bladder contractions. Benign prostatic hypertrophy (enlarged prostate), prostate cancer, urethral strictures, and bladder neck contractures after prostatic surgery are potential causes of outlet obstruction in men. Bladder outlet obstruction in women is caused by pelvic organ prolapse and surgical procedures compressing or tightening the bladder neck and urethra.

Surgical procedures involving the colon, rectum, prostate, and female reproductive organs are all potential causes for urinary incontinence. Damage to the bladder nerve pathways may be a result of an abdominoperineal resection. Bladder nerve supply or urethral sphincter nerve supply may be disrupted in gynecologic surgeries. The bladder position itself may even be altered. Examples of such gynecologic procedures include radical hysterectomy, benign hysterectomy, pelvic organ prolapse corrective procedures as well as anti-incontinence procedures.[9]

Bladder wall compliance is the ability of the bladder to stretch. Loss of compliance, then, is the loss of the bladder's ability to stretch with increasing volumes of urine. Muscular or connective tissue structural and functional alterations result in bladder wall noncompliance. Some of the more common causes of bladder wall noncompliance include interstitial cystitis, chemical cystitis, and radiation. Chemical cystitis may result from chemotherapeutic agents. Radiation in the pelvic region may damage the bladder wall. These alterations may be part of a medical malpractice claim involving an alleged delay in the diagnosis of cancer.

6. Methods of treatment

Treatment options for urinary incontinence are influenced by the underlying cause and pathophysiology involved. A thorough assessment needs to be conducted which includes such aspects as environment, dietary history, medication regimen, medical history, and surgical history. Treatment alternatives are focused on eliminating or controlling the cause of the incontinence.

Treatment for extrinsic factors resulting in incontinence, then, focuses on identifying the extrinsic factor and eliminating it. Toileting aids, such as bedside commodes, may assist in eliminating the incontinence in situations of restricted mobility and other conditions. In the presence of stool impaction, fluid intake should be increased and a bowel regimen established promoting regular elimination.

Tip

Treatment for intrinsic factors is more difficult. The treatment option identified based on the classification of incontinence may itself result in urinary incontinence.

Surgery for the correction of stress incontinence in a woman may also lead to the development of urethral obstruction. Anti-incontinence procedures may result in inappropriate placement or excessive tension on periurethral (around the urethra) sutures.[10] The obstructed bladder decompensates with time, resulting in detrusor instability, irritative voiding symptoms, and urge incontinence. Treatment options, then, must be carefully considered.

Urge incontinence treatment options include medications and behavioral management. Anticholinergic drugs are typically chosen to treat urge incontinence. The most commonly used medications include Ditropan (Oxybutynin), Detrol (Tolterodine), and Levsin (Hyoscyamine). Tofranil (Imipramine) is an antidepressant used in urge incontinence treatment. Behavioral management of urge incontinence includes such measures as bladder training, biofeedback, and electrical stimulation. Bladder training encompasses instructing individuals on methods to postpone voiding until in the proper position. Over time, the individual increases the length of time voiding is postponed until a more "normal" voiding pattern is established. Methods to postpone voiding include distraction, deep breathing, and pelvic floor muscle contracting. Biofeedback involves strengthening the pelvic floor muscles. These muscles are then used to inhibit detrusor contraction, preventing urine leakage. Detrusor contractility may also be inhibited using electrical stimulation.

In addition to behavioral management and medications, stress incontinence treatment options include surgery and devices. Behavioral management includes biofeedback, pelvic muscle exercises, pelvic muscle reeducation, electrical stimulation, and magnetic therapy. Biofeedback teaches an individual to isolate and contract the pelvic muscles. Biofeedback may be used in conjunction with pelvic floor exercises, which focus on contracting just the pelvic muscles. The repeated exercises increase the muscle bulk and muscle strength, resulting in increased urethral resistance and prevention of urine leakage. Another modality used to strengthen the pelvic muscles is pelvic muscle reeducation using vaginal cone weights. Vaginal cone weights are also believed to stimulate reflex pelvic muscle contraction. As an adjunct to behavioral therapy, medications are frequently used.

Surgical management of stress incontinence focuses on correcting urethral hypermobility or intrinsic sphincter deficiency. In the situation of urethral hypermobility, the goal is to improve anatomic sphincter support without creating obstruction. Three procedures may help with this goal achievement and are appropriate when no intrinsic sphincter deficiency is present. Retropubic suspension techniques involve elevating the lower urinary tract, especially the urethrovesicular junction. Needle bladder neck suspension is another technique used in urethral hypermobility. Still one other surgical option is anterior vaginal repair. This technique involves dissection of the anterior vaginal wall and plication of the pubocervical fascia (shortening of the fibrous tissue). In the event intrinsic sphincter deficiency is present, other surgical options exist. Periurethral bulking injections and sling procedures are recommended. In individuals unresponsive to these surgical techniques, artificial urinary sphincters are recommended.

Devices are used to reduce or prevent urinary leakage in conjunction with measures to correct the underlying cause of the incontinence. They are alternatives to absorption products that serve to contain the leakage. Stress incontinence in women may be treated using urinary control pads, continence shields, urethral occlusion inserts, bladder neck prosthesis, and vaginal pessaries. Penile cuffs and clamps are devices available for treating men. These devices are explained below.

The urinary control pad is a onetime only product consisting of a foam pad with adhesive. The control pad is placed over the urethral meatus and held in place by the adhesive gel. The adhesive gel creates an occlusion over the urethral meatus. A similar device is the continence shield. The continence shield is held in place by suction and is reusable. Another option to provide urethral occlusion is a urethral occlusion insert. This particular device is a balloon tipped catheter that is inserted into the urethra. The balloon is then inflated occluding the urethra and securing the catheter in place. A device inserted into the vagina is the bladder neck prosthesis. This prosthesis elevates the urethrovesical junction, mimicking the effects of bladder suspension surgery. The bladder neck prosthesis is similar to a vaginal ring pessary. Vaginal pessaries are intravaginal devices used in pelvic organ prolapse management. Additionally, pessaries may be used to support the urethrovesicular junction. Pessaries are often used in conjunction with estrogen therapy.

Stress incontinence treatment options for men include penile cuffs and clamps. Penile cuffs and clamps are devices designed to occlude the urethra. One such device is an inflatable bladder. The inflatable bladder is placed against the ventral side of the penis corresponding with the corpus spongiosum. Velcro secures it in place.

Behavioral management is a component of reflex urinary incontinence treatment. Individuals may be instructed on spontaneous voiding and reflex voiding. Catheterizations, intermittent and indwelling, are additional treatment options for reflex incontinence. Medications may be used in conjunction with other treatment options. Additionally, reflex voiding may be used in conjunction with catheterization.

In reflex voiding, the bladder empties spontaneously into a condom catheter connected to a drainage bag. Continence then is achieved through containment of the urinary leakage. As external collection devices are in various development stages for women, reflex voiding is typically an option for men only.

Spontaneous voiding is an option reserved for those individuals who experience detrusor hyperreflexia with sensory awareness filling. The individual perceives the urge to urinate followed by a period of hesitancy. If unable to toilet in a brief period of time, the individual will experience urinary leakage. Underlying neurological conditions may inhibit an individual's ability to toilet in a brief period of time. Thus, this issue must be addressed. Additionally, the individual needs to be advised urination cannot be prolonged over time. The individual must respond to the urge to void as quickly as possible. Some individuals will require instruction on the use of hand-held or bedside toilets.

For those individuals with partial control of the pelvic floor, biofeedback may be an option. Biofeedback is used for pelvic muscle reeducation. Selected individuals may benefit from transurethral or transvaginal electrical stimulation. Treatment of reflex incontinence with either biofeedback or electrical stimulation is still in its infancy stages. More clinical trials need to be conducted.

Complete bladder emptying can be achieved with catheterization. Individuals are instructed to evacuate the bladder at regularly scheduled intervals using a catheter. The catheter is inserted into the bladder to facilitate urinary drainage. Once urine is completely drained from the bladder, the catheter is removed. This procedure is referred to as intermittent catheterization. In some instances, intermittent catheterization may be used in combination with reflex voiding. Urinary leakage is eliminated through complete emptying of the bladder. Medications are used with intermittent catheterization to control hyperreflexic contractions. Hyperreflexic contractions contribute to urinary leakage between catheterizations. An indwelling catheter, or a catheter which remains in place in the bladder, provides another treatment option for reflex incontinence.

Many of the urinary incontinence treatment options discussed thus far may be used as treatment options in the case of urinary retention with overflow incontinence. Medications, intermittent catheterization, indwelling catheterization, biofeedback, and behavioral management are all treatment options available for urinary retention with overflow incontinence. An additional treatment option is a continent diversion. Continent diversions are discussed in the section exploring ostomies.

Behavioral management includes such measures as timed voiding and double voiding. Timed voiding involves voiding on a schedule. Timed voiding is beneficial for those individuals with reduced bladder filling sensation and detrusor contractility. Over distention of the bladder is avoided, eliminating urinary leakage. Double voiding eliminates urinary leakage by the individual voiding twice. After the initial void, the individual initiates a second void. Residual urine volumes are reduced, and urinary retention is avoided. Voiding can be initiated by the manual application of pressure over the suprapubic area. This procedure is referred to as the Credé maneuver. Still another behavioral strategy is pelvic muscle reeducation in conjunction with biofeedback.

Unfortunately, some individuals do not respond effectively to medication, behavioral management, or catheterization. For these individuals, continence may be restored by the creation of a continent diversion. A continent diversion involves the creation of an internal intra-abdominal reservoir. The reservoir is then penetrated with a catheter to facilitate urinary emptying. Penetration of the reservoir is performed four to six times per day.

Not all individuals respond to treatment modalities producing restoration of continence. For these individuals, the goal is the maintenance of skin integrity while preserving personal integrity. Skin integrity is maintained through the use of skin barriers and absorbent products. Skin care options include cleansers, moisturizers, moisture barriers, skin sealants or films, and powders. Absorbent products include pads and containment garments.

B. Fecal incontinence

Fecal incontinence is defined as a change in an individual's "normal" bowel habits, resulting in an involuntary passage of stool. Three classifications for fecal incontinence exist: complete, incomplete, and seepage and soiling.[11] Complete incontinence is one classification characterized by the incontinence of gas, liquid, and solid stool. Incomplete incontinence involves leakage of gas and stool. Leakage of small amounts of stool between bowel movements in a continent individual who is able to delay defecation is classified as seepage and soiling. Fecal incontinence caused by personal injury or medical malpractice is a distressing element of damages.

Conditions resulting in fecal incontinence include alterations in stool consistency, alterations in recognizing rectal filling and rectal contents, compromised sphincter function, and compromised rectal capacity and compliance. The following discussion addresses the etiology of each of these conditions as well as treatment options.

1. Etiology

Normally, the anal sphincter prevents the passage of stool without conscious relaxation of the sphincter. In the presence of an alteration in stool consistency and stool volume, the sphincter may become incompetent. For example, diarrheal conditions can result in incontinence. Conversely, constipation can result in incontinence with the occurrence of stool leakage around the fecal mass. The same is true in fecal impaction.

When volumes of water and electrolytes secreted into the bowel lumen overwhelm the bowel's absorptive capacity, diarrhea occurs. Secretory diarrhea can result from infections, malabsorbed substances, side effects of medication, malignant tumors, and prostaglandins. Diarrhea can result from any substance producing stimulant secretory effects. Conditions compromising intestinal absorption can also result in diarrhea. Low protein, extensive bowel resection, prolonged periods of nothing by mouth, protein-calorie malnutrition, and intestinal infections are all conditions contributing to alterations in the bowel's ability to absorb. Bowel motility plays a role in diarrheal conditions. An increase in bowel motility results in an increase in stool delivery rate to the rectum. Bowel motility disorders are associated with diabetes mellitus, irritable bowel syndrome, and infections. Diminished bowel motility contributes to diarrhea, as does fecal impaction. Fecal impaction is a rectal obstruction causing a relaxation of the internal sphincter. Bacterial action on the fecal mass produces a liquid stool. The result is seepage of liquid stool. Laxative abuse and *Clostridium difficile* infections also result in diarrhea.

Rectal filling and rectal content alterations affect bowel continence. Individuals are alerted to the need to defecate when anorectal sensation is intact. Sensory awareness can be compromised by neurological conditions, pudendal (genitalia) nerve damage, chronic rectal distention, and cognitive impairment.[12] Diabetic neuropathy, multiple sclerosis, and spinal cord injury are all neurological conditions associated with sensory loss.[13] Pudendal nerve damage can result from forcep vaginal deliveries, large babies delivered vaginally, and a prolonged second stage of labor. These situations cause an excessive stretch in the pudendal nerve, resulting in partial denervation. Chronic straining, as in the occurrence of chronic constipation, is another cause of pudendal nerve damage as a result of excessive tension on the pudendal nerve. Chronic constipation can also result in chronic rectal distention, which can result in fecal incontinence as a result of pudendal nerve stretching and constant tension. In many institutionalized elderly, fecal incontinence results from cognitive impairment.[12] Sensory nerve pathways are intact, but individuals are unable to respond appropriately or interpret the message to defecate.

At rest, the internal anal sphincter maintains fecal continence. In the presence of rectal distention, the external anal sphincter maintains fecal continence. Thus, a compromise of either sphincter can result in fecal incontinence. Internal sphincter compromise results in partial fecal incontinence. There is leakage of gas and liquid. External sphincter compromise results in full fecal incontinence. Both denervation injuries and sphincter disruption result in compromised sphincter function. Denervation injuries include spinal cord injuries, vaginal deliveries, and chronic straining. A women's first vaginal delivery can cause a traumatic disruption in the sphincter muscle, especially when forceps are used in the delivery.[14] Other causes of traumatic sphincter disruption include anorectal surgery and anorectal injury.

Rectal capacity and rectal compliance influence the rectum's ability to store stool until defecation. A significant increase or decrease in either the capacity or the compliance affects fecal continence. Chronic delay of defecation results in reduced sensitivity to defecation and increased compliance. These individuals no longer experience the urge to defecate. Pelvic radiation and ischemic disease can result in fibrotic changes of the rectal wall. The fibrotic changes reduce rectal capacity and compliance. Inflammatory diseases, such as gastroenteritis, also reduce rectal capacity and compliance.

2. Methods of treatment

Treatment options for fecal incontinence focus on the cause of the incontinence. Measures include strategies to restore normal function. Strategy options include disimpaction, restoration of normal stool consistency, behavioral management, and surgical management. Behavioral management strategies include environmental changes, bowel training programs, stimulated defecation programs, sensory-motor reeducation, and sphincter retraining. Surgical management strategies include sphincter repair, sphincter modification, sphincter replacement, and colostomy creation. These modalities are described below.

Disimpaction encompasses measures to remove the fecal obstruction. Fecal obstruction removal may be accomplished by the administration of softening and lubricating enemas, suppositories, or laxatives. In the event the fecal impaction is too large to pass manually, manual break up and removal may be necessary. Once stool has been evacuated measures to maintain a soft, stool consistency are instituted.

Initially, constipation management involves the elimination or correction of the underlying cause. A detailed assessment assists with this identification process. In addition, assessment assists with the identification of peristaltic inhibitors and identification of the need to institute measures to produce soft stool. Peristaltic inhibitors include inactivity and antimotility medications. Antimotility medications are either eliminated or reduced. Likewise, interventions to increase activity are implemented. A soft stool consistency is commonly obtained by increasing fluid intake and increasing fiber intake. Fiber intake may be increased through dietary modifications, daily intake of bran, or bulk laxatives.

Conversely in the presence of diarrhea, measures are instituted to improve stool frequency and consistency. Again, a thorough assessment will assist in identifying the underlying cause of the condition and interventions necessary to eliminate or to control the condition. Dietary modifications and bulking agents are typically used to improve stool consistency. Constipating foods include such items as cheese, yogurt, rice, bananas, apples, and wheat products. Other individuals require medications to improve their stool consistency or to reduce their colonic motility. Antidiarrheal and antimotility drugs, such as Loperamide and Lomotil, are commonly prescribed. Frequent diarrhea of mushy stool or episodic elimination of watery stool is usually caused by a dietary intolerance or malabsorption problem. For these individuals then, management involves the elimination of the intolerant foods.

Skin protection is a primary goal whenever diarrhea is present. Skin protection can be achieved by means of stool containment and by protective barriers. Stool containment devices involve the use of an external collection device or internal drainage systems. Internal drainage systems consist of a catheter along with an exterior drainage system. One end of the catheter is inserted into the rectum, and the other end is connected to the drainage system. Protective barriers provide a layer between the skin and the fecal discharge. Commonly used protective barriers include moisture barrier products.

Behavioral management of fecal incontinence focuses on environmental modifications and bowel training programs. Environmental modifications are defined as the modification of an individual's environment to support continence. Pathways to the restroom should be well lit and free of obstructions. Clothing may need to be altered to permit ease of removal. Various assistive devices, such as wall rails, may need to be installed. Bowel training programs may be as simple as retraining an individual to respond promptly to the urge to defecate or establishing a bowel defecation schedule. Stimulated defecation programs use a bowel defecation schedule along with a peristaltic stimulant to restore continence.

Sensory reeducation and sphincter reeducation are two other behavioral management options. In sensory reeducation, education is provided focusing on consciously recognizing rectal fullness. Biofeedback is sometimes employed as an adjunct therapy to sensory reeducation. Biofeedback may also be used in conjunction with sphincter retraining. Sphincter reeducation focuses on pelvic muscle exercises commonly known as "Kegel exercises."

Surgical interventions are typically used whenever other options fail. However, some indications do exist which would lead to surgical intervention as the first treatment choice. Surgical interventions are indicated in situations of traumatic childbirth, traumatic injuries, accidental injuries, and radiation enteritis. Sphincter repair is one surgical option. Traumatic obstetrical injuries, anorectal surgery, and accidental trauma are all indicators for surgical intervention requiring sphincter repair. For those individuals whose sphincter is anatomically intact and functionally incompetent, posterior sphincter plication would be the indicated surgical intervention.

In the existence of fecal incontinence as a result rectal prolapse, posterior sphincter plication may be indicated. Another surgical option is encirclement procedures. Encirclement procedures augment the anal sphincter function by providing a mechanical barrier. Thus, encirclement procedures are indicated for those individuals who have inadequate sphincter muscle mass or neurogenic incontinence with an intact sphincter.

Another option for those individuals with neurogenic incontinence is the antegrade colonic enema (ACE) procedure. A continent channel that can be catheterized is created between the abdominal wall and the cecum. Tunneling of the appendix or tabularized segment of bowel through the subcutaneous tissue and into the cecum assists with continence maintenance. Continence maintenance may be obtained by creating a nipple shaped valve by intussusception. Regular colonic washouts are then performed through the one way stoma.

Finally, two additional surgical options include the surgical creation of a colostomy and an artificial bowel sphincter. Many healthcare professionals consider a colostomy as a last alternative option. However for many, a colostomy will allow the individual to return to a normal life. Artificial sphincter creation is still in its infancy.

13.5 Life with Incontinence

Incontinence does not coincide with society's expectation of urinary and fecal continence. As a result, incontinence may have a serious psychological effect on an individual.

Tip

An individual's activities of daily living, ability to work or attend school, and sexuality are all affected upon by incontinence

---

Society's expectation of continence inflicts a stigma on an incontinent individual. The individual is not "normal" by society's standards. This stigma, in turn, can affect the individual's self-image and self-esteem. Many individuals experience anxiety and depression as a result of their incontinence.[16]

Tip

Incontinence can be perceived as a lack of personal control.[15]

Individuals may modify their fluid intake and change the activities they participate in as a result of incontinence. Any food an individual identifies as a cause of loose stools may be eliminated from the diet. At the very least, the food may be consumed selectively. In the occurrence of urinary incontinence, fluids such as those with caffeine may be eliminated or limited in consumption. Some individuals may feel the need to know where every restroom is located.[17] Sleep can be interrupted by the repeated need to urinate during the night.

Embarrassment and shame associated with incontinence can result in the individual isolating himself. He may choose to stay at home instead of risking an incontinence episode in public. Additionally, he may change his activities. For example, an individual may decide to participate in a recreational activity such as reading instead of swimming. Thereby, the individual minimizes the opportunity for an incontinent episode related to both the physical effort required to perform the activity as well as the location required to perform the activity.

Embarrassment and shame can also result in an individual feeling worthless. Incontinence may be perceived to mean the individual is imperfect. Thus, the individual may feel undesirable and unattractive. These feelings, then, affect the individual's sexuality.

Individuals may choose to wear an undergarment for the containment of leakage. This choice may prompt a change in clothing selection. Odor control may be of concern for those individuals wearing containment undergarments. Additionally, the need for ease of clothing removal can prompt a change in clothing style. Individuals who experience urge incontinence may need to remove their clothing quickly to avoid an incontinent episode.

Treatment of incontinence may require the individual to participate in a behavioral therapy. For example, the individual may now require bladder retraining. Activities of daily living are altered to incorporate this new need. In the event biofeedback is a component of the behavioral therapy, frequent visits to a healthcare provider may be necessary. Time must be planned and taken away from other activities. The length and duration of the therapy can affect the individual's ability to attend school or to work.

Tip

Work or school environments may not be conducive to the prevention of incontinent episodes.

Obstacles may physically stand in the way to the restroom. Time may not permit restroom breaks when necessary. Thus, the time it takes to heed the urge to void is prolonged. An individual's home may also need to be rearranged to provide for easy access to the restroom. Further, home and daily routines may need to be modified to permit medication consumption.

The need for containment products, therapy treatments, and frequent visits to a healthcare provider may affect the individual's finances. Limited healthcare coverage and reimbursement can further impair an individual financially. Finances can be further compounded by the effect the incontinence has upon the individual's ability to work. As a result, every component of life is affected by incontinence.

Altered bowel and bladder function enhances an individual's awareness of these two bodily functions many take for granted. On a daily basis, the individual's life is impaired. One's awareness is further heightened by societal expectations of continence. The attorney's questioning of the plaintiff during deposition or at trial helps the jury understand the consequences of being incontinent. Figure 13.4 provides questions that the defense attorney may wish to use during deposition or the plaintiff attorney may use during direct examination at trial. The trial attorney handling a case involving incontinence should sensitively but thoroughly evaluate the effect of the changed elimination on the individual's life.

13.6 Applying the Knowledge

Understanding scenarios as well as the pain and suffering inflicted on those affected by an ostomy and incontinence assists the legal profession in applying the knowledge to litigation. This application is further enhanced by the exploration of legal cases where verdicts have already been rendered. This section outlines some of the many legal cases that have been reported.

A. Ostomy-related litigation

Adhesions can often be treated on an outpatient basis through laparoscopic pelvic surgery. Laparoscopic pelvic surgery involves inserting a scope into the intestine. One of the potential complications associated with such a procedure is the perforation of the bowel wall. That is, a hole is made in the bowel wall that could result in fecal contents entering the abdominal cavity.

A thirty-six-year-old nurse underwent outpatient laparoscopic surgery for adhesions. Within twenty-four hours, she developed severe lower abdominal pain, nausea, and vomiting despite being on pain medication and antibiotics. Thus, she was admitted into the hospital for four days. While hospitalized, she continued to complain of abdominal pain. Her treatment consisted of further pain medication and antibiotics. Testimony revealed she had a high fever for three days and an elevated white blood count. In addition, the plaintiff claimed there was a failure to rule out a bowel injury as no diagnostic tests were performed. Diagnostic tests would have included a contrast enema, CAT scan, or x-rays.

The nurse continued to complain of abdominal pain for a few weeks after discharge. Hence, she was readmitted and transferred to another medical facility. Diagnostic tests there revealed an infection and a possible rectal perforation. Surgical treatment necessitated the removal of ten inches of bowel related to the infection and the formation of an ileostomy. Three and a half weeks later, the ileostomy was reversed. The nurse, however, continues to experience bouts of diarrhea. The jury returned a verdict for the plaintiff in the amount of $755,300 ($537,000 for past pain and suffering, $200,000 for future pain and suffering, and $18,300 for lost earnings) and $10,000 for the plaintiff's husband for loss of services.[18]

B. Incontinence-related litigation

In another laparoscopic procedure, the plaintiff experienced a lacerated left iliac vein related to the device being inserted into her abdomen at an improper angle. The resultant internal bleeding necessitated the perfor-

Sample incontinence questions

The following is a list of questions an attorney might ask to assist in identifying the pain and suffering experienced by the client with incontinence as well as that of the significant others. The list, while extensive, is not an exhaustive one and is only meant to be a guide for questioning.

When interviewing the person with incontinence and spouse or loved one, the interviewer may choose to refer to the specific type of incontinence (urinary or fecal). The general term of incontinence is used in the suggested questions below.

Pre-operatively

- When did your incontinence begin?
- Did anyone explain to you the possibility of incontinence as a side effect of the procedure?
- Did anyone discuss with you what incontinence is?
- Do you feel your questions were answered regarding your surgery and possible incontinence?
- Did anyone come to talk with you who was specially trained to take care of people with incontinence?

Post-operatively

- Did anyone come to talk with you who said was specially trained to take care of people with incontinence?
- Did anyone explain to you about incontinence and ways to manage episodes of incontinence?
- Did anyone explain to you about containment garments?
- What were you told, if anything, about where to buy supplies?
- Did anyone ever explain to you hygiene measures to avoid developing irritation?
- What were you told, if anything, about any changes you might need to make in your diet, clothing choices?
- Did anyone talk to you about disclosing to others you incontinence?
- Did anyone discuss with you about having intimate relationships with others?
- How often do you need to change your protective garment?
- Have you ever had an incontinent episode in public?
- Is the skin in your private area irritated?
- Have your clothes ever been soiled as a result of your incontinence?
- Do you think you have an odor that others can smell?
- How do you think others feel about you now that you have incontinence?
- How do you feel about yourself?
- Do you have difficulties with intimate relationships since you developed incontinence?
- Has being incontinent caused you humiliation or embarrassment?
- Did you have to change your clothing style or eating habits as a result of your incontinence?
- What do you fear the most as a result of being incontinent?
- Has the care of your incontinence been a burden on you financially?
- What changes, if any, have you had to make in your employment as a result of the incontinence?

Figure 13.4 *Questions for attorneys to ask clients about their incontinence*

mance of an emergency laparotomy. The plaintiff can no longer sit for lengthy periods of time and experiences bladder incontinence. Additionally, she has not been to work since the injury occurred four years ago. The jury awarded pain and suffering damages to the plaintiff in the amount of $1.2 million and to her husband in the amount of $100,000.[19]

Trauma to the genitourinary system resulting in urinary incontinence does not have to be the result of a surgical procedure. Incontinence may result from a less complex procedure such as the insertion of a Foley catheter. In addition, the procedure performed to correct the incontinence may result in incontinence.

The plaintiff in the case of *William Tucker v. Community Medical Center* claimed he suffered urethral strictures as a result of forceful Foley catheterization performed by both a nurse and a surgeon. He further claimed the urethral strictures caused urinary and sexual dysfunction as well as requiring bimonthly surgical procedures to release the strictures. The defense claimed that the bleeding was a result of preexisting urethral strictures that were caused by Foley catheterization when the plaintiff was an infant. The jury returned a verdict for the defendant.[20]

A female plaintiff sought damages for past and future medical bills, physical pain, mental anguish, disfigurement, physical impairment, loss of consortium, and exemplary damages as a result of a Foley catheter placed during delivery of her third child.[21] She noticed significant urinary incontinence after being discharge from the hospital. A urology referral resulted in the diagnosis of intrinsic sphincter deficiency.

She underwent a transvaginal sling bladder suspension to correct the problem. However, approximately one year later, the plaintiff began experiencing urgency and episodes of incontinence. These are both known complications of the surgical procedure. The plaintiff claims her urethral injury was the result of improper insertion, inflation, and monitoring of the Foley catheter. The jury, according to *Soele's Trial Report*, rendered a verdict in favor of the plaintiff for $2,549,200.[21]

13.7 Conclusion

While the above cases are just a sample of the litigation involving ostomies and incontinence, the cases are examples of how juries can respond to pain and suffering allegations. The pain and suffering is a result of an alteration in normal body functioning that many people take for granted: two bodily functions many people prefer to keep private. Yet when a claim of medical malpractice exists, these bodily functions and the events surrounding their changes become the focus of strangers.

Glossary

abdominoperineal resection. Incision involving the abdomen and the perineum.

adenomas. A tumor arising from glandular structures that is not malignant.

adynamic. Absence of peristalsis in various parts of the gastrointestinal tract.

anastomosis. Suturing one segment of the gastrointestinal tract to another.

asphyxia. Condition characterized by an increase in carbon dioxide in both the blood and tissues and a blood oxygen deficiency

cauda equina syndrome. Weakness in the legs, gait disturbance, incontinence, severe back and leg pain as a result of nerve root compression in the lumbar spinal canal.

colostomate. A person who has a colostomy.

colostomy. An opening in the large intestine; a stoma may be externally present on the skin.

continent diversions. Those diversions of urine that results in urine collecting in an internal reservoir.

corpus spongiosum. Urethral surface of the penis formed by a column of erectile tissue.

cortical. The outer layer such as the outer layer of an organ.

Credé's maneuver. Manual application of pressure over the suprapubic area.

cystitis. Inflammation of the bladder.

denervation. Interruption of the nerves.

detrusor. Bladder.

disimpaction. Use of measures to remove the fecal obstruction

diverticular disease. Disease involving the lining and the wall of the colon.

enterovesicular fistula. Tunnel between the bowel and bladder.
extrahepatic biliary atresia. Destructive disease of the bile ducts starting outside the liver.
fascial layer. Layer of fibrous tissue.
fibrotic. Formation of tissue containing fibers.
fistula. Abnormal passages in body tissue that may connect two internal organs or connect an internal organ to the body surface.
folliculitis. Peristomal skin complication where there is an inflammation within a hair follicle as a result of traumatic hair removal.
gastrointestinal polyposis. Numerous polyps or benign growths in the intestine.
hydronephrotic kidney. Kidney distended with urine
hyperplasia. A peristomal skin complication that is characterized by painful wartlike papules or nodules, commonly seen in urinary stomas.
hyperreflexic contractions. Spasms.
ileoanal anastomosis. Suturing the ileum (the end of the small intestine) to the anal canal.
ileostomate. A person who has an ileostomy; a stoma may be externally present on the skin.
ileostomy. Opening in the small intestine.
innervation. Nerve supply to a body part.
intussusception. Bowel telescoped into itself.
ischemic. Tissue affected by loss of blood.
ischemic disorders. Damage caused by lack of circulation.
Kegel exercises. Pelvic muscle exercises.
Kock continent ileostomy. Creation of an ileal pouch within the abdominal cavity. A portion of the ileum is also used to create a continent nipple valve and outflow tract under the skin. This particular reservoir is then accessed to facilitate fecal drainage.
leimyosacroma. A malignant tumor arising from smooth muscle.
meconium ileus. Newborn intestinal obstruction with thick meconium or fetal stool.
metastatic malignancies. Malignancies that have spread from adjacent or distant site.
micturition. Urination or voiding.
mucutaneous separation. Involves the separation of the stoma from the skin; the separation creates a defect; may occur in individuals with compromised healing abilities, such as in malnourished individuals, or when the opening in the skin is too large for the stoma.
necrotizing enterocolitis. Death of the intestinal mucosa.
necrosis. Cell or tissue death.
nocturia. Having to get up at night to urinate.
ostomate. Person who has an ostomy.
ostomy. Opening; a stoma may be externally present on the skin.
palliative treatment. Reduce pain and suffering.
paralytic ileus. Paralysis of the bowel or part of the bowel.
perforation. A hole.
perineum. Pelvic floor and the associated structures.
peristomal skin. Skin surrounding the stoma.
peritoneum. Wall lining of the abdomen and the pelvis.
peritonitis. Inflammation of the peritoneum.
plication. The use of tucks to shorten a structure
polyps. A growth or mass arising from a mucus membrane
primary colorectal malignancies. Malignancies originating from the bowel wall.
prolapsed stoma. Involves a telescoping of the bowel out through the stoma.
pudendal. External genitalia.
pyelonephritis. Inflammation of the kidney and the renal pelvis
radiation enteritis. Inflammation of the bowel caused by radiation.
rectovaginal. Between the rectum and vagina.
reflux. Backward flow.
reflex incontinence. Problems with storage and emptying, involves the involuntary loss of urine as a result of detrusor hyperreflexive contractions along with diminished or absent sensory awareness of the urge to void.
renal pelvis. The upper end of the ureter which opens into the kidney.
retraction. A stoma that is below skin level; frequently occurs as a result of excessive scar tissue formation, premature removal of the loop ostomy's support device, and weight gain.
retroperitoneal. Space behind the peritoneum of the abdomen

retroperitoneal fibrosis. Tissue composed of fibers located in the space behind the peritoneum

sacral micturition center. The sacral area of the spinal cord contains nerves that are a component of the neurological transmission between the brain and the bladder

sarcoma. A tumor arising from connective tissue; typically malignant.

serositis. Inflammation of the thin and watery tissue.

sphincter. Muscle that closes an opening.

stenosis. Narrowing of an opening.

stoma. An opening which has been created for drainage.

strictures. An abnormal narrowing of a passage.

urostomate. A person who has a urostomy.

urostomy. An opening in the urinary system; a stoma may be externally present on the skin.

ureteropelvic junction. Area where the ureter connects to the kidney.

urethral strictures. Abnormal narrowing of the tube through which urine flows.

volvulus. Twisted bowel.

vesicoureteral. Involving the bladder and ureter.

vesicovaginal fistula. A passageway between the bladder and vagina.

Endnotes

1. Bryant, R., and Buls, J., "Pathophysiology and Diagnostic Studies of Gastrointestinal Tract Disorders." In Hampton, B., and Bryant, R., eds., *Ostomies and Continent Disorders: Nursing Management.* St. Louis: Mosby, 1991.

2. Laska, L., editor, "Ureter Resected during Hysterectomy." *Lucinda and Jose Sandoval v. Daniel Kuo, M.D.*, Queens County (NY) Supreme Court, index no. 28618/99, *Medical Malpractice Verdicts, Settlements and Experts*, February 2002, 24.

3. Nugent, K., Daniels, P., Stewart, B., et al., "Quality of Life in Stoma Patients." *Diseases of the Colon and Rectum*, 42(12), December 1999.

4. Erwin-Toth, P., "The Effect of Ostomy Surgery between the Ages of Six and Twelve on Psychosocial Development during Childhood, Adolescence, and Young Adulthood." *Journal of Wound, Ostomy and Continence Nursing*, 26(2), March 1999.

5. Gooszen, A., Geelkerken, R., Hermans, J., et al., "Quality of Life with a Temporary Atoma: Ileostomy versus Colostomy." *Diseases of the Colon & Rectum,* 43(5), May 2000.

6. Carlsson, E., Berglund, B., and Nordgren, S., "Living with an Ostomy and Short Bowel Syndrome: Practical Aspects and Impact on Daily Life." *Journal of Wound, Ostomy and Continence Nursing*, 28(2), March 2001.

7. Slade, D., "The Voice of Experience." *Journal of Wound, Ostomy and Continence Nursing,* 27(4), July 2000.

8. Laska, L., editor, "Failure to Timely Diagnose and Treat Cauda Equina Syndrome." *Gustavo Landin and Patricia Landin v. Roland Zachow, P.A., Thomas Strawmyer, M.D., and Concentra Health Services, Inc. d/b/a Concentra Medical Center*, Harris County (TX) District Court, case no. 2000-00945, *Medical Malpractice Verdicts, Settlements and Experts*, May 2002, 10.

9. Aronson, M., and Sant, G., "Urinary Incontinence after Pelvic Surgery." In O'Donnell, P., editor, *Urinary Incontinence.* St. Louis: Mosby, 1997.

10. Trockman, B., and Leach, G., "Complications of Incontinence Surgery." In O'Donnell, P., editor, *Urinary Incontinence.* St. Louis: Mosby, 1997.

11. Waldrop, J., and Doughty, D., "Pathophysiology of Bowel Dysfunction and Fecal Incontinence." In Doughty, D., editor, *Urinary and Fecal Incontinence: Nursing Management,* Second Edition. St. Louis: Mosby, 2000.

12. Johanson, J., "Fecal Incontinence." In Johanson, J., editor, *Gastrointestinal Disease: Risk Factors and Prevention*. Philadelphia: Lippincott-Raven, 1997.

13. Rose, S., and Wald, A., "Fecal Incontinence." In Snape, W. Jr., editor, *Consultations in Gastroenterology.* Philadelphia: W.B. Saunders, 1996.

14. Roig, J., Villoslada, C., Lledo, S., et al., "Prevalence of Pudendal Nerve Neuropathy in Fecal Incontinence: Results of a Prospective Study." *Diseases of the Colon and Rectum,* 38(9), 1995.

15. Ashworth, P., and Hogan, M., "The Meaning of Incontinence: A Qualitative Study of Non-Geriatric Urinary Incontinence." *Journal of Advanced Nursing,* 18, 1993.

16. Wyman, J. Harkins, S., and Fanti, J., "Psychosocial Impact of Urinary Incontinence in the Community-Dwelling Population." *Journal of the American Geriatric Society*, 38, 1990.

17. Cochran, A., "Response to Urinary Incontinence by Older Persons Living in the Community." *Journal of Wound, Ostomy and Continence Nursing,* 25(6), November 1998.

18. Laska, L., editor, "Failure to Diagnose Bowel Perforation after Laparoscopic Surgery." *Gokey v. Levy*, Franklin County (NY) Supreme Court, index no. 307/97 *Medical Malpractice Verdicts, Settlements and Experts*, January 2002, 61–62.

19. Laska, L., editor, "Laceration of Left Iliac Vein during Exploratory Laparoscopy Causes Internal Bleeding, Chronic Pain, and Chronic Bladder Incontinence." *Carol Gross and John Gross v. Arthur Laver, M.D.*, Delaware County (PA) Court of Common Pleas, case no. ____, *Medical Malpractice Verdicts, Settlements and Experts,* February 2002, 24.

20. Laska, L., editor, "Negligent Catheterization." *William Tucker v. Community Medical Center*, Lackawanna County (PA) Court of Common Pleas, case no. 96 CV 4450, *Medical Malpractice Verdicts, Settlements and Experts*, May 2002, 26.

21. Laska, L., editor, "Negligent Insertion of Foley Catheter." *Catherine Leigh Huckaby and Daris Chea Huckaby v. Lake Pointe Partners, Ltd. f/k/a Lake Pointe Medical Center Ltd. d/b/a Lake Pointe Medical Center and Lake Pointe Health Services, Joanna Cinnamon, R.N., et al.*, Rockwall County (TX) District Court, case no. 1-00-592, *Medical Malpractice Verdicts, Settlements and Experts*, May 2002, 26–27.

Chapter 14

Pain and Suffering in the Intensive Care Unit

Ian Larry Cohen, MD, FCCP, FCCM

"Complete emotional tranquility is seldom attainable in this world."

6 Cal.App.4th at 801

Synopsis

Acknowledgments

I want to thank Patricia Iyer for the opportunity of participating in this important work. Her knowledge, experience and leadership are inspirational. And to my wife Dianne and my children who help me better understand the meaning of life.

14.1 Introduction

The intensive care unit (ICU) is a naturally high stress environment where the vast range of human emotions, including pain and suffering, is played out daily as life, death, and near death swirl together in a seemingly chaotic high tech symphony. Any reader who has spent a prolonged period of time at the bedside of a loved one in the ICU can attest to the frequently surreal and traumatic nature of an experience that is rarely forgotten. Critically ill patients may or may not recall their stay in the ICU, but few are left without prolonged or lasting physical or emotional scarring as a reminder of a near death episode. It is not just the patients and families who need to deal with or suffer from stress in the ICU; pain and suffering touches every member of the ICU team as well.

The amount of stress associated with any particular patient varies widely depending on a variety of factors, knowledge of which can serve to alleviate pain and suffering. A failure to recognize and reduce stress leads to increased risk of potential medical-legal consequences.

The primary objective of this chapter is to describe the workings of a typical adult ICU in detail sufficient for the reader to gain empathy from multiple perspectives. What follows is meant to assist the legal community in their efforts to support plaintiffs and defendants.

It is hoped that this chapter will help lead to better understanding of the critical care environment.

14.2 Understanding the ICU

A. What is an intensive care unit?

ICUs grew out of attempts in the 1940s and 1950s to bring critically ill patients together into one area after major catastrophes, such as massive fires and the polio epidemic. During these times, large numbers of victims, limited technology, and scarce training forced medical professionals to scramble in many directions to match up the patient's needs with medical resources. As surgical techniques advanced, particularly in the area of cardiac surgery, recovery rooms became increasingly pressured to provide higher levels of protracted care. It was clear that there needed to be specialized units for these types of patients, and over the '60s, '70s and '80s ICU bed growth was exponential.

Tip

An ICU can be best defined as an area of the acute care hospital that provides the following: high levels of long-term nursing support (usually one-to-one or one-to-two nursing to patient ratios), a team of individuals trained in critical care, high levels of technology, and an array of special procedures.

From its meager beginnings, ICUs have advanced two or three generations and are now frequently subspecialized. Though most community hospitals have only one general purpose ICU, many tertiary referral centers have a wide array of units including medical (MICU), surgical (SICU) cardiovascular (CVICU) neurological (NICU), trauma (TICU), pediatric ICU (PICU), burn ICU, and so on. These have various names in different facilities. The thing that really identifies an ICU remains the concentration of staff and technology in a specialized area of the hospital. The terms ICU and critical care unit are used interchangeably.

There is a small but growing number of ICUs that are referred to as EICUs. In these cases, critical care specialists provide remote monitoring in addition to the setup in the ICU. Thus several ICUs can be "watched" from a command center miles away, and the "e" doctor can order interventions. It is likely that this strategy will grow in the future.

In the USA, ICUs account for more than 10% of acute care hospital beds; at least 20% of hospitalized patients pass through an ICU once during their stay. Eighty to $100 billion dollars, or 8%–10% of healthcare expenditures, or approximately 1% of the U.S. gross domestic product, is spent on ICU care per annum. In fact, 25%–33% of hospital resources are allocated to ICU care. There is little doubt that the ICU is a high stakes player in the healthcare "game."

B. What is a critically ill patient?

Not all patients in ICUs are critically ill, and not all critically ill patients are in ICUs. Many ICU patients are admitted for a higher level of monitoring and may, in fact, be quite able to even get up and walk, if necessary. On the other hand, most critically ill patients have their onset of illness before they come to the ICU, and some may be transferred out of the ICU while still unstable. The latter typically occurs when life support is being withdrawn or when a patient is being moved to an intermediate care unit, often to make way for a more acutely ill individual.

Though there is a good deal of black and white in defining the critically ill, there is also a large area of gray. So much depends on the structure within any healthcare system, and even in the greater community. At the extreme, for example, a patient on a respirator and dialysis for the long term may be labeled as chronically critically ill and kept in the ICU at one hospital because of lack of other options. In another community the same patient might be cared for in a step down unit or long-term acute care hospital. In a third city the patient may be adequately supported at home. Each option will have consequences on pain and suffering, and the optimal use of these strategies will be most beneficial to patient outcomes.

Tip

The ICU environment cannot easily account for all the pain and suffering associated with the critically ill.

C. Physical layout of an ICU

ICUs rarely look like the sterile hotel-style chambers depicted on TV shows. They do, however, vary from a completely open architecture where nothing but curtains separate individual patients to individual patient rooms that are usually highly visible to a central nursing station. Most ICUs have at least a couple of highly filtered isolation rooms for specialized situations, such as when the patient is at very high risk for infection (e.g., after a transplant) or he or she is infected with a highly resistant or highly contagious "bug" (bacteria, fungus, or virus) that puts other patients at risk. Larger units are frequently divided into pods with multiple nursing stations.

D. Personnel involved in ICU care

Nursing level is a major part of defining ICUs; nurses are the cornerstones of ICU care and account for approximately two-thirds of ICU costs. In the U.S., most ICU nurses have gone through rigorous ICU orientation programs and many have taken special certification exams provided by the American Association of Critical Care Nurses (AACN). The vast majority of ICU nurses are RN level, but LPNs, nurses' aides, and ICU techs are sometimes found as support staff.

Intensivists, or critical care physicians, are specialists in critical care who have taken supplemental training or certification after completing medicine, surgery, or anesthesiology residencies. In many ICUs noncritical care physicians deliver the bulk of the care, often while also attending to their routine non-ICU daily duties. Frequently, the complex ICU patient is cared for by a whole array of physicians practicing individual specialties; in such cases a patient may have a surgeon, general internist, family physician, pulmonologist, cardiologist, nephrologist, infectious disease specialist, and hematologist all writing orders and managing individual aspects of the care at different times of the day.

There is strong evidence to support the existence of the benefits to using intensivists in the care of critically ill patients, including a 10% reduction in the chance of dying in the ICU. This type of evidence is causing numerous organizations, including the Leapfrog Group (a large project of numerous Fortune 500 companies, regulatory agencies, and third-party payers; on the Web at http://www.leapfrog group.org/) to encourage hospitals to provide appropriate intensivist support in their ICUs.

Many other individuals participate in the care of ICU patients and are essential to the operations of the ICU team. These include physician, nurse, therapy and pharmacy trainees, respiratory therapists, dieticians, pharmacists, social workers, clergy and administrative support personnel (e.g., patient-family advocates). In addition, physicians and their respective teams, see their patients daily. The patient and family may witness an endless stream of white-coated individuals who talk, poke, prod and pry into every nook, cranny and orifice of the physical, psychological, and social aspect of life.

E. Organizational aspects of the ICU

Almost all ICUs have a readily identifiable nursing chain of command with a nurse manager or head nurse who reports up the ladder of hospital nursing. Frequently, the nurse manager has one or more associates to help cover administrative issues on various shifts.

The physician chain of command is much more variable. On paper all ICUs have medical directors but in practice the roles of these directors and their designees are often exceedingly limited. Moreover, from a physician reporting perspective there is no standard approach. In highly specialized ICUs the director usually reports to a department chairman. The ICU director frequently reports to the hospital medical director (vice president for medical affairs or VPMA). Sometimes, the reporting structure isn't even defined. In other words, it is quite common to see circumstances where, from a doctor standpoint, everybody, anybody, or nobody seems to have command and control over the ICU environment.

Tip

The simple question "who's in charge?" can lead to interesting discoveries about how well a place is organized.

From the patient care perspective there are roughly three types of physician care models; these are the open model, the closed model, and the semi-closed model. In the open model each patient remains under the direction of the primary or admitting attending physician. This physician has the authority to admit to and discharge from the ICU and to direct all aspects of care. On the other end of the spectrum, in the closed model, only an ICU team of intensivists has the authority to admit to or discharge from the ICU and to direct all aspects of care. In the more common semi-open unit, the primary or admitting attending physician shares the authority with other physicians. This can vary widely from units that require mandatory consultations with other physicians for specific problems that arise to a near closed model where a group of intensivists oversees all aspects of care, including admission and discharge but the primary attending physician remains in the decision making loop.

The organizational variation from one facility to another is such that one cannot describe the organization of a typical or "standard" ICU with any great degree of meaning. Nevertheless, these physician organizational aspects can have profound impact on patient care. The better organized, the more consistent the approach to all patients, and the stronger the physician leadership, the better will be the outcomes.

Whatever the organizational design, the families of ICU patients, and even the patients themselves, will be at a high risk for confusion and frustration if the lines of care, decision making, and information are confounded. There needs to be an identifiable expert who can assure appropriate care and assimilate the information from others involved. Clearly this function is made easier by the presence of a strong intensivist program.

All the non-nursing and non-physician personnel usually work in other departments under a number of separate reporting chains. Their availabilities and roles will thus vary a great deal from place to place. In practical terms, this means that it is very difficult to define a rigid care standard in ICU for professions such as pharmacy, nutrition, physical and occupational therapy, or social work. For example, "Is it reasonable to have the care of a patient, with a prolonged stay in the ICU, reviewed by physical therapy and a dietician?" The answer is—far from clear.

F. Patient population characteristics

The average ICU patient in the U.S. is in the mid to late sixties, will stay in the ICU for three days and in the hospital for more than ten days and is at high risk for dying or having a reduced quality of life. Though averages are important, in that they can help elucidate trends, they are much less useful when it comes to understanding ICU experiences.

For the sake of this discussion there are five categories of critically ill patients.

1. People who suffer life-threatening medical problems in the community. This includes a wide array of people and problems including, severe infections, heart attacks, stroke, drug and alcohol-related emergencies, liver, lung or kidney failure, and many other less common disorders. Some may be in the intensive care unit due to a delay or failure of diagnosis and delay in treatment.
2. People with life-threatening, potentially surgical conditions, such as multiple trauma, head injury, ruptured or dissecting aorta, and acute abdominal emergencies. Some of these individuals may be in the ICU as a result of trauma that may be related to a personal injury suit.
3. Elective surgical patients who are undergoing high-risk procedures that normally require an ICU bed (e.g., coronary artery bypass surgery, lung resection, or removal of a brain tumor) or have enough existing medical problems to warrant admission to an ICU post-op (e.g., a patient with heart failure undergoing gall bladder surgery).
4. Patients who deteriorate while in the hospital and need to be admitted or readmitted to an ICU for medical or surgical problems. The list of conditions that cause these problems is long but, common things being common, is usually one of six—chest pain, cardiac rhythm disturbance, low blood pressure, infection, bleeding, respiratory failure, cardiac arrest, or some combination thereof. Patients who have unexpected problems at the time of low-risk elective surgery are also included. Medical malpractice cases may result from alleged deviations associated with the deterioration, such as failure to diagnose or appropriately intervene before the patient's condition became life threatening.

5. The chronically critically ill. This is a melting pot group of patients who continue to have critical care issues, such as requiring a respirator, for prolonged periods of time, sometimes indefinitely. In this group are patients who bounce in and out of ICUs on multiple occasions for reason such as recurring severe infections or bouts of respiratory failure. The hospital mortality rate of this group is extremely high, as is their experience with pain and suffering.

G. Technology—mechanical ventilation

Mechanical ventilation (artificial respiration, respirator, or ventilator) is technology that allows part or all of a patient's breathing to be supported. There are a number of different approaches and devices that can be used, depending on the patient's characteristics and physician preference but they fit into one of two categories—invasive or non-invasive ventilation. In the invasive approach, the patient is connected to a ventilator via a tube that is inserted into his or her airway. This tube can be inserted through the mouth or nose in which case it crosses the vocal cords and rests in the trachea with the external end connected to the machine. In adults the endotracheal tube is usually about ten inches in length.

The more long-term patient usually receives a tracheostomy tube that is inserted surgically into the trachea through the neck. This tube is much shorter and sits below the vocal cords.

In the non-invasive approach to mechanical ventilation, the patient is connected to the machine without a tube in the airway. The most common method is via a mask or nasal device that is fitted to achieve a good seal. This technology is widely used to treat sleep apnea (CPAP or BiPAP) but in that case its purpose is to help keep the airway open during sleep. When used successfully in patients with respiratory distress, the machine can relieve a good deal of the work and stress of breathing.

Another device that is occasionally used is the cuirass. This system is fashioned after the old iron lung that became popular during the polio epidemic. It is fitted around the chest, not unlike a suit of armor chest piece, and works by negative pressure to draw air into the lungs—much like a bellows.

In the ICU, non-invasive methods are increasingly being used, but the mainstay of ICU ventilator support is invasive ventilation. Indeed, if one were to select a predominate therapy to help define ICU care it would be invasive mechanical ventilation. It could even be said that there is an intricate association among the following factors—severity and duration of critical illness, length and degree of ventilator support, and pain and suffering. Though many patients on ventilators for prolonged periods have lung failure, many require the machine to help support them because they are so ill with other problems as well; the failure of their respiratory system is often secondary and dependent on the resolution of other underlying disorders.

Tip

The length of time on a respirator can serve as a rough approximation of the severity of a person's illness and degree of pain and suffering she may be experiencing.

H. Other technologies used in ICU

A host of technologies and devices can be found in the ICU. Some of these are used routinely and are considered part of standard ICU care; others are quite controversial with respect to balancing their risks and benefits for use in ICU patients; and, finally, some are considered "luxury" items—they are found in only selected centers.

Standard technologies include a number of simple, non-invasive, low-risk monitoring devices to track vital functions and sound alarms when certain limits are breached, such as EKG (or heart rate), blood pressure by cuff, respiratory rate, and oxygen saturation by pulse oximetry. Many patients have more invasive blood pressure devices—arterial lines—that measure blood pressure continuously. Cooling blankets, numerous high-end IV pumps, sequential compression stockings to prevent leg clots, and bedside computers are also commonplace.

More invasive and sometimes controversial technologies are used commonly. These include central venous pressure and cardiac function via pulmonary artery catheter (Swan-Ganz catheter). The major source for controversy is the latter use of the "Swan," fueled by concerns over excessive risks to benefit. The Swan-Ganz catheter is placed through one of the large veins in the neck, chest, or groin area. With the guidance of pressure waveform monitors attached to the Swan, and sometimes fluoroscopy, the catheter is guided through the right side of the heart and into the pulmonary artery. Concerns have been expressed because of the risk of injury (perforation of the lung, bleeding, rhythm disturbances, injury to the heart and pulmonary artery). This debate has probably led to a more limited, or at least more selective, use of these devices. Wide variation of the expertise of the physicians inserting and interpreting the pulmonary artery catheter has been a major part of the problem. Many experienced and well-trained intensive care practitioners find it to be an invaluable tool.

Dialysis is commonly performed in the ICU and is a cross between technology and procedure. In order to perform it, a large-bore specialized catheter needs to be placed into one of the large central veins. Dialysis can be performed in a conventional manner that is used for most long-term patients whereby the patient is attached to a machine for three to four hours for three times a week or daily in the more severely ill. A specialized dialysis nurse under the direction of a nephrologist usually performs this procedure after a physician places the catheter. Often a more "gentle" approach is used with CVVH (continuous veno-venous hemofiltration). This procedure is usually carried out by an ICU nurse, and the machine used is a simple pump and filter setup that runs continuously twenty-four hours a day. CVVH is better tolerated in patients with unstable blood pressures.

More "luxury" devices include metabolic carts (non-invasive tools for measuring the levels of oxygen use and carbon dioxide production—this can assist with nutrition and hemodynamic management), gastric tonometry (invasive measurement of stomach gas for measuring resuscitation levels), and other less invasive methods of measuring cardiac function instead of using a "Swan" (i.e., bio-impedance and esophageal probes).

Many more devices can show up in the ICU, including a wide array of specialized beds, x-ray machines, several different types of dialysis devices, a number of heart support system, and pacemakers. And, there are more things that can and will appear, such as barometric chambers used for decompression sickness and certain difficult to treat infections.

I. Procedures performed in the ICU

Nursing care comprises the vast majority of procedures that occur daily in the ICU. Many of these are routine, such as administration of medications, dressing changes, bathing, checking vital signs, rotating, suctioning the breathing tubes and lungs, assessment and management of discomfort, and oversight on all the bedside high tech equipment.

Tip

No one from the clinical team is in closer contact or does more with the patient than the nursing staff. The ICU nurse participates in practically everything that involves the patient.

The majority of procedures that physicians perform on ICU patients can be done readily in the ICU environment. Nonetheless, some take place outside the ICU by design, while others simply can't be handled within the ICU unless the unit is a rare specialty or research unit.

Of the numerous interventions possible, the majority of all procedures physicians perform in the ICU are:

- Airway intubation (for placement of a nasal or oral endotracheal tube for patients on ventilators); this usually requires topical (sprayed into the back of the throat) anesthetic and sedation to suppress the pain, gagging and suffocating that a person can feel.
- Arterial lines placed into arteries in the wrist, elbow, armpit, groin or foot (frequently used for patients with blood pressure instability or on ventilators); the procedure is usually performed with local anesthetic and occasionally some sedation if the patient is awake. The pain of the needles and sutures required is akin to starting a difficult IV and sometimes multiple sticks at multiple sites are required.

- Central venous catheters placed in large veins in the neck, chest, or groin (to provide fast access and possibly multiple access when regular IV, are inadequate); both these and a Swan-Ganz are placed using sterile technique. The patient's face is often covered with a sterile gown. This often causes a claustrophobic feeling or difficulty breathing from lying flat (especially if he has had heart failure). Local anesthetic is usually generously used, but the patient may feel significant pressure when the rather large catheters are threaded through the skin and muscle layers or pain when the needle goes deeper than the anesthetic.
- Pulmonary artery catheters (Swan-Ganz) placed through large veins as well (when the patient is at high risk for cardiac and blood pressure problems).
- Bronchoscopy (for clearance of mucus plugs and for helping to diagnose the cause of lung problems). Topical anesthetics and sedatives are used so that the patient will have little or no recall.

When performing any invasive procedures it is common practice to be fairly generous with intravenous sedatives when the patient is on a ventilator. Sedating the patient who is not on a ventilator is a more risky proposition because she is at risk for respiratory arrest. In some cases, anesthesia assistance is usually sought to help with conscious sedation management.

In most facilities the patient needs to be transported outside the ICU for various procedures or specialized tests. Certain x-rays, such as CT or MRI scans, are almost exclusively limited to x-ray departments. Nonetheless, many hospitals are able to provide a variety of portable procedures at the bedside of ICU patients, such as echocardiography, ultrasound, and ultrasound-guided fluid removal or biopsy. Tracheotomies are easily and increasingly performed at the bedside, but some surgeons prefer to do them in the operating room. Insertion of brain pressure monitoring devices, open lung biopsies, burn wound debridement, insertion of percutaneous endoscopic gastrostomy feeding tubes, limited gall bladder surgery, and limited abdominal exploration can be accomplished in the ICU.

Tip

Any time an invasive procedure is performed, special precautions need to be taken to ensure the patient's safety. Also, transporting critically ill patients around the hospital can be a high-risk venture; it too requires special precautions.

J. Drugs used in the ICU

Practically every conceivable class of drugs is used in the ICU, especially when an intravenous preparation is available. Again, most drug use can be categorized in a short list.

- Analgesics—pain relievers—are found commonly and in one or another form of narcotic. These drugs are usually given intravenously or by epidural, but skin patches are now available for more chronic situations. Non-narcotic products are also used, but less frequently, and usually after narcotics have been implemented to resolve the more acute pain problems.
- A wide variety of sedative agents are prescribed to help control or treat agitation. These are occasionally supplemented by paralyzing drugs (neuromuscular blocking agents) to help prevent lung damage in the most severely ill ventilator patients. When paralyzing drugs are used, the patient is unable to move any muscles, even if awake. Both narcotics and sedatives are frequently used continuously for days or even weeks and sometimes with continuous paralysis as well.
- Antibiotics are used widely, particularly high-cost, highly potent agents.
- A wide variety of drugs can be used to raise or lower blood pressure or improve heart function (often referred to as vasoactive agents).
- A host of relatively common but miscellaneous agents such as steroids, asthma inhalers, blood thinners, and antacid agents.
- Though arguably a drug, nutritional supplements are an important part of care and can be given intravenously (total parenteral nutrition, or TPN) by mouth or via the stomach or small bowel (total enteral nutrition, or TEN.) The latter is often given through a tube placed into the small bowel

by surgery, by endoscopy, or by hand, frequently under radiological guidance.

K. Standardized measurements of pain and suffering

The sickest or most acute ICU patients are usually intubated, on a ventilator, and unable to communicate fully because the breathing tube is obstructing the vocal cords. Consequently, it is very difficult to be exceedingly accurate when trying to assess pain, anxiety, delirium, etc., especially in the face of a myriad of events and pharmaceutical agents that can alter a patient's mental status. Nevertheless, many ICUs have become adept at using these semi-quantitative, subjective measurement schemes.

Tip

Scoring systems are used increasingly in ICUs to help diagnose and manage patient discomfort.

Pain scales are employed widely in health care and base the pain score on the patient's perception (e.g., "Rate your pain from 0 to 10 with 10 being the worst imaginable or in the colors red, yellow, or green.") Refer to Chapter 2, "Pain Assessment," for more details. Agitation scores assess the patient's level of consciousness from deep coma to severe agitation and combativeness. A recent addition to ICU is a delirium diagnostic tool (CAM ICU) and there is a good deal of interest in using more objective measuring devices, such as the BIS (sispectral) monitor to measure depth of sedation. When muscle-paralyzing drugs are used, most commonly to prevent lung injury from patient ventilator asynchrony (bucking or fighting the ventilator), it has become conventional to use nerve stimulators to help prevent excessive use of long acting drugs (train of four testing). None of these techniques is perfect, but used wisely and skillfully they can be of tremendous help in optimally managing a patient's comfort.

14.3 Stressors in the ICU—Causes of Pain and Suffering

It was the author's hope that with good descriptions in the prior section the next two sections will flow reasonably intuitively. Nonetheless, in order to explain fully the complex interplay mentioned in the introduction there are still blanks to be filled. Specifically, what are the factors associated with stress in the ICU?

A. Environment

Contrast a private, well-soundproofed room with quality climate control, a window with a beautiful view, and a $15,000 specialty bed with a large open style ICU with no easily visible windows and dingy old equipment.

Tip

Anything you can think of in the way of environment matters when it comes to comfort, and pain and suffering.

The ability of a patient to sleep comfortably, for example, is highly affected in the ICU, especially in an open unit where there is always something occurring to disturb sleep, such as noise and lights. Frequently extraneous events in the unit are severe (they involve a lot of bedside attention for an unstable patient) and quite frightening to onlooking patients and families.

B. Equipment and alarms

Every electronic device used for monitoring or therapy in the ICU is rigged to one or more alarms. Each device may sound for a variety of different parameters with differing types and intensities of sounds. Frequently the nurse intentionally waits for the alarm as a trigger to perform a task, such as change an IV bag. Alarms often sound because the cardiac lead came loose or the manually set alarm parameters are set too narrowly.

There is little sound standardization in ICU alarm equipment. Also, there is some but not extensive integration of all the bedside technology, and therefore a paucity of artificial intelligence to expedite the recognition and resolution of the problem. So, when an alarm goes off it may take some time to figure out which parameter is a problem, particular when a new or less commonly used device is present or the staff addressing the alarm is inexperienced in the ICU. For most of the staff, alarms are a constant reminder of what's at stake; after all, they are there for a reason. For the patient and family, alarms are a source of frequent and significant stress, especially when no one from the staff is rushing in to figure out what's happening.

C. Severity of illness

The patient who "sails" in and out of the ICU in a day or two after his uneventful coronary bypass surgery is in stark contrast to the young, multiple trauma and head-injured patient who has been in the ICU for six weeks, has had many trips to the operating room and dozens of x-rays and CT scans, a whole host of lines and catheters, is being kept alive on a ventilator with a tracheostomy, and is receiving CVVH dialysis for renal failure. The cumulative discomfort associated with each new x-ray, for example, is only one small part of the stress experienced by the sicker, longer stay patient.

Tip

There is no doubt that illness severity is a major driving force in causing stress.

D. Procedures and routine care

The ICU patient's day is commonly filled with processes and procedures that were mentioned earlier in the chapter. There is an element of tension or stress for everybody involved every time a patient is examined, a temperature is taken manually, a blood pressure cuff inflated, a bed bath performed, the endotracheal or tracheal tube is suctioned or repositioned, the patient is rolled to prevent pressure sores, he or she is transported for a test or simply gotten out of bed. For the staff, the fear is often of disrupting essential lines and invasive catheters or even accidentally dislodging the endotracheal tube (self-extubation) and making the patient uncomfortable. For the patient, it is fear of pain, discomfort, inability to breathe properly and—the unknown. This stress affects the patient unless heavy sedation is being given.

Even for the patient in the "first class room" described above, the lights may need to be turned on in order to check all the monitors or analyze an alarm. It is impossible to cover the myriad array of stresses related to daily staff-patient interactions, but it is possible to say that every one is a potential catalyst for increasing pain and suffering.

E. Tubes, catheters, and attached devices

Most people have seen or experienced firsthand one or more of the following: endotracheal tube, nasogastric tube, Foley catheter, feeding tube, chest tubes, abdominal drainage tubes, EKG wires, pneumatic anti-clot stockings, central venous, pulmonary and arterial catheters, dialysis, and mechanical ventilation. Imagine how uncomfortable it might be having all these tubes and devices, and even more, at the same time. This is especially true when some of the devices (e.g., the endotracheal tube) prevent or limit effective communication.

F. Recall

From the ICU perspective, recall refers to the vivid recollection of events. In some cases the experience can be delusional and confused, while other people can accurately describe situations, such as having their heart lifted during bypass surgery and comments made by the surgeon. The latter comes from too little amnesia-producing drugs during surgery, while the former often results from their prolonged or excessive use. Figure 14.1 includes some questions the attorney may ask the plaintiff and her family to determine the degree of recall and to find out more about the critical care experience.

Tip

Recall can produce a great deal of anxiety and angst for the patient and family.

The staff is also very significantly affected by recall, and at times embarrassed because of indiscreet comments that were overheard by the patient, such as off-color jokes, sexual remarks, disparaging remarks about the patient's body size, or frank and frightening comments about the patient's condition.

Paralyzing agents are used commonly in the ICU as well as in the OR. If inadequate levels of sedation are given the patient can be fully aware yet unable to move anything. This is an experience that is never forgotten. There have been situations in which patients were thought to be brain dead because they had vital signs but no signs of neurological function; the problem turned out to be that the paralyzing agents were

To patients (families may be able to answer some)

- Do you remember anything about being in the ICU?
- Do you have any recollection of being awake and not able to move?
- Were you ever tied to the bed? How did that make you feel?
- Were you able to change positions by yourself? Do you recall feeling frustrated that you were not being able to move without assistance?
- Was your pain adequately relieved or do you recall being in pain for long periods?
- Do you recall experiencing hallucinations, severe insomnia, and/or paranoia?
- Do you recall ever being unsure of where you were?
- Were you on a ventilator in ICU?
- Do you recall not being able to communicate your needs? Was it frustrating not being able to talk?
- Were there periods when you could not eat or drink? Do you remember being hungry or thirsty?
- Did you have surgery during this period? Do you recall unpleasant drainage coming from your wound?
- Were you able to signal the nurses when you needed the bedpan or urinal? Were you ever aware of being incontinent (wetting the bed or not being able to control your bowels)?
- Do you recall any unpleasant interactions with the hospital staff in the ICU?
- How long did it take you to walk again after the ICU?
- Are you experiencing any new unusual changes such as major mood swings, severe nightmares, panic attacks, and suicidal thoughts (or attempts)?
- Did you receive any counseling while in hospital from social workers, psychologists, or psychiatrists?
- Did you receive physical and occupational therapy in the hospital on a regular basis?
- Given the choice, if you were ill again would you wish to be taken care of in that ICU; and why or why not?
- What is your quality of life like now compared with before you were ill?

Questions for the families

- Were you kept well informed?
- Were you happy with the care the ICU team provided?
- Were there any specific incidents that you felt were harmful?
- Did your "loved one" seem to be comfortable and receiving adequate medication for pain, anxiety and sleep?
- Did you ever see your loved one tied to the bed? If so, how did that make you feel?
- Did your loved one ever become confused about where she was? How did that make you feel?
- Did you ever feel that too much medicine or too little pain medication was being given?
- When you voiced concerns did the appropriate members of the ICU team respond?
- Did you feel supported by the nurses, social workers, and clergy?
- Given the choice would you allow yourself or your loved one to be taken care of in that ICU; and why or why not?

Figure 14.1 *Questions for attorneys to ask clients about ICU*

long acting and had not worn off. Patients have reported hearing discussions about the hopelessness of their situation and the fact that they were brain dead!

G. Pain

Pain is a common problem and exists to some degree in most ICU patients. Because of the difficulty many critically ill individuals have in communicating, pain can easily be undertreated, overtreated, or mistreated. Under treatment is not uncommon and usually results from inadequately aggressive orders or the use of sedatives instead of pain medications to help quiet the patient.

Tip

There is little doubt that pain, in some semi-quantifiable manner, is a very important source of stress.

In many uncomplicated ICU patients, such as those admitted briefly following high-risk surgery, pain can be well controlled using patient controlled analgesic (PCA) devices such as venous or epidural PCAs. When patients are too ill or too confused to manage these devices, however, the bedside medical team is left to determine when pain is present, how much pain there is, and how the pain responds to analgesics. As mentioned elsewhere, this can be a daunting task to perform accurately.

H. Anxiety and fear

Being ill generates a good deal of anxiety and fear for obvious reasons, but the ICU environment is particularly stressful in this regard. Anxiety can be a primary problem, but it is frequently an important indicator of a problem that needs correcting, such as difficulty breathing, physical discomfort, or poorly managed pain. Noting that the patient is anxious is an important clue that something is amiss and certainly indicates a significant level of discomfort.

I. Delirium and psychosis

The thought processes of ICU patients can easily become disordered. This is most often associated with some degree of disorientation to person, time, and place. The patient may be behaving like an amnesia victim who is unsure of even the most basic of facts—like her own name or the names of her loved ones, date, day of the week, or where she is. This type of confusion is very common in the ICU, particularly in longer stay patients. Nonetheless, people do develop ICU psychosis and may be completely oriented despite the fact that they may be hallucinating or having frightening delusions. A delirious or psychotic patient can become dangerously agitated and suffer life-threatening problems if not properly addressed.

J. Sleep deprivation and sleep disturbance

> Sleep shall neither night nor day
> Hang upon his pent-house lid.
>
> Macbeth. Act I. Sc. 3.

Many who recall their experience as an ICU patient report the inability to sleep as one of the most distressing problems they remember. Some even report having felt they would welcome death just to sleep for a couple of hours. Sleep deprivation and aberrant sleep patterns are more the norm in the ICU. Frequently, patients may not sleep at all, they may have reversal of their day/night cycle and sleep during the day, and when they do sleep they do not experience the normal REM patterns of good healthy sleep. Sleep-deprived patients can become very difficult to handle. First, they can become very agitated and delirious. Even more serious, they can become very hypermetabolic (marked increase in metabolism and oxygen demand) with higher heart rates, blood pressures, and oxygen demand. Either way, sleep deprivation impedes the recovery of the critically ill.

K. Restraints

This word usually brings to mind the use of ties to bind the arms and legs to the bed or some kind of Posey vest device. Restraints can be frightening and, especially for the awake and confused patient, they can be physically injurious leading to impaired circulation, chafing, or even dislocation of joints. This is a very limited perspective, however. In a broader sense most ICU patients are restrained—if not by the kinds of straps used to prevent removal of medical equipment or climbing out of bed, then by chemicals, catheters, tubes, and wires. Even the patient whose pain and anxiety are well controlled may have the uncomfortable experience of confinement. Lying in one position for hours until rotated, afraid or unable to move, is not an easy feeling for anybody.

L. Loss of control

One of the most common complaints that an alert ICU patient voices is the need to urinate. The ICU staff will diligently explain that he has a Foley catheter in place and he just needs to relax. This is a minor aspect of patient care compared to all the other intrusions that take away routines of daily life from the patient. In many cases, just about all activities of daily living—even breathing or moving, as mentioned above—are taken out of the patient's control.

M. Family

Anxiety is a particular feature seen in the families of ICU patients. Much of the time, loved ones are already on pins and needles because of the seriousness of the underlying disease. When alarms go off, as they frequently do, panic often ensues as it seems like an eternity before one of the medical team responds. Day after day family members try to maintain a vigil that has required they break away from their normal routines. Those who cannot spare the time or money to be present frequently often feel the stress of guilt or exhaustion. The more severe the illness and the longer it continues, the greater the toll on the family. Add to this a constant flood of information from monitors and healthcare personnel and the need to make very serious decisions on the patient's behalf when he or she lacks the capacity (as is common).

Tip

It has been estimated that up to 75% of family members show very significant signs of stress-related pathology, such as acute depressive symptoms, when a patient's stay exceeds three days in the ICU.

Family dynamics can result in a great deal of demand for support from hospital staff; sometimes more support than the patient requires!

N. Staff

A busy day in the ICU has been described like the opening scene of the beach landing in the movie *Saving Private Ryan*. In the midst of life and death events, pressing routines, anxious families, numerous staff-staff interactions, and unexpected emergencies there is a never-ending battle to move patients in and out of beds that are being heavily triaged. (Triage is a process for sorting sick or injured people into groups based on their need for or likely benefit from immediate medical treatment. There is pressure to find beds for critically ill patients in other areas of the hospital such as the OR, ER, or floor.) Tensions and emotions can be palpable, especially among (but by no means limited to) less experienced members of the team.

Essential to all is the well-being of the ICU patient under their care. Nevertheless, individuals frequently differ on what is really best, and this can lead to serious conflict, or tension and anguish, if not managed properly.

Those who work in the ICU develop a gestalt for potential problems but even the most battle-worn veterans know that the best philosophy for survival is to expect the unexpected. Clearly, the ICU environment is a potentially stress-filled one for the staff.

O. Drug and alcohol withdrawal

There is a growing list of withdrawal-prone drugs that patients are using prior to their hospitalization. Withdrawal syndromes vary from agent to agent but some things are common (e.g., elevated heart rate and blood pressure, increased metabolism and increased respiratory rate).

Drug and alcohol abuse may result in the most severe withdrawal syndromes in which people become extremely agitated, and may be frankly psychotic or delirious. This can go on for days and can result in devastating or fatal events, such as stress-related heart attacks, falls, and other injuries to self and staff. Commonly prescribed drugs such as certain heart and blood pressure medications, some popular antidepressants, and even some ulcer medications are associated with withdrawal or severe rebound when stopped in some patients. Nicotine withdrawal is also of concern, and nicotine patches are commonly applied to those at risk.

P. Drug reactions

There really is no safe drug used in the ICU. Everything comes down to weighing risks and benefits when choosing to prescribe. Fortunately, the patient receives most drug doses uneventfully, but there is always a risk of some kind of adverse event, especially in those with other medical problems. Most readers have experienced, or know someone who has, an adverse drug reaction. The unpleasant result can be as benign as mild itching, nausea, burning at the infusion site, and so on, or life threatening.

Tip

Given enough time in the ICU, most patients will experience a number of adverse events related to drugs, albeit mostly mild problems that are of minor consequence in relative terms.

14.4 Consequences of Stress

In the introduction the activity of an ICU was allegorically referred to in orchestral terms. In this respect it is now time to tie together the various bits and pieces that have been dealt with in isolation and try to assess the results of the interplay of these factors. Like a symphony, or for that matter the human body, individual parts come together in a synergistic manner that simply do not add up to be the sum of the individual parts.

In section 14.2 the "concert hall" and its workings were described; Section 14.3 was dedicated to introducing each of the "musicians and their instruments;" now it's time to hear the music, or perhaps more appropriately, face the music; in other words, the consequences and outcomes.

A. Agitation

Agitation has been defined as violent motion, or strong or tumultuous emotion. Brought on by a variety of physical and emotional factors it is a clearly observable expression of disturbance. Nurses cannot see pain, anxiety, or psychosis, but they can certainly observe a patient trying to pull out his breathing tube or climb out of bed with a complex pile of technology attached. Therefore, agitation needs to be carefully evaluated as to its root cause—what stress factors are involved (e.g., low oxygen, difficulty breathing, pain, anxiety, delirium, withdrawal, sleep deprivation, drug reaction, environmental problems, and so on).

Then, the underlying causes need to be addressed and reversed. This often requires sedation. But, sedatives are commonly part of the problem. They typically cause amnesia and confusion, and their effects can last for many hours, even days in some cases.

B. Organ dysfunction and organ failure

Any or all the major organ systems can fail in ICU patients, but it is common to have organ dysfunction without total failure. The difference is that in failure there is inadequate function to sustain life without aggressive therapeutic intervention. There are therapies for failing organs. Dialysis, for example, can be maintained for years. In the case of severe heart failure there are devices that can be used for a bridge to heart transplantation, transplantation, and possibly even long-term artificial hearts. The lungs can be replaced by a ventilator or lung transplant; the liver can be replaced by transplantation. Eligibility for these various organ replacement options is complicated.

Patients who present with simple primary organ failure, such as end stage liver disease, are often suitable candidates, assuming an organ can be found and other requirements, such as age, are met. However, the person whose liver fails as the result of trauma, overwhelming infection, or metastatic cancer will almost certainly not make the list.

For the most part, the number and degree of organs failing correlates positively with severity of illness and negatively with survival. A common diagnosis in complex ICU patients is MODS (multiple organ dysfunction syndrome). In this syndrome the organs have not failed, but there is significant dysfunction in a number of systems; usually as a result of some severe preceding insult such as overwhelming or unrelenting infection, or shock.

Tip

MODS is a feared diagnosis because it is associated with a very high rate of hospital mortality.

C. Infection, bleeding, strokes, heart attacks, heart rhythm disturbances, and pulmonary embolism (blood clots to the lungs)

Though these problems can bring patients to the ICU, they are also not uncommonly seen in ICU patients who have been admitted to the ICU for other reasons. Not infrequently, these disease entities arise in patients with MODS and become part of the ever complicated cascade of tribulations. Infections are so common that it is hard to find a patient in the ICU more than five or six days who does not have or will not develop a life-threatening infection in the lungs, at a surgical site, or in a number of other sites, such as the sinuses or brain.

Bleeding is frequently seen in the ICU. It may be related to a complication of surgery, and sometimes this may be related to an avoidable error in technique. Often it occurs because the patient has an impaired ability to clot, and this is usually reversible. It may also result from some new stress related problem, such as ulcers. High-risk patients should receive drugs to prevent this well studied problem. In the case of patients whose clotting mechanisms are impaired by treatments used to take care of or prevent other problems listed here (e.g., pulmonary embolism or heart attack), the risk benefit margin may become extremely hazardous. For example, if a patient is on blood thinners for unstable coronary artery disease and then develops bleeding from a stress ulcer, it usually becomes impossible to persist with blood thinners.

D. Drug addiction and drug withdrawal

Since narcotics and sedatives are used so liberally in the ICU it is important to address the risks of iatrogenic drug addiction (i.e., the patient becomes addicted to a drug as a consequence of appropriate medical use).

Tip

Any patient on high doses of benzodiazepines or narcotics for more than five days ought to be considered dependent.

These cases are usually exemplified by the use of continuous high dose IV infusions of these agents; this is a common ICU practice that needs to be distinguished from the use of longer-term pain and anxiety management strategies as seen in palliative care or hospice. If managed improperly this can lead to long-term addiction problems or dangerous withdrawal syndromes. The skilled practitioner will ensure that these agents are used optimally, thereby avoiding excess, and that they are weaned safely. Nonetheless, it is quite common to find these agents being used sub-optimally. Just stopping them after ten days of high dose use, for example, can be very dangerous.

E. Prolonged disability and critical care polyneuropathy

Severely ill patients can have devastating loss of muscle and neurological function that may take weeks or months to recover. The result is profound generalized weakness. In many cases the damage is secondary to the catabolic (breakdown) effects of high stress states in which the person's own muscles are used as a source for much needed proteins and other fuels. Certain drugs, such a paralyzing agents (e.g., pancuronium or Pavulon and vecuronium or Norcuron) have also been implicated in this state, especially in the presence of steroid medications.

Additionally, many individuals suffer other injuries as a result of their original insult or from complications of therapy that can lead to substantial problems. Many of the problems mentioned above, for example, will result in permanent or long-term ramifications and an inability to return to prior levels of function.

Though still poorly understood, there are a number of hormonal abnormalities in the critically ill, and some can cause protracted problems. For example, it is not uncommon for sexual dysfunction to follow a patient for months after a severe illness, but this is not well described in the medical literature.

F. Depression and posttraumatic stress disorder (PTSD)

In the past few years there has been a good deal of interest in the long-term psychological sequelae of being critically ill. The PTSD these patients develop is very similar to that seen in combat veterans and can be associated with incapacitating episodes of fear, anxiety, and recall. The medical community is becoming more aware of these problems, but the kind of follow up necessary is usually beyond the scope of ICU personnel.

Consequently, critical care workers are often unaware of the status of problems in patients after they have left the unit.

Tip

It is clear that a disturbing number of survivors have prolonged evidence of depression and PTSD to a degree that they are unable to return to a satisfactory quality of life.

Though still unclear, it appears as if there are some interesting relationships evolving between what goes on in the ICU and the presence of these problems, even months or years later. First, there seems to be an important relationship with the use of sedatives and paralyzing agents and the presence of depression and PTSD. Second, patients who have clear recall of events appear to have less risk for these problems than those whose memories are disorganized and delusional.

The implications of these observations are not totally apparent. On the one hand, there is a need to reduce agitation and minimize pain and suffering in the ICU. On the other, however, is the emerging concern that this very treatment can come at the price of future psychosocial problems.

G. Death

The risk of dying in the ICU or non-ICU and non-home environment is highly variable. Very elderly patients with tracheostomies, for example, have a much poorer hospital survival and discharge to home rate than do younger patients. The majority of elderly survivors go to nursing homes. In general, the rate of survival will depend on the type of patient as outlined in Section 14.2. Patients undergoing elective surgery are in the best category, generally having a risk of dying of less than 1% or 2%. What is important about death for the critically ill is that it frequently comes after a very protracted course, during which there have been numerous ups and down for the patient, family, and staff. Or it comes so quickly no one has a chance to adjust.

Tip

A majority of patients, even with very advanced diseases or in the face of very high-risk surgery, do not identify a healthcare proxy or execute a living will.

Unfortunately, all too few people are adequately prepared for this eventuality. Many have not even discussed their views toward death and disability. This commonly leads to an enormous problem for the family and healthcare team who then feel the need to go to extreme lengths, beyond what the patient may have desired. This will almost certainly increase the risk for pain and suffering.

H. Staff burn out and family distress

The subject of family distress was covered in Section 14.3 and mentioned above. It is important to point out, however, that this distress travels with them in parallel to the patient's problems after they leave the ICU. Things done in the ICU to mitigate stress and enhance the outcome for the patient will also help improve the family's quality of life.

Staff stress can easily lead to a number of problems from a personal and administrative perspective. Problems in the healthcare professions with smoking, substance abuse, depression, and burnout are well known but also well camouflaged. No matter how carefully such problems are hidden, they will eventually surface and affect individual staff members as well as patient care. Simple loss of staffing due to stress related sick time—especially in a time of increasing budget constraints—will push others in the system that much harder.

14.5 Summary

The Society for Critical Care Medicine (SCCM) (on the Web at www.sccm.org/profresources/G_toc.html) is an excellent source of ICU practice guidelines. These have helped set standards for ICU design, organization, and a whole variety of patient care issues including management of pain, sedation, and paralyzing agents.

It is safe to say that all patients who spend significant time in an ICU will need to put up with some de-

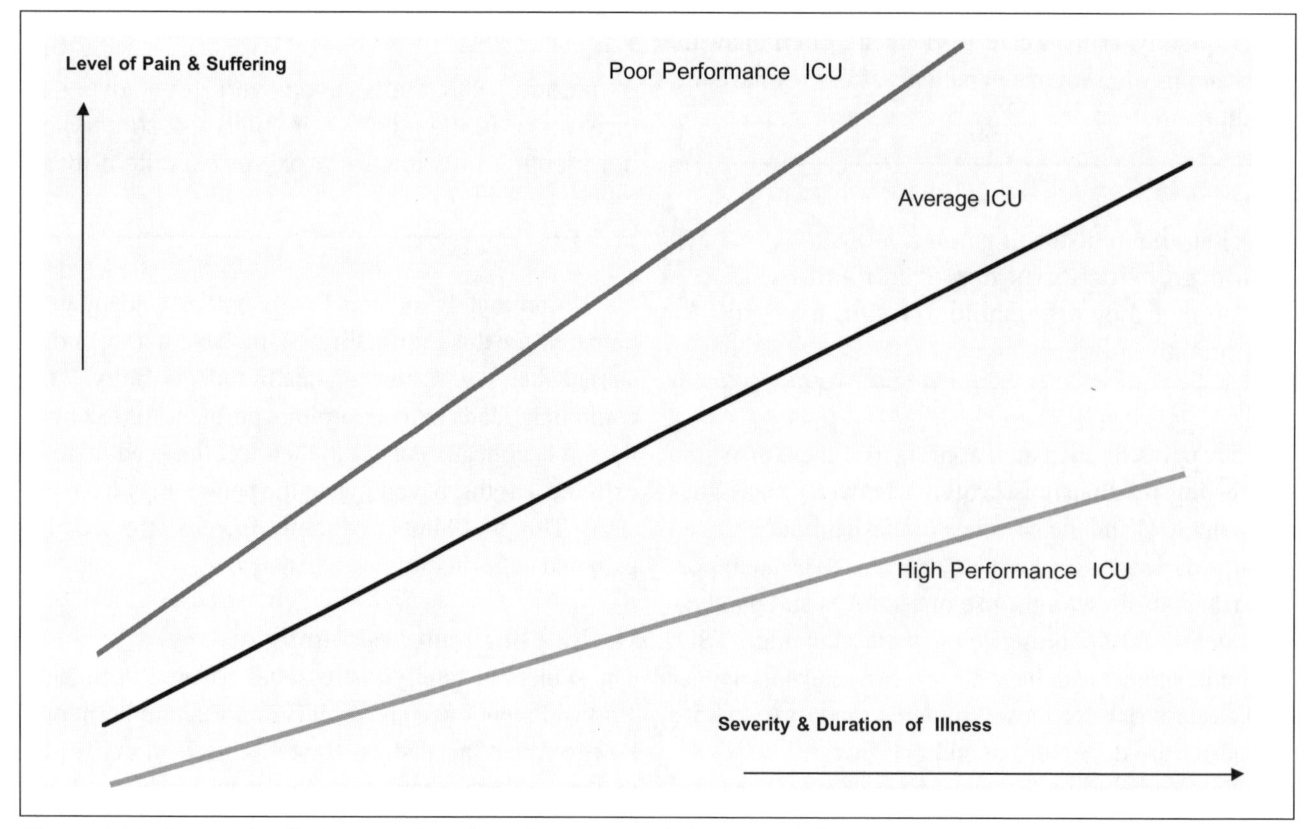

Figure 14.2 *Pain and suffering as a function of severity and duration of illness*

gree of pain and suffering, and this will spill over onto their loved ones. The degree of pain and suffering will depend heavily on a number of stressors and their consequences.

Critical care has been my sole specialty for nearly twenty years. During that time I've had the privilege to work with exceptional people from all disciplines and interact with many magnificent patients and families. I have also had the chance to visit a large number of other centers and interact with critical care people around the world. In their honor I hope the complexities of life for the critically ill, their relatives, and the devoted members of the ICU team are appropriately addressed. Further, I trust that the readers appreciate critical illness is a commonly unforgiving and uncooperative beast that can lead even the best to be unwittingly duped or simply overpowered.

I am continuously struck by opportunities to improve the way we approach the critically ill and for the need to view this problems systematically and from a system's perspective. It has become very clear that in the ICU, as in many other areas of health care, widespread and unexplained variations in practice and outcomes exist to a degree that needs serious attention.

Organizational aspects of ICUs play a very important part in determining outcomes. ICUs that are well-designed and well-run have strategies that emphasize standardized and patient-centered team care with rapid response systems from highly competent individuals; these units will undoubtedly perform better than those that operate in a fragmented manner. In simple terms, the best outcomes will be achieved when the right people do the right thing for the right patient at the right time in the right place.

The idea of institutional quality is demonstrated in Figure 14.2. In this hypothetical illustration the severity and duration of a critical illness is plotted against a quantity of total pain and suffering. The high performance ICU shows a good deal less pain and suffering for any level of illness. The average is meant to represent the mean of the two.

Though on a case-by-case basis it is difficult to judge where a hospital ICU might fit on this theoretical graphic, it is possible to examine cases to find areas of fragmentation where improvements can be made. I say this with something different in mind than simply looking at a deviation from standards of care. On the other hand, it is my wish to see these standards of care better defined and continuously advancing in a direction that assures improved care for the entire ICU population. This will allow us all to sleep better.

Additional Readings

Brilli, R., et al., "Critical Care Delivery in the Intensive Care Unit: Defining Clinical Roles and Best Practice Models." *Critical Care Med,* 2001; 29(10):2007–2019

Brook, A., et al., "Effect of a Nursing-Implemented Sedation Protocol on the Duration of Mechanical Ventilation." *Crit Care Med,* 1999;27:2609–15.

Greifzu, S., "Caring for the Chronically Critically Ill." *RN,* 65 (7), 42-48, July 2002.

Hamill-Ruth, R., and Marohn, M., "Perspectives in Pain Management: Evaluation of Pain in the Critically Ill Patient." *Critical Care Clinics,* 15 (1), 35, 1999.

Jacobi, J., et al., "Clinical Practice Guidelines for the Sustained Use of Sedatives and Analgesics in the Critically Ill Adult." *Crit Care Med,* 2002; 30:119–141.

Jones C., Griffith R., Humphris G., et al., "Memory, Delusions and the Development of Acute Posttraumatic Stress Disorder-Related Symptoms after Intensive Care." *Crit Care Med,* 2001; 29:573–80.

Kress J., Pohlman A., O'Connor M., and Hall J., "Daily Interruption of Sedative Infusions in Critically Ill Patients Undergoing Mechanical Ventilation." *New England Journal of Medicine,* 2000; 342:1471–7.

Mascia, M., Koch, M., and Medicis, J., "Pharmacoeconomic Impact of Rational Use Guidelines on the Provision of Analgesia, Sedation, and Neuromuscular Blockade in Critical Care." *Crit Care Med,* 2000; 28: 2300–06.

Nelson, B., et al., "Intensive Care Unit Drug Use and Subsequent Quality of Life in Acute Lung Injury Patients." *Crit Care Med,* 2000;28: 3626–30.

Schelling, G., Stall, C., Hammer, M., et al. "Health-Related Quality of Life and Posttraumatic Stress Disorder in Survivors of the Acute Respiratory Distress Syndrome." *Crit Care Med,* 1998; 26:651–659.

Scragg P., Jones A., Fauvel N., Psychological problems following ICU treatment. *Anaesthesia.* 2001; 56:9–14.

Truog R., et al. "Recommendations for End-of-Life Care in the Intensive Care Unit: The Ethics Committee of the Society of Critical Care Medicine." *Crit Care Med.* 2001; 29(12):2332–2348.

Internet Resources

Society of Critical Care Medicine www.sccm.org (a large number of important guidelines plus other information).

Leapfrog Group www.leapfroggroup.org (a very important initiative of Fortune Five Hundred companies to improve quality; valuable references to ICU).

Revisions to Anesthesia Care Standards: Standards and intents for sedation and anesthesia care. http://www.jcaho.org/standard/anesamb.html.

Additional References by Author

Chalfin D., Cohen IL, Lambrinos J. Economics of critical care. *Intensive Care Medicine* 1995; 21:952-961.

Cohen I., "Current Issues in Agitation Management." *John's Hopkins School of Medicine: Advanced Studies in Medicine.* June 2002; 9:332–337.

Cohen I., "Establishing and Justifying Specialized Teams in Intensive Care Units for Nutrition, Ventilator Management, and Palliative Care." *Critical Care Clinics* 1993; 9:511–20.

Cohen I., guest editor, "The Management of the Agitated ICU Patient." SCCM 2002; 30:S97–S123

Cohen I., "Weaning from Mechanical Ventilation: The Team Approach and Beyond." *Intensive Care Medicine* 1994; 20:317–318 [Editorial].

Cohen I., Bari N., and Strosberg M., "Reduction of Duration and Cost of Mechanical Ventilation in an ICU by the Implementation of a Ventilator Management Team." *Critical Care Medicine* 1991; 19:1278–1284.

Cohen I., Fitzpatrick M., and Booth F., "Critical Care Medicine: Opportunities and Strategies for Improvement." *The Joint Commission Journal of Quality Improvement* 1996: 22:85–103.

Cohen I., and Lambrinos J., "Mechanical Ventilation in New York State during 1990." *Chest* 1995; 107:1673–1680.

Kurek C., Cohen I., Lambrinos J., Booth F., and Chalfin D., "Clinical and Economic Outcomes of Patients Undergoing Prolonged Mechanical Ventilation in New York State during 1993: Analysis of 6,353 Cases under Diagnosis-Related Group 483." *Crit Care Med* 1997: 25; 983–8.

Nasraway S., Cohen I., Dennis R., Howenstein M., Nikas D., et al. "Guidelines on Admission and Discharge for Adult Intermediate Care Units." American College of Critical Care Medicine and Society of Critical Care Medicine. *Crit Care Med* 1998: 26; 607–10.

Chapter 15

Pain and Suffering in the Elderly Population

Suzanne Frederick, MSN, RN

Synopsis

15.1 Introduction

The prevalence of pain is twice as high in the elderly population as it is in individuals less than sixty years old.[1] Some studies show that 25%–50% of older people living in the community suffer from pain problems, whereas as many as 85% of nursing home residents suffer from pain. Pain is a serious problem in this population and may lead to multiple complications.[2] When older people experience a traumatic event or go through a serious illness, their pain and suffering is often compounded by recent losses of either a spouse or close friends and relatives or loss of their home and independence. The older person's traditional support system and coping abilities are stripped away. Events or illnesses that lead to pain and suffering may be devastating blows to the individual. Elderly individuals are also at particular risk for abuse and neglect leading to prolonged suffering.

This chapter presents clinical information about pain and suffering in the elderly in order to help the attorney more cogently screen cases for damages and present injuries. The attorney may have a case in which the elderly person was living at home or in a nursing home, or was being cared for in a hospital prior to the events in question. This individual may have chronic pain, upon which is superimposed acute pain due to trauma or an undiagnosed illness. The injury that caused pain and suffering might be an acute one, such as may occur in a fall or a motor vehicle accident. It may be a chronic issue, such as neglect or abuse directed at a nursing home resident. This chapter will provide reasons why the elderly are at increased risk of suffering from pain and poorly treated pain. Pain assessment in the elderly person, including the cognitively impaired elderly, is discussed at length. Barriers to adequate assessment are included. In this chapter, the attorney is given a description of the suffering experienced by the elderly as a result of pressure ulcers, fractures, and abuse and neglect. Signs and symptoms of pain are included. Clinical documentation standards regarding pain assessment and treatment are described. Pain management guidelines are also provided.

15.2 Causes of Chronic Pain in the Elderly

Most chronic pain complaints from the elderly are related to arthritis and musculoskeletal problems such as degenerative arthritis and low back pain. Cancer is also a source of significant pain in the elderly population. Headaches and leg cramps are not uncommon in the elderly but are caused by a variety of ailments. Peripheral vascular disease is a term indicating diseases of the arteries and veins of the extremities. Symptoms may include pain with walking. Problems causing pain with walking, such as arthritis, must be differentiated from arterial insufficiency with associated intermittent pain upon walking and swelling of the lower legs.[3]

According to the American Medical Directors Association, factors that are associated with chronic pain conditions in the elderly population include the conditions shown in Figure 15.1.

15.3 Pain Assessment and the Undertreatment of Pain in the Elderly

It may be difficult for healthcare providers to determine if an elderly person is suffering pain (and for the attorney or expert witness to determine this from the medical record). This difficulty contributes to undertreatment of pain and results in suffering. The American Medical Directors Association lists the following barriers to the recognition of chronic pain in nursing homes. These same barriers apply to the hospitalized elderly.

- **blunted response**. Older people might not exhibit the same signs and symptoms of a younger person. An older person may be less verbal and demonstrative about pain or abuse. When injured or abused, an older person may not report it to anyone. When asked about an injury or abuse, the older person may attempt to diminish the real suffering he or she is experiencing.

- **cognitive and communication barriers**. Older people may not be able to communicate verbally that they are in pain. Nurses may fail to recognize the behaviors that suggest the presence of pain and suffering.

- **cultural and social barriers**. The cultural and social background of the older person, family and caregiver greatly affect communication about pain and the treatment. Racial, ethnic, and gender biases of residents and caregivers may hinder patients from reporting pain and may reduce caregivers' sensitivity to the signs and symptoms of pain and suffering. For example, males tend to attempt to be more stoic and may be less vocal about their suffering. The British also tend to be more stoic.

- **coexisting illnesses and multiple medication use**. Illnesses such as depression, and multiple medication use can reduce the older person's ability to interpret or report pain. Multiple medication use may also alter the older person's response to pain, which, in turn, may decrease the caregiver's ability to recognize that the older person is in pain or is suffering.

- **staff training and access to appropriate tools**. Caregivers may not have the training and skills to assess pain or use valid tools available to assess for pain.

- **system barriers**. Adequate pain assessment and management of pain in nursing homes and hospitals requires a team approach of physicians, nurses, physical therapists, pharmacists and nurse aides. High turnover of direct caregivers, poorly functioning groups or teams of caregivers and insufficient commitment to pain management by leadership in healthcare facilities may result in a failure to recognize, assess and treat pain sufficiently.[4]

- degenerative joint disease
- rheumatoid arthritis
- low back disorders
- osteoporosis with recurrent compression factors
- diabetic neuropathy
- postherpetic neuralgia (pain caused by herpes infections)
- headaches
- oral or dental problems
- chronic leg cramps
- peripheral vascular disease
- post-stroke syndromes
- improper positioning
- use of restraints
- immobility and contractures
- pressure ulcers
- amputations

***15.1** Chronic pain conditions in the elderly*

The elderly are at particular risk for undertreatment of pain, particularly those in nursing homes. Two reasons for undertreatment of pain in the elderly are patient beliefs and communication problems. If the elderly and their caregivers believe that pain is a natural part of the aging process then the pain is unlikely to be treated.[2] If an older person has communication problems, due to a stoke or cognitive deficits, it is more difficult for the caregiver to assess the person's pain and degree of suffering.

There are many misconceptions in our society that may contribute to inadequate assessment and treatment of pain in the elderly. One common misconception is that pain is a natural outcome of growing old. The fact is that pain is not normal in the elderly. Another misconception is that an older person does not feel pain as much as a younger person due to a decreased sensitivity or perception of pain. However, there is no scientific basis for this belief. Many in our society also believe that if the elderly patient does not complain of pain he or she does not have pain. However, most elderly patients do not complain of pain because of not wanting to worry loved ones, not wanting to bother or anger caregivers, and fear of losing their independence. It is wrong to assume that if the elderly patient is busy with activities then he or she is not in pain. Likewise, it is wrong to assume that if the elderly patient is asleep or resting that patient is not in pain. Many older patients use sleep as a coping mechanism. They may also use activities as a short-term distraction for their pain.

Tip

The standard of care for hospitals and nursing homes requires that pain be assessed in a systematic and consistent manner. The attorney or expert witness who is analyzing the medical records of the elderly patient should determine if appropriate pain assessment was performed.

The determination of the presence or absence of pain cannot be based on a patient's behavior alone. The thought that elderly patients complain of more pain as they age is contradicted in studies that show that elderly patients actually do not report their pain enough. Elderly patients are often very stoic, and the degree of pain and suffering they are experiencing may not be readily evident. Pain assessment in the elderly is more complex than in younger patients due to the elderly patient's poor memory, depression, and sensory impairment.[1] However, the pathophysiology of pain is essentially the same in the elderly as in younger people.

The Joint Commission on Accreditation of Healthcare Organizations (JCAHO) requires that hospitals and nursing homes systematically assess and manage a patient's pain. Nurses are expected to assess pain as the "fifth vital sign." Adequate pain assessment in older patients can be challenging. One survey of nurses found that nurses do not have enough knowledge regarding the experience of pain and its management in the elderly.[5] Multiple concurrent illnesses, under-reporting of pain, and the presence of cognitive impairment make it difficult to assess the older person's pain.

The American Geriatrics Society[6] recommends that caregivers use a simple, objective assessment tool to assess pain in the elderly. The key factor is to identify an assessment tool that is applicable to the patient's needs and stick to it. Changing assessment tools may be confusing to an elderly patient. Some commonly used assessment tools include the numerical rating scale, visual analog scale, verbal descriptive scale, *McGill Pain Questionnaire*, and the FACES pain scale. But it should be noted that pain assessment tools have not been validated for use in the elderly. However, one study found that the visual analog scale and the FACES rating scale may be the best tools for pain assessment in populations with diminished verbal and abstract thinking abilities.[7] A study of communicative patients with moderate to severe dementia found that 62% of patients reported pain. Of those patients reporting pain, 83% were able to use at least one of five available scales to quantify their pain.[8] Therefore, if caregivers are patient, allowing time for cognitively impaired elders to assimilate clues and using visual cueing techniques to aid their patients, objective pain assessment is possible. See Chapter 2 for examples of assessment tools that may be useful with elderly patients.

Any pain assessment should include the patient's descriptions and the caregiver's observations of the patient's physical and behavioral responses. The nurse should ask the patient about the location, type (e.g., dull, sharp, burning), duration, and frequency of the pain. The nurse should determine what relieves the pain and what makes it worse. Even though pain assessment instruments, such as visual analog scales, word descriptor scales and behavioral scales based on facial grimacing and posturing have not been validated in older patients, numeric pain scales are commonly used to help the patient describe the degree of pain he or she is experiencing. The patient is asked to rank his or her pain on a scale of 0–10, or 0–5, with 0 meaning no pain at all and 5 (or 10) meaning the worst pain level. This also provides a method to monitor and track the patient's degree of pain in response to treatment.

Pain assessment must include looking for signs of pain that are reflected in the patient's behavioral and physiologic responses to pain. Behavioral responses to pain may include grimacing, withdrawal, crying, anxiety, restlessness, altered body position, twitching, and immobility. Physiologic responses to mild or moderate pain include muscle tension, elevated blood pressure, dilated pupils, pallor, shortness of breath, increased pulse, and sweating. Physiologic responses to severe pain include decreased blood pressure, decreased pulse, nausea and vomiting, dizziness, weakness, and even loss of consciousness.[3]

15.4 Pain in the Cognitively Impaired Older Person

A. Misconception that individuals with dementia do not feel pain

An important component in evaluating the value of an elderly person's case is the analysis of the patient's awareness of pain and suffering. Some attorneys believe that patients with cognitive impairments do not feel pain or that their pain perception is decreased. There is no evidence to support this belief. It is likely that patients with cognitive impairments frequently suffer from unrelieved pain and discomfort.[1] Research has shown that older people with cognitive impairments typically underreport pain, compared with elderly patients who do not have dementia. According to two recent studies conducted in nursing homes, approximately 25% of nursing home residents who reported pain daily were not being treated for the pain.[9] Elderly people with cognitive deficits have a difficult time reporting pain. Furthermore, caregivers may not believe their reports of pain. A simple way of conceptualizing the pain that a cognitively impaired patient experienced is to ask the question: Would this injury cause pain if it occurred to me? A fractured leg hurts the demented patient no less than the coherent one. The confused patient may not understand why there is pain or how to tell others that pain exists, but the pain is nevertheless real. Patients with cognitive impairments frequently suffer from unrelieved pain and discomfort. The failure to relieve the pain of the confused patient constitutes substandard pain management.

Tip

When evaluating the medical records of the cognitively impaired patient, determine if the nursing and medical staffs were performing pain assessments and administering pain medication.

B. Ways of assessing pain in the cognitively impaired elderly

When caring for cognitively impaired elders who are not able to communicate, caregivers should observe changes in facial expression, body movements, and daily activities in identifying behavioral changes possibly associated with pain. Caregivers must learn the patient's baseline activities to be able to note the changes in behavior.

Tip

The attorney may see documentation that indicates that the elderly person was grimacing, moaning, or rubbing a part of his body. All are indicators of pain.

One study of nursing home residents found that screaming and verbal agitation are indicators of pain and decreased with the treatment of pain. Another study showed that elderly patients in a nursing home who were on psychotropic medication for difficult behavior had a decrease in problem behavior when they were placed on routine acetaminophen and were able to have their psychotropic medications discontinued.[8]

Self-report is the most reliable indicator of pain, and every effort should be made to obtain pain ratings. A study of 758 cognitively impaired nursing home residents revealed that the complaints of pain from a cognitively impaired older person are generally no less valid than those of cognitively intact individuals.[1] The best approach is to accept the patient's report of pain and treat the pain as it would be treated in a patient with intact cognition. Communicating with cognitively impaired elderly people may be very difficult due to the decline in the person's ability to express and receive information. Caregivers are often reluctant to engage in communication with the person who is cognitively impaired. This reluctance by the caregiver contributes to inadequate pain assessment of the cognitively impaired person and therefore leads to unrelieved pain in the elderly person. A trusting relationship between the caregiver and the cognitively impaired elder will improve their communication and allow the caregiver to assess the patient better. The degree of comfort in a caregiving relationship affects the cognitively impaired person's ability to comprehend and respond to the caregiver's questions and care activities. When a caregiver communicates with a cognitively impaired elder by using harsh directives, or terse and demeaning put-downs, the elder will likely become noncompliant and will not communicate. A quick route to aggression with a cognitively impaired elderly person is to direct or command behavior. Types of direct and indirect verbal abuse include ignoring, shaming, or demeaning the cognitively impaired elder and the use of minimal and task-oriented communication. This type of caregiver behavior is a barrier to being able to assess pain adequately in this patient. Figure 15.2 includes ways to enhance the assessment process. The attorney may need to use these techniques to elicit information from a confused elderly person.

15.5 Consequences of Pain

Gait disturbances, falls, slowed rehabilitation, cognitive dysfunction, and malnutrition are conditions that are potentially worsened by the presence of pain.[10] Pain leads to the use of multiple medications. Significant complications, such as depression, impaired mobility, decreased socialization or withdrawal, sleep disturbance, impaired functioning, and increased healthcare utilization and costs have been associated with unrelieved pain in elderly patients.[1,9] Pain has been linked to anorexia and possible malnutrition.[8] Psychosocial and economic consequences of pain significantly affect the elderly population. Pain is a complication that often impedes rehabilitation and treatment and decreases the quality of life for the elderly.[3] Obviously, pain conditions increase medical expenses.

15.6 Suffering

Older people commonly experience a series of dramatic life changes including the loss of loved ones, loss of their home, loss of functional abilities such as mobility, dexterity and strength, and loss of finances and loss of cognitive abilities. When an older person suffers a loss, such as a loss of mobility due to a fractured hip, that loss is superimposed on these other losses. The older person's life changes compound the suffering from illness or trauma. These life changes and losses strip them of their normal support system and coping abilities, as is described in the following example.

Mrs. Smith, eighty years old, was married to Joe for fifty-eight years. Joe was her soul mate and they did everything together. However, Joe died suddenly in January. Mrs. Smith was not able to care for herself alone due to arthritis and general weakness. She felt that her only option was to enter a nursing home. Her daughter, who lived 100 miles away, insisted that she enter a nursing home closer to her. So in March, Mrs. Smith left her neighbors and lifelong friends, sold her home of thirty-five years, and moved into a nursing home closer to her daughter. On admission, the nursing

- Attract the older person's attention. Maintain eye contact.
- Use gestures, pictures, and facial expression to convey more meaning.
- Ask simple questions.
- Give time for comprehension.
- Ask the person directly what he or she means using a paraphrase of what he or she said.
- Provide "either/or" choices in questions.
- Supply missing words for the speaker.
- Acknowledge the older person's attempts to converse.

15.2 *Methods of communication when assessing pain in the cognitively impaired elderly (Hendryx-Bedalov, 2000)*

home assessed that she was at risk of falling and needed assistance with ambulation. In May, Mrs. Smith fell while getting out of bed to go to the bathroom. She sustained a complex fracture of her left hip and was sent to the hospital. She underwent surgery and remained in the hospital for a week. She had a terrible time coping without Joe. Following the surgery, she was not allowed to bear weight on her left leg for three weeks. She started physical therapy but experienced a great deal of pain. She was reluctant to bother the nurses for medicine and just thought that her pain was part of the process. She was unable to get comfortable enough to sleep at night. She didn't feel like eating. She felt so alone and depressed. She didn't want to get out of bed anymore. The nurses were busy and didn't have time to answer her call light so she was left to urinate in the bed. She couldn't completely turn herself in bed and was dependent on the aides to turn her. But the aides only came into her room at the beginning of the shift and were in such a hurry that she was treated in an abrupt and rough manner. Her skin started breaking down, and soon she developed a pressure ulcer on her sacrum. The ulcer quickly deteriorated because Mrs. Smith was infrequently turned and repositioned. An old friend came to visit her in the nursing home and Mrs. Smith was terribly embarrassed because she now wore diapers and her pressure sore smelled. Due to the fall which resulted in a hip fracture, Mrs. Smith endured extreme unrelieved pain and profound suffering as a result of being neglected. Her pain and suffering from abuse and neglect were unbearable because she did not have the support of her husband Joe or her friends.

Life changes and losses of normal support systems and abilities compound the problem of pain. Suffering caused by trauma such as falls and hip fractures or the development of pressure ulcers are also compounded by these changes and losses. Suffering occurs not only because of the physical pain from the fall and fracture, but also from having to be uprooted again and hospitalized for a long period, being restricted in movement, and having to go through physical therapy. Most likely, this trauma superimposed on suffering from losing a home, family and functional ability will lead to depression, loss of appetite, loss of willingness to participate in activities or even physical therapy, and overall apathy. Even more sadly, these events lead to a loss of hope in the older person. This potential cycle of events should be convincing enough to be aggressive about prevention of trauma and addressing suffering in nursing homes.

There is also a profound effect on the family of an elderly person who has pain and suffering. Pain is a major concern and source of distress for family caregivers. Families need support to cope with the physical and psychosocial stresses resulting from caring for loved ones.[1,11] The emotional and physical demands of caring for a loved one with pain at home or in a nursing home can be overwhelming.

15.7 Documentation of Pain in the Medical Record

The medical record should reflect pain assessment and management of a nursing home resident or hospital patient. Many facilities use a structured pain assessment form which shows the location of pain, type of pain, frequency, and treatment. A pain scale may be incorporated into the assessment form. Nurse's notes should include this information in addition to nursing interventions to relieve the pain and the patient's response to treatment. Medication administration records (MAR) should clearly reflect the time, dosage, and route of all pain medication given. In the nursing home, the back of the MAR should have nursing documentation of this information in addition to the resident's response.

The Minimum Data Set (MDS) is a comprehensive assessment of the nursing home resident. The MDS should reflect the resident's pain frequency for a defined assessment reference period. However, this documentation may be flawed. One recent study in a nursing home showed that nurses' aides routinely caring for a cognitively impaired older person identified the resident's pain more accurately than was reflected in the MDS.[9] Another study revealed that minority patients were less likely than Caucasians to have pain recorded in the MDS.[4] The undertreated pain in the elderly patient is often reflected in the medical record. Recordings of pain assessments or signs of pain can be found in the nurse's notes, MDS, or monthly nursing summaries. These are sections in the record in which only a nurse may document. Section J in the MDS provides information about pain symptoms including the frequency with which the resident complains or shows evidence of pain in the last seven days. The intensity of the pain is then described by rating the pain as mild, moderate, horrible or excruciating. The nurse is required to check the location of the pain from a list of nine locations plus "other." The frequency, intensity, and location of pain as stated in the MDS should be documented in the medical record as well as the treatment ordered to relieve the pain. Even when the nurses are appropriately assessing pain, they may still fail to treat the pain. For example, in the nursing home record, there may be well documented signs that a resident is experiencing pain or even clearly recorded pain assessments but there no pain medication or comfort measures have been given.

15.8 Pain and Suffering Associated with Pressure Ulcers

Pressure ulcers, also known as decubitus ulcers or bed sores, are areas of skin breakdown that usually occur over bony points in the body. These ulcers are caused by unrelieved pressure on the skin. According to the National Pressure Ulcer Advisory Panel, "pressure ulcers are a significant and increasing source of considerable human suffering."[12] Elderly patients make up the majority of hospitalized patients with pressure ulcers and usually account for almost the entire nursing home incidence of pressure ulcers.

Pressure ulcers are described in part by a staging system denoting the depth of the pressure ulcer. The stages range from Stage I, a reddened area on the surface of the skin, to Stage IV, ulceration that extends to the muscle and bone. Stage II ulcers may appear to cause more pain. However, deeper ulcers, Stages III and IV, cause severe tissue destruction and often become infected. (See Chapter 9, "Spinal Cord Injury," for definitions of the stages of pressure sores.) Therefore, pressure ulcers cause considerable pain and distress, as well as an increased cost of care. Pressure ulcers often create problems for the elderly. The reality of having a bed sore is emotionally traumatic for an older person. Pressure sores, especially infected ulcers, may cause a foul odor that is embarrassing. Pressure sores are an issue of dignity. Treatments of pressure sores lead to even more immobility and isolation due to pain, bulky dressings, and not being able to be positioned on the ulcer site. For example, when an older person develops an ulcer on the coccyx, he or she must be kept off the coccyx and may not be able to get into a chair in order to go out of his or her nursing home room and socialize. Wearing clothes may cause pain and discomfort to a person with a pressure sore.

In order for a pressure ulcer to heal, the older person needs additional nutrition and hydration. The protein requirements increase significantly with the number and stage of the pressure ulcers. When an elderly person develops a pressure ulcer, there is often a downward spiral of additional limited mobility, impaired body image, painful treatments, isolation and depression. Depression in the elderly frequently contributes to loss of appetite and even malnutrition which compromises the healing of the pressure ulcers. Facing all these problems without the support of a spouse or close friends, and at a time when the patient has already suffered so many other losses is extremely overwhelming and traumatic.

Treatment of Stage III and IV pressure ulcers usually causes severe pain and suffering and added healthcare costs including hospitalization and surgery. Stage IV ulcers can lead to osteomyelitis, which is an infection of the bone and is very debilitating and difficult to treat. These ulcers frequently contain devitalized or dead tissue and bacteria. Therefore, the ulcers must often be debrided. Pressure ulcer debridement is done by a variety of methods. These include sharp, mechanical, enzymatic, and autolytic debridement. Autolytic debridement is a method of assisting the body in naturally breaking down the necrotic tissue. Sharp debridement is the use of a scalpel, scissor, or other sharp instrument to remove the revitalized tissue. Small wounds can be debrided at the bedside by a trained professional wound care nurse, physical therapist, or physician. Extensive wounds are usually debrided in the operating room.

Mechanical debridement techniques include wet-to-dry dressing, hydrotherapy such as whirlpool, and wound irrigation. Enzymatic debridement is done by applying topical debridement agents to devitalized tissue on the wound surface. Autolytic debridement involves using synthetic dressings to cover a wound and allow devitalized tissue to self-digest from the enzymes normally present in wound fluids. Dressing changes and debridement procedures can cause extreme pain and emotional distress to any patient but especially an elderly person. Prior to any of the treatments described, the patient should be medicated for pain. The patient should be monitored and treated for pain following the procedure. See Chapter 12 for more information on the debridement of wounds. See Figure 15.3 for questions to ask regarding how the older person is coping with a pressure sore.

In a Texas case, a woman developed malnutrition, dehydration, contractures, and sixteen pressure sores. Five of these sores had deteriorated to Stage IV. The plaintiffs sought compensatory and punitive damages. The jury awarded $2,710,000 for pain and suffering, impairment, disfigurement and mental anguish of the decedent during the long period of ill health before her death. They jury additionally awarded $310 million in punitive damages.[13]

- How do you feel about having a pressure ulcer?
- Do you think you look different?
- Does it hurt?
- When does it hurt?
- Describe the pain (use the pain assessment tools described earlier).
- Do you worry about the smell of the ulcer?
- Are you afraid of dressing changes due to the pain?
- How does the pressure ulcer limit your movement?
- How has this affected your life?
- Are you able to get up and be with other people?
- Have you been hospitalized due to the pressure ulcer?
- Have you incurred additional expenses due to the pressure ulcer?

*Note: If the patient is not able to answer questions, similar questions can be asked of family members to establish damages.

***15.3** Questions for attorneys to ask to obtain information about how client is coping with the pressure ulcer*

15.9 Pain and Suffering Associated with Fractured Hip

Older people are at risk for accidents and related trauma such as a hip fracture due to falling. Hip fractures are a major cause of morbidity and mortality in the elderly. Forty-eight percent of the elderly with a fractured hip either die or become dependent on others within six months of the injury. Hip fractures cause more than 225,000 hospital admissions annually involving Medicare recipients and cost $7.3 billion annually. These figures are expected to double by the year 2040.[14] Acute pain associated with fractures does not change with age in otherwise healthy, elderly people.[1]

Hip fractures are the most frequent fall-related injury resulting in hospitalization in the elderly population. Hip fracture is a significant injury that may permanently change the patient's level of functioning and independence. Many who survive a hip fracture never return to their pre-fracture ambulatory status. Women have a higher incidence of hip fracture than men. The most common site of fracture is the head of the femur. Older adults' bones fracture more easily because they are more brittle. They also heal more slowly, increasing the risk of immobility complications.

Falls are the most common cause of hip fracture in older adults. Unsteady gait, uneven surfaces, medications, slippery conditions, and weakness are only a few causes of falls. Confused and restrained elders sometimes experience hip fractures while attempting to get out of bed. Nursing homes and hospitals should have a planned approach to fall prevention.

Complications of a hip fracture can be devastating to the elderly. The pain and suffering are extensive and long lasting. Complications of a hip fracture include pneumonia, deep vein thrombosis, fat embolus, pressure ulcers, immobility, voiding dysfunction including incontinence, and psychosocial problems such as depression and isolation. The older person frequently becomes dependent on others to meet his or her needs, including bathing, personal grooming, and assistance with mobility. See Figure 15.4 for questions to ask to obtain information about how the patient is coping with the fractured hip.

15.10 Pain and Suffering Associated with Abuse and Neglect

Elder abuse and neglect are serious and prevalent problems for older persons in the community and nursing homes. Abuse and neglect involve males and females, both well and frail, and encompasses all socioeconomic, racial, and ethnic groups. Cognitively impaired individuals are at even higher risk for abuse and neglect. A cognitively impaired elder may not be able to seek help or report the incident. The abused elder may be unwilling to report the abuse for fear of retaliation, not having his basic needs met, and being institutionalized or abandoned. The U.S. Department of Health and Human Services defines abuse as "the willful infliction of injury, unreasonable confinement, intimidation, or punishment with resulting physical harm or pain or mental anguish, or deprivation by an individual, including a caretaker, of goods or services that are necessary to attain or maintain physical, mental, and psychosocial well-being." The federal government defines neglect as any "failure to provide goods and services necessary to avoid physical harm, mental anguish, or mental illness."[3]

In a Texas case, a resident of a nursing home was allegedly neglected and abused, which led to malnutrition and the development of a Stage IV pressure sore. The plaintiffs claimed such extended abuse and neglect resulted in the patient's physical pain, mental anguish, physical impairment, disfigurement, and death. The case settled for a confidential amount.[15]

Signs of physical abuse are easier to detect than psychological abuse and exploitation. See Figure 15.5 for common signs of physical abuse and neglect.

- How does the fracture limit your ability to get around?
- Does it hurt?
- When does it hurt?
- Describe the pain (use the pain assessment tools described earlier).
- Are you afraid of falling again?
- How has this affected your life? Are you able to see your friends?
- Are you able to get up and be with other people?
- How long were you in the hospital due to the hip fracture?
- What additional problems have you had since the hip fracture? (i.e., pneumonia, stiff joints, inability to move your leg, contracture, or depression)

***15.4** Questions for attorneys to ask to obtain information about how client is coping with the fractured hip*

- poor hygiene and unclean body
- unshaven or uncombed hair
- poor skin hygiene
- patches of hair missing
- dehydration
- malnutrition
- weight loss
- pressure ulcers
- a foul body odor
- failure to comply with medical treatments
- bruises in different stages of healing and age
- burns in an unusual location or type
- physical or thermal injury on the head, scalp, or face
- burns from cigarettes or rope-type burns
- bruises and hematomas in an unusual location, bruising or swelling in the genitals, bruise in shape of fingerprints or the outline of an object
- bite marks
- presence of other injuries in different stages of resolution
- mental status and neurologic examination changes from previous level
- hemorrhages in the eyes
- fractures, falls, or evidence of physical restraint (such as strap marks, bruising across chest from a vest restraint, or contractures)
- difficulty in walking (poor ambulation may suggest sexual assault)
- behavior changes such as being extremely fearful or agitated, anxiety, anger, overly quiet and passive, or expressing fear of caregiver
- lacerations and fractures with unknown origin
- lacerations and fractures that have healed without appropriate medical treatment
- caregiver's explanations that do not match the injury.[3,15]

***15.5** Signs of physical abuse and neglect*

The effects of physical, sexual, and psychological abuse are far reaching in the elderly. Elders may experience extreme pain due to physical abuse. An untreated fracture may contribute to many other physical conditions, such as swelling, infection, and loss of mobility. All forms of abuse potentially affect the physical and emotional health of the elderly. Abuse increases the risk for anxiety disorders, depression, and withdrawal. The older person may also suffer from posttraumatic stress disorder as a consequence of abuse.

A Washington woman, who was a resident of a nursing home, was raped by an outside visitor. She sustained posttraumatic stress disorder, rape trauma syndrome, rape, emotional distress, agoraphobia, and ongoing nightmares and panic attacks. The action settled for $175,000.[16]

Depression and withdrawal contribute to isolation, immobility, anorexia and are associated with numerous physical maladies. Abuse may be the cause of malnutrition, dehydration, and noncompliance with prescribed medications and treatments. All reports of abuse, or suspected abuse, must be reported to the state agency or agencies responsible for nursing homes. All states have laws authorizing adult protective services to intervene in cases of elder abuse.[3,17]

15.11 Pain Management Principles in the Elderly

Nursing homes and hospitals are required by federal and state rules to take an interdisciplinary team approach to pain management. The American Medical Directors Association suggests that a systematic effort to recognize and treat pain in nursing homes is an essential indicator of quality of care. The elderly are at high risk for adverse effects of unrelieved acute pain due to the physiologic changes and other diseases that the elderly have in addition to the pain. For example, a patient with a respiratory condition such as chronic obstructive pulmonary disease (COPD) may experience increased shortness of breath due to unrelieved pain. This may even lead to an exacerbation of the COPD. Recent research has shown that aggressive pain control improves outcomes, decreases length of hospital stays, and reduces the cost of care in the elderly population.[1,4]

Caregivers are fearful of drug interactions and adverse effects and of over-medicating the elderly. Although opioids can be used safely in the elderly, many physicians and nurses are fearful of the potential side effects. The most dangerous side effect of opioids is respiratory depression.[1]

Pain management starts with adequate assessment and proper identification of the pain in the individual. Pain treatment care plans should be developed and implemented to ensure safe and effective pain management in the elderly.[1]

Tip

There are pain management standards that govern the care provided to the elderly. The attorney may obtain these during discovery.

The American Medical Directors Association[4] states that long-term care facilities must be committed to proper pain assessment and management. Facilities must develop comprehensive plans to address this issue. Policies and procedures that facilitate the recognition, assessment, treatment, and monitoring of pain must be written and implemented. Communication systems must be in place to ensure that information about a patient's pain is conveyed to the right people. Training all facility staff members, including non-direct caregiver staff, about recognizing and reporting a patient's pain is essential. A pain management team that is coordinated by a registered nurse is necessary to ensure that all patients are assessed and properly treated for pain. Documentation of ongoing pain assessment and treatment must be in every patient's medical record. Caregivers should have a high index of suspicion that a patient is in pain due to the numerous predisposing factors the elderly have for pain. Every patient should be assessed for pain systematically and regularly. Pain assessments should be performed on admission to a long-term care facility, at each quarterly review, at any time that a change in the patient's condition prompts the completion of a new MDS, and any time that pain is suspected.

The Agency for Health Care Policy and the American Pain Society (see Figure 15.6) produced pain guidelines that are considered by many professional

- Implement a valid and reliable pain assessment tool in clinical practice.
- Inform patients that treatment of their pain is important.
- Tell patients to notify someone if he or she is in pain.
- Set a goal with the patient for an acceptable level of pain intensity.
- Systematically document the pain experience. This should include factors influencing perception, evaluation of pain, and responses to pain, as appropriate.
- Assess pain on regular intervals, after initiation of treatment, at each new report of pain, and at a suitable interval after treatment.
- Treat the pain within fifteen minutes.
- Use both drug and non-drug therapies to treat pain, as appropriate.
- Determine if pain relief is acceptable to the patient.
- Institute a formal and collaborative institutional approach to pain management with clear lines of responsibility. [12,17]

15.6 *Pain guidelines recommended by the Agency for Health Care Policy and Research*

groups and legal experts to be the standard of care for pain management. These guidelines are critical to the prevention of undertreatment of pain in the elderly.[2]

15.12 Summary

Pain and suffering in the elderly are significant issues in healthcare that are finally getting the recognition is needed. Caregivers need to become more informed and skilled in recognizing and treating pain in older persons. When evaluating a case, attorneys and experts should examine facility pain management policies and procedures and training logs to determine whether the facility is following recommended guidelines for a systematic approach to pain management. Medical records should be reviewed for evidence of proper pain and suffering assessment, identification, care planning, treatment, and evaluation of the older person's response to pain. The implications for attorneys are that knowledge about pain and suffering will be used to evaluate the damages in a case.

Endnotes

1. Pasero, C., Reed, B., and McCaffery, M., "Pain in the Elderly." In *Pain Clinical Manual.* St. Louis: Mosby, 1999, 674–710.

2. Gaston-Johansson, F., and Johansson, F., "Under Treatment of Pain in the Elderly: Causes and Prevention." *Annals of Long-Term Care,* 7(5), 190–196, 1999.

3. Holmes, H.N., editor, *Mastering Geriatric Care.* Springhouse, PA: Springhouse Corporation, 1997.

4. American Medical Directors Association (AMDA), *Chronic Pain Management in the Long-Term Care Setting; Clinical Practice Guideline,* 1999.

5. Sloman, R., Ahern, M., Wright, A., et al., "Nurses' Knowledge of Pain in the Elderly." *J Pain Symptom Manage,* Vol. 21, 317–32, 2001.

6. "Management of Persistent Pain in Older Persons; AGS Panel on Persistent Pain in Older Persons." *Journal of the American Geriatrics Society,* 50 (Supplement. Number 6, S205–S224), 2002.

7. Freeman, K., Smyth, C., Dallam, L., and Jackson, B., "Pain Measurement Ccales: A Comparison of the Visual Analogue and FACES Rating Scales in Measuring Pressure Ulcer Pain." *Journal of Wound, Ostomy and Continence Nurses Society*, 28(6), 290–29, 2001.

8. Huffman, J., and Kunik, M., "Assessment and Understanding of Pain in Patients with Dementia." *The Gerontologist*, 40(5), 574–581, 2000.

9. Fisher, S., Burgio, L., Thorn, B., Allen-Burge, R., Gerstle, J., Roth, D., et. al., "Pain Assessment and Management in Cognitively Impaired Nursing Home Residents: Association of Certified Nursing Assistants Pain Report, Minimum Data Det Pain Report, and Analgesic Medication Use." *Journal of American Geriatrics Society*, 50(1), 152–156, 2002.

10. Ferrell, B.A., "Pain Management in Elderly People." *J Am Geriatric Society* 39, 64–73, 1991.

11. Hendryx-Bedalov, P., "Alzheimer's Dementia—Coping with Communication Decline." *Journal of Gerontological Nursing*, 20–24, August 2000.

12. *Management of Cancer Pain*, U.S. Department of Health and Human Services, Agency for Health Care Policy and Research (AHCPR) Publication No. 94-0592. Rockville, MD: 1994.

13. Laska, L., editor," Death of Nursing Home Resident Following Development of Pressure Sores, Contractures and Malnutrition." *Cecil Fuqua, as Executor of the Estate of Wyvonne Fuqua, Deceased v. Horizon/CMS Healthcare Corporation f.k.a. Horizon Healthcare Corporation*, Tarrant County (TX) District Court, case no. 4:98-CV-1087-Y, *Medical Malpractice Verdicts, Settlements and Experts*, August 2001, 37

14. Anders, R.L., and Ornellas, E.M., "Acute Management of Patients with Hip Fracture." *Orthopedic Nursing* 16(2), 31–46, 1997.

15. Laska, L., editor, "Malnutrition and Failure to Monitor and Treat Decubitus Ulcer Blamed for Death of Elderly Woman." *Daline Eason, et al. v. Silsbee Convalescent Center*, Harding County (TX) District Court, case no. 38,481, *Medical Malpractice Verdicts, Settlements and Experts*, June 2001, 36.

16. Laska, L., editor, "Failure to Properly Monitor Mentally Retarded Cerebral Palsy Resident—Resident Raped by Visitor." *Jane Doe v. Westwood Manor Retirement Center and Mark Wheaton*, Snohomish County (WA) Superior Court, case no. 98-2-07354-1, *Medical Malpractice Verdicts, Settlements and Experts*, August 2001, 37.

17. *Acute Pain Management: Operative or Medical Procedures and Trauma,* Agency for Health Care Policy and Research, U.S. Department of Health and Human Services, AHCPR Publication No. 92-0032. Rockville, MD: 1992.

Additional Reading

King, S.A., "Shattering the Myths about Geriatric Pain." *Geriatric Times*, 1(1), 2000. Retrieved from http://www.medinfosource.com.

"Meeting JCAHO Standards for Pain Control." *Nursing 2000*, 30(3), 2000.

Morrison, M., Moffat, C., and Bridel-Nixon, J., *Nursing Management of Chronic Wounds*, Second Edition. London: Mosby, 1998.

National Pressure Ulcer Advisory Panel, "Pressure Ulcers Prevalence, Cost and Risk Assessment, Consensus Development Conference Statement." *Decubitus,* (2) 24–28, 1989.

"Persistent Pain in Nursing Home Residents." *JAMA,* 285(16). Retrieved May 16, 2002 from http://jama.ama-assn.org, 2001.

Teno, J., Weitzen, S., Wetle, T., and Mor, V., "Study Finds Persistent and Severe Pain among Nursing Home Residents." Retrieved May 16, 2002 from http://www.brown.edu/Administration/News Bureau, 2001.

Chapter 16

Life Care Planning and Chronic Pain

Randall Thomas, PhD, CRC, NCC

Synopsis

16.1 The Field of Life Care Planning

A. Background

A life care plan (LCP) to project the needs of an individual with a catastrophic injury or chronic medical condition has gained popularity over the past twenty years. Currently, LCPs are used to project future care costs in workers' compensation, personal injury litigation, reserve setting, and discharge planning. Plaintiff and defense attorneys are using life care plans more frequently in cases where future care cost is an area of disagreement. The life care planner is the one expert witness who can "pull all the costs" together as well as identify the goods and services required for the client through his life expectancy.

Many of the conditions that cause pain and suffering require ongoing medical care. Those that are related to catastrophic injuries, chronic illnesses, or lingering suffering which ends in death are likely to cause significant expenses. The LCP provides the reader of the document a comprehensive look at the current and future goods and services that an individual will require as a result of her injury or illness.

LCPs gained popularity in the mid-1980s when introduced to the healthcare industry in *Damages in Tort Action*[1] and *A Guide to Rehabilitation*.[2] Soon after, a training program was developed to provide those in the rehabilitation community with instruction in the process and methods of life care planning. The first certification exam in life care planning offered for life care planners was administered in 1996.[3] The number of individuals providing life care planning services in the United States is unknown. The professional backgrounds of practitioners providing life care plan services vary. Practitioners include nurses, vocational rehabilitation counselors, physical therapists, occupational therapists, psychologists, physicians, and other professionals in the field of rehabilitation.[4] Life care planners may have various allied healthcare certifications, and the astute lawyer will be able to research the credibility of the various credentials of a potential life care planner.[5]

B. Definition

As LCPs have gained popularity, standards in the field of life care planning have emerged and have become better defined.[6] A standard definition exists, and a standardized process of developing LCPs is now evolving.

The generally accepted definition of a LCP is "a dynamic document based upon published standards of practice, comprehensive assessment, data analysis and research, which provides an organized, concise plan for current and future needs with associated costs, for individuals who have experienced catastrophic injury or have chronic healthcare needs."[7]

Tip

A LCP is a document prepared to project, to a reasonable degree of probability, the variety of goods and services that an individual will need at present and in the future as a result of an injury or medical condition.

The LCP includes medically related goods and services and nonmedical services such as architectural renovation and modified transportation. A LCP contains more than a projection of future medical care costs associated with acute medical conditions. The LCP outlines a program to reduce the frequency of medical complications, to enhance the participation of the individual within the community and society, to address quality of life issues, and to assist in maintaining the emotional and psychological health of the individual. The LCP identifies caregiving services required by the injured individual. In addition to preserving health, the services outlined in the LCP are intended to prevent family stress and burnout, which would then place additional emotional stress on the client.

A LCP is a proactive plan of care that is holistic in its approach. A LCP report may contain a descriptive report that is factually based and provides relevant historical data about the client, the client's medical, social, educational, and relevant family history. The narrative of the LCP describes the client's ability to participate in major life activity areas. The LCP may contain, as optional information, a summary of cost of recommended items, a vocational assessment with loss of earning capacity report, the life care planner's CV, and a bibliography of documents relied upon by the life care planner. The attorney requesting a LCP should clearly communicate to the life care planner if a loss of earnings capacity report (LOEC) is also required. Typically, the LCP and LOEC are two separate reports.

Tip

As life care planners become more visible within the litigation environment, the ability of the referral source, the opposing attorneys and the court to scrutinize a LCP (and the life care planner) increases. They will review the LCP with an even finer comb to find information for use at deposition or trial.

A LCP serves a number of purposes. Although many LCPs are currently completed because of pending litigation, there is an increased use of LCPs in nonlitigated settings such as elder care programs. The LCP can be used by the courts or parties involved in litigation as they try to evaluate the probable costs of care for an individual. However, an important purpose of the LCP is to educate the client, caregivers, parents, and other responsible parties about an individual's present and long-term needs.

The LCP should serve as a road map of care. Ideally, the LCP should be updated or revised any time there is a significant alteration in the level of functioning of the client or when the client reaches a significant developmental milestone, such as adolescence or young adulthood. The LCP is the best reasonable projection of future care needs given all that is known about the client and the disability and is based on a number of factors, including historical data from professional literature. To be listed as a "costed" item in a LCP, the recommended item should have a greater than 50% chance of being used.[8]

A step-by-step procedure for life care planning, outlined in *Life Care Planning and Case Management Handbook*,[7] provides guidance to attorneys and life care planners regarding the process of life care planning. It is important that the referring attorney recognize that the competent life care planner will review medical records and depositions, conduct an interview with the client, consult with treating physicians and therapeutic team members, and research costs for recommendations. While there may be some variation in the particular practitioner's process for data collection, these integral parts of LCP development should be present. On occasion, the life care planner retained by defense counsel may be denied an interview with the client. This failure to interview the injured party can be noted by the life care planner as a part of the limitations of the life care plan and does not prohibit the life care planner from completing the LCP.

Each life care planner should use a standard process when a LCP is developed. This process may include certain forms to be completed, letters or faxes to be sent to treating practitioners, forms to be signed for release of medical records, and forms for obtaining a comprehensive history from the client. The end result of the LCP process, however, should be the same: an objective and unbiased documentation of future care needs along with a proper foundation provided for the recommended items.

A LCP typically consists of a narrative section and a section of LCP tables or charts that describe the specific set of recommendations for the individual. The LCP should address the areas of care as shown in Figure 16.1. The areas of care in Figure 16.1 reflect the order the items are typically arranged in the LCP tables. Each item of care in each of the areas of the LCP will have specific information describing purpose, frequency, cost, and other relevant information such as the source of the recommendation and the source of the cost information.

- projected evaluations
- projected therapeutic modalities
- diagnostic testing and educational assessment
- wheelchair (mobility), wheelchair accessories, and maintenance
- aids for independent function
- durable medical equipment
- prosthetics and orthotics
- supplies
- medications
- home care and facility care
- medical care—routine
- acute medical intervention—surgical
- health and strength maintenance
- transportation
- architectural renovations
- vocational and educational plan
- potential complications

***Figure 16.1** Areas of the life care plan*

C. Practitioners in the field of life care planning

The vast majority of life care planners are nurses or vocational rehabilitation counsellors.[4] Life care planners may hold a variety of healthcare certifications. Examples of certifications typically held by life care planners include certified case manager (CCM), certified rehabilitation counselor (CRC), and certified life care planner (CLCP) designations. (Contact information for organizations that grant these credentials is shown in Figure 16.2.) The credentialing bodies for the CRC and CCM certifications are accredited by the National Commission for Certifying Agencies (NCCA). NCCA is the accreditation body of National Organization for Competency Assurance (NOCA). Established in 1977, NOCA is the leader in setting quality standards for credentialing organization.[9] A review of NCCA standards allows the attorney to determine if a specific certification body has met the guidelines that allow for accreditation by NCCA.[5]

For more information see:

Certified Rehabilitation Counselor
http://www.crccertification.com/
Certified Case Manager
http://www.ccmcertification.org/
Certified Life Care Planner
http://www.CDEC1.com
National Organization for Competency Assurance
http://www.noca.org/

***Figure 16.2** Additional resources for life care planning certification*

D. Limitations of the life care planner role

Many LCPs are prepared when the client is involved in litigation. It is critical within this environment that the attorney has confidence that the life care planner has established the proper foundation for a recommendation for services in the LCP. For some recommended items, the life care planner may have the capacity (i.e., the expertise, training and credentialing) to recommend a particular service. If not, the life care planner should document the foundation for a particular recommendation from consultations with treating or examining healthcare professionals, a review of medical records, a review of professional literature, and standards of practice within a particular field, or consensus guidelines.

A life care planner with a master's degree in rehabilitation can outline future vocational counselling services. However, it is typically beyond the scope of the life care planner to prescribe future medications or future surgery for a client. Rather, the recommendation for medical services is usually obtained from a physician, as the delivery and prescription of those services are within the physician's scope of practice, expertise, and training.

Tip

A LCP is a collaborative process. The life care planner will request a signed release from the client to communicate with the treating healthcare members. Requesting and obtaining recommendations from the various healthcare providers helps the life care planner establish a proper foundation for items identified in the LCP.

Life care planners, regardless of their professional background, should follow the standard process for obtaining recommendations for goods and services to include in a LCP. A physician life care planner may recommend a MRI for someone for whom he is preparing a LCP. However, the physician life care planner should also solicit recommendations for future care needs from the client's current treating physician, especially if the identified needs are outside the physician's speciality area. A physician life care planner that does not solicit recommendations from other healthcare providers is subject to difficulty in testifying as an expert witness regarding items in a specialty area outside her credentialing.

Many of the items listed in the life care plan can only be prescribed or delivered by a physician. A non-physician life care planner such as a nurse or rehabilitation counsellor should use caution if including these items in a LCP without a physician's recommendation. The life care planner, whether a physician or non-physician, should include recommendations in the LCP that are based on a standard process or procedure that has been accepted in the field. The recommendation should be based on the training, education, and experience of the person offering the recommendation. The life care planner should be familiar with the effect of *Daubert*[10] and *Kumho*[11] on expert testimony as described by the U.S. Supreme Court. An expert witness who is unfamiliar with *Daubert* has a higher risk of having his testimony limited or excluded in all federal courts and some state courts.

In a litigate environment, it is important the life care planner establishing the LCP recommendations does so in a manner that meets the rules of evidence related to expert testimony in the
jurisdiction. The retaining attorney is advised to discuss with the potential LCP expert potential "obstacles" to having the expert's report and testimony admitted. The referring attorney should consider having her expert's LCP independently reviewed by another life care planner retained as a non-disclosed consultant to the attorney. It is beyond the scope of the chapter to detail the various criteria related to expert testimony. However, as noted above, the life care planner and attorney should be very familiar with the *Daubert* and *Kumho* decisions.

Tip

In essence, the life care planner is expected to complete the plan in a consistent and reliable fashion and to have the proper foundation established for the items in the plan, especially physician related services such as surgery, medications, and aggressive medical treatment.

E. How items are selected and costed in a LCP

When preparing a LCP, the life care planner will request from the treating physicians their opinions regarding future care needs. In addition, the life care planner will request information from other treating healthcare team members such as physical and occupational therapists, treating psychologists, and the client and family members. The life care planner should document the request to the healthcare professionals, and also document in writing the response (if any) from the healthcare team members. The prudent life care planner will document any oral recommendations from the physician by forwarding the physician a list of the recommendations obtained during the consultation with the life care planner. By providing a list with a request for the physician to review and sign, the life care planner documents the oral communication and reduces the potential for miscommunication or a challenge by opposing attorney, that the oral recommendations were hearsay.

The life care planner should complete a home visit and client interview unless there are specific circumstances that prevent the client interview. One example of a valid reason to not complete a client interview would be if the defense attorney retains the life care planner, and after a request by the life care planner to arrange for a client interview, the interview is denied by the plaintiff's attorney.

In addition, the life care planner researches the cost of each item in the LCP. The life care planner must use caution to not select the highest or lowest cost source in an attempt to increase or decrease the total dollar value of a LCP. Typically, three costs should be provided for any item where the cost exceeds $500 per year. Providing three cost sources in the client's geographic area of residence enables the individual to have several options from which to choose when it is time to purchase an item. However, not all cost sources must be local. The criterion for including a cost source relates to the extent that the cost is reasonably available to the client. For example, the life care planner may chose to use an Internet cost source. Internet cost sources for medications are acceptable, and the costs are frequently reported in a LCP. However, the life care planner will likely use a current vendor as an additional cost source. Life care planners must be sensitive to very high or very low prices provided by vendors. These "outlier" costs, either too high or too low, should not be used as one of the three vendor costs in determining a reasonable average of cost or range of cost.

When researching costs, the life care planner will attempt to locate vendors within the client's geographic location. Due to the limited number of vendors in some areas, three local vendors may not be located. The life care planner may survey a nearby metropolitan area for vendor and cost information. When soliciting a cost from a vendor, the life care planner should request the current retail price for each item. There are several reasons for this standard practice. First, if the cost provided is a negotiated price or a discounted price, it may not accurately reflect what the client will pay for the item when she goes to purchase the item. A discounted cost available to a case manager or life care planner skilled in cost negotiation may not be the same rate that the client is asked to pay for the item in the future. In addition, after the LCP is completed, a case manager may not be involved in implementing the LCP and assisting the client to secure the best cost. When collecting cost data, the life care planner is seeking the price the client will most likely pay in the private market. Life care planners follow different procedures when reporting and describing the cost information in the LCP. Some life care planners report all information regarding the cost sources in the LCP. Other life care planners provide minimal information in the LCP regarding the cost sources, preferring to provide a source list within the client file. In either situation, life care planners should have written documentation in their client file about the cost sources.

Tip

In litigation, the life care planner knows that every recommendation will be closely scrutinized. Was the math correct? Were there any misspelling of words? Were the proper terms used? Did the life care planner "double dip" by including overlapping attendant care cost? How were costs obtained? Who was contacted? The list goes on and on.

16.2 Chronic Pain

Individuals with chronic pain frequently use medical and nonmedical services related to their chronic pain condition. As such, it is important that the life care planner provide reliable and valid cost data in the LCP. The Joint Commission on Accreditation of Healthcare Organizations (JCAHO) identified pain as a major, largely avoidable public health problem.[12] JCAHO has developed standards that create new expectations for the assessment and management of pain in accredited hospitals and other health care settings.[13]

Approximately 2%–4% of the general population is treated for chronic pain, and only 40%–50% of this population has adequate relief of pain. Chronic pain is diagnosed in both men and women and is present in individuals of all ages and cultural backgrounds. The annual cost of chronic pain is approximately $100 billion, including medical expenses, lost income, and lost productivity.

Individuals with chronic pain may have received treatment for acute pain, sometimes from a number of physicians. After trying various drugs and pain relief interventions without success, the individual's pain may be compounded by the emotional, financial, and psychological effects of the pain. Chronic pain often disrupts various aspects of daily life. Relationship difficulties often occur as a result of chronic pain. Financial difficulties typically exist as a result of the individual's limited ability, or complete inability, to retain employment. Dependence on prescribed drugs is often seen in this population. Depression is prevalent among clients with chronic pain.

Tip

In preparing a LCP for an individual with chronic pain, it is important for the life care planner to address both the medical and the resulting social and psychological aspects of chronic pain.

The goal of the LCP is to determine the probable medical and nonmedical goods and services that will be needed as a result of the chronic pain condition. Chronic pain can be a challenging area for the life care planner because of the involvement of numerous medical conditions that cause or exacerbate chronic pain and because the outcomes of the same treatment can vary from patient to patient.

16.3 Life Care Plan Areas and Items Related to Chronic Pain

The following is a list of items identified by the author to be considered under each area of recommendations in a LCP for a chronic pain patient. A cost range is provided for each item. The prices reflect a reasonable cost range but should not be used in reporting cost in a specific individual's LCP. It is also noted that there will be some cost variation by geographic location.

A. Projected evaluations

Projected evaluations include evaluations by non-physicians in the areas of allied health. Examples include physical therapy (PT), occupational therapy (OT), speech and communications therapy, psychology, and driver's evaluation. Evaluations in this area are important for the chronic pain patient because the evaluations serve as an ongoing monitoring system for the health and well being of the individual.

For the chronic pain patient, a physical therapy evaluation may be included on a yearly basis. The periodic or annual PT evaluation will be important as the individual with chronic pain ages and her physical capabilities begin to diminish. Also, a yearly psychological evaluation may be recommended to monitor changes in the emotional status of the individual. While the individual may be functioning well during the first yearly evaluation, living with chronic pain may begin to erode the individual's self-esteem or trigger depression at the time of the second or third yearly psychological evaluation. Practitioners who are familiar with chronic pain should perform these evaluations.

Following the annual evaluation, treatment recommendations for follow-up services should be made. While follow-up treatment sessions may not be required after each periodic evaluation, they should be considered by the practitioner in order to prevent future complications or deterioration of the individual's health status. It is the responsibility of the life care planner to focus on the maintenance of health and understand how each of these evaluations affects other areas of the individual's plan of care.

Involvement of the client with a chronic pain clinic is important. A good chronic pain program will ask the client to complete a medical history and physical, including drug and alcohol treatment history, will develop goals for increased functional activities, and will document the progress the client has made. The program will involve regular review of the client's functioning, pain relief, side effects of medications, and quality of life. If recommending a pain management evaluation, it is important for the life care planner to identify one or more quality programs that will meet the needs of the client with chronic pain.

The following cost ranges are offered as examples of the fees for the indicated evaluation.

pain management clinic evaluation (outpatient)
(cost: $250–$750)
psychological evaluation (3–6 hours)
(cost: $105–$150 per hour)
nutritional evaluation (1 hour)
(cost: $60–$120 per hour)
physical therapy evaluation (2 hours)
(cost: $105–$150 per hour)
occupational therapy evaluation (2 hours)
(cost: $105–$150 per hour)
vocational rehabilitation evaluation (4 hours)
(cost: $105–$150 per hour)
driver evaluation (2–4 hours)
(cost: $70–$110 per hour)

B. Projected therapeutic modalities

The projected therapeutic modalities area of the LCP details the specific allied health treatment services as opposed to evaluation services. The treating physician may have specific recommendations for ongoing services in this area for an extended number of years. Also, the occupational and physical therapists may have specific recommendations. The life care planner will solicit their opinions as a part of a standard LCP process. In many cases the projection of a specific time frame for services in this area is more problematic than in other areas of the LCP. That is, the foundation for a yearly PT evaluation through life expectancy may be a reasonable medical foundation, but a recommendation for weekly PT sessions (fifty-two per year) for the next thirty years becomes a more tenuous recommendation to support.

To demonstrate a reasonable foundation for future care services in the LCP, the life care planner should make a concerted effort to speak with the client's treating healthcare professionals. Requesting an interview or phone conference with the individual's treating healthcare team member is one of the most reliable methods to obtain recommendations based on the probable occurrence of therapeutic modalities. The life care planner should document the recommendations in a written format and confirm these recommendations with the allied healthcare team member. For example, if the individual is presently receiving counselling services, the life care planner should request a conference, either in person or by phone, with the treating counsellor. The treating counsellor should have an excellent foundation to outline a future schedule of services for the individual. However, there are times the client will not have been receiving psychological services. The life care planner with a background in psychology (e.g., psychologist or counsellor) may be able to recommend a future schedule of services based upon her interview and meetings with the client and a review of the medical records. Also, the treating physiatrist, or other qualified physician, may recommend a schedule of psychological services.

In general, it is preferable for the life care planner to seek the opinion of the healthcare professional currently treating the individual and solicit her opinion on the need for future services and a schedule for those services. For example, a physical therapist currently working with the chronic pain patient may have detected deterioration of range of motion and will recommend a certain number of sessions to be targeted toward increasing the individual's range of motion. The physical therapist may also be able to recommend a number of yearly sessions required to maintain range of motion.

A similar process to determine future care needs in occupational therapy should be used by the life care planner. Again, the client may not presently be involved in occupational therapy services. A life care planner with a background in occupational therapy may be able to offer an appropriate schedule. Also, the treating physiatrist or chronic pain physician may also be able to offer an appropriate schedule for occupational therapy.

Case management is a service included in the area of projected therapeutic modalities. Individuals with chronic pain often benefit from the services of a case manager to coordinate medical and pharmacological intervention.

Tip

Insuring that the individual does not fall through the cracks is particularly important with chronic pain patients. Often, individuals with chronic pain are seeking medical intervention from healthcare communities where there is little or no speciality in chronic pain. In this situation, the case manager will be a valuable resource for the individual to insure that chronic pain is being addressed appropriately.

In the area of projected therapeutic modalities, the LCP may describe a range in the frequency and duration of the recommendation. For example, recommendations for psychological counselling may indicate "twelve to twenty-four sessions per year," a fairly wide range in the recommended number of sessions. The reader should not view the indication of a range of services with alarm. A range of frequency for a specific item may best describe the most probable need. On occasion, a range of frequency for services is a better description of the probable care needs than are a specific number of sessions.

In summary, the method by which a life care planner arrives at the recommendation should be evident and documented. That is, the life care planner should be able to describe the method and process employed, and demonstrate that this process is used on a consistent basis.

behavior modification and counselling
(cost: $90–$150 per hour)
counselling for family
(cost: $90–$150 per hour)
case manager
(cost: $75–$105 per hour)
nutritional counselling
(cost: $60–$90 per hour)
driver training
(cost: $70–$100 per hour)
physical therapy session
(cost: $105–$150 per hour)
occupational therapy session
(cost: $105–$150 per hour)
recreational therapy session
(cost: $100–$130 per hour)
vocational guidance services
(cost: $75–$105 per hour)

C. Diagnostic testing and educational assessment

This area of the LCP describes educational services and educational diagnostic services. Medical diagnostic services are not included in this area. Items in this area include the educational goods and services for a child or adult client. Typically the items listed are greater in frequency for a child since children with chronic pain are more apt to need these services than will an older adult. Recommendations in this area for a child will take into consideration the services provided by the local public school under the Individuals with Disabilities Education Act of 1975 and the Individuals with Disabilities Education Act (IDEA) Amendments of 1997. The act is federal and applies to all school districts throughout the United States. Services under IDEA are provided based upon the child's identified special educational needs, and not on the child's disability category or financial status.

The services provided to the child are designed to improve the child's educational goals. The focus of IDEA is not medical care for the student. As the life care planner describes future health related needs, she should differentiate between the services based on educational needs and medical needs. That is, if the school district provides physical therapy sessions for educational purposes, then the cost of those services will not be included in the bottom line dollar figure because the school pays for the services and there is no right of subrogation in the school to recover these expenditures. However, there may be a recommendation for additional PT services to meet the medical needs of the child. If so, these additional physical therapy services would be listed and costed in the LCP.

Educational testing or supplemental tutorial services may be considered if the individual with chronic pain has missed school due to pain or has suffered cognitive impairment due to pain or pharmacological intervention. Children with chronic pain often have other significant medical conditions causing pain, such as cancer or a spinal cord injury. (See Chapter 9, "Spinal

Cord Injury," for more information.) It is important for the life care planner to evaluate the needs of the child that result from both conditions.

A consultation with school officials and a review of the Individual Education Plan (IEP) allow appropriate goods and services to be documented.

Tip

It should be noted that seldom will school officials acknowledge the need for services beyond those listed in the IEP since the school will be responsible for these services. From a practical standpoint, there is variation from state to state in the extent to which school systems fund special programs and a variation in the goods and services provided by various school systems.

Individuals with Disabilities Education Act (IDEA) services
(cost: no fee)
educational testing
(cost: $350–$700 per year)
supplemental tutor
(cost: $18–$35 per hour)

D. Wheelchair (mobility), wheelchair accessories and maintenance

Impairment in mobility is commonly seen in the chronic pain population. While the need for a wheelchair or mobility device may not be as self-evident as it is for an individual with a spinal cord injury, a mobility device may be just as important for someone with chronic pain. Again, the life care planner should focus on the quality of life and the prevention of medical complications. The life care planner should inquire about the client's daily activities and mode of ambulation. Specifically, the life care planner will inquire about what activities increase the client's pain levels. Often, standing or walking are noted to be causes of pain. While a young client with chronic pain may continue to ambulate unassisted, the limitations of chronic pain combined with the effects of aging may necessitate a mobility device at a younger age than in a non-handicapped individual.

When the recommendation is made for a mobility device, the life care planner should inquire regarding the most appropriate equipment for the specific individual. Individuals with chronic pain may be able to ambulate independently in their primary residence. However, because of an increase in pain when standing or walking or a reduction in stamina due to pain and fatigue, the individual may require a power scooter, such as a Hoveround, or a manual wheelchair, for outings. The current mobility needs of the individual, as well as what the need may be in future, must be considered. Life care planners understand the relationship between age and disability and will make recommendations for mobility devices based on this understanding. It is important for the life care planner to discuss mobility and the need for mobility equipment with the client's treating practitioners. While the physician may recognize the need for a mobility device, the physical therapist may be able to provide the life care planner with details about the type of equipment needed and the accessories that may be required for the individual.

Following a determination of the mobility need, the life care planner establishes the appropriate schedule for routine maintenance of the equipment. Typically, an annual maintenance allowance is allocated in the LCP for power, manual, or shower wheelchairs. The maintenance allowance is allocated based on the expected life of the device to provide for repair costs, replacement of tires and batteries, or general service to the equipment.

In addition to maintenance, accessories to the mobility device are usually considered. If a manual wheelchair is recommended, portable ramps may be needed for someone who uses the mobility device for outings, as many personal residences are not equipped with ramps. A component of the wheelchair that may be important to the client with chronic pain is the seating system. If recommended, replacement and revision costs for the seating system must be considered as well as the annual maintenance cost. The identification of each individual's need for mobility devices is an important area of consideration for the life care planner and should be done following an observation of the individual's residence, and vehicle, and a discussion of his daily activities.

manual wheelchair
(cost: $1,500–$4,500)
manual wheelchair maintenance
(cost: $100–$250 per year)
power wheelchair
(cost: $8,000–$24,000)
power wheelchair maintenance
(cost: $800–$1,200 per year)
power wheelchair batteries
(cost: $250–$350 per year)
power scooter
(cost: $3,500–6,000)
power scooter maintenance
(cost: $100–$200 per year)
power scooter lift for car
(cost: $700–$900)
shower wheelchair and maintenance
(cost: $950–$1,700/$50–$75)
seating system
(cost: $3,500–$7,500)
portable ramps
(cost: $450–$600)
wheelchair tray
(cost: $85–$150)
push cuff gloves
(cost: $35–$50)

E. Aids for independent function

As the life care planner conducts the home visit and interview with the client and caregivers, the need for independence-enhancing aids will become evident. If the individual reports that pain often causes him to require additional time to put on his shoes, the life care planner will consider items such as a long-handled shoehorn to increase the client's independence. Similarly, if dressing and undressing are difficult for the individual due to limited range of motion or pain, an adaptive clothing allowance may be recommended to increase the individual's ease in dressing.

The client's physician may not recommend items in this area, as the physician rarely has the opportunity to see the client function in her home. Observation and discussion between the life care planner and client may lead the life care planner to recommend small adaptive aids that may greatly enhance the patient's independence. Also, the occupational therapist is a very good source for probable items in this area. The life care planner should include items that increase the chronic pain client's sense of independence, reduce depression, reduce social isolation, and reduce deterioration of function.

computer and workstation
(cost: $1,000)
handheld reacher
(cost: $16–$40)
ice packor heat pack
(cost: $10–$20)
grab bar
(cost: $30–$80)
handicap parking emblem
(cost: $1.00)
padded raised toilet seat
(cost: $110)
tub bench
(cost: $230)
adaptive clothing
(cost: $565 allowance per year)

F. Durable medical equipment

To begin the process of determining what durable medical items to include in this area, the life care planner surveys what the client already owns or is currently using. While conducting a home visit, the life care planner may observe that the client ambulates in the home with a walker.

Tip

It is important that the life care planner note the condition of the current equipment in order to determine when the equipment will need to be replaced. For example, the client may have been issued a bath chair that cannot be used because it does not fit into the client's bathroom. Such observations are critical to the life care planner in formulating recommendations.

The need for durable medical equipment by a client with chronic pain is typically a result of the client's loss of function. The client may comment that on good days he can ambulate independently. However, on bad days, he requires the assistance of a cane or walker. The durable medical equipment needs will vary from client to client. Variation may occur due to age, living conditions, severity and frequency of pain, or lifestyle. While a TENS unit may be recommended with one client with chronic pain as a result of a back injury, it may not be recommended for another. However, the life care planner should be able to explain the variation between plans based on use of a consistent process of developing each LCP.

power medical bed and rails, and maintenance
(cost: $1,500–$2,100/$66.25)
walker
(cost: $95)
cane
(cost: $36)
mattress
(cost: $1,500–$4,500)
fracture frame
cost: $400–$500)
Hoyer lift
(cost: $1,237–$1,300)
Hoyer lift maintenance
(cost: $95–$125)
Hoyer lift slings
(cost: $85–$112)
over-bed table
(cost: $85–$120)
TENS unit
(cost: $375–$400 + supplies)
transfer board
(cost: $85–$150)

G. Prosthetics and orthotics

A prosthesis is an artificial device used to replace a missing body part or function, such as a limb. An orthotic device or orthosis (commonly known as a brace or splint) is an orthopedic device that is applied externally to the limb or body. The purpose can be to provide support, protection, or replacement of lost function.

Orthotics and prosthetics are applied physical disciplines that address neuromuscular and structural skeletal problems in the human body with a treatment process that includes evaluation and transfer of forces using orthoses and prostheses to achieve optimum function and prevent further disability. The orthotist and prosthetist work directly with the physician and other allied health professionals in the field of rehabilitation. Please note that specific ranges of costs are not provided for this area. The cost can vary significantly based on the specific prescription provided by the physician. In addition, replacement intervals are dependent on the use of the device and the age of the client.

hand or wrist splint
(cost: variable)
TMJ (temporomandibular joint) brace
(cost: variable)
AFO (ankle foot orthosis)
(cost: variable)
KAFO (knee ankle foot orthosis)
(cost: variable)
HKAFO (hip knee ankle foot orthosis)
(cost: variable)
RGO (reciprocating gait orthosis)
(cost: variable)
SAO (smart ambulation orthosis)
(cost: variable)

H. Supplies

As described in the durable medical equipment section, it is important that the life care planner survey the supplies that the client presently uses. The life care planner must also differentiate common supplies, such as lotion that is used by many individuals, and lotion that is used by the chronic pain patient for massage of the affected area.

As a result of physiological damage, for example, a client may experience periodic incontinence and may require adult briefs throughout his life expectancy. (See Chapter 13, "Ostomy and Incontinence," for more information.) In addition, compression garments may be recommended for a patient with chronic pain who is inactive. The supply section of the LCP is typically a small portion of the overall cost of the plan; however, these items may be critical in increasing the client's self-esteem and general comfort level.

abdominal binder
(cost: $35–$60)
catheter and related products
(cost: varies depending on specific product)
Jobst stockings
(cost: $30–$40)
lotion
(cost: $3–$5)
position pillows
(cost: $15–$20)

I. Medications

Medication is an important part of the management of chronic pain, yet it also is a difficult area to address. Information about drug dependence in the chronic pain population has been extensively published. Detection of dependence is not the role of the life care planner. Rather, it is the role of the life care planner to obtain medication records and discuss with the healthcare practitioners what the future pharmacological management of the client will be. Several groups of medications, including pain medication, sleeping medication, depression-related medication, and muscle relaxants may be used to treat the individual with chronic pain. It is important that the life care planner inquire of the physician how often the client is monitored in the office, what the plan for future treatment may involve, and what will occur in the future if the medication is no longer effective.

Please note prices for generic medications are not provided for the following medications.

pain medication
Oxycontin 40 mg #30* (cost: $300)
Darvocet 100/650 mg #30 (cost: $25)
Tylenol #3 300/30 mg (Codeine) #30 (cost: $10)
anticonvulsants (used for pain management)
Neurontin 300 mg #90 (cost: $50–$100)
Tegretol 100 mg #60 (cost: $20)
steroids
Prednisone 10 mg #30 (cost: $8)
antidepressants
Prozac 40 mg #30 (cost: $160)
Zoloft 50 mg #30 (cost: $67)
Paxil 30 mg #30 (cost: $75)
Elavil 25 mg #30 (cost: $18)
muscle relaxants
Soma 350 mg #30 (cost: $91)
Flexeril 10 mg #30 (cost: $35)
Skelaxin 400 mg #30 (cost: $26)
Valium 5 mg #30 (cost: $26)
(* "#30" refers to 30 pills or tablets.)

J. Home care and facility care

The individual's functional limitations and ability to remain safe when unattended primarily determine the need for attendant care for the client with chronic pain. Again, if the life care planner is evaluating an older individual, it is important that the life care planner differentiate between needs arising from advanced age and the needs arising from the chronic pain condition. It is important to discuss the need for attendant care with the healthcare team.

The level of attendant care (e.g.., certified nursing assistant or licensed practical nurse) recommended is an important area of inquiry for the life care planner. Based on the individual's level of functional impairment, cognitive status, medication regimen, and needs for assistance, either the nurse practice act or home health care act of each state will typically describe the qualifications required by the caregiver if the caregiver is an employee of a home healthcare agency.

It is preferable to obtain the costs for attendant care from three local vendors. This provides a cross section of cost information for attendant care. The life care planner should be familiar with the cost associated with private hire if private hire is an option.[14]

With a privately hired caregiver, there are other costs to consider. Since the attendant is not employed through an agency, other costs include business paperwork such as an accountant, taxes, unemployment insurance, advertising and interviewing, background checks, liability insurance, and health insurance. Additional case management hours would be necessary to screen and supervise this individual if an agency is not involved. In addition there need to be arrangements made for vacation time and sick days for the hired attendant. Considering these costs, the private hire attendant's cost per hour may approximate the agency rate per hour.

Tip

Typically, chronic pain alone does not lead an individual to be placed in a long-term care facility. This may be the case if the client has multiple healthcare needs other than the chronic pain. The goal of pain management will be to increase or maintain the person's level of independence in the community.

The proper foundation, in litigation for these items can be established by the life care planner soliciting the opinions of the treatment team and providing recommendations based on the life care planner's education, training, and experience.

personal care attendant
  (cost: $10–$14/hr—agency hire)
certified nurse's aide/home health aide
  (cost: $14–$18/hr—agency hire)
licensed practical nurse
  (cost: $20–$27/hr—agency hire)
registered nurse
  (cost: $35–$45/hr—agency hire)
private hire attendant
  (cost: varies)

Please note that the above cost reflects an agency rate and that cost varies widely based on region of the country, with costs typically higher on either coast.

Tip

The attendant care portion of the LCP can be the area of the highest cost in the LCP and should be well researched by the life care planner.

K. Medical care—Routine

The recommendations made in the "medical care—routine" area are most often provided by the chronic pain client's treating physicians. When developing the LCP, the life care planner will solicit recommendations from members of the client's healthcare team. The life care planner will ask the healthcare team members about the need for future medical appointments, routine medical diagnostic testing, and the probability of future hospitalizations or surgical interventions. The primary physician treating the pain is a good resource for determining the need for referral to specialists. In addition, the physician will recommend specific medical diagnostic tests such as MRI, x-rays, and so forth.

Often, the individual with chronic pain has received treatment from a general practitioner or other healthcare treatment team member who is unfamiliar with chronic pain. In this event, the life care planner may discuss with the referring party the limitations of the general practitioner in treating pain. Ideally, a pain management specialist will be involved with the individual diagnosed with chronic pain and will be the primary source of recommendations for future care for the client. It is noted that a general practitioner or other specialist familiar with pain may be well qualified through many years of experience treating pain.

pain management physician office visit
  (cost: $65–$155 per visit)
surgeon office visit
  (cost: $90–$155 per visit)
neurologist office visit
  (cost: $90–$155 per visit)
physiatrist (PM&R)
  (cost: $90–$155 per visit)
orthopaedist office visit
  (cost: $95–$155 per visit)
general practitioner office visit
  (cost: $50–$80 per visit)
podiatrist office visit
  (cost: $40-$70 per visit)
urologist office visit
  (cost: $60–$100 per visit)
x-rays
  (cost: $75–$100 each)
MRI (including radiologist fees)
  (cost: $2,000–$2,500)
allowance for travel expenses
  $0.34–$0.40 mile
allowance for lab and tests (e.g., CBC, chemistry panel)
  (cost $150 per event)

L. Acute medical intervention—Surgical

In addition to routine healthcare assessment and maintenance, the treating physician may also recommend future acute medical interventions or surgical procedures. Such procedures may include the implantation or revision of an intrathecal morphine pump to provide a steady amount of medication internally. However, if this recommendation is made, the life care planner must consider the life expectancy of the pump as well as physician and facility fees for implantation and revision of the pump. It is best to discuss with the physician who will perform the surgery to learn where she will perform the surgery. The life care planner can follow up with that facility to obtain fees. Obtaining fees for such a procedure from only the physician's office will not represent the totality of the cost that will be involved in the procedure.

Intrathecal pain therapy:

cost for morphine pump
(cost: $5,300–$9,400)
pump implantation (facility and physician fee)
(cost: $4,500–$9,000)
medication refill for pump
(cost: $1,600)
spinal column stimulator—implantation
(cost: $30,000–$45,000)
Botox
(cost: $400 per vial of 100 units)
Botox injections (includes physician fee)
(cost: $900–$1,500 per session)
epidural steroid injection
(cost: $1,100–$1,500 per injection)

M. Health and strength maintenance

Remaining active is an important goal for the patient with chronic pain. Providing the client with the means for an activity in the convenience of his home is ideal. It provides the opportunity to incorporate daily activity sessions on a frequent basis despite transportation, weather, or other barriers. Typically, in-home exercise equipment is available at a reasonable cost and can be maintained with relative ease. In some cases, a physician may recommend hydrotherapy. Such services are provided at many YMCA facilities or rehabilitation centers and involve very little monthly cost.

exercise equipment allowance
(cost: $500–$2,500 allowance)
gym membership
(cost: $20–$40/month)

N. Transportation

In some cases, an individual with chronic pain may require a wheelchair or scooter for mobility. As a result the client may need a van that can accommodate the wheelchair for transportation.

If the client has the ability to drive, the van may need to be modified to allow the person to drive while remaining in the wheelchair. Such modifications may include hand controls, a lift, and a lowered floor or raised roof and tie downs.

Both minivans and full-sizes vans can be modified. The additional cost for a van is typically included in the LCP. The additional cost of the non-modified van can be determined by taking the difference in the cost of a regular car and a van. Therefore, the additional cost of the van would be included, since the van is necessitated by the individual's medical condition. The life care planner will also include any special modifications, such as a wheelchair lift.

When discussing with the vendor the inclusion of certain equipment, the life care planner should inquire about the warranties regarding the modifications. The life care planner must plan for maintenance as a result of wear and tear for the years that the warranty does not cover the equipment prior to replacement of the vehicle, typically at eight years.

vehicle (additional cost for van)
(cost: $5,000–$10,000)
vehicle (allowance for modification)
(cost: $5,000–$8,000)
vehicle modifications and maintenance
(cost: $1,000–$1,500 per year)

O. Architectural renovations

When home renovations are needed for an individual with chronic pain, the goals of the modifications are safety, convenience, and prevention of accidents such as falls. When the life care planner conducts a home visit, he will note the layout of the house and have the individual or family member provide a tour of the property. Often, the individual with chronic pain remains in only one room or one area of the home due to stairs, inclines, or other barriers that the individual cannot safely navigate. A close review of the bathroom is important, especially around the shower or bathtub. A person who reports numbness or loss of sensation can be at risk for slipping or falling in an area with wet or slippery floors. Therefore, the addition of nonslip mats or grab bars may be simple, inexpensive recommendations that save the individual from further health problems resulting from falling. When establishing the cost of an item such as grab bars, it is important for the life care planner to include both the cost of the item and the cost for installation. In addition, replacement of the item must be considered if the individual uses the item on a daily basis.

ramps
(cost: $275 to $550)
grab bars
(cost: $75 to $125)
grab bars installation
(cost: $150)
widen doorways
(cost: $250 to $750)

P. Vocational and educational plan

Individuals with chronic pain may have the ability to continue in gainful employment. The life care planner will determine if there are vocational services that will be of benefit to the client. Typically, the life care planner will consult with a master's level vocational rehabilitation counsellor and ask for a professional opinion regarding the educational or training needs related to the client's vocational goals.

vocational assessment
(cost: $1,250–$2,500 per evaluation)
job coaching
(cost: $25–$75 per hour)
career counselling
(cost: $75–$125 per hour)
vocational or technical program
(cost varies)

Q. Potential complications

Proper foundation, in litigation, for potential complications can be established by the life care planner or the treating or examining physician. The cost for the potential complication is not included in the bottom line cost of the future care services since the complication is potential and not probable. Examples of potential complications for individuals with chronic pain include:

- hospitalization for depression
- hospitalization for suicide risk
- dependence on drugs or alcohol
- hospitalization for orthopaedic injury resulting from falls

The example of a LCP shown in Appendix 16.1 is offered for review to demonstrate the LCP recommendations for a client with multiple failed back surgeries. Mr. Doe is forty-four years of age and has had three back surgeries. Mr. Doe is diagnosed with chronic pain, depression, and failed back syndrome.

16.4 Conclusion

In conclusion, astute attorneys will be aware there are accepted procedures for the completion of a life care plan. The attorneys will be able to examine critically the process used by the life care planner and recognize both the strengths and weaknesses of the plan. The plaintiff's attorney should obtain a second opinion regarding the life care plan completed by the retained expert before tendering the plan to defense counsel. This independent review can be accomplished by a non-disclosed life care plan consultant to the attorney, and the results of the review would not be discoverable by opposing counsel.

Life care plans for individuals with chronic pain may vary significantly from patient to patient because of the unique nature of chronic pain. Attorneys should carefully explore the medical foundation for extensive and often expensive treatment recommendations, such as an implantable morphine pump.

Life care plans can be of significant help to define the cost of future care for the patient. However, the retained life care planner should be cautious to follow a consistent process. The attorneys involved must be prepared to critically examine the plan for reliability, consistency, and overstating or understating of recommendations. Perhaps most importantly, the attorneys must be able to determine the extent to which the life care planner has followed an ethical and professional process to complete the plan of care.

Endnotes

1. Deutsch, P.M., and Raffa, F., *Damages in Tort Action*, Vol. 8. New York: Matthew Bender, 1981.

2. Deutsch, P., and Sawyer, H., *A Guide to Rehabilitation*. Purchase, NY: Ahab Press, 1985.

3. McCollom, P,. and Weed, R., "Life Care Planning: Yesterday and Today." *Journal of Life Care Planning,* 1(1), 7, 2002.

4. Neulicht, A., Riddick-Grisham, S., Hinton, L., Costantini, P., Thomas, R., and Goodrich, B., "Life Care Planning Survey 2001: Process, Methods and Protocol." *Journal of Life Care Planning,* 1(2), 97–148, 2002.

5. Thomas, R., "Determining the Value of Your Certification." *Inside Case Management,* Vol. 9. No. 4. Gaithersburg, MD: Aspen, 2002.

6. Weed, R., and Berens, D., editors, *Life Care Planning Summit 2000 Proceedings*, Athens, GA: Elliott & Fitzpatrick.

7. Weed, R., editord, *Life Care Planning and Case Management Handbook.* Winter Park, FL: CRC Press, 1999.

8. Thomas, R., *Life Care Planning: A Standard Process*. The American Association of Legal Nurse Consultants, Annual Conference, Reno NV, 1999, 123–138.

9. National Commission for Certifying Agencies (NCCA), (http://www.noca.org).

10. *Daubert v. Merrell*, 509 U.S. 579, 1135 S.Ct. 2786, 125 L.E.2d 469)1993).

11. *Kumho Tire Co., Ltd., v. Carmichael*, 526 U.S. 137, 199 S.Ct. 1176, 143 l.E.2d 238 (1999).

12. Joint Commission focuses on Pain Management, see http://www.jcaho.org/news+room/health+care+issues/jcaho+focuses+on+pain+management.htm.

13. Background on the development of the Joint Commission standards on pain management, see http://www.jcaho.org/news+room/health+care+issues/index.htm.

14. Thomas, R. and Kitchen, J., "Life Care Planning: A Comparison of Private Hire and Agency Cost." *The Rehabilitation Professional/NARPPS Journal*, 12 (2), 47–52, 1997.

Appendix

Example of Life Care Plan for an Individual with Chronic Pain

National Center for Life Care Planning
PO Box 2446
Madison, MS 39130
(601) 956-3868 • Fax: (601) 952-0072

Life Care Plan

a client

Projected Evaluations

DOB: Jan 1, 1956
D/E:
Date Prepared: Oct 22, 2002
Primary Disability: Chronic Pain and failed back

Item / Service	Age Year	Frequency/ Replacement	Purpose	Cost	Comment	Vendor
Physical Therapist Evaluation	Beginning 47 2003 Ending * 74 2030	1 per year	Determine physical therapy status & needs, i.e., contractures, range of motion, atrophy	Per Unit $125.00 Per Year $125.00	Recommended by Treating Pain Doctor and Physical Therapist	1

Please note this life care plan is abridged due to space limitations. Example items are provided for the various areas of the life care plan.

Item / Service	Age Year	Frequency/ Replacement	Purpose	Cost	Comment	Vendor
Occupational Therapist Evaluation	Beginning 47 2003 Ending * 74 2030	1 per year	Determine functional status & needs,	Per Unit $125.00 Per Year $125.00	Recommended by Treating Physiatrist	2
Psychological Assessment	Beginning 47 2003 Ending * 74 2030	Yearly - 3 hour evaluation to Life Expectancy (LE)	assess the patient's needs and the route therapy should take	Per Unit $100.00 to $150.00 Per Year $300.00 to $450.00	Recommended by Psychologist	3
Recreational Therapist Evaluation	Beginning 47 2003 Ending * 74 2030	1 per year to Life Expectancy (LE)	Determine Recreational therapy needs, i.e., avocational interests to enhance quality of life	Per Unit $150.00 Per Year $150.00	Recommended by Treating Physiatrist	4

 * Dates are inclusive, i.e., 1997-1999 equals 3 years.

National Center for Life Care Planning
PO Box 2446
Madison, MS 39130
(601) 956-3868 • Fax: (601) 952-0072

Life Care Plan

a client

Projected Therapeutic Modalities

DOB: Jan 1, 1956
D/E:
Date Prepared: Oct 22, 2002
Primary Disability: Chronic Pain and failed back

Item / Service	Age Year	Frequency/ Replacement	Purpose	Cost	Comment	Vendor
Counseling - Client Including adjustment, sexual, and family issues	Beginning 47 2003 Ending * 51 2007	12 interventions per year for the next 5 years	Enhance psychological and behavioral statusof client	Per Unit $100.00 Per Year $1,200.00	Recommended by Treating Pain Doctor and Psychologist	5
Counseling for Family	Beginning 47 2003 Ending * 51 2007	6 sessions per year for 5 years	Enhance psychological functioning of the family.	Per Unit $100.00 Per Year $600.00	Recommended by Psychologist	6
Occupational Therapy	Beginning 47 2003 Ending * 74 2030	3 seesions per year to LE	Maximize function in ADLs secondary to chronic pain	Per Unit $90.00 to $120.00 Per Year $270.00 to $360.00	Recommended by Treating Physiatrist	7
Physical Therapy	Beginning 47 2003 Ending * 51 2007	4 sessions per year to life expectancy	Maximize function in ADLs	Per Unit $90.00 to $120.00 Per Year $360.00 to $480.00	Recommended by Treating Physiatrist and physical therapist	8
Message Therapy	Beginning 47 2003 Ending * 47 2003	One session per week for 1 year	Assist in pain control	Per Unit $65.00 to $85.00 Per Year $3,380.00	Recommended by Treating Pain Doctor	9

lcp3 (8) ©1994-1998. * Dates are inclusive, i.e., 1997-1999 equals 3 years.

National Center for Life Care Planning
PO Box 2446
Madison, MS 39130
(601) 956-3868 • Fax: (601) 952-0072

Life Care Plan

a client

Diagnostic/Educational Testing

DOB: Jan 1, 1956
D/E:
Date Prepared: Oct 22, 2002
Primary Disability: Chronic Pain and failed back

Item / Service	Age Year	Frequency/ Replacement	Purpose	Cost	Comment	Vendor
No Items Identified	Beginning			Per Unit		
	Ending			Per Year		10

lcp3 (8) ©1994-1998. * Dates are inclusive, i.e., 1997-1999 equals 3 years.

page 3

National Center for Life Care Planning
PO Box 2446
Madison, MS 39130
(601) 956-3868 • Fax: (601) 952-0072

Life Care Plan

a client

Orthotics/Prosthetics

DOB: Jan 1, 1956
D/E:
Date Prepared: Oct 22, 2002
Primary Disability: Chronic Pain and failed back

Item / Service	Age Year	Frequency/ Replacement	Purpose	Cost	Comment	Vendor
No Items Identified	Beginning Ending			Per Unit Per Year		11

lcp3 (8) *** Dates are inclusive, i.e., 1997-1999 equals 3 years.**

National Center for Life Care Planning
PO Box 2446
Madison, MS 39130
(601) 956-3868 • Fax: (601) 952-0072

Life Care Plan

a client

Orthopedic Equipment

DOB: Jan 1, 1956
D/E:
Date Prepared: Oct 22, 2002
Primary Disability: Chronic Pain and failed back

Item / Service	Age Year	Frequency/ Replacement	Purpose	Cost	Comment	Vendor
No Items Identified	Beginning			Per Unit		
	Ending			Per Year		12
No Items Identified	Beginning			Per Unit		
	Ending			Per Year		13

 * Dates are inclusive, i.e., 1997-1999 equals 3 years.

National Center for Life Care Planning
PO Box 2446
Madison, MS 39130
(601) 956-3868 • Fax: (601) 952-0072

Life Care Plan

a client

Aids for Independent Function

DOB: Jan 1, 1956
D/E:
Date Prepared: Oct 22, 2002
Primary Disability: Chronic Pain and failed back

Item / Service	Age Year	Frequency/ Replacement	Purpose	Cost	Comment	Vendor
Handicap Parking Sticker	Beginning 47 2003	1 per year or as needed	Increase independence in mobility	Per Unit		
	Ending * 74 2030			Per Year		14
Grab Bars in bathroom (includes installation)	Beginning 47 2003	1 per 5 years	Safety	Per Unit $100.00 to $150.00	Recommended by Occupational Therapist	
	Ending * 74 2030			Per Year $20.00 to $30.00		15

 * Dates are inclusive, i.e., 1997-1999 equals 3 years.

National Center for Life Care Planning
PO Box 2446
Madison, MS 39130
(601) 956-3868 • Fax: (601) 952-0072

Life Care Plan

a client

Medication(s)

DOB: Jan 1, 1956
D/E:
Date Prepared: Oct 22, 2002
Primary Disability: Chronic Pain and failed back

Item / Service	Age Year	Frequency/ Replacement	Purpose	Cost	Comment	Vendor
Neurontin 300 mg or similiar	Beginning 47 2003 Ending * 74 2030	3 tabs per day or 90 tablets per month	For pain and spasms	Per Unit $75.00 Per Year $900.00	Recommended by Treating Pain Doctor	16
Medication, Routine - (Darvocet N-100) or similiar	Beginning 47 2003 Ending * 74 2030	4 per day or 120 per month	For pain	Per Unit $100.00 to $1,200.00 Per Year	120 tablets cost 100 dollars	17

lcp3 (8) ©1994-1998. *** Dates are inclusive, i.e., 1997-1999 equals 3 years.**

National Center for Life Care Planning
PO Box 2446
Madison, MS 39130
(601) 956-3868 • Fax: (601) 952-0072

Life Care Plan

a client

Home Care

DOB: Jan 1, 1956
D/E:
Date Prepared: Oct 22, 2002
Primary Disability: Chronic Pain and failed back

Item / Service	Age Year	Frequency/ Replacement	Purpose	Cost	Comment	Vendor
Personal Care Attendant (PCA)	Beginning 47 2003 Ending * 74 2030	3 hours per day	Maintain safety and well-being of client and assist with daily care	Per Unit $11.00 to $12.00 Per Year $12,045.00 to $13,140.00	Recommended by Treating Physiatrist	18

Unit Cost X 3 hours per day = $33.00 X 365 days per year = $12045.00

Unit Cost X 3 hours per day = $36.00 X 365 days per year = $13140.00

Item / Service	Age Year	Frequency/ Replacement	Purpose	Cost	Comment	Vendor
Support Care, Handyman Service	Beginning 47 2003 Ending * 74 2030	2 hours per month		Per Unit $50.00 Per Year $600.00	25.00 per hour 50.00 per month	19

lcp3 (8) ©1994-1998. *** Dates are inclusive, i.e., 1997-1999 equals 3 years.**

National Center for Life Care Planning
PO Box 2446
Madison, MS 39130
(601) 956-3868 • Fax: (601) 952-0072

Life Care Plan

a client

Future Medical Care Routine

DOB: Jan 1, 1956
D/E:
Date Prepared: Oct 22, 2002
Primary Disability: Chronic Pain and failed back

Item / Service	Age Year	Frequency/ Replacement	Purpose	Cost	Comment	Vendor
Physician - Psychiatrist	Beginning 47 2003	1 per year	routine Assessment	Per Unit $75.00 to $125.00	Recommended by Treating Physiatrist	
	Ending * 74 2030			Per Year $75.00 to $125.00		20
Case Manager	Beginning 47 2003	2 hours per month $80.00 per hour or $160.00 per month	Coordinate services.	Per Unit $160.00	Recommended by Treating Physiatrist	
	Ending * 74 2030			Per Year $1,920.00		21
Diagnostic Studies - X-Rays(MRI, CAT scan)	Beginning 47 2003	yearly Allowance	Management of chronic pain	Per Unit $1,000.00	Recommended by Treating Pain Doctor	
	Ending * 74 2030			Per Year $1,000.00		22
Internal Medicine-	Beginning 47 2003	1 per year		Per Unit $75.00 to $100.00	Recommended by Treating Physiatrist	
	Ending * 74 2030			Per Year $75.00 to $100.00		23
Neurologist	Beginning 47 2003	PRN		Per Unit	Recommended by Treating Physiatrist	
	Ending * 74 2030			Per Year		24

lcp3 (8) ©1994-1998. *** Dates are inclusive, i.e., 1997-1999 equals 3 years.**

page 9

National Center for Life Care Planning
PO Box 2446
Madison, MS 39130
(601) 956-3868 • Fax: (601) 952-0072

Life Care Plan

a client

Future Medical Care Routine

DOB: Jan 1, 1956
D/E:
Date Prepared: Oct 22, 2002
Primary Disability: Chronic Pain and failed back

Item / Service	Age Year	Frequency/ Replacement	Purpose	Cost	Comment	Vendor
Orthopedic Surgeon	Beginning 47 2003 Ending * 74 2030	To Be Determined by treating physician on PRN basis		Per Unit Per Year	Recommended by Treating Physiatrist	25
Physiatrist	Beginning 47 2003 Ending * 74 2030	2 visits per year		Per Unit $100.00 to $150.00 Per Year $200.00 to $300.00	Recommended by Treating Physiatrist	26
Travel Expenses	Beginning 47 2003 Ending * 74 2030	100 miles per month for medical expenses	Travel for health care	Per Unit $0.45 Per Year $540.00		27

50 milesUnit Cost X 100 miles per month = $45.00 X 12 months per year = $540.00

 *** Dates are inclusive, i.e., 1997-1999 equals 3 years.**

National Center for Life Care Planning
PO Box 2446
Madison, MS 39130
(601) 956-3868 • Fax: (601) 952-0072

Life Care Plan

a client

Acute Medical Intervention

DOB: Jan 1, 1956
D/E:
Date Prepared: Oct 22, 2002
Primary Disability: Chronic Pain and failed back

Item / Service	Age Year	Frequency/ Replacement	Purpose	Cost	Comment	Vendor
Chronic Pain Management Program	Beginning 47 2003	one Inpatient stay per lifetime	Pain Managment	Per Unit $20,000.00 to $30,000.00	Recommended by Treating Pain Doctor	
	Ending * 47 2003			Per Year $20,000.00 to $30,000.00		29

lcp3 (8) ©1994-1998. *** Dates are inclusive, i.e., 1997-1999 equals 3 years.**

National Center for Life Care Planning
PO Box 2446
Madison, MS 39130
(601) 956-3868 • Fax: (601) 952-0072

Life Care Plan

a client

Surgical Intervention

DOB: Jan 1, 1956
D/E:
Date Prepared: Oct 22, 2002
Primary Disability: Chronic Pain and failed back

Item / Service	Age Year	Frequency/ Replacement	Purpose	Cost	Comment	Vendor
Intrathecal Morphine Pump _ - Hospital fees and Cost of Pump	Beginning 47 2003 Ending * 47 2003	One time Only	Pain Management	Per Unit $20,000.00 to $25,000.00 Per Year $20,000.00 to $25,000.00	put in wo trial 20-25 hosp and pump md 3500 trial. . .1500 range	30
Intrathecal Morphine Pump _ Refill each 2 months	Beginning 47 2003 Ending * 74 2030	6 times per year to LE	Pain Management	Per Unit $600.00 to $900.00 Per Year $3,600.00 to $5,400.00		31
Intrathecal Morphine Pump _-Surgeon Fees	Beginning 47 2003 Ending * 47 2003	One time Only	Pain Management	Per Unit $3,500.00 Per Year $3,500.00	put in wo trial 20-25 hosp and pump md 3500 trial. . .1500 range	32
Intrathecal Morphine Pump - Trial Test	Beginning 47 2003 Ending * 47 2003	One time Only	Pain Management	Per Unit $1,500.00 Per Year $1,500.00	put in wo trial 20-25 hosp and pump md 3500 trial. . .1500 range	33
Chronic Pain Services *Refill Implanted Pump Each 28 days*	Beginning 48 2004 Ending * 74 2030	To Be Determined by treating physician on PRN basis		Per Unit Per Year		34

 *** Dates are inclusive, i.e., 1997-1999 equals 3 years.**

National Center for Life Care Planning
PO Box 2446
Madison, MS 39130
(601) 956-3868 • Fax: (601) 952-0072

Life Care Plan

a client

Vocational/ Educational Plan

DOB: Jan 1, 1956
D/E:
Date Prepared: Oct 22, 2002
Primary Disability: Chronic Pain and failed back

Item / Service	Age Year	Frequency/ Replacement	Purpose	Cost	Comment	Vendor
Vocational Counseling	Beginning 47 2003	24 sessions for one year	Enhance ability to remain employed	Per Unit $90.00	Recommended by Treating Physiatrist	
	Ending * 47 2003			Per Year $2,160.00		35
Vocational Rehabilitation Evaluation	Beginning 47 2003	One time only	Assist with vocational adjustment and/or avocational interests; to evaluate vocational	Per Unit		
	Ending * 74 2030			Per Year		36

 * Dates are inclusive, i.e., 1997-1999 equals 3 years.

National Center for Life Care Planning
PO Box 2446
Madison, MS 39130
(601) 956-3868 • Fax: (601) 952-0072

Life Care Plan

John Doe

Vocational/ Educational Plan

DOB: Jan 1, 1955
D/E:
Date Prepared: Oct 22, 2002
Primary Disability: Chronic Pain, Failed back syndrome

Item / Service	Age Year	Frequency/ Replacement	Purpose	Cost	Comment	Vendor
Vocational Counseling	Beginning 48 2003	24 sessions for one year	Enhance ability to remain employed	Per Unit $90.00	Recommended by Rehab Counselor	
	Ending * 48 2003			Per Year $2,160.00		32
Vocational Rehabilitation Evaluation	Beginning 48 2003	One time only	Assist with vocational adjustment and/or avocational interests; to evaluate vocational	Per Unit $850.00 to $1,500.00	Recommended by Rehab Counselor	
	Ending * 48 2003			Per Year $850.00 to $1,500.00		33

lcp3 (8) ©1994-1998 * Dates are inclusive, i.e., 1997-1999 equals 3 years.

National Center for Life Care Planning
PO Box 2446
Madison, MS 39130
(601) 956-3868 • Fax: (601) 952-0072

Life Care Plan

John Doe

Summary Cost

DOB: Jan 1, 1955
D/E:
Date Prepared: Oct 22, 2002
Primary Disability: Chronic Pain, Failed back syndrome

	Item/Service	Beginning Date	Ending Date	Cost Per Year Avg.**	Number of Years	Total***
Projected Evaluations						
1	Physical Therapist Evaluation	2003	2030	$127.50	*28	$3,570.00
2	Occupational Therapist Evaluation	2003	2030	$127.50	*28	$3,570.00
3	Psychological Assessment	2003	2030	$375.00	*28	$10,500.00
4	Recreational Therapist Evaluation	2003	2030	$150.00	*28	$4,200.00
5	Pain Management Program Evaluation	2003	2003	$1,100.00	*1	$1,100.00
					Sub Total	$22,940.00
Projected Therapeutic Modalities						
6	Counseling - Client Including adjustment, sexual, and family issues	2003	2007	$1,200.00	*5	$6,000.00
7	Counseling for Family	2003	2007	$600.00	*5	$3,000.00
8	Occupational Therapy	2003	2030	$315.00	*28	$8,820.00
9	Physical Therapy	2003	2007	$420.00	*5	$2,100.00
10	Message Therapy	2003	2003	$3,380.00	*1	$3,380.00
					Sub Total	$23,300.00
Wheelchair(s) / Mobility / Maintenance						
11	Manual Wheelchair	2003	2003	$2,400.00	*1	$2,400.00

lcp7, lcp11 (11) ©1994-1998 * Dates are inclusive, i.e., 1997-1999 equals 3 years. ** Cost per year is annualized if item is periodic replacement

Page 1

National Center for Life Care Planning
PO Box 2446
Madison, MS 39130
(601) 956-3868 • Fax: (601) 952-0072

Life Care Plan

John Doe

Summary Cost

DOB: Jan 1, 1955
D/E:
Date Prepared: Oct 22, 2002
Primary Disability: Chronic Pain, Failed back syndrome

	Item/Service	Beginning Date	Ending Date	Cost Per Year Avg.**	Number of Years	Total***
12	Manual Wheelchair Maintaince	2003	2030	$175.00	*28	$4,900.00
					Sub Total	$7,300.00
Orthotics/Prosthetics						
13	No Items Identified					
					Sub Total	
Durable Medical Items						
14	Electric Powered Medical Bed with height adjustment, inclinable head, foot and side rails	2003	2030	$206.50	*28	$5,782.00
					Sub Total	$5,782.00
Aids for Independent Function						
15	Handicap Parking Sticker	2003	2030		*28	$0.00
16	Grab Bars in bathroom (includes installation)	2003	2030	$25.00	*28	$700.00
					Sub Total	$700.00
Medication(s)						
17	Medication, Routine - Neurontin 300 mg or similiar	2003	2030	$900.00	*28	$25,200.00
18	Medication, Routine - (Darvocet N-100) or similiar	2003	2030	$1,200.00	*28	$33,600.00
19	Chronic Pain Services Refill Implanted Pump Each Month	2004	2030	$14,400.00	*27	$388,800.00

lcp7, lcp11 (11) ©1994-1998 * Dates are inclusive, i.e., 1997-1999 equals 3 years. ** Cost per year is annualized if item is periodic replacement

Page 2

National Center for Life Care Planning
PO Box 2446
Madison, MS 39130
(601) 956-3868 • Fax: (601) 952-0072

Life Care Plan

John Doe

Summary Cost

DOB: Jan 1, 1955
D/E:
Date Prepared: Oct 22, 2002
Primary Disability: Chronic Pain, Failed back syndrome

	Item/Service	Beginning Date	Ending Date	Cost Per Year Avg.**	Number of Years	Total***
					Sub Total	$447,600.00
Home Care						
20	Personal Care Attendant (PCA)	2003	2030	$12,592.50	*28	$352,590.00
					Sub Total	$352,590.00
Future Medical Care Routine						
21	Physiatrist	2003	2030	$250.00	*28	$7,000.00
22	Neurologist	2003	2030		*28	$0.00
23	Orthopedic Surgeon	2003	2030		*28	$0.00
24	Internal Medicine-	2003	2030	$87.50	*28	$2,450.00
25	Case Manager	2003	2030	$1,920.00	*28	$53,760.00
26	Diagnostic Studies - X-Rays(MRI, CAT scan)	2003	2030	$1,000.00	*28	$28,000.00
					Sub Total	$91,210.00
Transportation						
27	Travel Expenses	2003	2030	$540.00	*28	$15,120.00
					Sub Total	$15,120.00
Architectural Renovation(s)						
28	Home Renovations Allowance	2003	2003	$10,000.00	*1	$10,000.00

lcp7, lcp11 (11) ©1994-1998 * Dates are inclusive, i.e., 1997-1999 equals 3 years. ** Cost per year is annualized if item is periodic replacement

Page 3

National Center for Life Care Planning
PO Box 2446
Madison, MS 39130
(601) 956-3868 • Fax: (601) 952-0072

Life Care Plan

John Doe

Summary Cost

DOB: Jan 1, 1955
D/E:
Date Prepared: Oct 22, 2002
Primary Disability: Chronic Pain, Failed back syndrome

	Item/Service	Beginning Date	Ending Date	Cost Per Year Avg.**	Number of Years	Total***
					Sub Total	$447,600.00
	Home Care					
20	Personal Care Attendant (PCA)	2003	2030	$12,592.50	*28	$352,590.00
					Sub Total	$352,590.00
	Future Medical Care Routine					
21	Physiatrist	2003	2030	$250.00	*28	$7,000.00
22	Neurologist	2003	2030		*28	$0.00
23	Orthopedic Surgeon	2003	2030		*28	$0.00
24	Internal Medicine-	2003	2030	$87.50	*28	$2,450.00
25	Case Manager	2003	2030	$1,920.00	*28	$53,760.00
26	Diagnostic Studies - X-Rays(MRI, CAT scan)	2003	2030	$1,000.00	*28	$28,000.00
					Sub Total	$91,210.00
	Transportation					
27	Travel Expenses	2003	2030	$540.00	*28	$15,120.00
					Sub Total	$15,120.00
	Architectural Renovation(s)					
28	Home Renovations Allowance	2003	2003	$10,000.00	*1	$10,000.00

lcp7, lcp11 (11) ©1994-1998 * Dates are inclusive, i.e., 1997-1999 equals 3 years. ** Cost per year is annualized if item is periodic replacement

Page 3

Chapter 17

The Expert Fact Witness

Patricia Iyer, MSN, RN, LNCC

Synopsis

17.1 Introduction

This chapter will address the role of the nursing expert as an expert fact witness who summarizes medical records and explains the symptoms, diagnoses, and treatment rendered to the plaintiff. The expert fact witness can testify about the pain and suffering (or lack thereof) documented in the medical records of an individual injured as a result of personal injury, medical malpractice, products liability, toxic torts, workers' compensation and so on.

Information presented in this chapter is based on the author's experiences as of the time of writing this chapter in preparing over 125 expert fact witness summaries of medical records since 1990. For the purposes of this chapter, the patient and plaintiff terms may be used interchangeably, although it is acknowledged that in reality the plaintiff may be someone other than the injured patient.

17.2 Pain and Suffering Testimony

In addition to the use of a nurse to testify about liability or to prepare a life care plan, a nurse is also useful for preparing a summary of the plaintiff's pain and suffering. Instead of bringing in a parade of treating physicians or other experts, the attorney can retain a nursing expert fact witness who can review and summarize the medical records and present them in their entirety.

The attorney's purpose may be to provide the jury with a clear, concise, understandable account of the events in the medical records in order to persuade the jury to accept the attorney's depiction of the damages.

Physicians tend to concentrate on explanations of specific medical treatments and procedures and minimize pain and suffering. Unlike a nurse, a physician makes brief periodic visits to a patient's bedside. They are rarely at the bedside for an extended amount of time, do not perform all the painful procedures that nurses do, and do not share the same holistic perspective of nurses. A nursing expert fact witness, who is a legal nurse consultant, is more likely to visualize and present a broader, more comprehensive, and more empathetic view of the events described in the medical records. Legal nurse consultants have expertise in both the legal and medical/nursing fields. This dual expertise makes them excellent choices to fulfill this testifying role.

The nursing expert fact witness who is selected to perform this function should have excellent oral and written communication skills, the ability to be analytical and well organized, and the ability to convey complex material in a clear manner.

A. Legal basis

Rule 1006 of the Federal Rules of Evidence permits the use of summaries. The rule provides that when there are voluminous writings, recordings or photographs which cannot be conveniently examined in court, a chart, summary, or calculation may be presented. The originals must be made available for examination or copying by the opposing party, and the judge may order their production in court. In many instances the use of summaries is the only practical means of presenting the contents of voluminous evidence to the judge and jury. There must be a reasonable guarantee that the summary is accurate and that the person who prepared the summary is available to testify at trial as to the method of preparation of the report or to give an explanation of the summary (Fed Rule of Evid. 1006). Further information about the legal basis for this role is found at the end of this chapter.

B. Use of pain and suffering summaries

The pain and suffering report is usually prepared on behalf of the patient and is particularly helpful in malpractice and personal injury cases. They are particularly effective in the situations shown in Figure 17.1. The report provides the attorney with a comprehensive overview of the contents of the medical record, with a specific focus on the problems the patient experienced. The summary is useful for the liability witnesses in the case, who may use it to refresh their recollection about the medical events when preparing for deposition or trial.

Tip

The summary may reduce the need and cost of the liability experts to perform a complete review of all of the medical records.

Pain and suffering reports are effective when:

- There are extensive medical records covering a long admission to the hospital or several admissions over a number of months or years.
- The plaintiff is unable to describe his or her own pain and suffering due to death, disability, lack of communication skill, or memory deficits.
- The plaintiff experienced marked pain, has required extensive narcotic or analgesic medication, or had multiple medical and nursing interventions, surgical procedures, complications, noxious sensations, or emotional suffering.
- The attorney wants the nurse to educate the jury about the plaintiff's unpleasant experiences
- The attorney wants to build maximum impact by having a nurse testify to the patient's pain and suffering rather than putting the patient on the stand and risk having the plaintiff being perceived as whining.

***Figure 17.1** Examples of when pain and suffering testimony is useful*

C. Procedural pain

The expert fact witness evaluates the medical record for evidence of pain and suffering. Unpleasant sensations are associated with the medical treatment provided to alleviate the pain associated with injuries. The medical treatment that becomes necessary to diagnose and treat negligently inflicted injury becomes an additional source of discomfort. There are myriad ways that healthcare providers add to the pain and suffering of patients who are being treated for injuries. This iatrogenic (caused by healthcare providers) pain and suffering has many sources. A few will be described below. For example, insertion and removal of medical devices can cause pain. A research study at State University of New York at Stony Brook[1] identified the following four emergency medical procedures that caused the most pain:

- nasogastric intubation (insertion of a tube into the stomach by way of the nose)

- incision and drainage of an abscess
- reduction (setting) of a fracture
- insertion of a urinary catheter

The sensations associated with removal of tubes were studied in a group of hospitalized patients. Thirty-one had Jackson Pratt drains (small football-shaped drains attached to a long hollow tube with its end in the surgical wound) and thirty-one had chest tubes (tube the size of a man's thumb that is in the chest cavity). Both groups reported similar sensations when the tubes were removed: pain, pulling, pressure, and burning.[2]

D. Suctioning

Suctioning involves inserting a flexible clear tube down the nose or mouth. Once the tube has passed beyond the back of the throat where the gag reflex is located, suction is applied to remove accumulated secretions from the lungs. Deep suctioning involves advancing the catheter far into the airways of the lungs. The presence of thick yellow secretions necessitates frequent suctioning, as often as every thirty to sixty minutes. The risk of developing thick mucous plugs, which block off the airway, is reduced with frequent suctioning.

Tip

Patients often gag and cough when being suctioned and demonstrate that they cannot breathe easily when the suction catheter is in the lung.

E. Assessment of level of consciousness and infliction of pain

Neurological injuries are often associated with a change in the patient's level of awareness or consciousness. Examples of medical malpractice-associated injuries that could cause altered level of awareness include:

- the patient who showed beginning signs of a stroke, which were not detected by his nurse practitioner who may have been able to refer him to the local emergency room for treatment to arrest the progression of the event
- the infant who is born with brain damage due to failure of the nurse to recognize the ominous patterns on the fetal heart monitoring strip
- the elderly patient who suffers a fractured skull and intracranial bleeding when she falls off the unsupervised loading dock of the hospital

---

Tip

In order to identify a change or improvement in level of consciousness when the patient is unable to communicate effectively, healthcare professionals are taught how to inflict pain. This specific type of pain is referred to in medical records as noxious stimuli.

Light levels of pain may be inflicted by rolling or pressing a pencil over the fingernails or toe nails. Pinching the skin may be used also, although if done repetitively, it can result in bruising. When the patient reacts to this type of pain, the medical record may state that the patient "localized" the pain, meaning she withdrew from painful stimulation. Deeper levels of pain are used when light pain does not elicit a reaction. This more vigorous infliction of pain is performed by pinching the shoulder muscle, pressing the fingers on the bony ridge above the eyes, or using the knuckles to press on the sternum. Older and less common methods include pinching the nipples, scrotum or inner thigh. Patients who are unable to localize or withdraw from the pain may grimace. No response to painful stimuli is synonymous with a deep level of sedation or coma.

F. Cases

The following case histories demonstrate the range of cases which can benefit from this type of report. All names in the following examples have been changed.

- At age thirty-four, Betsy Gordon was riding a bike along a rural road. She was struck by a bus traveling about 50 or 55 miles per hour. She was thrown at least ten feet and found in a wheat field. Her bike helmet was crushed and she sustained pelvic fractures. The case settled just before trial.

- Carrie Quinn, age thirty-seven went to her physician when she noted that she had a breast lump.

The doctor dismissed her concerns. The patient was ultimately diagnosed with breast cancer after spread to lymph nodes had occurred. The case settled approximately a month before the patient died.

- Justin Fisher, age forty-five, twisted his knee when he slipped off of a wet truck bed. Multiple orthopaedic procedures on his knee were needed to restore his function. He developed a permanent limp and weakness of the knee. The workers' compensation claim settled.

- Mary Jane Weaver, age sixty-eight, had gynecologic surgery performed. The day after surgery, feces were pouring out of her abdominal wound, and she was in a state of shock. When she was taken back to surgery, multiple holes in her bowel were discovered. The case settled.

- Kathy Peterson, age thirty-two, was standing on the sidewalk when a car driven by an eighty-year-old woman went out of control. The car struck another vehicle, which hit Mrs. Peterson and threw her into the street. The case settled.

- Jeffrey Sills, age forty-two, lived in a mobile home with his girlfriend and grandchild. After getting his propane tank filled, he stood outside and lit a cigarette. He suffered severe burns when the tank exploded and ultimately died eight days later, conscious until the last eight hours of his life. All but one of the defendants settled. The case went to trial against the last defendant, and the defense won.

- Ester Lawrence was a seventy-nine-year-old woman who was riding in a car with her husband when it was hit broadside. There was a two-and-a-half-foot intrusion into the passenger compartment. Both Mr. and Mrs. Lawrence suffered severe chest injuries and died within a week of each other.

- Christopher Nathan was a thirty-year-old employee of a produce company. He was on an electric pallet jack when a truck hit him. He was pinned between the forklift and the vehicle. The case went to trial, and the plaintiff prevailed.

- Winifred Gary, age sixty-two, became paralyzed in the hospital due to an epidural soft tissue mass causing compression on the spinal cord. Surgery was unsuccessful in reversing the paralysis. The patient died after several months in the hospital. The case settled.

- On the day Carol Porter was celebrating her sixty-third birthday, she was driving her car when it was hit broadside on the driver's side by an eighteen-wheel tractor-trailer. There was a three-foot intrusion of automobile parts into the interior compartment of her car. It took forty minutes to extricate her from her vehicle. The case settled before trial.

- Ellen Winston was a sixty-eight-year-old woman who tripped and twisted her ankle. She suffered at trimalleolar fracture. She suffered fracture blisters, which progressed to extensive wounds on her foot. The case settled.

- Karen Allen, age forty-eight, went to the operating room for a routine hysteroscopy, laparoscopy, and vaporization of endometriosis. The surgeon's use of a laser resulted in burns and extensive scar tissue to her colon. Several feet of bowel had to be removed, resulting in chronic diarrhea. The case settled.

17.3 Format for the Pain and Suffering Report

The summary of the medical records can follow several formats. This section of the chapter provides information about several common components of the expert fact witness's report. The content, format, and length of the report should be based on the amount of medical documentation available and the seriousness of the injuries. Lengthy, detailed reports may be warranted in a case in which the plaintiff dies after a lingering illness lasting months but may not be necessary in a case with minimal, nonpermanent injuries.

Tip

The expert fact witness's assignment is to summarize the records and explain details of medical treatment that would not ordinarily be understood by laypeople.

The expert fact witness should refrain from speculating about what the plaintiff would have been thinking or experiencing. Drawing on medical training and experience, the expert is able to make conclusions about sensations associated with medical procedures. For example, nursing expert fact witnesses know that certain procedures cause pain, such as injections, debridements, and wet-to-dry dressing changes, and that other procedures cause noxious sensations. The expert fact witness draws on this information in analyzing records.

The expert fact witness should avoid purple prose or dramatic, inflammatory descriptions of the patient. For example, the expert should not include statements such as "the patient moved her bruised and battered body inch by agonizing inch over to the side of the bed." The tone of the report should be professional. A summary "cannot be a jury argument in disguise." C. Mueller and L. Kirkpatrick, *Evidence*, §10.16 at 1232. See also *Gomez v. Great Lakes Steel*, 803 F.2d 250, 257 (6th Cir. 1986) (criticizing admission of a summary that was "more akin to argument than evidence."). However, the summary "need not be an 'encyclopedic' survey of all the evidence." Id., quoting *United States v. Bentley*, 825 F.2d 1104, 1108 (7th Cir.), cert. denied, 484 U.S. 901 (1987) (upholding use of charts that summarized trades in silver and copper futures).[2]

The report should "fairly condense the underlying material." C. Mueller and L. Kirkpatrick, *United States v. Loney*, 959 F.2d, 1332, 1340–42 (5th Cir. 1992). The summary "cannot embellish with information not contained in the originals." Id.; see also *United States v. Drougas*, 748 F.2d 8, 25 (1st Cir. 1984) (summaries with information "not present" in the underlying records deemed inadmissible); *United States v. Seelig*, 622 F.2d 207, 213-16 (6th Cir. 1980) (upholding the admission of a chart of selected high-volume purchases made from defendant pharmacist, despite defendant's claim that the chart was "skewed," but disallowing the use of a separate chart that had compared defendant's sales with those of eight other pharmacies).[2]

The report should be clearly structured. Headers and subheaders organize the material for the reader. The use of an easy to read font, such as Times New Roman or Arial, is advised. A list of exhibits at the beginning of the report helps the reader anticipate the key information that will be provided. Exhibits may consist of scanned sections of medical records, photographs, medical illustrations, tables, and graphs. Several examples of such exhibits are included in this chapter.

Tip

Ideally the exhibits should be designed so that they can be enlarged and used as exhibits at the time of trial, as discussed in Chapter 19, "Trial Exhibits: Preparation and Use."

A. Cover and table of contents

A cover that captures a key aspect and personalizes the case may be used. Figure 17.2 shows Betsy Gordon after being hit by the bus being carried to a helicopter waiting to transport her to a tertiary care facility. Covers may show a before-and-after photo, which may be effective in a delay in diagnosis of cancer case after chemotherapy has altered the appearance of the patient. Covers should be tasteful. A photograph of a partially severed limb, for example, may be construed as too graphic for the cover of the report.

A table of contents may be useful if the report is lengthy. See Figure 17.3 for the first page of a table of contents of Justin Fisher's report.

The report typically begins by listing the documents that were reviewed in preparation of the report. This would include the medical records from hospitalizations, outpatient visits to doctors, physical therapy, and so on. A listing of exhibits may follow. A chronology of key events may be placed early in the report in order to provide an overview of the details that will be contained in the report. Figure 17.4 is one such brief chronology of Mary Jane Weaver, the patient whose surgeon left multiple holes in her bowel during gynecologic surgery.

Betsy Gordon
Date of Accident: June 10, 1999

Figure 17.2 *Cover page of report for Betsy Gordon*

Justin Fisher
Table of Contents

Page #

Figure 17.3 *Table of contents for Justin Fisher*

B. Introduction and description of the accident

In a personal injury, products liability, or workers' compensation case, the initial injury most likely occurred outside a healthcare facility. References in this chapter to an accident refer to this type of injury.

The expert fact witness's report typically begins by providing background information about the injured patient. These data help the reader identify with the injured person and put into context the details of medical care that are described in the report.

Example:

> On 6/9/00, Kathy Peterson was a 32-year-old woman who was standing on the sidewalk on Broad Street in Redwood City at around noon. She was 5'4" and weighed 125 pounds. Mrs. Peterson was employed by a surgeon with an office on Broad Street in Redwood City and was the mother of a 4-year-old daughter. She had surgery for bunion repair approximately 11 years before this accident, and had no medical problems.

The description of the accident, injury, or alleged medical malpractice incident or care follows. In the case of a personal injury incident, the information is gathered from an analysis of rescue squad and emergency department records. Details of the injury are explained in simple terms.

Example:

> At the time of his burn, Mr. Jeffrey Sills was a 42-year-old man who was involved in a fire in a trailer. The first medical people to see him at the scene of the fire were the ambulance attendants. They arrived at 10:29 a.m. These individuals observed that he was awake and alert and oriented times × 3 (he knew who he was, where he was and the date.) He did not lose consciousness after being burned and was in severe pain. The patient was assessed by the squad member as having first, second and third degree burns over 75% to 85% of his body.

(A first degree burn is defined as a superficial partial thickness burn. A second degree burn consists of a partial thickness burn. A third degree burn is a full thickness burn. See Figure 17.1 for an indication of the depth of each type of burn.)

Italics may be used to highlight explanations of medical terms.

Example:

> At the time of his first visit to the orthopaedic surgeon following the twisting knee injury, Mr. Justin Fisher had two effusions (*accumulations of fluid into the tissue*), medial joint-line pain (*pain along the middle of the knee*), decreased range of motion (*joint movement*) and a positive Lachman test. [The Lachman test, used to determine ACL (*anterior cruciate ligament*) injury, is performed with the knee flexed 20 to 30°, and one hand grasping the thigh and stabilizing it. The tibia (*lower leg bone*) is pulled forward with an anterior (*front*)-directed force, and the examiner notes tibial movement. A soft endpoint (*displacement of the tibia*) indicates a positive test and rupture of the anterior cruciate ligament.] (See Exhibit 2, Illustration of Lachman's test.) The x-rays were negative (*no bone abnormalities were seen*). The diagnoses were possible ACL tear of the right knee and possible meniscal tear (a hole in the meniscus, or crescent-shaped fibrocartilaginous structure of the knee) of the right knee. The plan was for an MRI (*magnetic resonance imaging*) of the right knee and home physical therapy. (An MRI provides 3-D images of the body's interior, including muscle, bone, blood vessels, nerves and organs.) The patient was not to return to work until approximately 9/23/99.

C. Evaluation and description of injuries in the emergency department

The expert fact witness's report should contain a description of the initial evaluation of the plaintiff's injuries after the accident. These medical details will be located on the emergency department and trauma flowsheets. The expert fact witness translates this information into simple terms.

Example:

> Injuries of Mrs. Lawrence
>
> A. Head: There was a gaping laceration of her forehead that extended down to the subcutaneous tis-

Mary Jane Weaver
Chronology of Events

Date	Event
	Beachwood Hospital
10/24/01	Dr. B. performed a trachelectomy, failed vaginal hysterectomy, failed abdominal hysterectomy, left salpingo-oophorectomy, anterior repair, bowel repair, and lysis of adhesions.
10/25/01	Return to OR; Dr. H. performed an exploratory laparotomy, small bowel resection (in two places), control of multiple enterotomies, control of pelvic hemorrhage. Admitted to ICU postoperatively.
10/27/01	Mechanical ventilation was discontinued.
11/02/01	Transferred to medical-surgical unit; TPN was started.
11/05/01	CT scan of the abdomen to evaluate the abdominal wound drainage; a drain was placed in the wound.
10/31/01	The abdominal wound was debrided at the bedside.
11/08/01	The abdominal wound was debrided at the bedside.
	Beachwood Rehabilitation Hospital
11/16/01	Admitted to Beachwood Rehabilitation Hospital for rehabilitation, wound care, and TPN.
	Beachwood Hospital
11/20/01	Admitted to Beachwood Hospital with enterocutaneous fistula.
11/26/01	Return to OR for closure of small bowel fistula and delayed primary wound closure.
	Beachwood Rehabilitation Hospital
12/22/01	Admitted for rehabilitation, wound care and TPN.
01/22/02	Progress notes indicated the development of a second fistula in the abdominal wound site.
03/06/02	The drainage increased from the abdominal wound fistula. There was a heavy amount of thick green drainage.
	Beachwood Hospital
03/10/02	Admitted with a draining fistula. Mrs. Weaver was considering surgery.
03/13/02	Return to OR for exploratory laparotomy and ileocecal resection and anastomosis.
03/25/02	Discharged home with a plan for visiting nurse twice a day for wound care.

TPN = total parenteral nutrition
OR = operating room
ICU = intensive care unit

Figure 17.4 *Chronology of events for Mary Jane Weaver*

sues. There was a bruise in her scalp area. A laceration/puncture site was present over her left eyebrow.

B. Shoulder: Mrs. Lawrence's left clavicle was broken. There was a large bruise on her shoulder.

C. Chest: There were multiple bruises on Mrs. Lawrence's chest and back. More than a dozen fractured ribs, which ordinarily protect the heart from injury, were present. The fracture fragments were widely separated, which was described as a "flail" chest (crushed rib cage). On 12/5/99, a tear in her aorta was detected. This is the major blood vessel that carries oxygenated blood out of the heart. There was extensive air under the skin in the left chest wall and under the arm. There were also scattered bruises on her back.

D. Arms: There were multiple areas of bruising and scattered lacerations on all of Mrs. Lawrence's extremities. The patient's left elbow had two puncture wounds that were 1 cm (one-half inch). Her left wrist was fractured. The bones were pushed out of alignment. There was a laceration on her left hand involving her fifth finger. Her fingers were swollen and discolored.

E. Abdomen: There was either a pancreatic laceration or a contusion of the duodenum (portion of the intestines directly below the stomach). The exact location of the injury was not determined.

F. Legs: There was a large bruised area on Mrs. Lawrence's left leg. An abrasion was present on her left leg and right knee. Her right knee was bruised. There was a fracture of her right hip. The bone was pushed into the hip socket (impacted).

G. Upper back: There was a laceration on Mrs. Lawrence's upper back. She had pain in the back of her neck and upper back. X-rays of her thoracic spine showed collapse of several mid thoracic vertebrae, which was due to either acute traumatic injury or osteoporosis.

Extensive injuries can be defined on a schematic drawing of the patient. Figures 17.5 and 17.6 are a composite of the injuries that Mrs. Lawrence sustained in the car accident, based on her medical records. Portions of the medical record that show drawings of injuries may be included in the report. These can be scanned and inserted into the body of the report. See Figure 17.7 for a drawing of a forehead avulsion wound on Kathy Peterson's head after being struck by the runaway car.

Photographs of bruising and lacerations may be included in the report. Figure 17.8 shows Betsy Gordon's bruised hip after being hit by the bus and Figure 17.9 shows photographs of Christopher Nathan's crushed leg. The photos were scanned and inserted into the report.

D. Treatment in the emergency department

The treatment of the patient's injuries occurs simultaneously with the evaluation of the extent of damage. The report should contain a section describing what was done to stabilize the patient in the emergency department.

Example:

Initial Assessment, Condition and Treatment

When the trauma team evaluated Ms. Gordon, her medical records show that her injury was described as "bicyclist versus bus". Her initial condition included a decreased level of consciousness, with a closed head injury suspected, and pelvic pain. After her clothes were cut off, her skin was dry and cool. A left knee laceration was seen. Ms. Gordon was attended to by the trauma physicians and resident, the anesthesiologist, respiratory therapists, and radiology department. On arrival, her blood oxygen level had dropped to 74%. Her respirations were shallow. She was placed on a cardiac monitor. While Ms. Gordon was in the emergency department from 10:21 a.m. to 11:30 a.m., her blood pressure varied from a low of 70/43 to a high of 140/70 when she was transferred to the Surgical Trauma Unit. Her pulse rate varied from 76–125/minute.

While the diagnosis of her injuries was occurring, the following treatments were performed:

- A nasogastric tube was inserted. (This is inserted through the nose and causes an intensive gag-

continued on page 362

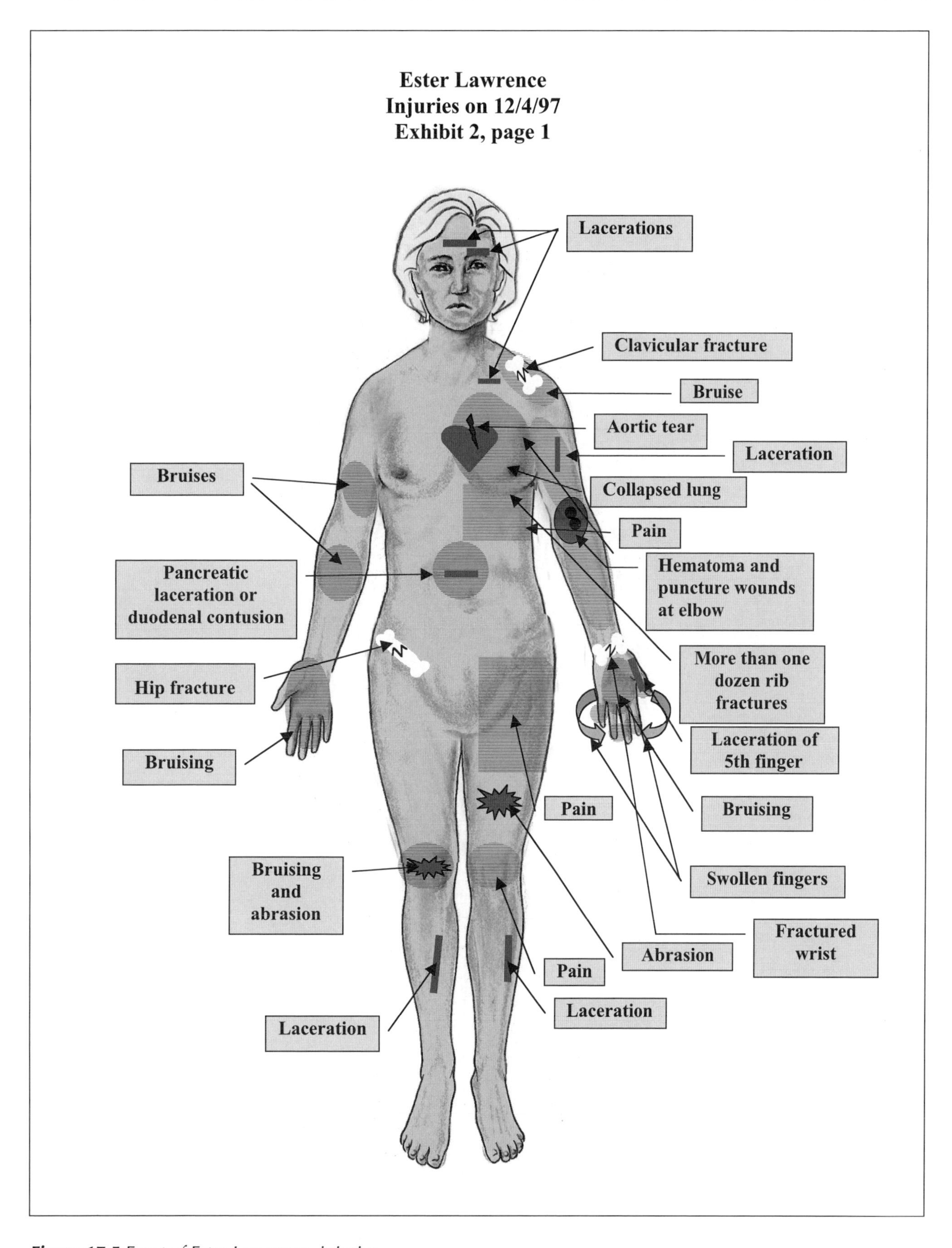

Figure 17.5 *Front of Ester Lawrence, injuries*

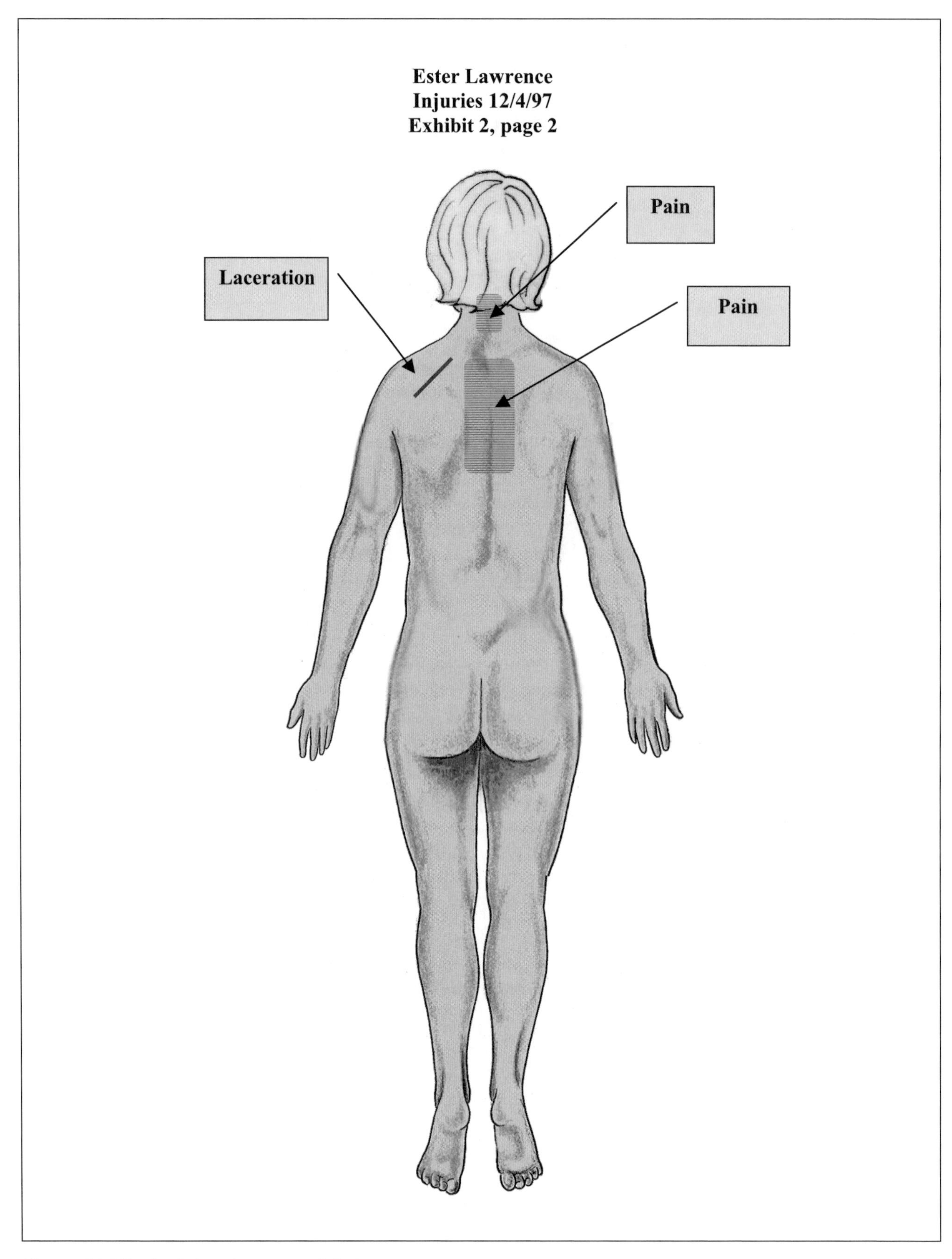

Figure 17.6 *Back of Ester Lawrence, injuries*

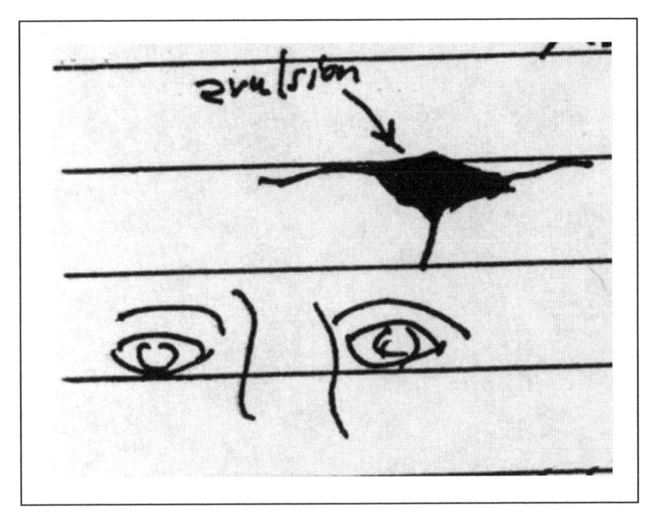

Figure 17.7 Scanned image of forehead avulsion

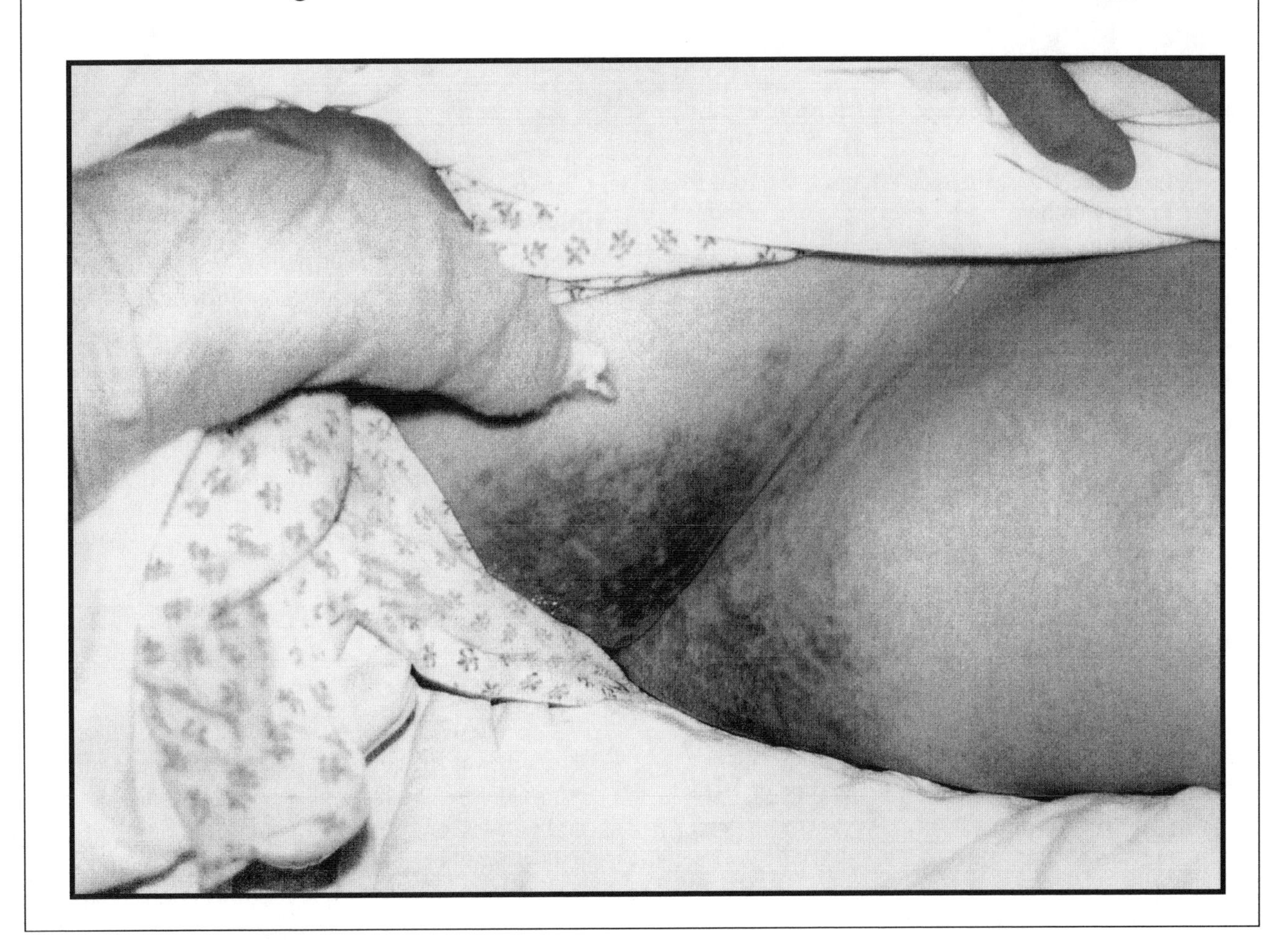

Figure 17.8 Betsy Gordon's bruised hip

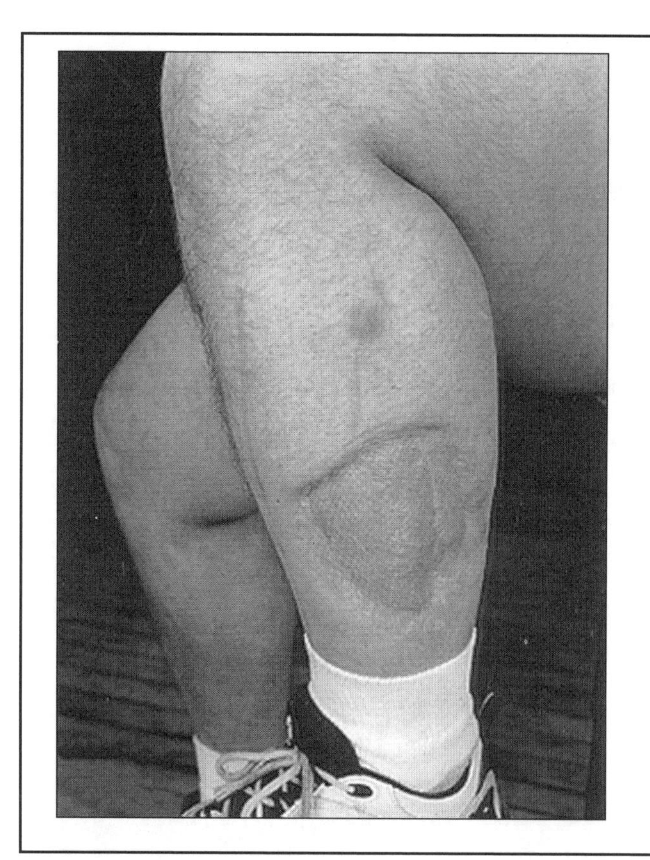
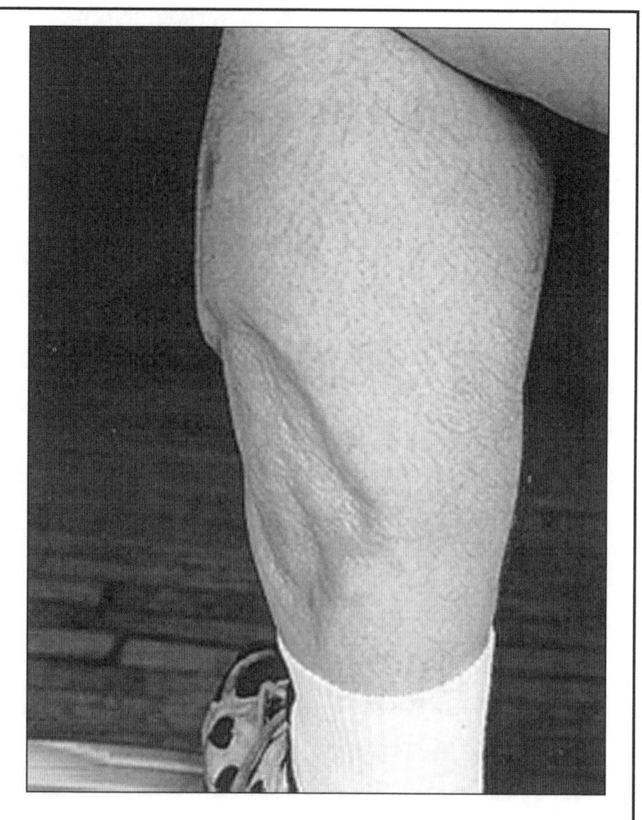

Figure 17.9 *Scanned photographs of Christopher Nathan's leg*

ging sensation as it slides down the throat into the stomach.)

- A catheter was inserted through her urethra into her bladder.
- An arterial line was put in her wrist. (The arteries are exquisitely tender. It causes intense pain when the artery is pierced with a needle).
- Blood work was drawn.
- A urine test was done.
- An endotracheal tube was inserted into her throat and attached to a ventilator. She was given a drug to paralyze her. This kept her awareness of sensations intact, but prevented her from moving.
- Intravenous needles were inserted into her right hand, right arm and right groin.
- A tetanus injection was given in her left arm.
- Her blood sugar was tested by a fingerstick.
- Fentanyl (fast acting narcotic) was given, which caused a drop in her blood pressure.

E. Chronological summary of status and problems

The body of the expert fact witness's report describes the evaluation of the patient's condition and the major problems experienced during the course of care. This can be described in a chronological fashion or in a problems-oriented approach. The following example, related to Mrs. Winifred Gary, the woman who became paralyzed in the hospital, presents the content in a chronological format.

Example:

March 1–12, 2002

As the month began, Mrs. Gary was without fever. She was awake, alert and responsive. Diarrhea continued for the last two weeks of her life. The social worker, who had been spending time with the patient and her family, noted that her friend thought it was unfair that Mrs. Gary had to continue to live without any hope of getting better. An entry on 3/3/02 pointed out that her herpes lip lesions had returned and were oozing fluid. There were also lesions on her chest which may have been from intravenous needle entry sites. A doctor was called to see the patient on 3/3/02 for an increase in temperature to 101.3 degrees and a drop in blood pressure to the "70s." The patient responded to intravenous fluids. Blood was seen in her stools again at that point with a corresponding drop in her hemoglobin.

On 3/4/02, there was a long phone call between the attending physician and Mrs. Gary's family. Her prognosis was "clearly worse than it was 1–2 months ago." She had a fever, gastrointestinal bleeding, a clot in her leg, and respiratory failure. Her friends thought she wanted to stop the ventilator and die. After further discussion with the family, a decision was made to pursue supportive measures only and to continue the ventilator. She was not to have cardiopulmonary resuscitation, drugs to raise her blood pressure or to be defibrillated. When Mrs. Gary was asked her opinions she was unable or unwilling to address these issues and wanted to rely on her family.

Mrs. Gary was more awake on 3/6/02 when she was receiving 1 mg or Morphine per hour. She did not indicate approval of the idea of stopping the ventilator if it meant she would die. However, on 3/7/02, Mrs. Gary pulled the ventilator off of her tracheostomy tube multiple times. That same day she pulled the balloon/cuff off of her tracheostomy. A new one was inserted and her hands were restrained. The following day she was scratching her skin, but denied having pain.

Mrs. Gary was transferred out the intensive care unit on 3/8/02. The family contacted the physician that day to request that the ventilator be turned off. The consensus was that Mrs. Gary did not want to continue with treatment and that she was willing to go off of the ventilator even if it meant that she died as a result. The Heparin to treat the blood clot and the antibiotics to treat her blood infection were stopped. Mrs. Gary indicated her wish to have the ventilator stopped and recognized that she might die as a result of this. The ventilator was stopped and the morphine drip was continued for comfort care.

On 3/9/02, the morphine was running at 20 mgs per hour. She was breathing at the rate of 6–10 breaths per minute.

On 3/10/02, the morphine was running at 36 mgs per hour. She was breathing at the rate of 5–10 breaths per minute. Her temperature was 101.2 degrees and she was suctioned frequently for thick white secretions.

On 3/11/02, on the night shift, Mrs. Gary's morphine was running at the rate of 48 mgs per hour. Her breaths sounds were coarse (there was a lot of fluid in them). Her heart rate was 120 beats per minute. Her morphine was increased to 54 mgs per hour by the end of the night shift. During the day shift, her morphine was running at 56 mgs per minute. She had minimal urine output. She looked comfortable. That day her family decided they wanted to bring her home. The social worker was to speak with them about specific arrangements that needed to be made to accomplish that. Mrs. Gary's Morphine rate was increased to 60 mgs/hour.

On Mrs. Gary's last day alive, 3/12/02, her morphine was running at 64 mgs per hour. Her urine output had dropped and she was in acute renal failure. At 1:15 p.m. she stopped breathing and had no heart beat. She was pronounced dead.

F. Presentation of major problems

When the pain and suffering experienced by the plaintiff is divided into a few simple areas, a checklist can be created based on an analysis of the medical records. See Figure 17.10.

The narrative section of the report provides a description of each of the major problems.

Example:

Major Problems

An analysis of Mr. Sills' medical records indicates that he experienced many of these problems in addition to several complications. Figure 17.6 shows the major problems that he experienced in the first three days after the burn.

Problems	10/1	10/2	10/3	10/4	10/6	10/7	10/8
Inability to eat	✓	✓	✓	✓	✓	✓	✓
Inability to walk	✓	✓	✓	✓	✓	✓	✓
Pain	✓	✓	✓	✓	✓	✓	✓
Inability to breathe on own	✓	✓	✓	✓	✓	✓	✓
Inability to use bathroom	✓	✓	✓	✓	✓	✓	✓
Inability to talk	✓	✓	✓	✓	✓	✓	✓
Anxiety	✓	✓	✓				
Right leg cold and numb	✓	✓	✓				
Restlessness	✓	✓	✓				
Bruised arms		✓	✓	✓	✓	✓	✓
Discolored legs		✓	✓	✓	✓	✓	✓
Oozing fluid from skin			✓	✓	✓	✓	✓
Oozing fluid from stumps				✓	✓	✓	✓
Open blisters on right leg			✓	✓	✓	✓	✓
Generalized swelling	✓	✓	✓	✓	✓	✓	✓
Necrotic incisions					✓	✓	✓
Swelling of face and arms	✓	✓	✓	✓	✓	✓	✓
Incontinent liquid stool			✓	✓	✓	✓	✓
Discolored area on sacrum				✓			
Sacral ulcer					✓	✓	✓
Fever over 100°				✓	✓	✓	✓

[shaded box] = Surgery

Figure 17.10 *Simple listing of major problems*

a. Pain

Mr. Sills experienced pain both as a consequence of having received the burns and as a result of going through a series of painful debridements and dressing changes during his stay at Community Medical Center. (Debridement is cutting away of dead skin.) His pain was treated with intravenous Buprenex. He received three intravenous injections on 10/26, eleven intravenous injections on 10/27, and four injections of 10/28 before being transported to Burn Center. [See Figure 17.7 for a listing of pain medications that he received during his last week of life.] During this admission he complained of pain in his left foot, in the neck area, buttocks, legs, and penis.

b. Low Blood Pressure and Rapid Heart Rate

For the first three days in the hospital, Mr. Sills' blood pressure was low. His systolic pressure (the top number in a blood pressure reading) ranged from 60–120 when he was first admitted to ICU and periodically dropped to low levels. During the admissions at each hospital, his heart raced and remained at over 120 beats per minute for most of his last week of life.

c. Edema (Swelling)

Mr. Sills developed massive swelling of his arms, legs and face. This was partly due to the fluid shifts as a result of the burns and partly caused by the massive amounts of intravenous fluid that were given to him. His arms were raised on arm elevators in an effort to reduce the swelling.

d. Respiratory Congestion

Immediately after his admission to ICU, Mr. Sills was noted to have congestion in his lungs. This was heard in the form of crackles, wheezes and rattles. His lungs remained congested throughout his stay at both hospitals. The initial suctioning of his lungs brought up grey/black secretions.

e. Loss of Pulses

Over the course of the patient's first night in the hospital, Mr. Sills developed a loss of pulses in his wrists and feet and decreased sensation in both hands. Emergency surgery was performed at around 6:30 a.m. on 10/27 after Mr. Sills was rushed to the operating room. Emergency escharotomies were performed, which consisted of slicing open the front and side of his legs and arms. The left leg was sliced open on both sides to the ankle. The right leg was cut open to the calf. Both of his arms were sliced open in two parallel lines from the shoulder to the thumb and to the little finger. The wounds were left open and unsutured. The two edges of the wounds were approximately 3 inches apart. After his return to ICU, his wounds were draining bright red blood. His sheets were moist with blood and clear fluid.

On 10/27, the nurse caring for Mr. Sills on the day shift provided detailed descriptions of the burned areas. The nurse noted that there were blisters on his ears and that lots of grey skin remained. He was complaining of pain in his neck area, which was briefly relieved by Buprenex. Hair from his eyebrows and lids was singed and missing and an area of his scalp had singed hair. His right arm was reddened and scarlet and was devoid of hair or nails. He was oozing a large amount of blood from the lateral slices in his arm. On his left hand, he had a little more skin remaining and had retained one nail. Dressing changes on his back showed that his skin was grey colored. Blisters were present around his hips, which were open and draining clear fluid. There was lots of oozing from the escharotomies on his legs. The nurse observed that Mr. Sills experienced more pain when his legs were dressed and gave him two intravenous injections of Buprenex. The nurse observed that the patient complained of pain when the dressings on his buttocks were changed. The tip of his penis was burned and painful and grey skin was falling off.

f. Bloody Drainage From Dressings

Clear bloody fluid oozed from the dressings covering Mr. Sills' wounds before his surgery. This soaked through the dressings and drained onto the sheets covering Mr. Sills. The drainage intensified after the emergency surgery that was performed on 10/27. On 10/28 at midnight, the drainage from his left wrist increased, necessitating suturing of his left wrist area. His wounds continued to bleed throughout both admissions.

g. Loss of Pulses and Sensation After Surgery

The emergency escharotomies were not permanently successful in preventing further problems. Mr. Sills complained of loss of sensation in his right finger tips at 5 a.m. on 10/28. This was preceded by several hours of having cool extremities and reduced or absent pulses. At 5:30 a.m., the doctor arrived on the unit. After the patient was given intravenous Buprenex, the doctor performed a bedside escharotomy on his right arm. Within six hours, Mr. Sills was on his way to Burn Center by helicopter.

G. Description of problems divided into categories

When medical records indicate that extensive pain and suffering resulted from several major problems, the symptoms can be organized into subsections. Each subsection would then be described.

Figure 17.11 shows this type of organization of problems for Mrs. Gary, the woman who became paralyzed in the hospital. Graphical presentations of treatment for major problems may also be included. See Figure 17.12 for an example of the presentation of the blood loss and blood replacement for Betsy Gordon, the woman who was hit by the bus.

H. Evidence of emotional reactions

As noted above and in other chapters, much of the suffering associated with an injury is documented in the medical records. Suffering can result from unrelieved symptoms, such as nausea and vomiting, diarrhea, and itching. Suffering may be exhibited in the form of agitation, anxiety, and depression. The nurses and physicians may document statements made by the patient, as well as their own observations about the distress they observe. This material may be summarized in a narrative format. Incorporating direct quotes from the medical records into the report is appropriate. The following material is extracted from the expert fact witness report summarizing the care given to Mrs. Carol Porter, whose car was broadsided by another car.

Example:

A sampling of comments from the nurses' notes reveals that Mrs. Porter was anxious on a number of occasions. For example, on 2/25, she was observed to be anxious. She was "screaming and yelling out loud. Stated 'need my mouth swabs and I am in pain'." The nurse increased the drip rate of the continuous epidural infusion, which reduced Mrs. Porter's pain. On 2/28, she was described as mouth breathing, anxious and complaining of pain. A chin strap was placed on her face to force her mouth closed so that she could not breathe through her mouth. This improved her oxygen level. Comments about her anxiety level are included in notes of most of the shifts of nurses who cared for her. On 2/28, she was given Xanax for an anxiety attack.

On 3/2, the social worker went to ICU to see Mrs. Porter. She stated she wanted to be transferred to Major Medical Center so that she could be closer to her friends and family. She stated her supports were very important to her. She was said she was very lonely and worried about her husband. She had been her husband's caregiver prior to her accident. Her husband was recovering from recent surgery and a long illness. The social worker learned in talking to Mrs. Porter's son that the patient's husband was hospitalized followed a myocardial infarction at Major Medical Center. The family was concerned about Mrs. Porter's reaction and had not told her yet. When Mrs. Porter's son was assured that the staff would provide support, they agreed that transferring the patient to Major Medical Center might be beneficial to her state of mind.

On 3/3, Mrs. Porter's doctor wrote that she would be told today that her husband had not woken up from a cardiac arrest the night before. The doctor wrote "I presume that this will be taken very hard by the patient and we may have a backslide physiologically." That day, Mrs. Porter was visited by her family, who spoke to her about the condition of her husband. Arrangements were made to transport her to Major Medical Center. Although the preferred method of transportation was a helicopter, that was not possible due to weather conditions. The epidural catheter was removed on 3/3 in anticipation of her transfer. Mrs. Porter was sent with paramedics by ambulance to Major Medical Center on 3/4.

continued on page 368

Major problems organized into subsections
December 1999 – March 2000

	1999				2000									
Month	**December**				**January**				**February**				**March**	
Week	**1**	**2**	**3**	**4**	**1**	**2**	**3**	**4**	**1**	**2**	**3**	**4**	**1**	**2**
Discomfort														
Fever*	✓						✓	✓	✓	✓	✓	✓	✓	✓
Rapid heart rate**	✓						✓			✓	✓	✓		
Swelling of feet	✓	✓	✓	✓		✓	✓	✓	✓	✓	✓	✓	✓	
Swelling of body								✓	✓	✓	✓	✓	✓	
Ulcerations on lips			✓									✓	✓	
Nausea		✓				✓			✓					
Diarrhea				✓		✓		✓		✓	✓	✓	✓	
Vomiting						✓								
Blood in stool							✓	✓					✓	
Rash in groin			✓											
Sacral ulcer						✓								
Incision opened		✓	✓	✓	✓	✓	✓	✓	✓	✓				
Scratching self														✓
Oozing pus from incision		✓	✓											
Pain														
Epigastric pain	✓	✓	✓	✓	✓	✓	✓	✓	✓	✓	✓			
Back pain		✓		✓	✓	✓								
Throat pain			✓			✓								
Leg pain						✓			✓					
Chest pain									✓					
Feet pain		✓												
Pain (site not specified)													✓	
Right hip skin tear										✓				
Respiratory Changes														
Short of breath	✓		✓		✓	✓				✓				✓
Lung congestion	✓				✓	✓	✓	✓		✓	✓	✓	✓	✓
Rapid respirations***	✓					✓						✓		
Aspiration of liquid					✓						✓			
Dependence on Others														
Unable to eat		✓	✓	✓	✓	✓	✓	✓	✓	✓	✓	✓	✓	
Unable to get out of bed	✓	✓	✓	✓	✓	✓	✓	✓	✓	✓	✓	✓	✓	
Unable to breathe on own						✓	✓	✓	✓	✓	✓	✓		
Behavior														
Confusion	✓	✓	✓	✓	✓	✓					✓			
Anxiety	✓	✓	✓			✓		✓	✓	✓	✓			
Lethargic	✓	✓	✓	✓	✓	✓			✓		✓		✓	
Depression		✓	✓	✓	✓		✓	✓	✓		✓			

Figure 17.11 *Major problems organized into subsections* *(continued on next page)*

	1999				2000									
Month	**December**				**January**				**February**				**March**	
Week	**1**	**2**	**3**	**4**	**1**	**2**	**3**	**4**	**1**	**2**	**3**	**4**	**1**	**2**
Pulled out nasogastric tube		✓	✓ ✓ ✓	✓										
Crying		✓	✓					✓	✓					
Pulled out subclavian line				✓										
Pulled out endotracheal tube						✓								
Pulled out PICC line									✓					
Pulled off ventilator													✓	
Pulled out tracheotomy tube													✓	
Had to be restrained			✓	✓		✓	✓							
Agitated			✓				✓			✓	✓		✓	
Hallucinations			✓		✓									
Difficulty sleeping								✓						
Tremors										✓	✓	✓	✓	

* Fever = 100° or higher
** Rapid pulse = 100 beats/minute or higher
*** Rapid respirations = over 24/minute

(shaded) = PEG insertion surgery on 1/14/00
(shaded) = Tracheostomy surgery on 1/26/00

Figure 17.11 *(continued)*

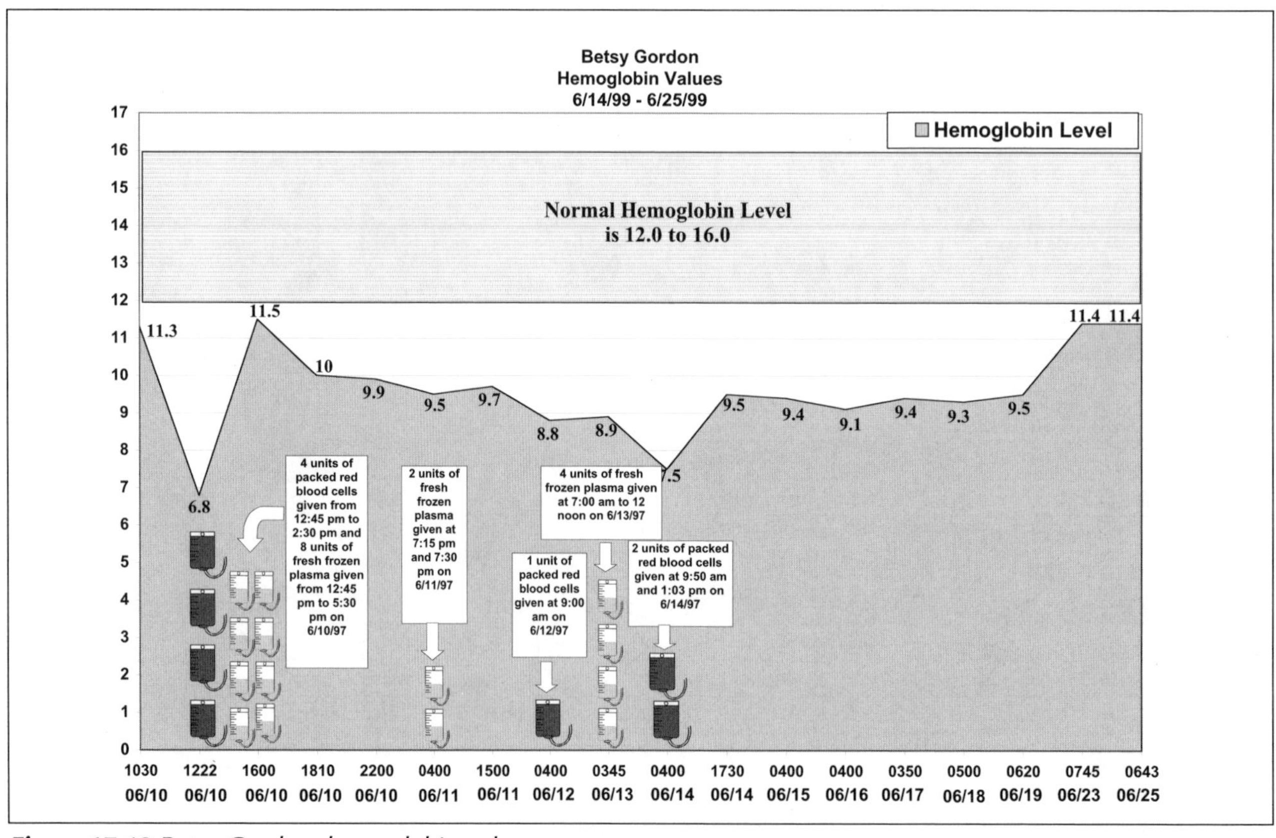

Figure 17.12 *Betsy Gordon, hemoglobin values*

There are multiple entries in Mrs. Lawrence's medical records, which document her high level of anxiety and agitation. A sampling of these entries follows.

DATE	SOURCE	ENTRY
12/06/02	Critical care flow sheet	Right arterial line dislodged by patient.
12/06/02	Critical care flow sheet	Patient agitated and restless, throwing legs off CT table, sitting up. Medicated with Versed 1 mg with good relief. Appropriate attempts to remove endotracheal tube. Patient extremely restless. Ativan 2 mg IV given. Restraints applied to feet.
12/07/02	Critical care flow sheet	Attempting to remove endotracheal tube. Agitated at times. Restless, pulling at IVs and tubes...Agitated, given Morphine secondary to agitation. Still agitated, given 2 mgs Morphine. Still agitated, given 2 mg Ativan. Given 4 mgs Morphine for agitation. Still agitated at times, given Ativan. Increasingly restless, heart rate increased to 120.
12/09/02	Nurses notes	Morphine given every 2 hours to maintain calm demeanor and reduce thrashing patient does when anxious.
12/09/02	Critical care flow sheet	Wrist restraint intact on right wrist secondary to pulling at (intravenous) lines, endotracheal tube. Medicated with Morphine 4 mgs IV secondary to complaints of generalized discomfort. Anxious, pulling at lines and restraints when not sedated. Sedation was repeated, as patient was very agitated after bath and (being) turned.
12/10/99	Nurses notes	Patient still with periods of great anxiety which increases heart rate and blood pressure.
12/11/02	Critical care flow sheet	Agitated with any and all stimulation. Attempting to pull out invasive lines. Wrist restrained with close supervision.
12/11/02	Social work	Daughter states patient is usually an anxious person and may need close support while she and husband are hospitalized.
12/12/02	Critical care flow sheet	Continues to require soft restraint of right arm secondary to pulling at gown, Foley and ___. When patient is very restless she causes herself to become hypertensive and to go into ST sinus tachycardia-rapid heart rate)
12/12/02	Nurses notes	When patient is agitated at that time she goes into SST (superventricular tachycardia-rapid heart rate)
12/13/02	MD Progress notes	Patient agitated, responsive to verbal stimuli. When

***Figure 17.13** Emotional reactions summarized in a table (continued on next page)*

DATE	SOURCE	ENTRY
		calm responds to commands. Family gives history of patient having agoraphobia/anxiety disorder.
12/13/02	Critical care flow sheet	Attempting to pull out oral endotracheal tube, leads, gown, Foley catheter. …Becomes agitated and restless when anxious.
12/13/02	Nurses notes	Patient with increased restlessness, attempting to pull tubes/(cardiac monitoring) leads/clothes. Increased anxiety with systolic blood pressure over 200.
12/16/02	MD Progress notes	Very slow wean (from the ventilator) complicated by anxiety when aroused.
12/20/02	Critical care flow sheet	Still with periods of agitation. Pulling soft (restraint) off ventilator and tracheostomy despite right hand restraint.
12/21/02	Critical care flow sheet	Very agitated/periods of crying. Pulling at tracheostomy.
12/22/02	Critical care flow sheet	Ativan given for agitation with mild relief provided.
12/23/02	Nurses notes	Mouths words, however words are indecipherable. Agitated, pulls at nasogastric tube and Dobhoff tubes and ventilator. Right upper extremity with soft wrist restraint intact. Medicated with 2 mgs Morphine. Patient still agitated, kicking up feet.
12/23/02	Critical care flow sheet	Nasogastric tube removed by patient.

***Figure 17.13** (continued)*

Evidence of emotional reactions and suffering may be summarized in a table. Entries from several parts of the medical record may be included, as shown in Figure 17.13 which describes the reactions of Ester Lawrence, the woman who was part of a couple involved in a car accident.

I. Level of awareness

The medical record can be used to establish if the patient had conscious pain and suffering or some level of awareness. Documentation of the level of consciousness can be primarily found in the nursing and physician progress notes.

Tip

The Glasgow Coma Score may be documented. This is a standardized method of evaluating level of responsiveness and motor abilities. The highest possible score is 15; the lowest possible score is 3. If a patient is incubated and cannot speak, the symbol "T" is used.

The documentation of level of awareness or consciousness should be correlated with the treatment being rendered in order to determine what stimuli the patient would have been exposed to during that time frame. The documentation concerning level of awareness or consciousness can be presented in a simple checklist chart, as shown in Figure 17.14, the data for Jeffrey Sills, the man who was burned in the trailer fire.

J. Pain

The initial evaluation of an accident victim may overlook the need to relieve pain. The expert fact witness should evaluate how much time transpired from the time of entry into the medical care system to the point of the first administration of pain medication.

Example:

> Mrs. Lawrence complained of multiple sites of pain while she was in the emergency department. She was given morphine for the first time at 4:45 p.m., two hours after she arrived in the emergency department.

Review of the documentation will reveal the types and amounts of pain medication that were administered to the patient. This information may be displayed in a simple text-based chart (Figure 17.15) or in a chart that incorporates graphics (Figure 17.16). When a considerable amount of pain medication is needed, sometimes it is useful to display this information graphically, as shown in Figure 17.17.

Pain may arise from the injuries and as consequences of the medical and nursing care that was provided. The expert fact witness's report may include a narrative description of the pain associated with the procedures.

Example:

> Major Problems 12/5/99–12/17/99
>
> Mrs. Lawrence experienced several problems during her last three weeks of life. These are broadly divided into the categories of discomfort, agitation, impaired oxygenation, impaired skin integrity, bleeding and dependence on others.

Jeffrey Sills

LEVEL OF CONSCIOUSNESS
October 26 - November 2, 1999

	10/26	10/27	10/28	10/29	10/30	10/31	11/1	11/2
Alert, oriented, nodding head to questions	✓	✓	✓			✓		
Asking questions, alert, cooperative		✓						
Alert, oriented, answers questions correctly			✓	✓	✓	✓		
Anxious, agitated				✓		✓	✓	
Talking		✓	✓	✓	✓			
Responded to family		✓	✓	✓	✓			
Sedated, chemically paralyzed					✓	✓	✓	✓
Responded to painful stimulation	✓	✓	✓	✓	✓	✓	✓	✓
Responded to loud voice						✓		
Unresponsive								✓

Figure 17.14 *Evidence of level of consciousness in Jeffrey Sills*

Medications for Symptoms	2/24	2/25	2/26	2/27	2/28	3/01	3/02	3/03	3/04
Pain:									
Marcaine		✓							
Bupivicaine and Sufentanyl		✓	✓	✓	✓	✓	✓	✓	
Percocet								✓	
Morphine by pump	✓	✓							
Morphine by injection					✓	✓			
Anxiety:									
Xanax			✓		✓	✓	✓	✓	✓
Ativan				✓					

Figure 17.15 *Text-based display of medications for symptoms*

A. Comfort

There were several sources of pain and discomfort associated with Mrs. Lawrence's injuries and treatment.

1. Injuries

Mrs. Lawrence had a fractured clavicle, which could not be casted. Whenever she was turned, she would have experienced pain. Mrs. Lawrence's ribs were fractured in several places. When a limb is fractured, the act of applying a cast reduces movement and reduces pain. It is impossible to place the rib cage in a support or cast to prevent movement and reduce pain. The act of breathing with fractured ribs causes pain. Mrs. Lawrence's wrist was fractured and placed in a cast. When the cast became tight on 12/6/99, her hand became swollen and cool. The cast was cut off and a splint was applied. This consists of two rigid plaster, plastic or metal supports which are held in place with an ace bandage or Velcro and cloth. A splint does not provide as much stability as does a cast. The splint was kept on her arm until 12/22/99, when the cast was reapplied. The medical records stated in many places in the nurses' notes that Mrs. Lawrence had little movement in her left arm. It is unclear if this was due to nerve damage or pain.

In addition to her fractures, Mrs. Lawrence had multiple abrasions, lacerations and bruises, which would have been painful. These were noted on her body for the entire duration of her hospitalization. Mrs. Lawrence developed abdominal pain on 12/20/99 and 12/22/99.

Mrs. Lawrence was able to grimace when she experienced pain, and respond when asked if she was having pain.

2. Medical Treatment

There were multiple painful medical procedures and diagnostic tests performed on Mrs. Lawrence, as illustrated on the Treatment Calendar. The procedures, which are uncomfortable or painful, include:

A. Insertion of Foley Catheter: This procedure involves invading the most private area of the body as it is passed up the urethra to the bladder. The catheter must be cleaned and manipulated by the nursing staff on a daily basis.

continued on page 372

Ester Lawrence
Medications for Symptoms
2/10/98–3/10/98

KEY

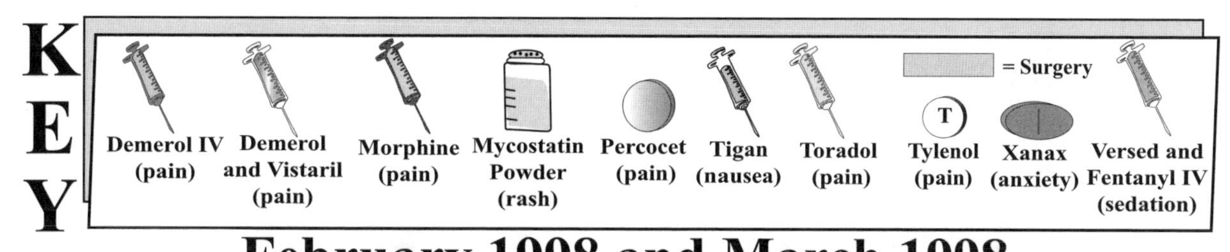

February 1998 and March 1998

Sun	Mon	Tues	Wed	Thur	Fri	Sat
		Feb. 10	11	12	13	14
15	16	17	18	19	20	21
22	23	24	25	26	27	28
Mar. 1	2	3	4	5	6	7
8	9	10				

Figure 17.16 *Graphics-based display of medications for symptoms*

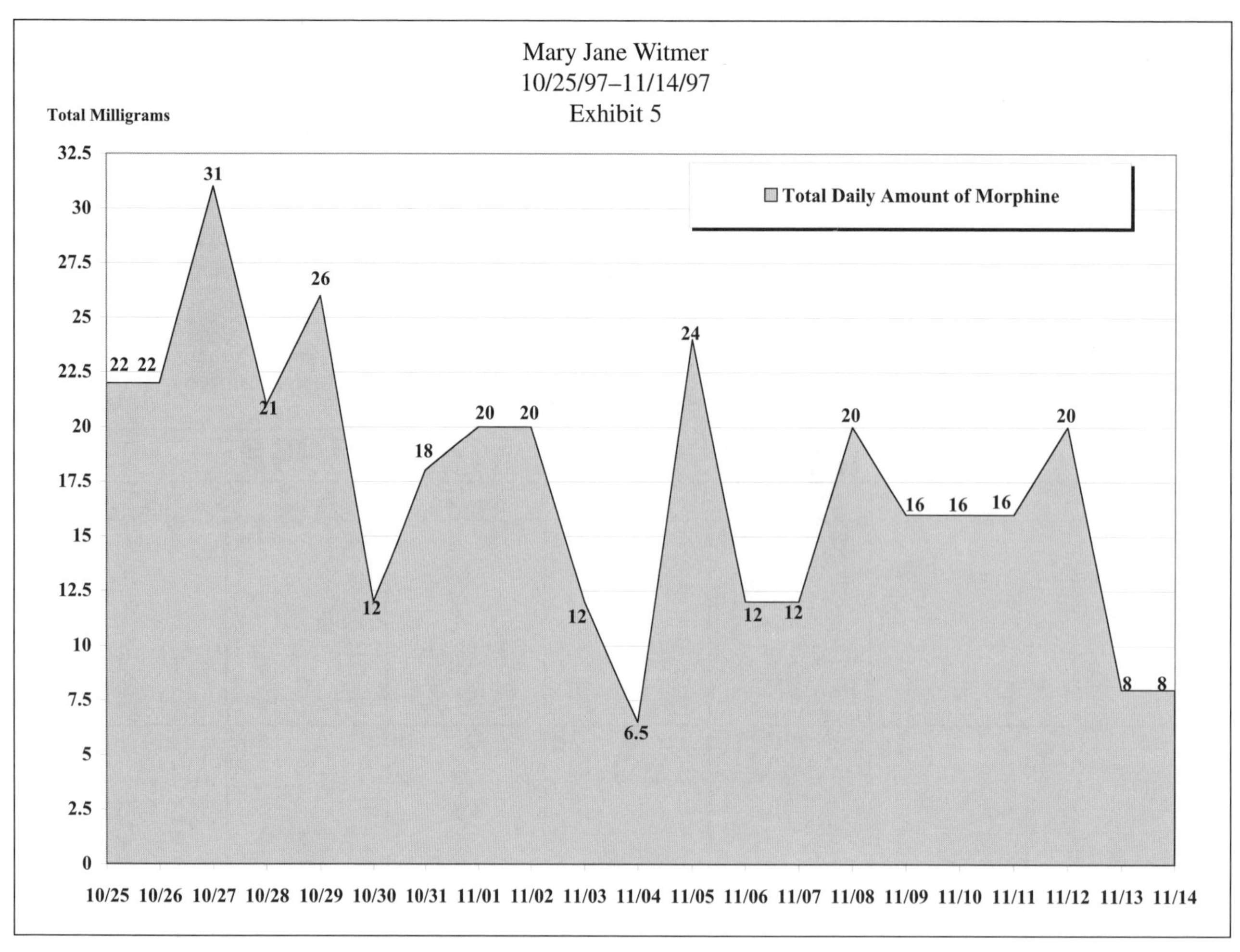

Figure 17.17 *Total amount of morphine received daily*

B. Insertion of Intravenous Needles: Intravenous needles were inserted into Mrs. Lawrence's arms and neck. The insertion of the needles is painful.

C. Two Large Chest Tubes: These were inserted in the operating room. One of the chest tubes was removed on 12/18/99, and the second one was taken out shortly before Mrs. Lawrence died. The tubes, which are the size of a man's thumb, are sutured to the skin. The manipulation of the tubes to prevent fluid clots is painful, as is also the removal of the tubes.

D. Arterial Blood Gases: Multiple blood samples of arterial blood were analyzed for the level of Mrs. Lawrence's oxygenation. These were withdrawn by manipulating the arterial line that was present in her wrist or groin. The manipulation of the arterial line can be painful.

E. Multiple Punctures: Several times each day Mrs. Lawrence's skin was pierced by needles. Multiple tests were performed by withdrawing blood from Mrs. Lawrence's arms and hands. Prior to the accident, Mrs. Lawrence's diabetes was controlled by pills. The stress of her injuries required administration of insulin. Her skin was pricked for drops of blood up to four times a day to test her blood sugar. She received as many as four insulin injections a day. She was given Heparin injections (usually administered into the skin of the abdomen) and Vitamin K injections. During the last six days of her life, the arterial line, which she pulled out, could not be replaced. It was necessary to use a needle to pierce her arteries to obtain blood for blood gases. Arteries are exquisitely sensitive to pain. On 12/18/99, the physician made multiple attempts to insert an arterial line. All were unsuccessful.

F. Nasogastric Tube: The nasogastric tube is inserted into the nose and must be swallowed by the patient to bring it to the stomach. The medical record showed that Mrs. Lawrence had the nasogastric tube inserted on 12/5/99, 12/12/99, 12/15/99, and 12/22/99. The insertion of a nasogastric tube causes a sensation of gagging when the tube touches the gag reflex in the back of the throat. Mrs. Lawrence pulled the nasogastric tube out of her nose on 12/10/99 and 12/23/99, the day she died.

G. Philadelphia Collar: A cervical collar was put on Mrs. Lawrence's neck in the emergency department of Kelly Hospital. This was a precaution to immobilize her neck. The cervical collar restricts the ability to move the head, and is uncomfortable to wear. A nurse's note commented that a dressing was placed under her collar to protect her chest incision from friction from the collar. The collar was kept in place until 12/10/99.

H. Multiple X-Rays: Throughout her stay, Mrs. Lawrence had multiple x-rays. Most of these were done as portable x-rays, which would have involved lifting or turning her to slide the hard x-ray plate under her body.

I. Multiple Cultures: Specimens were taken of her sputum and urine to check for bacteria. Urine cultures are drawn from the Foley catheter, which involves manipulation of the tubing. Respiratory cultures are obtained by suctioning the lungs and trapping the fluid into a container.

J. Suctioning: Removal of fluid from the lungs is an uncomfortable and frightening procedure for patients. The patient must be removed from the ventilator while suctioning is occurring. When a patient is being suctioned, she is unable to breathe. Mrs. Lawrence's lung secretions were described as thick. She was suctioned many times each day.

K. Chest Physical Therapy: Mrs. Lawrence required chest physical therapy during her last week alive. This involves striking the chest with cupped hands to move secretions (called percussion). Given that Mrs. Lawrence had multiple fractured ribs, this procedure would have been painful for her.

L. Bronchoscopy and Tracheostomy: On 12/19/99, after receiving sedation and drugs to chemically paralyze her, a large tube with a light on one end was inserted down Mrs. Lawrence's endotracheal tube. This tube, called a bronchoscope, was used to examine her lungs. Next, her neck was dissected down to her trachea. After her trachea was dilated, a rigid plastic tube was inserted into her trachea. This was attached to the ventilator.

M. Disimpaction: On three occasions, hard stool was manually removed from Mrs. Lawrence's rectum. Removal of hard stool is a painful procedure.

Images and icons may be used to graphically display information about painful treatments and diagnostic tests. Figure 17.18 shows one month's worth of treatment needed after fracture blisters turned into deep open wounds on Ellen Winston's foot. Figure 17.19 was created to show the multiple punctures needed for treating Ester Lawrence. When multiple trips to the radiology department are needed for diagnostic tests, each involving painful movements, a figure like 17.20 can be created.

K. Summary of status at key times

After describing major problems and limitations, it is often helpful to take a step back and provide an overview of the patient's status at key times. The summary of the status may describe the patient's symptoms on admission and discharge from the hospital, rehabilitation facility, and nursing home. Summaries of progress during outpatient treatment help provide an overview of progress.

The following is an overview of Betsy Gordon's status on discharge from the hospital and admission to a rehabilitation facility (after being hit by a bus).

Example:

Status on discharge

Before she was transferred to a rehabilitation facility, Ms. Gordon was allowed to get up using a platform walker. This had an armrest that permitted the patient to rest her weight on her right arm to keep weight off of her leg. Since her left shoulder was

continued on page 377

Ellen Winston
1/14/98–2/10/98

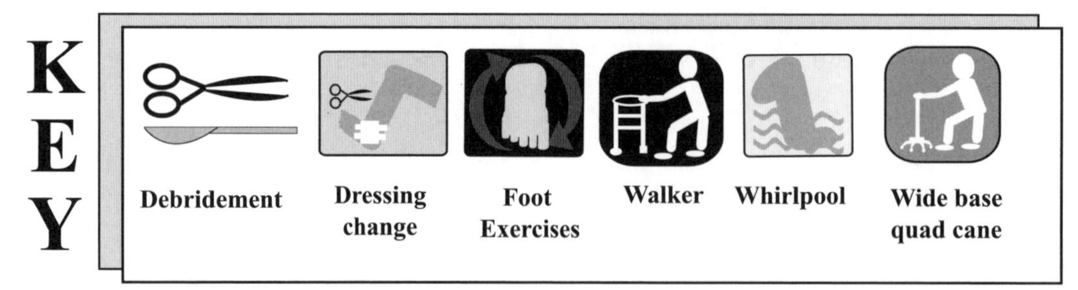

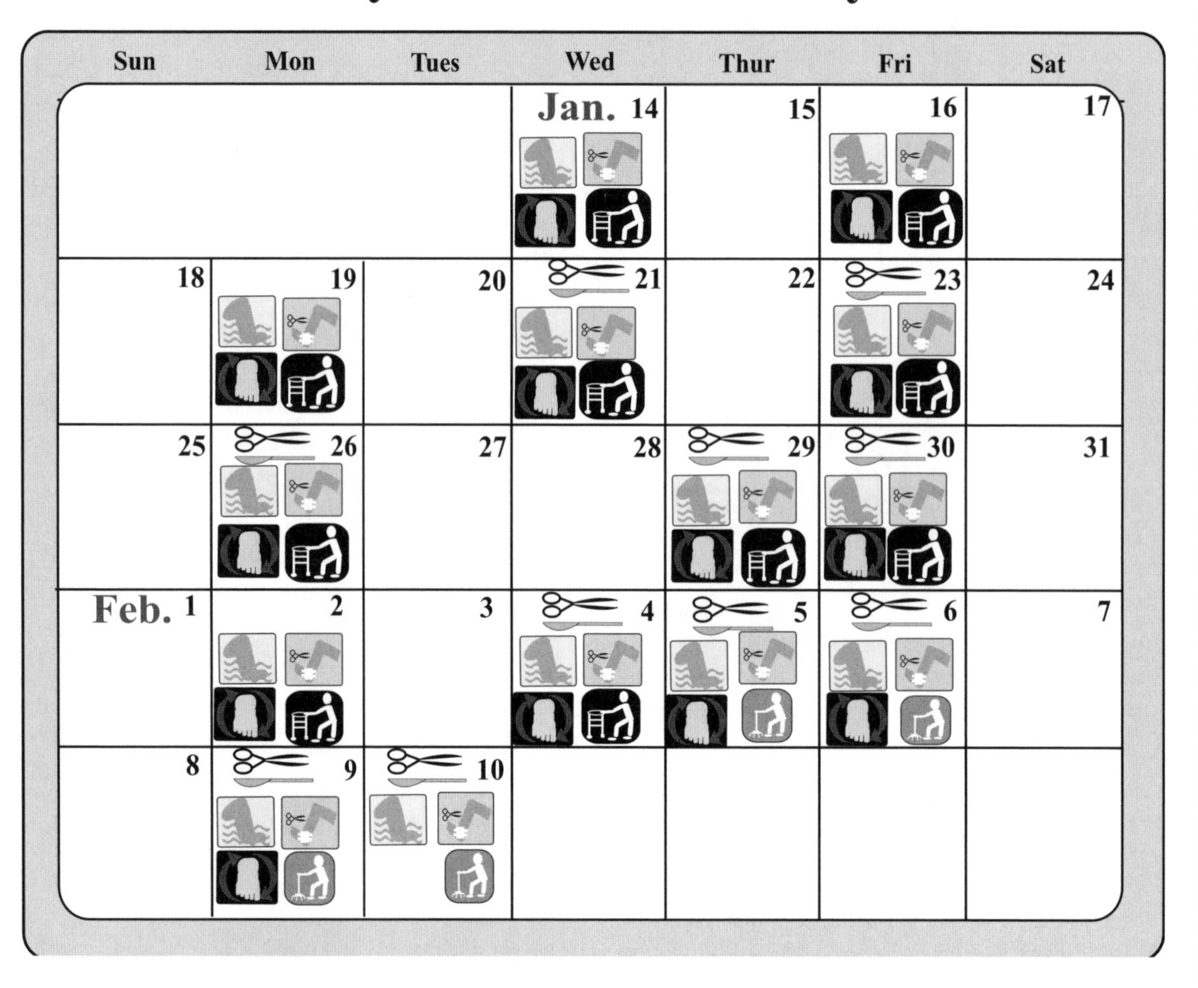

Figure 17.18 Graphics-based display of painful foot care

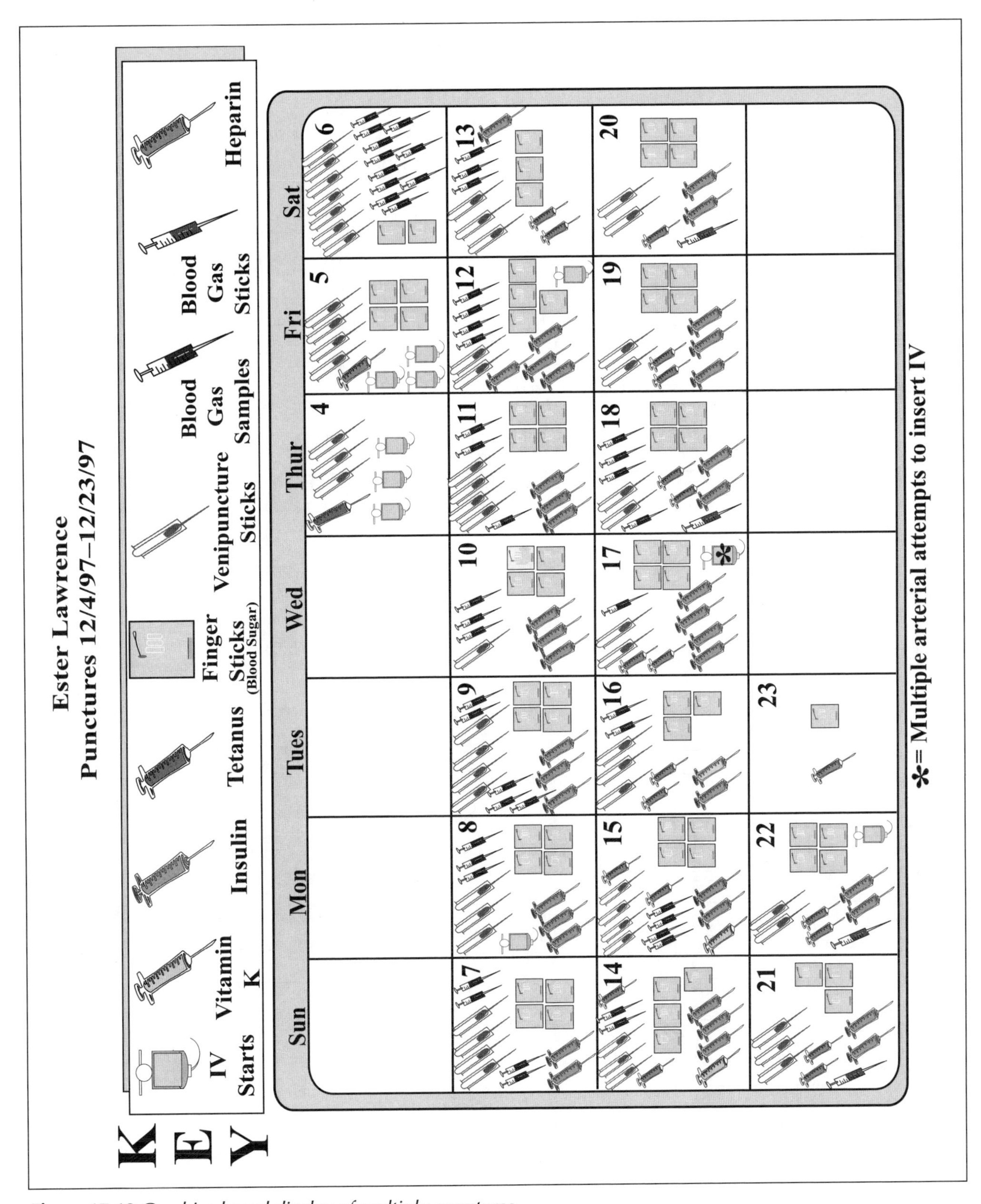

Figure 17.19 *Graphics-based display of multiple punctures*

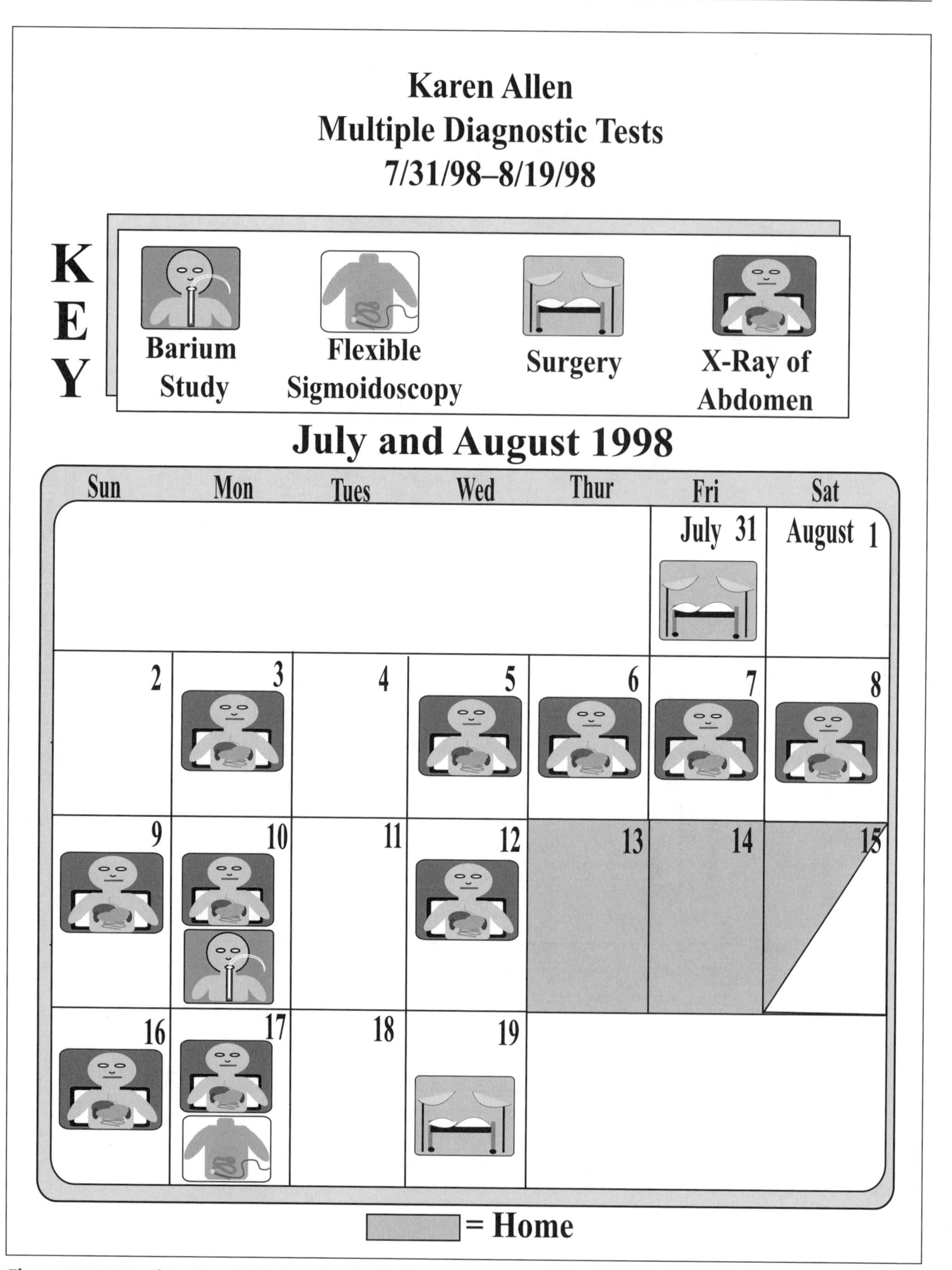

Figure 17.20 Graphics-based display of multiple diagnostic tests

fractured, she could not bear weight on her left arm. She was not allowed to bear weight on her right leg and was allowed to weight bear as tolerated on her left leg. Assistance was needed for bathing and dressing. She needed 3 people to help her transfer from one location to another. A splint was to be placed her knee when she was out of bed and her left arm was to be in a sling. She was unable to sit on the toilet and instead used the bedpan for bowel movements.

The patient was on the following medications at the time of discharge:

1. Percocet 1–2 pills every 4–6 hours for pain
2. Colace (stool softener) twice a day
3. Milk of Magnesia twice a day as needed
4. Dulcolax (laxative) suppository as needed
5. Robaxin (reduces pain and muscle spasms) every six hours
6. Coumadin (blood thinner)
7. Multivitamin with iron
8. Mycostatin powder as needed (antifungal) to affected skin

Richlands Rehabilitation Hospital 6/29/99–7/16/99

A. Condition on Arrival

Ms. Gordon was transferred to Richlands Rehabilitation Hospital on 6/29/99, 19 days after being hit by the bus. She had multiple problems on admission.

1. Medical Condition

A short arm cast was on her right hand. Pain was present in her left leg at the hip and knee. There was a healed surgical incision on her knee and a healing surgical incision on her lower abdomen. There were healed incisions at the chest tube insertion sites in her left chest. Ms. Gordon was alert and oriented. The nurse noted her sacrum was reddened.

2. Physical Limitations

Ms. Gordon was unable to bear weight on her right leg. She was to weight bear as tolerated on her left leg. A platform walker was required. (This has an armrest.) She was to bear weight as tolerated on her left arm (the one with the fractured shoulder). The range of motion of her right hip and left shoulder was limited. She needed help with transfers and had not tried to walk. It required maximum help of four nurses to get her into bed.

3. Occupational Therapy Initial Assessment

Ms. Gordon was evaluated by the occupational therapist on 6/30/99. The patient's goal was "to walk again." She needed minimal assistance with eating after her tray was prepared for her and all containers and utensils were put within her reach. She was independent in grooming. Moderate help was needed with bathing. She needed maximum assistance with toileting and dressing her upper and lower body. She needed maximum assistance to go from a standing to a sitting position, or from bed to wheelchair. She needed maximum help to go from a sitting to a lying down position. Her standing balance was fair. Several goals were established to increase Ms. Gordon's functional abilities.

4. Physical Therapy Initial Assessment

On 6/30/99, Ms. Gordon was evaluated by the physical therapist. Ms. Gordon stated her goals were to be able to walk, to use the bathroom and get out of bed herself. "I want to be self-sufficient." She needed moderate assistance of three people to stand from a wheelchair to a platform walker with her right arm on the platform. Moderate help of two people was needed to move her from the wheelchair to a mat and to go from a lying to a sitting position. She complained of dizziness, pelvic and low back pain during the evaluation when she was sitting. Several goals were established to improve her level of functioning.

L. Description of death

Having explained the injuries, treatment, and condition of the patient from the point of the accident or medical malpractice event, the expert fact witness may conclude the report by describing the patient's condition at the time that the medical records end. In some cases, the records end with the patient's death.

Tip

In keeping with the professional tone of the report, the death should be explained in terms of the clinical details without adding dramatic embellishment.

Example:

Description of Death

Mrs. Lawrence's heart stopped beating at 11:00 a.m. on 12/23/99. At 8:00 a.m., she removed the nasogastric tube out of her stomach. She was receiving intravenous fluids and was given Morphine. At around 10:00 a.m., the physician removed the chest tube. She was taken off the ventilator, and within minutes her oxygen level dropped. An ambu bag was attached to her tracheostomy tube to give her oxygen and she was given breaths manually with the bag. Her oxygen level continued to drop to 80%. Her heart rate dropped into the 50s with frequent irregular beats. A cardiac arrest effort ensured, including medications and being shocked with the defibrillator. After 15 minutes of effort with no response from the patient, the resuscitation was stopped.

Example:

Description of Death

A series of chest x-rays were taken while Mr. Sills was being cared for at Burn Center. The initial x-rays showed relatively clear lungs. By 10/31, the radiologist had diagnosed the beginning of pneumonia. The condition worsened as time went on. During the last 24 hours of his life, Mr. Sills began losing the battle to survive. His heart rate was rapid. At 11 p.m. on 11/1, he appeared to be working at breathing and was fighting the ventilator. He tried to sit up in bed. Versed was given to him to calm him down. His lung sounds indicated the progression of his pneumonia, as the nurses heard coarse lung sounds. The physical therapist documented on the day shift of 11/2 that the plan was to send him to the operating room on 11/4 for debridement of his wounds and application of cadaver skin. Mr. Sills died at 7:12 P.M. on 11/2. In the hours before his death, his heart rate was rapid, and his blood pressure began dropping. He was given Neosynephrine in an attempt to raise his blood pressure. A Swan Ganz catheter was inserted into the right side of his heart and threaded into the pulmonary artery in an effort to monitor his status more closely. Mr. Sills's urinary output began dropping at about 4 p.m. He was observed to be retaining carbon dioxide and was not able to get enough oxygen in his system. His body temperature dropped to 95.5 (at 5:30 P.M. His brother was in to see him at that time. Over the course of the next two hours, his blood pressure and blood oxygen level began to steadily drop. Two chest tubes were inserted. Efforts to reverse the process were not successful. At 7:12 p.m., his heart stopped and he was declared dead.

M. Summary paragraph

The final paragraph of the report should summarize the major points made in the report.

Example:

Summary

Over the course of Mrs. Lawrence's last three weeks of life, she experienced pain, went through emergency surgery, and lost control over her body. She was dependent on others for her most basic needs including eating, elimination, movement, and breathing. Her body was invaded by medical equipment, pierced by needles, and handled by a variety of healthcare workers. Her behavior showed continued agitation and anxiety over the duration of this time with multiple attempts to push away and remove the medical equipment that was needed to sustain her life.

Example:

Summary

Mr. Sills experienced significant amounts of pain and suffering in the aftermath of the fire at the trailer. He suffered from pain and a variety of complications associated with the extensive nature of his burns. Throughout all of his stay at Community Medical Center and the vast majority of his stay at Burn Center, he remained alert and oriented.

Example:

Summary

Mrs. Gary's last six months alive were spent entirely in the hospital, with the exception of a week at home between her two admissions to Holy Cross Hospital. She experienced all of the sensations associated with medical treatment as well as symptoms and problems created by her medical complications. Her ability to move, communicate, and care for herself was severely compromised by her multiple medical problems. She experienced pain in many areas of her body, gastrointestinal distress, respiratory symptoms, rapid heart rates, and skin breakdown. Mrs. Gary reacted to these problems with anxiety and depression. She came to rely on the visits of her family and friends, who witnessed her slow decline. Mrs. Gary was aware of the implications of the termination of the life support and participated in the decision that would lead to her death.

17.4 Overcoming Motions to Prevent Expert Fact Witness Testimony

The attorney may wish to provide the judge with a copy of the nurse's report for the judge's review. The defense attorney can be expected to object to the introduction to the report and the expert's testimony. The defense counsel usually does not want the jury to focus on the pain and suffering experienced by the victim of alleged malpractice for fear that sympathy will be evoked and prejudice the jury's determination of liability and damages. Objections that may be raised by defense counsel are listed below.

A. Objection: Use of treating healthcare workers

This argument states that the plaintiff's attorney should present the treating doctors and nurses to provide the testimony on the patient's experiences.

This argument can be countered by pointing out the impracticality of having dozens of healthcare professionals come to court. In addition, the professionals would most likely not remember this patient and would end up relying on the records. The nursing expert is uniquely qualified to rely on the records to summarize the patient's experiences.

The possibility of calling treating physicians to the witness stand to discuss medical care does not require the exclusion of the testimony of the expert fact witness. Keeping in mind practicality, a singular presentation from an expert fact witness offers an efficient and less costly alternative to presenting each doctor in turn to explain his or her portions of the medical records. A singular presentation is also apt to be more cogent than piecemeal accounts from each of the treating and examining physicians. Even if the plaintiffs or defendants choose to call those physicians at trial and admit the underlying records in toto, the expert fact witness's testimony may still be admitted as a secondary evidence summary.[4]

B. Objection: Repetitive with the plaintiff's testimony

The patient can describe his or her own pain and suffering.

This argument can be countered by asserting that the use of a nurse as a witness does not prevent the patient from also testifying about pain and suffering. However, the nursing expert's focus is not only on the information in the medical records but also on interpreting the information for the jury. The patient lacks the medical knowledge to explain the medical records to the jury. In cases of extended hospitalizations, the patient may be dead. If alive, the patient may have forgotten the details of what happened, spent part of the time in a coma, or sustained injuries which prevent the patient from communicating with the jury.

The expert may use models, drawings, and other exhibits to explain the medical and nursing care that the plaintiff experienced. The use of this demonstrative evidence will help the jury understand the experiences of the plaintiff. The plaintiff is not likely to be able to provide this type of testimony.

C. Objection: There are only two types of witnesses: Fact witnesses and expert witnesses

A fact witness has personal knowledge of the issues of the case. An expert witness expresses an opinion about the conduct of the healthcare professionals. The testimony of an expert fact witness does not fit into either category. Without personal knowledge of the plaintiff, the testimony of the witness should not be admitted.

The expert fact witness did not render nursing or medical care or participate in the treatment of the patient. There are no opinions set forth in the summary of medical records. If the subject matter of expert testimony falls distinctly within a particular field or profession, the individual offered as an expert generally must be a licensed member of that profession. A nurse is not qualified to make comments about the entries of a physician or on the significance of a physician's entry in a medical chart. There is no field of specialty in the interpretation of medical records.[4]

This argument can be addressed by asserting that there are at least three kinds of evidentiary summaries that may be presented in a courtroom. First, there are "primary evidence summaries" that are typically used to condense voluminous materials that cannot be conveniently examined in court. *United States v. Bray*, 139 F.3d 1104, 1112 (6th Cir. 1998); see also 1 Devitt, Federal Jury Practice and Instructions 14.02 (4th ed. 1992). See also Fed. R. Evid. 1006. Second there are "pedagogical-device summaries," more commonly described as "demonstrative aids" which are presented to summarize, clarify, or simplify proofs admitted in the case. These devices include chalkboard drawings, graphs, charts, calculations, or models, but are not themselves admitted into evidence, and instead are used as aids to presenting and understanding the evidence. *United States v. Bray*, 139 F.3d at 1112; 1 Devitt, supra at § 14.02. See also *White Industries v. Cessna Aircraft Co.*, 611 F. Supp 1049, 1069 (W.D. Mo. 1985) distinguishing between "pedagogical" demonstrative aids that undertake to "summarize or organize other evidence" and Rule 1006 summaries offered in lieu of the supporting materials. Third, a trial advocate may present "secondary-evidence summaries." There are hybrids of the first two categories, admitted "not in lieu of the evidence they summarize but in addition thereto." *United States v. Bray*, 139 F.3d at 1112; see also *Untied States v. Citron*, 783 F.2d 307, 317 n. 10 (2d Cir. 1986). Secondary-evidence summaries are permitted where, "in the judgment of the trial court such summaries so accurately and reliably summarize complex or difficult evidence . . . as to materially assist the jurors in better understanding the evidence." *United States v. Bray*, supra, 139 F.3d at 1112. Such devices are "not prepared entirely in compliance with Rule 1006 and yet are more than mere pedagogical devices." *Id.* The summary of an expert fact witness should be analyzed under the first and last of these evidential categories (i.e., either as a primary-evidence summary under Evid. R. 1006 admitted in lieu of the medical records or as a secondary-evidence summary designed to accompany the admission of these records).[2]

A nurse has the technical and specialized knowledge that will assist the trier of fact to understand the evidence. Evid. R. 703. The nurse need not be a physician to describe the medications or treatments the patient received or to translate the common medical symbols appearing on the patient's charts. Also, the nurse need not offer any expert opinions in her limited trial role as a summary provider. As Rule 703 explicitly recognizes, an expert may testify in the form of an opinion "or otherwise."[2]

D. Objection: Jury can read records

This argument states that the jury can review the medical records that the plaintiffs enter into evidence and consider those records during their deliberations.

This point can be refuted by asserting that the role of the expert fact witness is to assist the jury in the damages phase of the trial. The witness extracts information from medical records and explains them to the jury so that they are in more understandable terms. Medical records are extensive and highly technical. Records are replete with technical medical jargon which would not be readily understood by lay jurors without substantial definition and explanation. If the records were admitted as exhibits at trial without explanatory testimony, they would be apt to cause serious confusion in the jury room.[2]

An evidential summary may be presented in the form of a written document or by live testimony. Live testimony can often be more readily understood and accessed by a lay jury than dry written materials. Moreover, such testimony may be more effectively impeached by an adversary than a stack of paper exhibits.[2]

The medical records must be voluminous and not conveniently examined in court. There is no requirement in Rule 1006 that they be literally impossible to examine before a summary or chart may be used. Rather than imposing such a harsh standard of impossibility, "all that is required for the rule to apply is that the underlying writings be 'voluminous' and that in-court examination not be convenient." *United States v. Scales*, 594 F.2d 558, 561-65 (6th Cir. 1979).[2]

E. Objection: Use expert witnesses to present information

The plaintiff's expert witnesses can discuss the medical records and any entries that the plaintiffs find relevant or significant in support of their case.

This argument can be addressed by pointing out that the expert fact witness's report focuses on a detailed summary of the medical record. The expert witness's report typically provides a brief summary of the medical issues and then defines the standard of care and the deviations from the standards of care. The other expert witnesses concentrate on liability issues when reviewing the records. Moreover, when a physician expert witness reviews records, he or she is evaluating care provided by physicians. Nursing care, which makes up the bulk of the care provided in hospitals, rehabilitation facilities, and nursing homes, is best summarized by nurses.

F. Objection: Prejudicial nature of the testimony will outweigh the probative value

This rule prevents exposing the jury to prejudicial material presented as a representation of the plaintiff's injuries.

The attorney may counter this argument can by asserting that the subject matter of a personal injury or medical malpractice claim is not pleasant, but it is very relevant to the plaintiff's damages case. The plaintiff is to present the expert fact witness's testimony in a balanced, fair, and dispassionate manner. The summary of the medical records, and the exhibits created as a part of that process, should avoid incorporating particularly graphic photographs and other material that may be deemed prejudicial.

Appendix 17.1 presents a hypothetical motion in limine based on a brief and the response to the defense attorney's objection to having the expert fact witness testify in the Betsy Gordon case. These arguments were not heard since the case settled before trial. It can be anticipated that the types of arguments raised by the defense attorney are typical reactions to this offered testimony.

17.5 Summary

Pain and suffering may result from injuries. The consequences of these injuries can include pain from a variety of sources arising from the injuries and from treatments. The medical treatment designed to treat the injuries often creates even more discomfort. Suffering also results from the effects the injuries have on the patient's quality of life. The pain and suffering nursing expert witness can be an effective addition to the expert testimony used in malpractice and personal injury cases. Reports can include key concepts and documents, helping the trier of fact to understand the totality of the plaintiff's experiences.

Endnotes

1. "Rating Procedural Pain." *American Journal of Nursing*, 99 (9–10), September 1999.

2. "Patients' Experience of Tube Removal." *American Journal of Nursing*, 99 (8), 24AA, August 1999.

3. Judge Sabatino, Superior Court of New Jersey Law Division, Mercer County, May 9, 2002.

4. Letter by Joseph Lang, Esq. of Lenox, Socey, Wilgus, Formidoni, Brown, Giordano and Casey, to Clerk of Mercer County, October 15, 2001.

Additional Reading

Agency for Healthcare Policy and Research, *Acute Pain Management: Operative or Medical Procedures and Trauma.* Rockville, MD: U.S. Department of Health and Human Services, 1992.

Bach, S., Noreng, M., and Tjellden, N., "Phantom Limb Pain in Amputees during the First Twelve Months Following Limb Amputation, after Preoperative Lumbar Epidural Blockade." *Pain,* 1988, 33, 297.

Barsky, A., "Approach to the Angry Patient." In Goroll, editor, *Primary Care Medicine*, Third Edition, Philadelphia: Lippincott-Raven, 1995.

Clark, C., "Posttraumatic Stress Disorder: How to Support Healing." *American Journal of Nursing*, 1997, August, 97 (8), 27.

Cleeland, C., et al., "Pain and Treatment of Pain in Minority Patients with Cancer. The Eastern Cooperative Oncology Group Minority Outpatient Pain Study." *Annuals of Internal Medicine,* 1997, 127 (9), 813.

Etches, R., "Pain Control in the Perioperative Period." *Surgical Clinics of North America,* 1999, April, 79 (2), 297.

Iyer, P., and Beerman, J., "The Expert Fact Witness." In Iyer, P., editor, *Principles and Practices of Legal Nurse Consulting*, Second Edition. Boca Raton: CRC Press, 2003.

Jablonski, R., "If Ventilator Patients Could Talk." *RN*, 1995, February, 32.

Loeb, J., "Pain Management in Long-Term Care." *American Journal of Nursing,* 99 (2), 48, February 1999.

McCaffery, M., and Ferrell, B., "Opioids and Pain Management: What Do Nurses Know?" *Nursing,* 99, 48, March, 1999.

McCaffery, M., "Pain Control." *American Journal of Nursing,* 99 (8), 18, August 1999.

Ng, B., et al.," The Effect of Ethnicity on Prescriptions for Patient-Controlled Analgesia for Postoperative Pain." *Pain,* 66 (1), 9, 1996.

Pasero, C., "Using Continuous Infusion with PCA." *American Journal of Nursing,* 99 (2), 22, February 1999.

Pasero, C., "Epidural Analgesia in Children" *American Journal of Nursing*, 99 (5), 20, May 1999.

Wiebelhaus, P., and Hansen, S., "Burns." *RN,* 62 (11), 52, November 1999.

Young, D., "Acute Pain Management Protocol." *Journal of Gerontological Nursing*, 1999, June, 10.

Appendix to Chapter 17

Hypothetical Argument Supporting Qualification of Expert Fact Witness

I. Opening Statement by Paul Pierson, Esq., Plaintiff's Attorney

Ladies and gentlemen of the jury, thank you for your attention. The evidence will show that my client, Betsy Gordon, was thirty-four years old on a beautiful day in June in 1999. Betsy was a star athlete who loved to participate in triathlons during her free time. She prided herself in her strength and fitness. Betsy worked at a children's center taking care of emotionally disturbed kids. Her job involved being on her feet all day, bending and lifting. She had to be able to respond quickly if the children needed holding or to prevent them from hurting each other.

Betsy is an only child. After going to college, Betsy moved into her own home, a mobile home. She was proud of her independence. Although she had a loving relationship with her parents, she enjoyed having a place of her own.

On June 10, 1999, Betsy was riding her bike on the shoulder of a country road. The evidence will show that the bus left the travel portion of the road surface. Betsy was hit from behind by a 30,000 pound bus that was traveling at 55 miles per hour. She was thrown fifteen feet through the air and landed in a nearby field. The medical evidence we will present will show that Betsy suffered devastating injuries to her pelvis, hip and knee. She had multiple other broken bones. She underwent months of rehabilitation and physical therapy. You will hear testimony from Betsy that she was forced to move back with her parents when she first got out of the rehabilitation hospital. She had to give up her independence and become dependent on her parents for her most basic needs. She was unable to walk without the assistance of a walker, and then a cane. It took months before she was able to drive again and almost a year before she was able to get back on a bike.

The evidence will show that the bus driver, Richard Felton, did not see Betsy before he hit her. He has admitted that he was at fault. We are here to decide how Betsy should be compensated for the loss of her health, for her months of treatment, and for her permanent pain and limitations in her knee. Betsy would love to turn the clock back and have her fitness again. She would give anything to be able to alter the events and relive that day and not be on that road at the time Richard Felton was driving down the road. However, Betsy cannot change what happened. She cannot turn back the clock.

You will hear her orthopaedist, a world famous doctor, testify that Betsy's injuries will get worse as she ages. She already has signs of post traumatic arthritis and can expect to have prosthetic knees and hips in the future. You will hear that Betsy had $125,000 in medical bills and had a wage loss of between $300,000 to $1.2 million. You will hear that she lost out on a promotion at work and that there are limitations to what she can do now.

You have been asked to participate in helping Betsy resolve this accident. Betsy does not want your sympathy. You are the only people in the world who will hear the full story of what happened to Betsy after the accident. You are the only people who are in a position to compensate Betsy for what she has lost. This is Betsy's only chance to obtain compensation for her injuries. She won't be able to come back in fifteen years when she requires her total knee replacement or her total hip surgeries. This case is about pain and suffering.

It is about the destruction of bones by a bus. It is about months and years of pain. This case is simply entitled *Bus versus Bike.* When a bus and a bike collide, the person on the bike always loses.

At the end of our testimony, we will ask you to make a decision about how Betsy will be compensated for her devastating injuries. It is my hope that you will be fair and generous in your decision making. My client is entitled to recover for pain and suffering, embarrassment and humiliation, for her medical costs and lost income and for everything that she endured as a proximate result of the bus striking her.

II. Opening Statement by Diane Dunne, Esq., Defense Attorney

Ladies and gentlemen of the jury, I represent the bus driver. We are here today because of an unfortunate accident. Accidents are just that—accidents. My client did not get up that morning saying to himself, "Who can I hit today?" The very unfortunate accident was our fault. We admit that. We are here to decide what to do about Betsy. You will hear testimony that Betsy has made an excellent recovery. She rides her bike and drives her car. Betsy is very active today—perhaps more active than many people. She is not in a wheelchair, and she can work. I would ask that you keep that in mind when you complete your job on the jury.

Judge: Mr. Pierson, before you call your first witness, I understand there is a motion to be heard. Jury, you may be excused. When you return to the jury room, remember my earlier instruction that you are not to discuss this case amongst you. Mrs. Dunne, I understand you have filed a motion to preclude the testimony of Nurse Iyer. You may present your position.

Diane Dunne: Your honor, the defense objects to the use of Nurse Iyer as an expert in this trial. She was not involved in the plaintiff's treatment in any way. There are no nursing issues involved in this case. There are no claims of medical malpractice in the care of this patient. Since plaintiff intends to call her treating physicians as witnesses, Nurse Iyer's testimony is cumulative of the testimony of her doctors and the plaintiff herself. Nurse Iyer's report, exhibits and slide show are highly prejudicial and inflammatory, and given the cumulative nature of the report, that prejudice far outweighs any marginal probative value.

Nurse Iyer's background and expertise are strictly in nursing. She lacks any specialized medical education or experience. The practice of professional nursing is defined as "diagnosing and treating human responses to actual or potential health problems through such services as case finding, health teaching, health counseling, and provision of care supportive to or restorative of life and well being, and executing medical regimens as prescribed by a licensed physician or dentist." Nurse Iyer lacks the skill, training, knowledge, or experience to summarize the plaintiff's medical records. The medical records consist of medical diagnoses, treatments, and prognoses. A medical doctor, and not a nurse, is competent to provide analysis and summary of *medical* records. Nurse Iyer cannot provide such a summary. She is merely a nurse. Plaintiff's treating physicians are the appropriate personnel to explain the surgical procedures, diagnoses, and other purely medical details, as distinguished from nursing events. Nurse Iyer's mere familiarity with these matters does not qualify her to provide an appropriate, accurate, and reliable medical summary.

The primary purpose of expert testimony is to assist the trier of fact in understanding complicated matters, not simply to assist one party in winning the case. An examination of Nurse Iyer's report, exhibits, and slide show clearly demonstrates that she anticipates doing nothing more than selectively repeating the medical record without bringing any nursing expertise to bear upon issues pertinent to the fact finder. Nowhere in the report does Nurse Iyer comment upon Plaintiff's nursing regimen or any nursing care related issues. The plaintiff is perfectly capable of testifying about her course of treatment and symptoms.

Finally, Nurse Iyer's report and slide show contain photographs of the injuries of Betsy Gordon. These photographs are highly prejudicial. Her report contains a diagram of Ms. Gordon's fractured hip. This drawing is so rudimentary that it can not properly be qualified or explained except by its author. Without the exhibit's caption, it is questionable whether anyone would know what it is.

Judge: Counsel, are you finished?

Diane Dunne: Yes, your honor.

Judge: Mr. Pierson, you may respond.

Paul Pierson: My esteemed adversary argued earlier that Nurse Iyer was not qualified to summarize medical records. As Ms. Dunne herself noted, the practice of nursing includes health teaching and the provision of care supportive to or restorative of life and well-being, and executing medical regimens as prescribed by a licensed physician. In order for Nurse Iyer to function as a nurse, she must be able to interpret and analyze medical records. Part of the role of the registered nurse is to be able to use and explain equipment such as Foley catheters, Hoyer lifts, Rotorest beds, nasogastric tubes, and the other equipment that is explained in her report. Patient education is a basic function of all nurses. Nurse Iyer will be applying her expertise in patient education to help the jury understand the medical and nursing details of Betsy Gordon's care.

Nurse Iyer's testimony is permitted under Rule 702. It states "If scientific, technical or other specialized knowledge beyond that possessed by a layperson will assist the trier of fact to understand the evidence or to determine a fact in issue, a witness qualified as an expert by knowledge, skill, experience, training or education may testify thereto in the form of an opinion or otherwise." As a registered nurse with thirty years of experience, Nurse Iyer has specialized knowledge beyond that possessed by the jury. She has expertise in understanding and interpreting medical records.

Your honor, my adversary has argued that nowhere in Nurse Iyer's report does she comment on nursing care related issues. As you will note from reviewing her report, she comments on several nursing care related issues, including the symptoms my client experienced after she was run down by the bus driven by Mr. Felton.

Judge: Now Mr. Pierson, let's stick to the arguments. Save the dramatics for the jury.

Paul Pierson: I'm sorry, Your Honor. Nurse Iyer's report describes the many sources of discomfort my client experienced, her difficulty eating, her emotional distress, her dependence on others, just to name a few. These are all issues nurses are educated to treat as part of their role in providing care to patients such as my client. Further, my adversary has argued that my client, Betsy Gordon, is capable of testifying about her medical treatment and symptoms. My client was sedated for part of her admission, although capable of feeling and reacting to her medical treatment. She lacks the specialized knowledge and training that Nurse Iyer has, and is unable to explain to the jury why certain treatments were performed on her. Nurse Iyer has the educational background to be able to explain the drawing of Miss Gordon's fractured hip, one that my adversary objected to as rudimentary. Clearly Nurse Iyer was able to understand it, when my adversary could not! This is exactly why the jury needs Nurse Iyer to help them understand what happened to my client. It is unclear how the defense can assert that Ms. Iyer serves no useful purpose whatsoever when, in fact, when she has just assisted the defense counsel understand the nature of Ms. Gordon's pelvic fractures.

Further, the defense has had five months to obtain a counter expert, and they have no one. There is not a single defense expert who in any way questions the accuracy, appropriateness or reliability of the medical information in Ms. Iyer's report. The defense's orthopaedic surgeon reviewed Ms. Iyer's report as part of his medical opinion. He does not, in any manner, criticize her report. I'd like to stress that the defense argues that the plaintiff can testify to her course of medical treatment. My client, who had just been struck by a 30,000 pound bus going 55 miles per hour, was in no condition to even think! In a case such as this, where the plaintiff was in the hospital for three weeks, there would be testimony from at least twenty-five to thirty different healthcare professionals including doctors, nurses, and therapists to accurately convey that which Ms. Iyer is conveying in the course of approximately one hour's worth of testimony. To request that photographs of the plaintiff's injuries not be utilized at the time of the trial under the guise that they are prejudicial is simply wrong. In fact, it would be prejudicial to the plaintiff to not be able to accurately display the full extent of her injuries to the jury. These are simply photographs of bruises. Simply because the bruises may be a foot in circumference does not make them more prejudicial to the defense.

I would also cite Rule of Evidence 1006, which states that the contents of voluminous writings, recordings, photographs, which cannot be conveniently examined in court may be presented in the form of a chart, summary, or calculation. Nurse Iyer's report and testimony will assist the jury in understanding my client's voluminous medical records.

Judge: Are you finished?

Paul Pierson: Yes, your honor.

Judge: Mrs. Dunne, do you have anything further?

Diane Dunne: Yes, if the court please. I want to add that Nurse Iyer continually states her personal interpretation of the plaintiff's medical treatments. She frequently comments on plaintiff's injuries, using such terms as "large amounts of bruising," "extensive bruising," "fortunately did not disrupt her elbow joint," "maximum assistance," "moderate assistance" and "minimal assistance." The subjective nature of Nurse Iyer's characterization of plaintiff's injuries demonstrates that the sole purpose of this testimony is to excite the passions of the jury rather than to provide an accurate, brief and objective summary of the medical record which is too voluminous for the jury to otherwise comprehend.

Judge: Are you now finished?

Diane Dunne: Yes, Your Honor.

Judge: Counsel, any response?

Paul Pierson: Yes, Your Honor. The comments which my esteemed colleague has just cited are taken directly from the medical records of my client. The terms are not Nurse Iyer's but those of the doctors, nurses and therapists who attended my client. Why, if Mrs. Dunne would like to see, I can point out each term and where it is located in the medical record.

Judge: That will not be necessary, Mr. Pierson. I am satisfied that Nurse Iyer has performed a thorough review of the medical record. I agree that she possesses specialized skill, knowledge, experience and training well beyond that of the average layperson. She is familiar with medical terminology and has worked with medical records in the course of her duties as a nurse. She has taken direction from medical professionals and implemented instructions and orders. I do not wish to spend excessive court time bringing in a parade of doctors and nurses to testify about the treatment they rendered to the plaintiff.

Furthermore, I agree that the medical records are voluminous in this case and filled with symbols, abbreviations, and terms not understood by the average layperson. I find that the medical records are difficult to interpret without Nurse Iyer's testimony. I do not believe that Betsy Gordon's doctors are prepared to render such detailed and extensive testimony, as Nurse Iyer will in this case. I find that the Pennsylvania Rules of Evidence permit this type of witness to testify. Further, I do not find the photographs of the plaintiff to be prejudicial. The images of normal anatomy are also acceptable, as they are intended to provide the jury with an understanding of the issues in this case. Her testimony is permitted and I will allow the jury to hear her. Further, I will allow the jury to see the photographs of the plaintiff which are part of the slide presentation. Anything further Mrs. Dunne?

Diane Dunne: Judge, Nurse Iyer's' report does not constitute evidence in this case. We respectfully ask the court to prohibit Nurse Iyer's report from being entered into evidence or being placed with the jury while they deliberate.

Judge: I disagree. Nurse Iyer may testify and her report will be placed into evidence. Mr. Pierson, you may call Nurse Iyer to the stand.

Chapter 18

Trial Exhibits: Legal and Strategic Considerations

Patricia Iyer, MSN, RN, LNCC, Stephen Appelbaum, CEP, EPIC, and John M. Parisi, Esq.

Synopsis

18.1 Introduction

> A lawyer who has not added visual communication to his or her courtroom presentation is virtually committing malpractice. "It's too slick" and similar excuses don't fly. There is no longer any issue that your presentation has to be both verbal and visual. Not only is there no study which says, "no" to visual communication, every study says YES—visual communication is necessary.[1]

Demonstrative evidence has come to play a larger role in trials for several reasons. The pioneering efforts of Melvin Belli in the last half of the 20th century towards the effective use of visual aids set the stage for the attorney to begin to "think outside the box" in terms of courtroom persuasion. The law, by tradition, has been a profession of words and oratory in the courtroom, but we are living in a visual society today. The "baby boomers" have been brought up in front of television sets and are more accustomed to seeing and hearing the news than reading it from a printed page. The success of the newspaper *USA Today* is an example of the use of visual support (in the form of maps, charts, and graphics) to supplement the printed story.

Even television has maximized the use of visual support for the spoken word, by broadcasting the actual event as opposed to the reporter's summary and retelling of the events. When introducing a story for a news segment, there will usually be a graphic icon or symbol of some kind on the screen next to the reporter to anchor visually the general nature of the story. Because demonstrative evidence can be a powerful influence in determining the outcome of a case, use of exhibits is vital to courtroom persuasion. Demonstrative exhibits do not have to be complicated or expensive to be effective. A simple line drawing can provide great assistance to a witness describing the care the plaintiff required. A photograph of a scar can nonetheless provide details that would otherwise be very difficult to describe by verbal testimony alone.

18.2 Types of Trial Exhibits

There are three primary types of trial exhibits: real evidence, demonstrative evidence, and visual aids. Although different terminology is used to describe these various types of exhibits, all three are generally recognized.

A. Real evidence

Real evidence consists of actual objects or writings that constitute facts in the case. Examples of real evidence in a case involving injuries would include actual physical objects, such as restraints, the original medical record, an incident report, or a prosthetic device. These tangible items of real evidence are probative in and of themselves, are admitted into evidence and become part of the trial record. Once admitted, real evidence is generally made available for the jury to view and is usually taken to the jury room during deliberations.

B. Demonstrative evidence

Demonstrative evidence is defined as "evidence in the form of objects that have in themselves no probative value but are used to illustrate and clarify the factual matter at issue."[2] As with many definitions there is a technical answer as well as a practical explanation. More simply, demonstrative evidence refers to exhibits created or obtained for the trial of the case. These exhibits are not derived from the event that is subject of the litigation but are usually created after the fact by counsel for the purpose of illustrating, describing, or teaching the jury about the events or issues in the case. Demonstrative exhibits commonly include diagrams, charts, graphs, models, movable figures, computer graphics, videotape, and any other exhibit that makes a witness's oral testimony more easily understood by the jury.

Tip

In today's court system, demonstrative evidence is discussed in terms of the "visual support" of evidence presentation, although the other senses, especially hearing, are eligible for inclusion, albeit on a less frequent basis.

For a demonstrative exhibit to be admissible, its proponent must establish that (1) the exhibit will assist a witness in testifying or (2) that the demonstrative exhibit will help the judge or jury better understand the evidence. Before using demonstrative evidence, counsel should request the court's permission to do so out of the jury's presence. Demonstrative exhibits are often admitted into evidence and become part of the permanent trial record. Some judges may not permit demonstrative exhibits to be used by the jury during deliberations because they are not part of the "real" evidence of the case.

C. Visual aids

Visual aids are primarily created and used by attorneys to communicate information and ideas to help the jury understand the client's case. Visual aids are generally not considered to be real or demonstrative evidence and are not considered or admitted into evidence. Visual aids may be used during final argument, opening statement, and testimony. Examples of visual aids include a prepared chart summarizing evidence, overhead transparencies summarizing expert testimony, part of an opening statement used with an overhead projector, or an enlargement of the verdict form to be described during final argument. Other examples are a white marker board, flipchart, easel, or other blank surfaces on which counsel lists terms, dates, names of witnesses, or other summaries of testimony of a witness during direct or cross-examination.

The difference between demonstrative exhibits and visual aids is not very clear, and some judges treat them in the same fashion. However, visual aids are not usually marked as exhibits and are not received into evidence as part of the court record. It is advisable to tell the court in advance that the attorney plans to use the visual aids, especially if they will be used during opening statement or during testimony. The judge has discretion to permit or deny the use of visual aids in the courtroom. Since they are not admitted into evidence, visual aids are generally not given to the jury during deliberations.

18.3 Purposes of Trial Exhibits

A. Preservation and presentation

Many attorneys do not consider the preparation of trial exhibits until the very end stages of the case, as the days and hours tick away to the start of the trial. In fact, the preparation of demonstrative evidence should begin on the first day the attorney is involved in the case.

Effective demonstrative evidence starts with the proper preservation of all aspects of the case that can be visually documented. Transient elements of fact need to be recorded and documented as soon as possible.

B. Burden of proof

As is true with liability and causation, it is also the plaintiff's burden to prove damages with reasonable certainty. Demonstrative evidence is used to that end. Courts take various approaches to the evaluation of whether a jury's award for future pain and suffering is supported by the evidence. For example, under Kansas law the standard of evaluation by which an award for pain and suffering is measured is such amount as reasonable persons estimate to be fair compensation when that amount appears to be in harmony with the evidence arrived at without passion or prejudice. *Kerns by and through Kerns v. G.A.C., Inc.*, 875 P.2d 949, 255 Kan. 264 (1994). Because pain and suffering, as noneconomic elements of damages have no known dimensions (mathematical or financial), the only standard for evaluation is such amount as reasonable persons estimate to be fair compensation for the injuries suffered. Administration of this criterion is entrusted to the impartial conscience and judgment of jurors, who may be expected to act reasonably, intelligently, and in harmony with the evidence. Under Kansas law, as is true in most states, an award for future pain and suffering will be overturned only if the award shocks the collective conscience of the appellate court.

In *Hoover v. Innovative Health of Kansas, Inc.*, 988 P.2d 287, 26 Kan. App. 2d 447 (1999), the Kansas Court of Appeals upheld the jury's determination of an award for pain and suffering for a woman who had fallen on four separate occasions in a Kansas nursing home. The plaintiff, Bessie Moore, entered the nursing home in May of 1992. Her daughter brought suit against the nursing home in August of 1994 alleging that her mother had fallen and suffered injury on four separate occasions as a result of the nursing home's negligence and carelessness. Specifically, the plaintiff alleged that her mother was injured in August of 1992 when she fell from a wheelchair; October of 1992 when she was discovered on the floor by her bed; February of 1993, when she suffered a broken leg of unknown origin; and March of 1993, when she fell from the toilet. After a six-day trial, a jury found the nursing home at fault for each of the four incidents and awarded the following damages:

- $500 for pain and suffering and $5,000 for disability, mental anguish, and disfigurement for the August 1992 wheelchair incident;
- $50,000 for pain and suffering and $200,000 for disability, mental anguish, and disfigurement for the October 1992 incident where Moore was found on the floor by her bed;
- $7,500 for pain and suffering and $25,000 for disability, mental anguish, and disfigurement for the February 1993 broken leg; and
- $40,000 for pain and suffering and $100,000 for disability, mental anguish, and disfigurement for the March 1993 broken hip incident.

In rejecting the defendant's argument that the verdict was excessive and not supported by the evidence, the Kansas Court of Appeals cited the trial court's finding on this issue, which included:

> The defendant argues that there is insufficient evidence to support the jury's award of damages to the plaintiff for disability, disfigurement and mental anguish.
>
> . . . [t]he plaintiff, Pat Hoover, testified that she was called to the nursing home following the wheelchair incident and her mother was crying, was afraid, and couldn't say what was wrong. In September, following the wheelchair fall, the nursing home called Pat Hoover and asked her to approve an evaluation of Ms. Moore by a psychiatrist because she was becoming combative. The nursing home notes made by the social worker state that Ms. Moore no longer wanted to participate in activities and was depressed. Dr. Fulbright (Ms. Moore's personal physician) testified concerning her condition and the full nursing home records

> were available for the jury to review. They indicate changes in her behavior and condition. This evidence is sufficient to support the award by the jury of $500 for pain and suffering and $5,000 for mental anguish.
>
> Following the back injury Ms. Moore became a total assist patient. Her physical condition deteriorated. She had to be assisted in every activity. She was given medication for pain. Evidence concerning her condition came from the testimony of Dr. Fulbright, Dr. Reeves, Pat Hoover, and other nursing home personnel, and from the nursing notes contained in the nursing home records. Dr. Reeves and Dr. Dennis testified to the seriousness of the back injury and to the amount of pain that a "burst" fracture, where a piece of bone is injected into the spinal canal, would cause for the patient. The doctors testified that Ms. Moore would not suffer less pain because of her age and condition. She could no longer participate in any of the nursing home activities. There is sufficient evidence to support an award of damages by the jury for disability and mental anguish.
>
> Defendant argues there is no evidence that Ms. Moore had pain, suffering, disability, disfigurement or mental anguish as a result of the broken femur. The physicians called by the plaintiff testified that a broken femur is a painful injury. It is one of the heaviest bones in the body. There are nurse's notes following the injury which indicate that (Ms. Moore) was in pain. [The use of nurse's notes as evidence is addressed in Chapter 19, "Trial Exhibits: Preparation and Use."] The reason she was taken to the hospital in the first place was because she was in pain and distress. The defendant's argument is that since Ms. Moore was totally disabled before the leg injury she could not become more disabled after the injury. Clearly, whatever use she had of her leg before the injury was restricted even further by the injury. There is evidence from which the jury could find that Ms. Moore suffered pain, increased disability, and increased mental anguish as a result of the leg injury.
>
> Defendant argues that any pain or mental anguish suffered by Ms. Moore as a result of a broken hip is duplicative of pain she was already suffering from her previous injuries. Ms. Moore had surgery as a result of the broken hip. Her movement was further restricted. She had a surgical scar. She developed a decubitus ulcer, which the various experts testified is painful . . . . There is evidence to support the jury's finding that plaintiff suffered damage for pain and suffering, disability, disfigurement, and mental anguish as a result of the hip injury.

The Court of Appeals upheld the award, noting that the plaintiff's witnesses presented ample evidence of Ms. Moore's pain and suffering, disfigurement and mental anguish and that the credibility of the witnesses and the appropriate amount of damages to compensate the plaintiff was for the jury to decide. The court found no abuse of discretion on the part of the trial court in upholding the award of noneconomic damages rendered by the jury based on the evidence. The *Hoover* case serves as an example of the type of evidence that will be required to support a verdict of pain and suffering when challenged on appeal.

C. Persuasion

The plaintiff's attorney's purpose in using exhibits to present damages is to persuade the jury that the event or circumstances that gave rise to the injury had a demonstrable impact on the plaintiff. The defense attorney's purpose is to use exhibits to negate, minimize, or shift attention away from the claims of pain and suffering. Demonstrative exhibits work because they

- clearly and concisely educate the viewer (minimizing language, educational, or age barriers),
- give the presenter control of presenting specific information,
- emphasize the damages,
- emphasize or de-emphasize an emotional response, and
- create a long-lasting visual memory, whether positive or negative.[3]

Emotional appeal to the jurors is not enough if the attorney does not have evidence to satisfy the jurors. Jurors are impressed with hard data in the evidence. Demonstrative evidence organizes medical bills, photographs, x-rays, and other data that jurors can see and touch. This is among the most persuasive evidence they will receive. Jurors use the hard data to support the unconscious, emotional decision about how they desire the case to turn out.

Tip

If an attorney makes an emotional appeal which wins the jury's favor and then fails to offer validated evidence, jurors may subliminally punish counsel and client alike for leading them astray emotionally.[4]

D. Use of primacy and recency for persuasion

1. Primacy

The attorney uses the concepts of primacy and recency to persuade the jury. The psychological principle of primacy says that those facts which people first believe they tend to continue to believe. The primacy portion of the trial is considered by most experts to be from voir dire through the first witness.[4] Opening statements are a key portion of the trial for convincing or dissuading the jury about the plaintiff's injuries.

> The demonstrative evidence introduced during the earliest moments of testimony of a witness, during the earliest part of the day and the earliest part of the trial, will be received, retained and recalled better by jurors than other demonstrative evidence.[5]

Jury consultants have universally found that jurors are highly influenced by what they hear in the first ten minutes of one's presentation at trial. Therefore, many defense attorneys build their opening statements to concentrate solely on attacking liability issues. The defense plan usually calls for waiting until the end of the trial to focus on damages. The defense attorney's lack of commenting on damages during the opening statement may be construed as accepting the plaintiff's damages claims.[6] By recognizing the importance of primacy, the defense attorney's strategy changes to include introducing exhibits early in the trial that refute or minimize damages.

2. Recency

The psychological principle of recency refers to the tendency to remember longest that which was heard last. Recency refers to ease of recall, whereas primacy refers to the influence of the timing of information on forming beliefs. Studies of jurors show that they can recall with specificity the opening and closing portions of a trial and have vague recall of the events that occurred in the middle of the trial. The skillful attorney will use the principle of recency by finishing on a high note at each portion of the trial.[5]

E. Aristotle's principles of persuasion

Aristotle presented four principles of persuasion.

1. Well dispose your audience to you and ill dispose them to your enemy

Trial exhibits permit the trial attorney to make her points about the pain and suffering experienced as a result of the injury. Well-planned use of a variety of trial exhibits provides the chance for the attorney to demonstrate a mastery of the damages of the case. Selection of appropriate, easy-to-understand exhibits displays consideration for the needs of the jury. A complex exhibit that is difficult to understand will frustrate the jury and reflect negatively on the attorney. Presentation of trial exhibits in a coordinated, effective way shows the professionalism of the attorney.

2. Maximize your salient points and minimize your weaknesses

The plaintiff's attorney is careful to not overreach or exaggerate the damages. Information about damages needs to be presented in a fair, ethical, and unbiased fashion. Trial exhibits prepared by the plaintiff's attorney may focus primarily on the initial effects of the injury in a case involving severe damages, with an eventual return to health. Acknowledgment that the plaintiff recovered and returned to work, as shown on a timeline, is essential for maintaining credibility and weakening the opponent's opportunity to attack the amount of the damages. The defense attorney's strategy may include acknowledging the seriousness of the injuries and using exhibits to focus on disputing liability.

3. Refresh the memory of your audience frequently

Trial exhibits present key components of damages with a variety of witnesses: plaintiffs, treating healthcare professionals, expert fact witnesses, family, coworkers, or friends. Planning trial exhibits involves looking at the entire damages aspect of the case and determining how to present or refute exhibits that depict the damages sustained by the plaintiff.

4. Execute the required level of emotion

The word pictures that the plaintiff's attorney creates, combined with the tangible physical evidence in the form of trial exhibits, create an emotional appeal. As described below, the plaintiff's attorney has to be careful that the trial exhibits are not labeled as prejudicial.

If an attorney makes an emotional appeal that wins the jury's favor but is unable to provide the evidence (in the form of trial exhibits derived from medical records documenting damages, for example), the jury may subconsciously punish the attorney and her client.

The defense attorney must counter demonstrative evidence that is designed to elicit sympathy, bias, and prejudice and help the jury recognize when such improper innuendo is being placed before them.[4]

F. Engage the senses

The trial attorney must involve the senses of the jurors to engage their interest in the plaintiff's story. The great Chinese proverb is that a picture is worth a thousand words. The truth of that statement is well known to trial lawyers. Visual materials convey ideas and facts to jurors far more effectively and persuasively than presenting a case through trial testimony alone. It has been demonstrated by social scientists that although jurors retain approximately 15% of what they hear, they will retain almost 85% of what is presented to them by both auditory and visual means. The skilled advocate will learn to create word pictures in the minds of the jurors through the use of demonstrative evidence, evocative language, storytelling techniques, very careful word selection, and the use of rhetorical devices.[4]

18.4 Evidentiary Considerations

After all of the hard work, planning, and cost involved in producing exhibits, it becomes imperative that the attorney be allowed to use them in the courtroom. These considerations drive the production of trial exhibits and influence all decisions regarding their format and content.

During discovery and trial preparation, counsel must select the exhibits to use as real and demonstrative evidence. In many jurisdictions, preliminary witness and exhibit lists are exchanged between the parties. Even if preliminary exhibit lists are not exchanged, final exhibit lists are often required as part of a pretrial order. Obviously, to comply with such a rule, counsel must select the exhibits she intends to use well in advance of trial.

Tip

Before deciding to use an exhibit, counsel must be convinced that the exhibit will enhance a witness's testimony. Unless an exhibit assists a witness in describing or explaining her testimony, it should not be used. Obviously, if the exhibit detracts from the testimony or confuses a fact finder, it should not be used.

A. Relevance

It is axiomatic that admissible evidence must be relevant. The Federal Rules of Evidence define "relevant evidence" as evidence that has "any tendency to make the existence of any fact that is of consequence to the determination of the action more probable or less probable than it would be without the evidence."[7] Relevant evidence can be excluded from a trial when the probative value of the proffered evidence is substantially outweighed by the danger of unfair prejudice to the other parties, confusion of the issues, or misleading the jury. It can also be excluded if admission would result in undue delay, a waste of the court's time, or needless presentation of cumulative evidence.[8]

Relevant evidence may be either direct or circumstantial. Direct evidence is that given by witnesses who testify based on their personal experience. Witnesses will testify to what they saw or heard. Direct evidence can also consist of physical evidence relevant to the case. Examples would include the actual sponge left inside a patient during surgery, a prosthetic leg needed after an amputation from bedsores, or the patient's MRI scan film showing a hemorrhage after a fall.

In contrast to direct evidence, circumstantial evidence is derived from inferences reasonably made from other admissible facts. The classic example of circumstantial evidence is footprints in the snow. Even without the eyewitness testimony of a witness who saw someone walking, the prints themselves are circumstantial evidence of a person's presence at the scene. In a nursing home case, an exhibit documenting a large number of unexplained bruises or falls for a patient could be used as circumstantial evidence to infer that the patient was unsupervised, abused, or both.

Relevance depends in part on the particular type of evidence sought to be admitted and the issues of each case. When offering an exhibit into evidence, counsel must explain why the exhibit is relevant to an issue in the case. Counsel must also be ready to explain how the proffered exhibit will help the jury better understand that issue or assist the witness in providing testimony.

B. Authentication

A legal foundation is required to demonstrate to the satisfaction of the court that the exhibit is authentic and is indeed what it is represented by the attorney to be before it will be admitted into evidence. This is ordinarily done by the testimony of a witness with sufficient knowledge to lay the proper foundation.[9] The foundation required for the introduction of an exhibit is fairly easy to meet and is usually done through a witness who has knowledge that the tangible object or document is what it is claimed to be.[10] The minimum evidentiary foundation needed to establish admissibility for an item of real evidence exists when a witness can identify the object by its distinctive characteristics and can state that the object is in substantially the same condition as it was at the time relevant to the proceeding. Pursuant to Fed.R.Evid. 901(b)(4), identification can be made by the witness based on "distinctive characteristics" such as "appearance, contents, substance, internal patterns or other distinctive characteristics . . . ." For real evidence consisting of physical objects, products, appliances, and so on counsel must establish the prerequisite elements to get the exhibit admitted into evidence. For example, for a back brace needed after a fractured vertebra, the attorney must demonstrate that the exhibit is relevant to the case and elicit testimony that the witness recognizes and can identify the exhibit, that the witness can recall what the exhibit looked like at the time relevant to the proceedings, and that the exhibit is in the same or substantially the same condition as when the witness previously saw it.

As far as the admission of documents into evidence, the following items must be established by the attorney: (1) the document must be relevant to the case; (2) the document bears some identifying characteristic which enables the witness to identify it; (3) the document must be authentic (i.e., an original or admissible copy); and (4) the document is in the same condition it was when made and has not been altered. Copies are now generally admissible the same as an original pursuant to Fed.R.Evid. 1003.

Tip

The attorney must establish that a photograph is relevant to the case, that the witness is familiar with the scene depicted, and that the photo fairly accurately depicts the scene at the time of the event at issue. It is no longer necessary, in most jurisdictions, to have the photographer in court to authenticate most photographs

---

Any witness who is familiar with the subject matter of the photo can testify to its accuracy. Exceptions to this might be when a special lighting technique or photographic procedure is used that may need to be explained to the satisfaction of the court as a result of an objection on the part of adverse counsel in an attempt to exclude the photo. Certainly if the photograph was made with a wide-angle lens, the photographer might be needed to explain what the proper viewing distance would be at which to hold or place the print to eliminate any suggestion of distortion. Especially with wide-angle lenses, the prints can appear to be unnatural looking to the eye without the proper instructions. Adverse counsel might easily pick up on this appearance and attempt to disqualify the prints as being "distorted," and the attorney offering the exhibits should be prepared to present foundation testimony so that the prints will get in.

The same holds true for photographs purporting to show lighting conditions. Adverse counsel will object because the photographer can make the prints as light or as dark as he chooses by simple "manipulation" in the darkroom or computer. Care must be taken to note the appearance of the lighting at the time the photos are made so that they can be credibly authenticated at the time of trial.

A similar foundation is required for diagrams. In addition to relevance, the attorney must show that the witness recognizes the scene depicted in the diagram, that the diagram will assist the witness in explaining testimony or will aid the jury in understanding the testimony, and that the diagram is reasonably accurate and is not misleading.

Exhibits can be used to summarize evidence, such as a chart detailing the financial needs of a plaintiff, the testimony of multiple witnesses, or a summary description of the medical records. These exhibits are allowed pursuant to Fed.R.Evid. 1006. The foundation that must be laid to admit a summary exhibit is that the document is relevant, the witness has knowledge of the information that is summarized, and the witness has reviewed the exhibit and verified it is an accurate summary of the evidence. Additional information about the use of summaries prepared by an expert fact witness is found in Chapter 17, "The Expert Fact Witness."

C. Materiality

Materiality was an important consideration for the admissibility of evidence under common law. The concept of materiality has been codified in Federal Rules of Evidence 401 and 402. Materiality is based on the concept that admissible evidence must be of "consequence" to the case. What is of consequence to the case depends on the scope of the pleadings and the theories of the case, as well as the substantive law.

D. Unfair prejudice

Relevant evidence is not always admissible. It may be inadmissible if it is unfairly prejudicial. Obviously, all evidence is prejudicial in the sense that it hurts one party and helps the other. It is only when the probative value of the evidence is "substantially outweighed by the danger of unfair prejudice" that the evidence can be excluded.[8] For demonstrative evidence, an objection of unfair prejudice is usually directed at exhibits displaying injuries or an accident scene in overly graphic or gruesome detail. Photographs of corpses, traumatic injuries, bodily parts, and other similar items are subject to attack on the grounds of being prejudicial. Photographs showing pained facial expressions or grimaces may also be excluded as prejudicial if the expressions would inflame the average person.[11]

The trial judge determines whether the proposed evidence or exhibit is unfairly prejudicial. A judge's decision is discretionary and will be reviewed under a narrow abuse of discretion standard. Under an abuse of discretion standard, the judge's decision will be given great deference on appeal. Thus, if counsel is concerned that an opponent will attempt to introduce a particularly gruesome or unfairly prejudicial exhibit, a motion in limine is probably the most effective way of addressing its admissibility. A motion in limine gives the trial judge the opportunity to consider the objections to the exhibit outside the pressures of an ongoing trial. It also allows a ruling before the "cat is out of the bag" and the jury has already seen or heard of the evidence sought to be excluded. On the other hand, the proponent of an exhibit that is graphic by its very nature, such as photographs of burns, may seek an evidentiary hearing with the court before trial to get rulings on admissibility of the photographs.

Waiting until trial to get a ruling should be avoided if counsel has any concern about the exhibit's admissibility. By getting the court's ruling in advance, counsel for the proponent of the evidence can prepare for trial knowing whether or not the photographs will be admissible. The court's ruling may also direct counsel to modify the proposed exhibit to make it admissible. Presenting the same photographs in black and white film may reduce these objections.

Tip

Graphic photographs should be used sparingly. If overused, they lose their effect and may draw an objection that they are cumulative. Consider that overly gruesome photographs or exhibits can backfire with the jury. If the jury feels it is being manipulated, the effect of an otherwise persuasive exhibit can be lost.

E. Hearsay

Counsel must also consider whether the proposed exhibit contains inadmissible hearsay that will prevent its use at trial. See Fed.R.Evid. 801 and 802. While an in-depth discussion of the hearsay rule is well beyond the scope of this chapter, the counsel needs to be mindful of the potential that inadmissible hearsay evidence contained in an exhibit will prevent its admission into evidence if an opponent properly objects to the admission of the exhibit.

Greatly oversimplified, there are three essential elements in a hearsay statement: (1) the statement must be an oral or written assertion (or nonverbal conduct intended to be an assertion); (2) the statement must be made out of court; and (3) the out-of-court statement must be offered to prove the truth of what the statement says.[12] If any one element is absent, the statement is not hearsay.

Oral testimony, written documents, and even photographs can constitute hearsay. If an exhibit contains a "statement" that is oral, written, or nonverbal conduct intended to assert what has occurred out of court and is offered to prove the truth of what the statement says, it contains hearsay and will be excluded on proper objection unless it falls under one of the exceptions to the hearsay rule contained in Fed.R.Evid. 803.

Some out-of-court statements are simply not hearsay. Pursuant to Fed.R.Evid. 801(d)(1) and (2), prior statements by witnesses who testify at trial, party admissions (or any statement attributed to a party by another witness), and statements of prior identification are not hearsay if the person making the statement testifies at trial and is subject to cross-examination. Thus, enlargements of statements made by a party and depositions of parties and witnesses testifying at trial are not subject to the hearsay rule. Likewise, videotaped deposition segments used to cross-examine an expert who provides conflicting testimony on the stand would be allowed.

F. Exceptions to hearsay

Even if a statement is hearsay, it may nonetheless be admissible because of one of the exceptions to hearsay found in Federal Rules of Evidence 803 and 804. These rules have codified twenty-nine separate exceptions, and state law may recognize even more. These exceptions to the hearsay rule are important in determining whether an exhibit containing hearsay is admissible. For example, under Rule 803(3), describing medical history, including past or present pain or symptoms, made to a medical professional for purposes of medical diagnosis are not excluded under the hearsay rule. One of these exceptions covers statements made for the purposes of medical diagnosis or treatment and include describing medical history, past or present symptoms, pain, or sensations.[13]

Patient diaries qualify under the exception to hearsay. These constitute a memorandum or record "concerning a matter about which a witness once had knowledge but now has insufficient recollection to enable the witness to testify fully and accurately, shown to have been made or adopted by the witness when the matter was fresh in the witness's memory and to reflect that knowledge correctly. If admitted, his memorandum or record may be read into evidence but may not itself be received as an exhibit unless offered by an adverse party."[14]

Another important exception to the hearsay rule are business records pursuant to Fed.R.Evid. 803(6). Records kept in the ordinary and regular course of business or other organizations are admissible under this exception. For such documents to survive a hearsay objection, counsel must show: (1) the entries were made at or near the time of the event or act; (2) a person with knowledge recorded the information or transmitted the information to someone who recorded it; (3) the records were kept in the ordinary course of a business activity which is a regular practice of the business; (4) the custodian or other qualified witness testifies to the above facts; and (5) the records are otherwise reliable and trustworthy.

18.5 Considerations in Selecting Courtroom Demonstrative Evidence

A. Planning

1. Timing

Careful planning is essential for the successful use of any demonstrative evidence. A brainstorming session at least three months before the trial helps to develop a detailed list of the most important demonstrative evidence ideas.[15] The purpose of the exhibit will drive the preparation and its use. As stressed in this chapter, collection of evidence begins at the early stages in the case. The litigation support personnel will be at their best with sufficient time to work with the attorney to develop the case themes, to focus on the key points in the damages and to allow for review and revisions of the demonstrative evidence. Sufficient time has to be permitted for proofreading to avoid inaccuracies that will invalidate the exhibit. A good rule of thumb is to estimate how much time will be needed to prepare the exhibit and then to double that amount of time. This is essential for incorporating the perspective of the witness who will be using the exhibit and avoids costly mistakes.

2. Size

The final size of the exhibit must be considered before completing the plans. Be sure to discuss with the person preparing the exhibit all the options regarding size, mounting, supporting, and transporting the exhibit. Attorneys who drive small sporty cars will be more concerned with this than those who have the family van available to take to court. Exhibits can be hinged for ease of transportation, and carry cases are made that can accommodate up to eight-feet-long exhibits that fold. The size of the courtroom will be influential in finalizing the exhibit size. A huge enlarged photograph may dominate a small courtroom. A small exhibit may be lost in a large room. The size must be large enough for the jury to be able to see. Large exhibits may need to be broken into pieces in order to transport them. Foamcore boards may be hinged so they will fold.

3. Budget

After developing a budget for the production or purchase of demonstrative evidence, consider if there is a less expensive alternative. Some exhibits can be prepared in such a way as to make them reusable. Ask whether the potential value of the case justifies the amount of money needed to produce the demonstrative evidence. Exhibits may be borrowed from another attorney, physician, or medical school. Some attorneys in the area may be willing to share the costs of a key piece of evidence.

Litigation is expensive, and exhibit preparation can be one of the largest expenditures. The cost of exhibits can become prohibitive, both in terms of the time needed to make them and the cost to produce them. Obviously, the expense of the exhibit, both in terms of the amount of time and money it takes to produce it, should not exceed the exhibit's overall usefulness at trial. The value of a case in large measure dictates the sophistication and expense of the exhibits used.

In an effort to control costs, some firms hire their own graphic artists to produce exhibits in-house. This arrangement permits close supervision of the production process. The reliability and flexibility of this arrangement work well for the law firm frequently using graphics in trials. Staffing and equipping an in-house graphics department requires a large initial outlay of money. Some attorneys prefer to work with outside vendors. These consultants are consistently exposed to what other firms are doing and can share different perspectives with the attorney.[16]

4. Right amount

An attorney should be mindful of the number and kinds of exhibits the other side is going to use. Some jurors may feel the presentation of many expensive exhibits is a sign of weakness. This may be particularly important if the opponent will tell a simple story with few or no exhibits. Sophisticated persuasion is different from slick salesmanship. The use of too few exhibits creates the risk that the jury will be unable to follow the testimony regarding the plaintiff's pain and suffering. The use of too many exhibits can result in the jury becoming confused, frustrated, and overwhelmed. They may stop paying attention. Limit the number of exhibits.[3] Consider the risk to the defense of putting on a major production to counter the plaintiff's case. The jury may interpret this to mean that if the defendant is spending a lot of money it must be plenty worried about the plaintiff's case. One of the benefits of using computer technology for production of demonstrative evidence is that the efficiency and effectiveness of the presentation are improved, but the courtroom presentation can remain low key.[6]

B. Effect

Medical evidence can have a dramatic effect on the jury. A mix of enlargements of medical records, medical illustrations, computer images, day-in-the-life film, and photographs will keep the attention and interest of the jury.

To gauge the success of an exhibit, show the demonstrative evidence to laypeople well before the settlement conference or trial. The attorney's concept of a perfectly clear exhibit may not be supported by those who are unfamiliar with the case. Show the evidence to people who know nothing about the damages that are being claimed. The reactions of laypeople to photographs of the plaintiff will help determine if the images are prejudicial. The staff of a law firm, although conveniently accessible, may not be the best audiences as they are frequently exposed to injury photographs. Have focus groups or other objective observers may provide useful reactions to the exhibits. This requires preparation and coordination but can be time and money well spent. A trial run to determine how the exhibit plays before a live audience can pay big dividends at trial. The feedback of the focus group will help determine if the exhibit is clear and fair. The information provided by a focus group can be used to decide if an exhibit should be modified or used at all. It is also useful to determine how the exhibit may be perceived and understood by the real jury. Whether an exhibit might backfire, or may be persuasive to the other side's case, should be determined before offering it.

Jurors are always alert to the possibility that they are being misled by an unfair exhibit. A focus group helps to uncover such an impression so that the offending exhibits can be fixed before trial.[11]

At trial, introduction of a particularly vivid photograph should be timed to have the maximum effect on the jury. Some attorneys recommend showing photographs of amputations, burns, or pressure sores immediately before or after lunch. Such exhibits should be covered and out of sight until it is time to present them to the jury.

C. Comfort level

When using some of the new computer-based technologies, discussed in further detail below, consider the operator's skill and comfort level. If trial counsel finds that the operation of the equipment is too distracting, an experienced assistant must be available to use the exhibits and troubleshoot. The exhibits are needed to assist the trier of fact but should never be so elaborate that the trial attorney is distracted from the primary responsibilities in presenting the case. The attorney should be thoroughly familiar with the equipment that will be used in the courtroom. She should know where to place the exhibit in the room, how to adjust the easel, and how to handle pieces of medical equipment. This practice time will dramatically increase the attorney's comfort level and will provide a chance to correct any confusion. The attorney who is not comfortable with the equipment should use an assistant to set up and run the equipment.

The equipment in the courthouse should not be relied on to be available or to work. Purchase or rent reliable equipment. Have a backup laptop computer with all the needed files if this presentation method is being used in the courtroom. Bring replacement bulbs for projectors, extra extension cords, and tape to cover wires.

D. Mark and agree on exhibits with the adversary before trial

The opposing counsel should have an opportunity to see the exhibits before trial. Objections to the exhibits can be handled outside the presence of the jury. This will eliminate the judge and jury feeling as if the attorney is wasting time.[17]

18.6 The Plaintiff in the Courtroom

The trial attorney should carefully time the exposure of his client to the jury. In a non-catastrophic case, the plaintiff and available family members seated behind the plaintiff and his counsel will become fixtures in the courtroom. During voir dire or in the opening, counsel will explain that this is the most important day in his client's life. It is also the only opportunity the plaintiff has to obtain the full measure of damages that must compensate him, his spouse, and family for the losses the plaintiff will suffer for the rest of his life.[18]

Only in cases of catastrophic injury such as quadriplegia or in infant brain-damage cases, with attendant risk of jury desensitization, should the attorney limit the exposure of the injured plaintiff to the jury. For example, prolonged jury exposure to the heart-wrenching sounds of a toddler with spastic quadriplegia breathing through a tracheostomy tube with ventilator assistance will be less effective than a shorter well-timed presentation. Reference to the infant's condition during the earlier segments of the trial creates anticipation. The jury should only be actually exposed to the severely damaged plaintiff once or twice during trial for a few minutes each time. The presentation should be done in a low-keyed and dignified manner. The jurors should be cautioned about the shocking nature of what they will see. Presenting such a plaintiff in a dignified way undermines any attempt by defense counsel to argue that counsel is manipulating the jury's sympathy for the purpose of obtaining or increasing the award. Plaintiff's counsel should apologize for causing the jurors' discomfort by showing them the plaintiff's condition.[18]

Hely and Weiseman[19] note that there are risks to the plaintiff's attorney who keeps the plaintiff in the courtroom. A plaintiff who sits at counsel table will be persistently in the spotlight. This may be unwise if the plaintiff reacts to the testimony in ways that the jury does not find appealing or if the plaintiff herself is unappealing. The jury may note that the plaintiff sitting in the wheelchair is able to do more that the jury would have supposed.

Tip

One strategy is for the plaintiff's attorney to bring the plaintiff to the courtroom during voir dire. The plaintiff is introduced to the panel. The court is then asked that the plaintiff be excused and not have to return until she is called to the witness stand to testify.

After testifying, the plaintiff should not be seen again by the jury until the jury deliberations begin and the jurors find the victim sitting with the victim's family in the courtroom anxiously awaiting the jury's verdict. The absence of the plaintiff during the trial can be explained by a medical expert or psychologist. The jury can be told that it is not in the plaintiff's best interest to hear about the accident and have to relive the events or to hear testimony about the devastating long-term effects.[4] The trial may be very traumatic for a plaintiff. One trial lawyer found that his client was having difficulty listening to the medical experts about the problems he would be dealing with for the rest of his life. He asked his attorney to accept the settlement offer in order to get the trial over with.[19]

Recognizing that as the jury becomes more familiar with the plaintiff the effect of the injuries is lessened, the defense attorney must make every effort to let the jury see the plaintiff as much as possible throughout the trial. Familiarity may help to drive away the visual horror that fuels large verdicts. To help build this level of familiarity, the defense counsel may consider asking the judge to allow a showing of the day-in-the-life film to all prospective jurors during the voir dire process. See *Roberts v. Sisters of Saint Francis Health Services, Inc.*, 198 Ill.App.3d 891, 556 N.E.2d 662 (1990). Some defendants have also successfully blunted the trial shock of a token appearance of a terribly injured plaintiff by requesting the court, in limine, for an order requiring the plaintiff's presence in the courtroom during voir dire. See, e.g., *Luke v. Cleveland Clinic Foundation*, 1996 Ohio App.LEXIS 1202.[6]

Defense counsel should help the jurors understand that the plaintiff or surviving family may display signs of suffering through emotional outbursts during the trial (crying, anger, grieving). Jurors may find that their hearts go out to the injured person. Defense counsel may comment that while these feelings are understandable, human, and acceptable, a display of tears is not a measure of the facts or evidence on which the jury's decision may be based. The jury should feel comfortable knowing that it can empathize with the plaintiff's loss without awarding money.[6]

18.7 The Remote Witness in the Courtroom

The absence from court of a badly injured or infirm plaintiff may suggest her disinterest in the outcome of the proceedings. In the past, lawyers accepted such a circumstance as unavoidable and struggled to minimize its effect on the jury. Today, using video conferencing, lawyers can present "virtual" plaintiffs and witnesses in court.

This technology may be particularly appropriate for the child witness who may be intimidated by the courtroom setting. An incarcerated plaintiff or one in a mental institution may also be an appropriate candidate to testify via videoconferencing.[12]

Jurors who are made to understand that such presentations are unusual and allowed only under compelling circumstances pay rapt attention. The drama inherent in these moments, used judiciously, adds impact to testimony. A brief videoconference introduction of a catastrophically injured client should be made during the opening statement. The jury sees the extent of the injuries and is made aware that the plaintiff is present. The plaintiff reappears as the last witness. Now less shocked by the plaintiff's condition, the jury can focus its attention on what is likely to be the most dramatic testimony of the trial. Finally, if the trial has been lengthy, the plaintiff's appearance during summation can be a graphic reminder of his plight.

Effective videoconference testimony requires preparation and practice. Have an experienced professional assemble the technical elements (hardware, software, and communications lines) in a careful and timely manner. Multiple videoconference practice sessions can create a strong witness and hone the attorney's presentation. Practice is particularly important to expose the impact of videoconferencing on trial dynamics. The attorney may have to develop new techniques to cue a remote witness or quickly stop unresponsive or damaging testimony.[20]

18.8 Use of Demonstrative Evidence When Asking for Money

Exhibits have been planned, produced, and displayed to present the themes of the case. The noneconomic damages have been portrayed. It is now time for closing arguments and for the plaintiff's attorney to ask for an award.

The plaintiff's attorney's ability to ask for a specific amount of money is governed by state law. For example, in *Wilson v. Williams*, 374 P.2d 53, 261 Kan. 703 (1997), the Kansas Supreme Court overruled earlier precedent and found that plaintiffs' counsel, during closing argument, could make a "per diem" argument to the jury. Kansas law had previously prohibited a "per diem," or formula, argument which occurs when counsel argues for an award of future pain and suffering based on time units which are then multiplied by a price of pain per unit to arrive at the total being claimed. In overturning the Kansas long-standing prohibition against a per diem argument, the court noted that the rule was a minority position. Thirty-two states had considered the issue, and only seven prohibited a "per diem" argument, two of which, Pennsylvania and New Jersey, prohibited the court and parties from mentioning in closing argument any amount, total, or per diem for unliquidated noneconomic damages. The court noted that Kansas has always permitted a total sum to be argued to the jury, including the total amount desired for unliquidated damages such as pain and suffering, and has also permitted an argument as to the plaintiff's life expectancy, which is just as speculative as a suggested per diem amount for unliquidated pain and suffering damages. The court pointed out that juries are instructed that counsel's closing argument is not evidence and that trial courts should not permit charts or other exhibits they used in oral argument, but not admitted into evidence, to be taken into the jury room. Finally, the Kansas Supreme Court noted that if a party could show that a jury had arrived at a sum for pain and suffering by placing a specific value on a unit of pain, the Kansas court would not grant a new trial. Finding that prohibiting such an argument did not make sense, the Kansas Supreme Court overruled the earlier precedent and joined the majority of states allowing a per diem argument to be made by counsel in closing argument regarding a lump sum to be awarded by the jury for future pain and suffering. Specifically, the court held:

> That part of Caylor II which prohibits mathematical formula comments and charts during oral arguments is overruled. However, this opinion does not authorize expert testimony on the subject, and the trial court should continue to give (the Kansas instruction), which instructs a jury that there is no mathematical formula to determine nonpecuniary damages. Further, the trial court should instruct the jury that counsel's opening and closing arguments are not evidence.[21]

Tip

If permitted by state law, during closing argument, the jury can be presented with a prepared chart using a formula that can be used to calculate damages and suffering. This can be displayed on an enlargement attached to a rigid backing, a transparency, or a computer screen. The elements of noneconomic loss can be listed and defined: disability, impairment, loss of enjoyment of life, suffering, and pain.

In a motor vehicle accident case, the client's pain can be broken down into pieces. The fear, anxiety, shock, and pain suffered at the time of the impact has value. If the client was looking in terror at the defendant's onrushing vehicle, that has value. Actual blood, broken mirrors or seatbacks, and other indicators of physical contact between the client and the vehicle's interior add value. Fear for the safety of any loved ones in the car has value. The anxiety of being placed on a stretcher and taken away in an ambulance has value. The feelings experienced when a child is put on a stretcher have even more value. The anxiety, stress and worry at the hospital have value. The day-to-day pain and worry during therapy has value.[22]

Studies of jurors show that one of the methods used by jurors during deliberations in order to gain the attention of their fellow jurors is to use demonstrative evidence. Demonstrative evidences helps the jury understand each of these phases of pain and suffering and assign dollars to them. Counsel can hold a piece of demonstrative evidence during summation, establish eye contact, and advise the jury, "When you come to evaluate noneconomic loss, remember the plaintiff's exhibit 6 . . ." This is followed by the straightforward common sense argument which the attorney wants the jurors to make in the jury room with this piece of demonstrative evidence.[4]

18.9 Jury Instructions on Pain and Suffering

Forensic psychologists advise attorneys that jurors may not deliberate on the issue of evidence of damages for the reason that jurors do not like to confront physical pain and suffering, mental anguish, physical disability, and physical disfigurement. They do not like to see it, hear testimony about it, or sit down in a room with strangers and discuss it and attempt to put a monetary value on it. It is the attorney's duty to instruct the jurors as to their duties. The jurors must understand that they have to confront the injuries and their sequelae and to award full compensation, to follow the law with respect to an award of damages, and to render justice.[4]

In the vast majority of jurisdictions, the award of damages for past and future pain and suffering is left to the discretion of the jury, subject to the review of the trial court and ultimately, by any applicable approved jury instructions. For example, the Appellate Courts Missouri Approved Instruction 4.01, a general damages instruction, applies to all personal injury actions, other than those involving healthcare providers, and provides:

> If you find for the plaintiff, then you must award plaintiff such sum as you believe will fairly and justly compensate plaintiff for any damages you believe plaintiff sustained and is reasonably certain to sustain in the future as a direct consequence of the occurrence maintained in the evidence.

There are a couple of important points to be made about this instruction. First, the jury is not told to award anything specifically for pain and suffering. Rather, it is for the lawyer to argue for an amount of an award based on the evidence presented during the case. Second, the evidence must establish that the plaintiff has sustained pain and suffering in the past and that to a reasonable degree of certainty is going to sustain pain and suffering in the future. Third, the plaintiff must establish that the plaintiff's pain and suffering are a direct result of the occurrence for which plaintiff has brought the action and not some other cause. The notes to this jury instruction state that during an instruction conference the parties and the court should state on the record what damages are supported by the evidence and can properly be argued to the jury by counsel.

An award of pain and suffering caused by an injury other than the occurrence complained of would be error. The attorney cannot argue that pain and suffering for an old ankle injury in a case involving a broken arm. Nor can the attorney argue for damages that are not supported by evidence presented at trial. Thus, if counsel intends to argue for an award of past and future pain and suffering, there must be testimony or other evidence in the record that the plaintiff sustained a physical injury, that the injury is the kind that causes pain, that the plaintiff sustained pain as a result of that injury, and that the plaintiff is likely to sustain pain in the future. Although not absolutely required, it is obviously a good idea to present medical testimony that the injury sustained by the client is sufficient to produce the pain and suffering being complained of, and that the pain complained of began at the time of the injury, persisted until the time of trial and is likely to persist into the future.

In actions against healthcare providers Missouri requires that the amounts awarded by a jury for economic and noneconomic damages be itemized both for the past and the future. Noneconomic damages are defined as "those damages arising from nonpecuniary harm such as pain, suffering, mental anguish, inconvenience, physical impairment, disfigurement, and loss of capacity to enjoy life." M.I.A. 2105. While not required to be presented in non-healthcare provider cases, these categories serve as useful guides for counsel in determining the type of evidence needed to be presented at trial to prove the plaintiff sustained pain and suffering.

The Pattern Instructions of Kansas 3rd are used to instruct juries in all personal injury cases. Instruction 171.01 applies in personal injury cases and provides:

> Elements of Personal Injury Damage
>
> In determining the amount of damages sustained by the plaintiff, you should allow the amount of money which reasonably compensates the plaintiff for plaintiff's injuries and losses resulting from the occurrence in question. The amount of damages you determine should include any of the following showed by the evidence:
>
> a. Pain, suffering, disabilities, or disfigurement, and any accompanying mental anguish suffered by the plaintiff to date [and those plaintiff is reasonably expected to experience in the future];
>
> In determining the amount of damages you should consider plaintiff's age, condition of health before and after, and the nature, extent and duration of the injuries. For such items as pain, suffering, disability, and mental anguish, there is no unit of value and no mathematical formula the court can give you. You should allow such sum as will fairly and adequately compensate plaintiff. The amount to be allowed rests with your sound discretion.

Kansas law divides damages into noneconomic loss, medical expenses, and economic loss. These are defined in Pattern Instructions of Kansas 3rd 171.02, which states:

> In interpreting and applying the last instruction, there are three types of damages that you may allow:
>
> 1. Noneconomic loss. This type of damage includes:
> (a) Pain and suffering; and
> (b) Disability, disfigurement and
> (c) Any accompanying mental anguish suffered by plaintiff to date (and those plaintiff is reasonably expected to experience in the future)
> . . .
>
> You will be given a verdict form in which you must itemize the amounts of noneconomic, medical and economic damages awarded to date and those awarded for future injuries and losses.

Kansas case law has indicated that loss of enjoyment of life is not a separate category of nonpecuniary damages in a personal injury action and that it is error to submit a separate instruction or provide a separate verdict form entry for loss of enjoyment of life. However, in a proper case, loss of enjoyment of life is a valid component or element of pain and suffering or disability. *Leiker v. Gafford*, 778 P.2d 823, 245 Kan. 325 (1989). See also, *Gregory v. Carey*, 791 P.2d 1329, 246 Kan. 504, 514 (1990).

The Kansas damage instructions 171.01 and 171.02 clearly indicate that the plaintiff must be cognizant of the elements of damages allowable under state law and what evidence is required to demonstrate that the plaintiff has sustained pain, suffering, disability, disfigurement, mental anguish, loss of enjoyment of life, and other noneconomic or nonpecuniary damages. Damage instructions for other states will likewise provide useful guidance on what elements of damages are allowed in a particular jurisdiction and what evidence must be presented to submit the issue of future pain and suffering to a jury and sustain or challenge an award on appeal. Demonstrative evidence is crucial in convincing the jury of pain and suffering.

18.10 Conclusion

Demonstrative evidence will find its mark in many different ways; in as many ways as there are different personalities of trial lawyers. Planning trial exhibits must take into account the timing, budget and other practical considerations. An awareness of the legal considerations of relevance, prejudice, and other admissibility issues will help the trial attorney select the appropriate exhibits. Careful planning will avoid wasting time and money.

Endnotes

1. Gass, J., "The Eight Dimensions of Trial Work." *For the Defense*, April 2002, 19.

2. www.findlaw.com.

3. Watts, S., "Technology Creates Winning Visual Evidence." *TRIAL*, September 2000, 68.

4. "Jury Persuasion." www.mcle-online.conm/courses/juryargs /modules/module02.htm.

5. Nations, H.L., "Powerful Persuasion." www.howardnations.com/persuasive juryarguments/i-c-d.htm.

6. Iwan, L., and Huber, M., "Mistakes to Avoid in the Defense of Damages." *For the Defense,* March 2002, 38.

7. Federal Rule of Evidence 401.

8. Federal Rule of Evidence 403.

9. Federal Rule of Evidence 901(a).

10. Federal Rule of Evidence 901(b)(1).

11. Siemer, D., *Tangible Evidence: How to Use Exhibits at Deposition and Trial*, Third Edition. South Bend, IN: National Institute for Trial Advocacy, 1998.

12. Federal Rule of Evidence 801.

13. Federal Rule of Evidence 803(4).

14. Federal Rule of Evidence 803(5).

15. Krehel, G., "Think First, Draw Second: Planning Better Visuals." *Trial*, April 2000, 58.

16. Jones, A., "In-House Graphics Department a Boon to Law Firm." *New Jersey Law Journal,* February 18, 2002, 25.

17. Joye, M., "Avoiding Ten Pitfalls of Demonstrative Evidence." *Trial*, November 2000, 94.

18. Appelbaum, S., Iyer, P., Parisi, J., Davis, S., Weisgal, H., and Neggers, W., "Demonstrative Evidence." In Iyer, P., editor, *Nursing Malpractice*, Second Edition. Tucson: Lawyers & Judges Publishing Co., 2001.

19. Hely, J. and Weiseman, J., "Trustworthiness." In *A Trial Strategy Manual for the Plaintiff's Injury Case in New Jersey.* New Brunswick, NJ: New Jersey Institute for Continuing Legal Education, 1998.

20. Davis, S., "A Practical Guide to Videoconferencing." *Trial*, March 2000, 48.

21. Wilson, 261 Kan. at 710.

22. "Handling an Auto Injury Case." www.mcle-online.com/courses/picases/modules/.

Chapter 19

Trial Exhibits: Preparation and Use

Patricia Iyer, MSN, RN, LNCC, Stephen Appelbaum, CEP, EPIC, and John Parisi, Esq.

Synopsis

19.1 Introduction

The selection of the most appropriate type of demonstrative evidence to present pain and suffering is both an art and a skill. The experienced trial attorney builds on a wealth of experience in using demonstrative evidence, but a less experienced attorney may be at a loss when it comes to the creative use of demonstrative evidence. This chapter provides an overview of several types of trial exhibits. It concludes with a description of traditional as well as electronic methods for use in the courtroom.

19.2 Types of Exhibits

There are several types of useful demonstrative aids, including patient diaries, photographs, videotapes, radiology studies, medical records, graphic illustrations, anatomical models, medical illustrations, medical equipment, and computer animations.

A. Patient diaries

The client and family may be asked to keep records of treatment and symptoms following an injury. This information will assist the plaintiff's attorney in ensuring that medical records of treating physicians and other healthcare providers are obtained at appropriate points. The diary helps to fill in details of the client's life and can be useful when creating a timeline, as discussed later in the chapter. Pages of a diary may be enlarged for the jury. See Figure 19.1 for such a patient diary page.

B. Photography

Photographs should be taken as soon as possible to document any acute injuries. The attorney or her photographer may wish to take photographs of the injured client in the attorney's office, the client's home, or the hospital.

1. Photography in the attorney's office

The background of the photograph should be kept as simple as possible. The personal injury attorney should consider keeping an appropriate background suitable for the use of photography.

Tip

In the absence of a plain background, the client should be kept as far away as possible from bookshelves or other distracting backgrounds when being photographed. If the room is large enough, this allows light to fall off behind the client, creating an almost completely dark background.

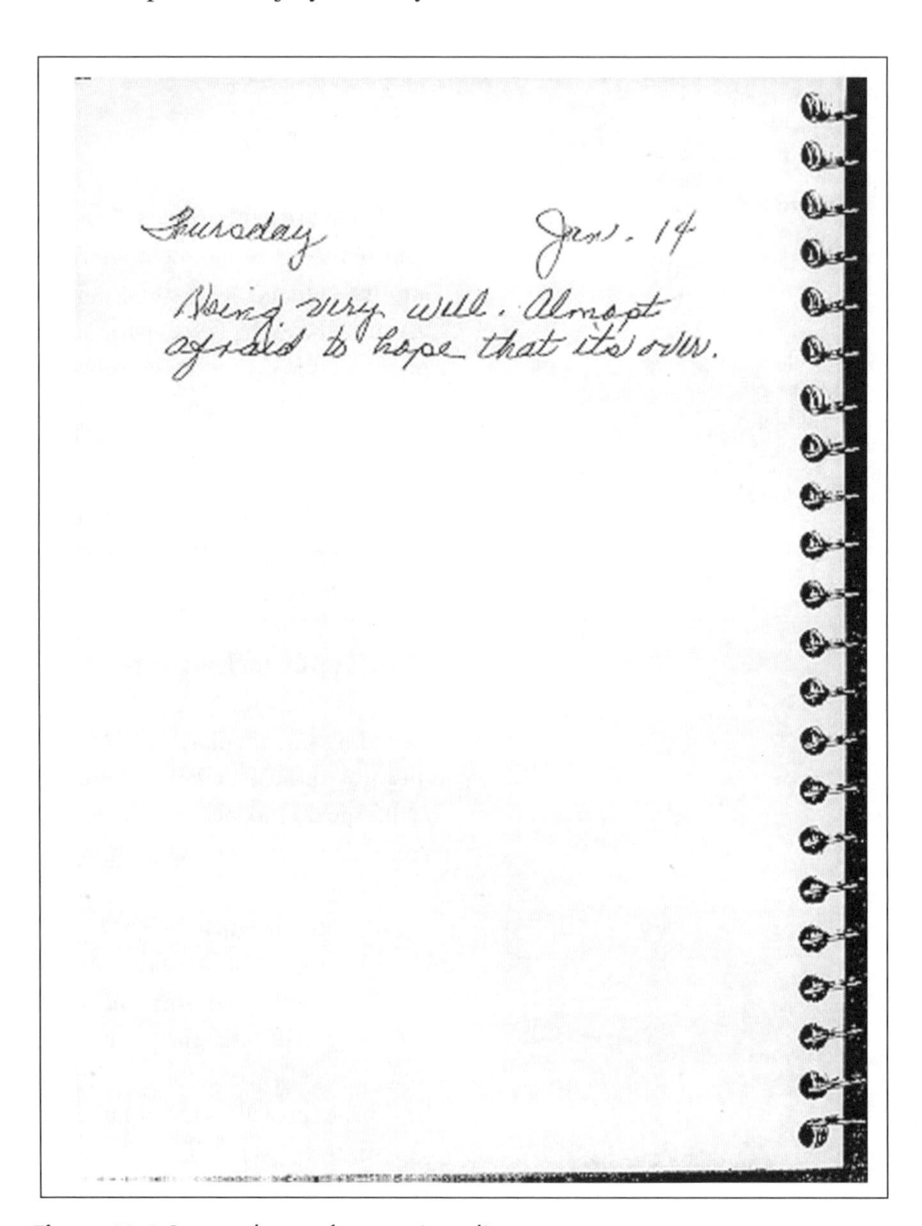
Thursday Jan. 14
Doing very well. Almost
afraid to hope that it's over.

Figure 19.1 *Scanned page from patient diary*

2. Photography in the plaintiff's home

The same approach of creating a dark background should be taken in the plaintiff's home. The attorney should inspect the surroundings for any personal items that might be distracting or controversial.

3. Photography in the hospital

Be aware that each hospital has a specific procedure for permitting photography of patients for legal purposes (as opposed to hospital internal purposes, an area which is probably covered in the admission forms signed by the patient or family member.) In some facilities, the permission for photography is either handled by nursing, administration, public relations or security. The attorney should review the procedure before sending a photographer to see or photograph the patient. When a treating physician's permission is needed, get the written authority before sending the photographer. Usually, the preferred time for this type of photography is in the afternoon, as the patient is usually receiving some type of treatment or test in the morning. Advising the nurse manager of the intentions can avoid scheduling problems.

Overall photos should be made of the patient's room. Photographs should be taken of the equipment or appliances used in the care of the injured subject. These photographs can be shared with the expert fact witness, who will identify the pieces of equipment shown in the picture. This is particularly effective when there are multiple wires, lines and tubes attached to the patient.

Tip

The timely taking of photographs to document injuries may convey that the plaintiff personal injury attorney is aggressive, prepared, and professional.

Just because the attorney has obtained photographs does not mean that they will be inevitably shown to a jury if a case is not settled. Mock trial research has shown that jurors can be turned off by professional photographs taken in the hospital shortly after an accident. This may imply that the patient has obtained a lawyer the day after the accident.

4. Amateur or professional photographer

The attorney needs to consider whether to take photographs herself or to hire someone. If there is any possibility that the attorney may be called as a fact witness or other concerns of conflict of interest, the photographs should be taken by another person.

Thirty-five-millimeter or digital cameras provide the opportunity to get excellent photographs with a minimum of knowledge. If the photographer is using traditional film, a local one-hour laboratory is useful to permit an evaluation of the output and to retake photographs if needed. The attorney should establish a relationship with a local laboratory that will be able to accommodate his needs for quality and delivery time. This is also important when the attorney needs additional photographs on short notice as requested by an expert or the adversary.

Tip

If using the services of a professional legal photographer, the attorney should clearly explain the nature of the injuries to be documented. Sometimes clients may not recognize the need to photograph all external injuries as recorded in the medical records.

---

5. Injury photographs

Photographs may be essential in establishing damages and the mechanism of injury. For example, an accident involving the slamming of knees into the dashboard should result in bruising on the knees. In cases involving soft tissue injuries, consider the timing of taking photos. Some burns or bruises mature and become more vivid a few days after an injury. Communication with the client and her family is important in order to identify the optimum time for taking photos.

Injury photographs will be taken in color film. There may be instances where the environment being photographed is illuminated by a mixture of tungsten, fluorescent, and window light. Color film reacts differently to each type of light source, and the resulting photo could look like what is found at the end of the rainbow. A color bar chart (Figure 19.2), commercially available, should be included if the accuracy of the color reproduction is important. The color lab printer can then match the known colors in the chart, which will assure the proper representation of all the other colors in the scene. A photo should be taken with and without the chart in the frame. All photographs involving injuries and bruises should also contain at least one frame with a color bar chart. This is especially important because of the relationship between skin tones and scars or bruises. The shot with the chart is there only for evidentiary reasons in case the photo is challenged by opposing counsel.

Supplemental flash units should be used to overcome any ambient light that might affect color reproduction. For example, fluorescent room lighting might look too green if the flash unit is not powerful enough to overcome the intensity of the room lights. Again, professional consultation can mean the difference between an admissible and an inadmissible exhibit.

The photographer should pay attention to the direction of the light source. Flash units built into the camera tend to flatten the appearance of the subject, hiding the appearance of raised marks or swelling. Photos should be made with equipment that allows the light source, the subject, or both be moved. The flash can be placed overhead and to either side of the subject to record the depth and texture of injuries more accurately. See Figures 19.3 and 19.4 for examples of how lighting affects the ability to see a scar resulting from an infected surgical incision. (Light source positioning may mean the difference between a flat, two-dimensional image and one that emphasizes the depth of a scar.)

When photographing injuries in later stages, or disfigurement and cosmetic injuries after surgeries have been completed and healing has occurred, lighting is critical. Photographs should be taken with lights shining on the area at a 45-degree angle to the surface. This will evenly illuminate all parts of the client. After these photographs are taken, the photographer should take additional pictures from three vantage points: a long shot, a medium shot, and a close-up. Next, an additional set of photos should be taken with one light shining on the subject to demonstrate depth, texture, and dimensions of the injured area. One of the problems with using photographs to document residual scarring is that while the human eye sees three dimensionally the single lens of the camera creates two-dimensional images. It is therefore extremely important to remember this when attempting to capture injuries with a camera with the expectation that the photos will look the same as the way the subject appeared in person.

The attorney should keep a record about each photograph that is taken. This should include the

- name of the photographer,
- time and date,
- type of camera,
- lens,
- type of film used,
- shutter speed,
- lens aperture used,
- description of the lighting used, if any, and
- distances from the camera to various points of importance in the photo.[1]

This information will be invaluable as the case progresses. It is important to be able to answer questions about these key details when challenged by the judge or opposing counsel.

6. Lenses and print size

There is a popular belief that the use of wide-angle or telephoto lenses distorts the reality of a scene. Actually, the distortion results from the improper relationship of lens choice, viewing distance and print size. To determine the proper print size, and viewing distance for photographs, forensic photographers use a formula based on the focal length of the lens. For practical purposes, this formula allows the photographer to create fair and accurate representations of scenes using wide-angle (short focal length) lenses. These permit the recording of larger areas of space.

Tip

The proper lens selection is critical in injury photography.

---

7. Digital photography

A digital camera does not use film but instead creates a digital file that can be read by a computer. The file can be printed on any black and white or color

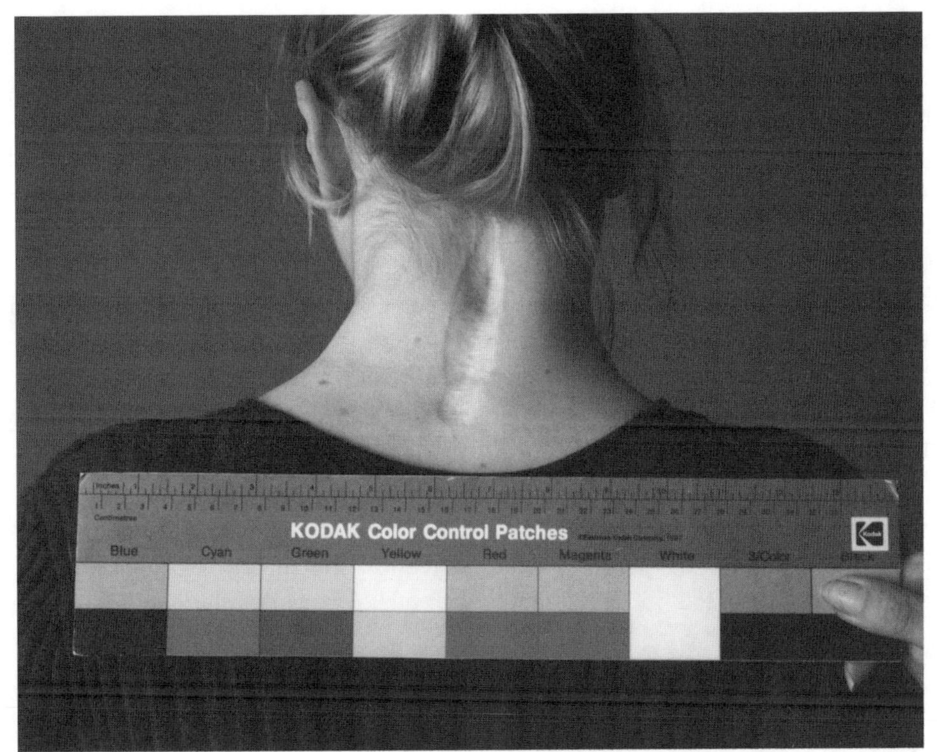

Figure 19.2 *Color chart, courtesy of the Evidence Store, Union, NJ*

Figure 19.3 *Cross lighting that demonstrates the texture and depth of a scar, courtesy of the Evidence Store*

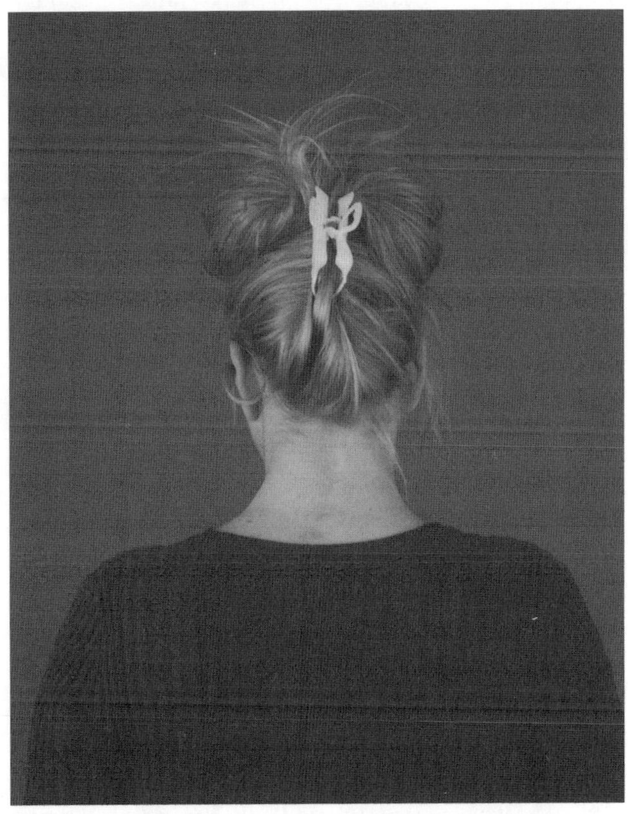

Figure 19.4 *Balanced, 45-degree lighting, courtesy of the Evidence Store*

printer. When using digital cameras, the attorney should be aware of the possible future objections to these photographs, since there are no traditional negatives to inspect if requested. Bruises can be easily enhanced, scars can be reddened, or injuries altered in other ways through manipulation of the image in the computer. The defense attorney who receives the photographs should be aware that this can be done. If there are questions about the accuracy of the image, compare digital photographs with the documentation of injuries in the medical records. Images should be stored on a separate disk containing only the photographs related to that case.

8. Use of photographs in the courtroom

At the later stages of the case, the presentation of photographs must be addressed with care. The witness who is testifying about the photographs will state that the photograph is a fair and accurate representation of what he or she saw.

There are several ways to present photographs to the jury. One way is to pass photos around to the jury. This approach is flawed for a number of reasons. The jury is seeing the pictures after they are described by the witness. The jurors may be distracted by elements in the photographs, and the process of passing them around slows the pace of the trial. The judge may instruct the attorney to begin questioning the witness while the jury is still looking at the photographs. This forces the jurors to decide to look at the photos or listen to the witness. If the jurors are near- or farsighted, they may have to hold prints at arm's length or close to their noses to see them clearly, especially if they forgot their reading glasses that particular day.

It is important for the attorney to be aware of these issues to allow for the proper presentation of photos. A number of solutions are available. Some attorneys prefer to have key photographs enlarged to view by all while the client's condition is being described. A print that is 8 × 10 inches for normal handheld viewing needs to be about 30 × 40 inches when placed six feet away from jurors. Essentially, when the viewing distance of a photo or document is doubled, there is a need to double the size to maintain legibility and proper perspective. This size makes it easy for all jurors to see the photographs at the same time. An objection may be raised to photographs that are larger than life. It is important to differentiate between photographs used for evidence and those used for demonstrative evidence. Photographs used for evidence include pictures showing the presence of a condition or injury. Photographs used for demonstrative evidence may depict a scar that is larger than life size. This would be ideal for a plastic surgeon to use to demonstrate the nature of the final result after multiple surgeries. Keloids (raised, lumpy scars), and post surgical infections may result in a less than satisfactory condition. According to Siemer,[1] when enlargements increase the size of the object being photographed beyond its normal size, the foundation should include a justification for this to avoid an objection. The jurors may remember the size of the object they saw in the photo and fail to understand testimony about the actual size of the object. The usual explanation is that the enlargement is needed for clarity or in order to see important details.

An album of photographs may be assembled for each juror so that photographs do not have to be passed around the jury box. As described in Section 19.4, a document camera attached to an LCD projector or monitor may be used to show a photograph on a screen.

Tip

When using projectors, the attorney should keep in mind the need to darken the room. If lights are not dimmed, the image may appear too washed out. This is especially important when presenting injury photographs, as scars and other defects may be invisible in a bright room. Turning off the lights may result in better contrast, but watch out for sleepy jurors, particularly after lunch.

A take-apart photographic exhibit may be prepared to demonstrate the care needed by a paralyzed patient being tended to in his home. A photograph may be taken of the plaintiff surrounded by his medical equipment. For example, a ventilator-dependent tetraplegic may be attached to a ventilator, a feeding pump, intravenous pumps, and a suction machine. The jury may first see the entire photograph, which has been enlarged and mounted on a rigid board and placed on a freestanding exhibit unit. The pieces of equipment will consist of separate parts that are attached by Velcro strips to the underlying picture. A witness may remove each piece of equipment to discuss the functions of the equipment. The pieces of equipment are stark reminders of the dependency of the plaintiff and of the fear of a power failure. The exhibit can also be used to show a picture of the plaintiff without all the surrounding pieces of equipment. As each piece is attached to the picture, the witness can explain why it is necessary to maintain the plaintiff's life. This approach can also be performed using a computer to add or subtract each piece of equipment.

In a lengthy trial with many witnesses, some judges will arrange to have instant photographs taken of each witness. These pictures are placed on a chart with the witness's name, date of testimony, and job title. This system helps the jurors remember their impressions of individual witnesses.[2]

C. Videotape

Technology has moved swiftly through the modern practice of law, and the use of videotape has changed the way many firms prepare and try their cases. It has created its share of problems, too, in that many practitioners tend to overuse or misuse the medium because of its relative simplicity for even the novice photographer. The advancements in making high quality video cameras that are smaller, lighter, and generally easier to use make this type of documentation relatively easy and cost-effective. There is generally no need for additional lighting with most video cameras. The cameras are small and almost invisible to the subject so that the patient will not be intimidated or upset by the presence of larger, more intrusive equipment. The newer, small camcorders have viewing screens that hinge on the side, eliminating the need for the photographer to even have the camera up to the eye, and most units have steadying systems that eliminate much of the amateur's shaky, jerking movements.

"Let's get a video" seems to be the battle cry for all forms of documentation without understanding the ultimate goal of the process or the need for future retrieval and presentation of information. This section examines the ways videotape can assist the attorney in the specific areas of documenting pain and suffering.

1. Videotaping in the hospital

Videotape should be used as soon as possible to record any abnormalities in speech, body movement, or any dynamic trait that may have been changed as a result of the injury. Interaction between the patient and family members and simple question and answer sessions of brief duration are important areas that should be filmed. If the patient is able to communicate clearly, an informal question and answer by a family member can preserve information immediately after the incident. The patient may be able to recall conversations that took place with and among caregivers during treatment and care, especially when the caregivers believe that the patient is unable to hear conversations spoken in normal volume.

Tip

If the individual has difficulties with speech, ambulation, or use of his arms, videotape can also be helpful in documenting the condition and demeanor of the patient in ways not possible with still photos.

Videotaping the patient in the hospital can include the filming of life support equipment. The filming should capture testing of responses and reflexes in more catastrophic cases, such as with patients with brain damage, to record accurately their reactions or lack of response. This will assist in dealing with potential issues of conscious pain and suffering. Videotaping of hydrotherapy, burn debridements, and dressing changes can be extremely powerful. Few jurors could fail to react to watching a debridement of a pressure ulcer or burn. Procedures involving the injection of medications into a patient's body can provide graphic videotape footage.

2. Videotaping in the plaintiff's home

Videotaping completed in the client's home can include footage of the assistive devices (wheelchairs, canes, walkers) the client needs to move from place to place as well as the limitations presented by the layout of the apartment or house. Due to the nature of their injuries, some clients are unable to traverse stairs or other barriers to be able to gain access to certain rooms.

This may limit the ability to interact with the family, such as not being able to eat a meal in a dining room. In other situations, the client's bed may be moved into the living room or dining room, thus affecting the ability of the rest of the family to use this space.

It is also effective to videotape the client or caretaker performing detailed aspects of care at home, such as dressing changes, tube feeding, the administration of antibiotics, or irrigating colostomies, or putting on prosthetic legs. These procedures are usually included in a day-in-the-life videotape.

3. Videotaping for settlement brochures

One of the more aggressive uses of videotape footage is the incorporation into a videotaped or electronic settlement brochure. Videotaping done at intervals over the course of the patient's recovery can be useful in capturing the slow, painful recovery. The taping may include treatments, physical therapy visits, ambulation difficulties, and so on. It may not be necessary to show this tape to the jury due to evidentiary concerns. Settlement tapes can be used without the restrictions that may apply in the courtroom.

A video montage of the subject's life before the injury can be an effective negotiating tool. Photos or video footage from family gatherings for special occasions, holidays, and so on can be made into a presentation that contrasts with the patient's current condition. An informal interview with the client describing changes in lifestyle as a result of the accident may be helpful. The video footage that results may be inadmissible at trial but can be useful for the settlement brochure.

It is to the attorney's advantage to be creative with the use of video. Preservation is more crucial within shorter time frames, such as when the patient's life expectancy is brief due to the nature of the injuries or his age. The attorney should determine if any videotape of the accident scene was taken. News coverage of the accident may be available from the local television show.

Tip

Settlement presentations using video technology are extremely effective because they combine the emotion of the seriousness of the injury with the persuasive liability facts of the case that can often prevent the matter from going to trial.

Experts can be shown summarizing their theories of liability as well as the medical witnesses explaining the issues related to the damages. Defense attorneys as well as insurance claims people can preview the "damage" that will be done by the plaintiff's trial team and better assess the risks of taking the case to a jury.

4. Instructional videotapes

Much good resource material is available from various commercial sources and organizations that can be helpful in educating the jury about a particular procedure or medical issue. Teaching films can convey the details of a procedure that could not be demonstrated in the courtroom. For example, the jury can watch the surgical correction of a fractured hip or how skin is removed from healthy tissue for grafting. Groups such as the American Academy of Orthopedic Surgeons maintain a vast library of educational audiovisual material and videotapes showing surgical and diagnostic procedures. The Learning Channel and Discovery Channel have video material of surgeries that can also be purchased for courtroom use to educate juries. Nursing and medical publishers and professional associations are good sources of information. If admissibility is a problem in the jurisdiction, the use of such tapes should not be ruled out. They are still available for the limited use of settlement negotiations as part of a video settlement package.

5. Day-in-the-life videotapes

The taking of video depositions and the production of day-in-the-life films should be considered if warranted by the injury and resulting change in lifestyle and the patient's condition would preclude a personal appearance if the case goes to trial. A day-in-the-life videotape is particularly effective in cases involving catastrophic injury. A professional videographer should be used for this project. Jurors are used to seeing polished footage on television and are likely to judge amateurish video footage accordingly. Keeping the day in the life video short is important to maintain effectiveness. A length of seven to ten minutes is recommended by Heninger.[3] The plaintiff should do simple things such as get out of bed, walk, or eat. The video should be tastefully done so as to not embarrass the plaintiff or jurors, advises Heninger.

Particularly effective scenes, such as those showing the equipment needed to care for a catastrophically injured patient at home, may be enlarged into photographs that are placed on rigid backing on an easel. The witness, who may be a home care nurse, can point to equipment and explain its use.

Videotapes may be effectively used when the plaintiff is blind or deaf as a result of the accident. A videotape can be created of a significant event in the plaintiff's life, such as a birthday party or Christmas. If the plaintiff is blind, the audio portion of the videotape will be played for the jury with the monitor blank. If the client is deaf, play the video without sound. A night-in-the-life audiotape may be created when a case involves around-the-clock care. The full night can be recorded and then edited to a few minutes. For example, the parents of a severely impaired infant may speak into the tape recorder, announcing the time at intervals, with the audiotape picking up the sounds of crying or silence.[3]

McClellan[4] advises that the plaintiff's attorney needs to achieve the dual goals of evoking sympathy and meeting legal standards of admissibility. The day-in-the-life film should not include taping of pre-existing injuries, which would give the defense counsel grounds for objecting to the relevance of the tape. The counsel should put herself in the position of the judge and ask herself if she would admit each portion of the tape if she had to rule on its admissibility. It is generally accepted that unless the defense attorney is attending the taping, the plaintiff's attorney should not be present. It is customary for the plaintiff's attorney to give notice of the taping in advance, however in these times when day in the live videos are more commonplace, most defense attorneys choose not to attend.

TIP

Some attorneys raise objections to these videos using the case of *Balian v.General Motors* as their foundation. While the case may or may not apply to this type of taping, it is generally better to err on the side of caution and advise adverse counsel than risk the tape being excluded at trial.

At some time in the editing process, the tape should be viewed by unbiased, non-attorney reviewers to provide feedback on the effectiveness of the presentation and to comment on any portions that may be objectionable. If the attorney is using a focus group or mock trial to prepare the case, the video should be shown at that time for feedback. These panels will provide the most accurate reading on the value of the presentation, and on what parts should be included or excluded, as well as comment on its general length.

Digital videotape formats now allow maximum flexibility for most postproduction needs. The images are stored on cards, memory sticks, or rewriteable CDs. The camera is then plugged into the computer using the USB port. The images can then be reviewed. Some editing of the video is necessary to delete repetitive sections, but the attorney has to be careful to not go too far. Paonita[5] noted,

> Once you've got your images into the computer, you might have to manipulate them to make them viewable. But here, you run into a quandary. To bring out the important part of the image, you'll probably need to crop them. At the same time, you don't want to have pictures that are obviously manipulated, because that decreases their value in court. And don't even think of using an image-editing program, such as Adobe Photoshop, to doctor an image. Such manipulations undermine your case's credibility.

6. Objecting to videotapes

The court may overrule any objection to the film not being relevant. Defense counsel is likely to have more success in an objection based on the prejudicial effects outweighing the probative value. This objection will force the court to consider whether the film is accurate and objective and how the probative value compares with the prejudicial effect.[4] Close-ups of facial expressions showing pain or tears, extreme close-ups of open wounds, or a soundtrack containing cries of agony are likely to be judged as prejudicial. Any mention on the tape of the case or the cause of the injury will also draw an objection from the defense. Videotapes are sometimes objected to on the grounds that they are cumulative. If the tape adds nothing new or incorporates a great deal of prior photographic evidence, this objection may succeed. To avoid this potential objection, the videotape can be offered early in the trial before a substantial quantity of other evidence about pain and suffering has been presented.[1]

Tip

Recognizing the power of a day-in-the-life film, defense counsel should vigorously fight to prevent it from being admitted into evidence

---

The defense counsel may argue that the scenes of the plaintiff trying to walk on her artificial legs, for example, are statements of the plaintiff about her condition offered to prove the truth of her condition and not subject to cross-examination. Several courts have upheld this objection, finding that the videotape was a statement rather than tangible evidence like a photograph of an inanimate object. Faced with this objection, the plaintiff's attorney may find helpful the exception under Fed.R.Evid. 803(3) for statements about mental, emotional, or physical conditions, or the catch-all provision of Rule 803(24).[1]

The incorporation of still photographs of the plaintiff before the accident, with the video images of the plaintiff's current condition may draw objections from the defense. A judge will likely require that the tape is inadmissible unless the "before" material is edited out.[1]

Plaintiffs' attorneys will be putting in many hours of viewing and editing time to get the final product to flow and communicate their messages. Any objection that can be sustained by the court because of prejudicial editing or cinema techniques will lessen the effectiveness of the film. The defense attorney should be aware of techniques possibly used by the plaintiff that would subjectively exaggerate the injuries. These include use of dramatic lighting, unnatural camera angles, or other Hollywood-style cinema techniques. The defense attorney will want to be present during the taping to ensure the integrity of what is being seen on the camera. The integrity may be affected by possible direction by the videographer, reshooting a scene, and other objectionable techniques.

The motion in videotapes may be objectionable if a tape is played at a speed faster or slower than normal so that the people or objects depicted on the tape are not moving at the speed they were when the tape was made. Motion in videotapes may also be objectionable if frames have been removed or edited, distorting the motion shown on the tape.[6] An example of objectionable editing would be footage of a plaintiff walking on her new prosthetic legs at a slower speed than occurred when the filming was done.

7. Surveillance videotaping

Surveillance videotaping is a tool available to the defense attorney when there is doubt about the validity of the plaintiff's injuries. A person with a camera is paid to sit and observe the plaintiff's residence in the hopes that the plaintiff will be caught doing something that is contrary to the claimed limitations.

Tip

The attorney needs to select the videographer carefully to ensure that this person is using professional equipment. If the subject claims "that's not me on the tape," the tape quality has to be high enough to be able to refute that claim. Although action and adventure Hollywood movies show how videotape can be enhanced to show minute details, the reality is that these techniques are not available to the general public.

The videocamera's time and date generator, while useful as an electronic note-taking device, should not be relied on for accuracy. These settings can be changed. If the batteries are taken out of the camera, the date and time setting will be inaccurate unless reset. A more effective method of documenting a reliable date would be to film the headlines of the daily newspaper.

Many defense counsels fear that jurors will be angered by surreptitious videotaping of the plaintiff. Jurors, on the contrary, may welcome the videotape that presents information that contradicts the plaintiff's claims. The keys to the use of such films are to avoid any editing and to only use them when they graphically show the plaintiff is untruthful about physical or cognitive disabilities. If the films are relatively benign, or if the film requires the jury to infer something that is not clearly shown, films can be of greater harm than good.[7]

Surveillance videotaping may be expensive and yield nothing usable.

In *Nuzzo v. Shoprite*, a retired seventy-six-year-old woman slipped in a supermarket. Although she did not fall, she injured her back so badly that she needed two surgeries. Her attorney presented evidence that she still had limited movement at the time of the trial. The defense commissioned a surveillance videotape of Nuzzo to illustrate that there was no evidence of injury in the plaintiff's daily physical activities. But the plaintiff's attorney said the video helped his case because it showed that Nuzzo's movements were indeed affected. The plaintiff's attorney demanded $757,000 just before trial. The defense countered with a $250,000 offer on the first day of trial. The case settled for $462,000 on the third day.[8]

In a Utah case, a plaintiff in her thirties claimed pain and dizziness in her ears following treatment with intravenous Gentamicin. Her experts testified she was unable to resume gainful employment due to the severity of her injuries. The defense tested the plaintiff through its own neuro-otolaryngologist and claimed that she was malingering. The defense alleged that surreptitious videotaping confirmed this claim, although the plaintiff was allegedly never taped walking without assistance. The action settled for a confidential amount, including a lump sum and lifetime annuity.[9]

Even when the videotape shows limitations, the jury may choose to ignore that evidence.

In a New York case, a cab driver had a hernia repair. He claimed that during a second procedure to remove an enlarged mass at the incision site, he suffered a neurological injury to his right arm. The patient had suffered polio as a boy and had a paralyzed and underdeveloped left arm. The defendants contended that the plaintiff's arm was properly positioned on a padded arm board during the surgery. The also claimed that many physicians and nurses documented that the plaintiff was using his right arm following the operation. The defendants produced a surveillance video showing the plaintiff driving a car and using his right arm to perform various daily functions. Nevertheless, the jury awarded $966,273.[10]

A precedent was established in New Jersey when a court assessed attorneys' fees to sanction a workers' compensation insurer that tried to use covert video surveillance and other subterfuges to terminate benefits. The Appellate Division, in *Mahler v. Johnson & Johnson,* A-256-00 on February 27, 2002, affirmed an award of $50,800 in attorneys' fees and $3,359 in costs to a sixty-one-year-old former worker who, the insurer claimed, was faking her disability. A workers' compensation judge found her to be completely disabled from reflex sympathetic dystrophy nine years after a mail cabinet fell on her left arm and shoulder. She was awarded weekly permanent disability benefits for life. The carrier, in 1997, tried to modify the award, offering to prove by video surveillance that the claimant was feigning disability. The ninety minutes of tape, recorded on thirteen separate days during fourteen months, showed her walking to her mailbox and gardening. On five of the thirteen days, the claimant never left the house. The most dramatic of the taped actions, which included weeding and sweeping with special devices, was throwing a cardboard box at the curb. The judge refused to terminate her benefits, calling the carrier "obsessed" with proving that Mahler was faking to obtain benefits. The judge was troubled by the fact that a nurse, ostensibly sent to help care for Mahler, was effectively a spy for the insurer. Even that being so, she saw only "some modest walking about."[11]

8. Videotaping expert testimony

Videotapes can substitute for experts or witnesses who cannot testify in person at trial. The expert may use a variety of demonstrative evidence, including models, medical illustrations, diagrams, and medical equipment to enhance the testimony. Counsel can retrieve selected portions of the tape and play them in the courtroom. Lengthy pauses, objections, or irrelevant background information should be edited out. New technology allows the camera shot of the witness to be enhanced with a typed transcript which runs next to or below the image of the witness. This is particularly effective when cross-examining an expert witness in the courtroom with a videotaped deposition transcript. Videotapes may be presented in the courtroom through a large television monitor placed in front of the jury. Courtrooms equipped for today's technology may incorporate a series of monitors in front of the jurors, judge, and opposing counsel. The room does not have to be darkened for clear visibility. The videotape can be locked on one image while a point is being explained by a witness.[1]

Video teleconferencing provides new options to the attorney. It can permit an out of state physician to testify via a live hookup, thus saving on travel expenses and time. After being brought up to speed on the trial the expert can be prepared to address the case as it is unfolding in the settlement discussions or at trial.

D. Radiology and diagnostics

Paper prints from x-rays and other diagnostic films can be easily made and distributed to insurance adjusters and attorneys. Not only do these images reinforce the facts of the condition or injury, they enhance the perception of a well-prepared, creative advocate. Prints and exhibits based on the films themselves can be included in settlement brochures, arbitrations, and settlement conferences as precursors to more elaborate trial presentations.

Tip

One of the most critical forms of visual evidence preservation is usually done before the attorney first gets involved in the case. Diagnostic tests such as x-rays, MRI or CT scans, and EKGs yield visual proof of the injury, which can be used during the lawsuit to support written or oral evidence.

The distinction between positive and negative images is an important consideration when working with x-ray films or MRI and CT scans. Films themselves are not really "negatives" in the traditional photographic sense. X-ray films are what the doctor uses to assess injury. They are not intermediate images that are later transformed. This is critical especially in cases of medical malpractice in which a dark spot that was missed on an x-ray had better be a dark spot on the final exhibit, not reversed into a "positive."

Some attorneys believe that fractures look more impressive when the image is reversed on paper. However, the human eye is drawn to the lightest part of any visual image. Therefore the most important part of the x-ray image, the bone, should remain light, not dark. A positive x-ray image forces the fracture line to compete with what now is a massive white background image. This is even more crucial when the films show some form of internal fixation or other hardware of treatment. On the original x-ray film, metal or plastic objects show up as light objects and are generally more impressive for the same reason.

Light boxes of the kind typically seen in a hospital are too small to show a film to the jury. X-rays may be presented in the courtroom in a variety of ways. They may be scanned, enlarged, and mounted on a rigid board. A visual presenter, as described in Section 19.4C, may be used. Consisting of a camera and plate, the image is projected on a monitor. An x-ray may also be videotaped by putting the negative on the light box and using a video camera to zoom in on the image. The image may also be scanned and saved on a computer for presentation using a laptop computer.

Most forms of diagnostic films can be used as the foundation for enhanced exhibits such as colorizations or illustrative interpretations. These will be addressed below in Section H on medical illustrations. No matter what format is used to present the films, it is important to have the doctor who will describe the exhibits at trial pick out which images should be presented. There are often many more views than are needed as exhibits. Counsel must have the treating doctor or expert take an active role in the selection of exhibits. Because of busy schedules, this selection process should occur in one or more pretrial meetings or perhaps for a few minutes in the doctor's office following his or her deposition. If the deposition is videotaped, have the prints made ahead of time, so that any marking made at the deposition can be preserved for the trial.

Diagnostic test results such as EKG strips can also make effective trial exhibits. Copies of the strips can be enlarged and mounted on rigid backing with overlays or laminate material added to give the witness a way to mark the exhibit during trial. Color markers can be used to highlight areas of irregularity and contrast them with normal readings. Lines can be added across the strips to mark the high and low ranges of normal results.

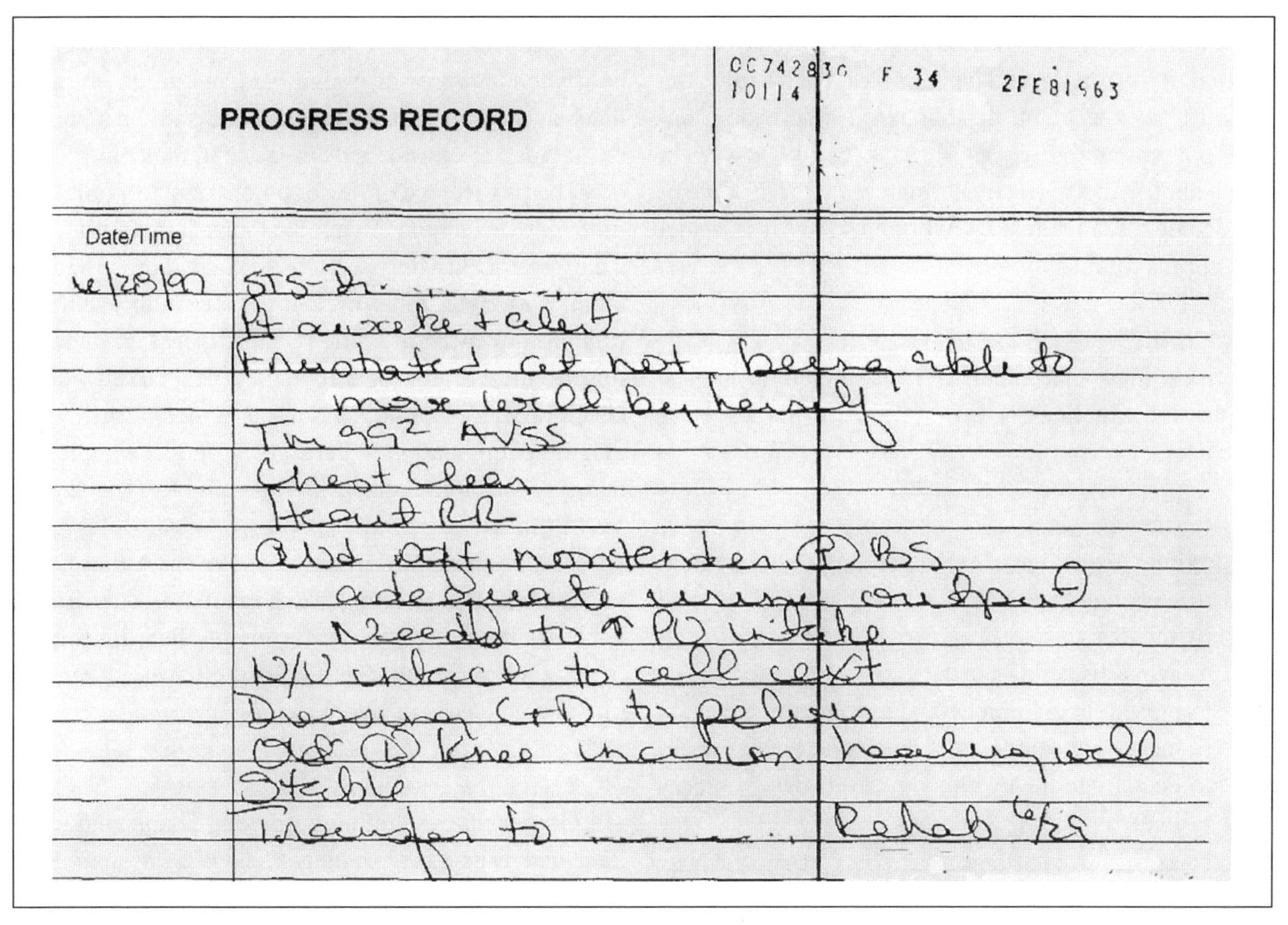

PROGRESS RECORD

OC742830 F 34 2FE81563
10114

Date/Time	
6/28/90	STS-Dr.
	Pt awake + alert
	Frustrated at not being able to
	move well by herself
	Tm 99^{2} AVSS
	Chest Clear
	Heart RR
	Abd soft, nontender, (+) BS,
	adequate urine output
	Needs to ↑ PO intake
	N/V intact to all ext
	Dressing C+D to pelvis
	Old (L) Knee incision healing well
	Stable
	Transfer to ... Rehab 6/28

Figure 19.5 *Scanned nurse's note*

E. Medical records

One critical source for demonstrative evidence is the patient's medical record. The presence or absence of information, comments, key events, and entries regarding times, medications, and dosages can be used effectively to reinforce the claims of pain and suffering. Comments regarding pain and suffering are found in the nurses' notes, see Figure 19.5, physician progress notes, physical therapy notes, and the entries of other therapists. Refer to Chapter 1, "Organizing and Analyzing Medical Records," for more information.

Both the plaintiff's and the defense counsel should evaluate medical records for evidence of pre-existing injuries that may be used to minimize damages. High on the list of mistakes is the failure to obtain a complete set of medical records from all service providers in the plaintiff's immediate area. The Internet, IDEX, references in records to other medical personnel, and services which identify all medical facilities within a radius of the plaintiff's home are useful in locating medical records.[7] These records should be scrutinized for pre-existing conditions and evidence of treatment for pain. These entries can be used as demonstrative evidence by the defense attorney at trial to attack pain and suffering claims.

Hely and Weiseman[12] suggest that pre-existing conditions can be addressed by the plaintiff's attorney by bringing a fragile wine glass and a child's plastic cup or mug to court for summations. Both are placed just at the edge of counsel table. At the appropriate place in the summation, the attorney refers to the two drinking vessels, commenting that the defense has argued that the plaintiff's problems stem from a condition she had before the careless acts took place. Referring to the two drinking vessels, the attorney says "At the edge of this table are two perfectly suitable things from which you can drink. Neither leaks. Both can quench thirst quite well. If the child's mug were to get knocked just a little, it falls to the ground. I can pick it up and use it again and again. But if the wine glass were to get knocked over the edge, it will completely shatter. It is fragile and vulnerable. That's how the plaintiff was before all this happened. She had an underlying vulnerability, but she functioned and went about her life in a perfectly normal way until the date of the accident." This analogy works because it is visual and not just oral.

F. Graphics

Graphics may take many forms, including tables, graphs and timelines. There are several purposes for graphics:

- to show the data
- to induce the viewer of the graphics to think about the substance of the data rather than get distracted by the design
- to avoid distorting the data
- to present many numbers in a small space
- to make large amounts of data coherent
- to encourage the eye to compare different pieces of data[13]

Tip

There is almost no case that cannot benefit from the preparation of graphics that can be used during opening statement, as visual support during testimony, or during closing argument.

---

1. Tables

Tables are effective when presenting small amounts of data. Figure 19.6 is an example of such a table. Tables may also be used to present a chronology of events, such as a list of operations or hospital admissions. As shown in the figure, consistency in presentation of information is important. All dates should either be written in words or in numbers, but not in both formats on the same exhibit. The columns in the table can be adjusted to eliminate dead space in the column.

The persistence or development of symptoms over time may be included in a large table. Dates defined on a daily or weekly basis may be located at the top of the table, with symptoms or complications in a column running down the left side of the paper. The intersection of the column and row may be marked with a check or shaded to indicate the presence of the symptom or complication. There are several examples of this type of table located in Chapter 17, "The Expert Fact Witness."

The amount of information placed in a table should be limited. Use of up to twenty rows is desirable. Tables that require more information than this should be broken into smaller units. Shading every other row increases the ease of interpretation of the data.

Date	Medications for pain	Number of doses
11/12/00	Morphine	6
11/13/00	Morphine	5
11/14/00	Morphine	5
11/15/00	Morphine Percocet	3 4
11/16/00	Percocet	6
11/17/00	Percocet	6

Figure 19.6 *Table format for listing medications*

2. Graphs

Graphs may be used to represent a large amount of data and aspects of damages, such as weight loss, amount of pain medication needed measured in milligrams, drops in hemoglobin, or increases in white blood cell counts indicating recurrent infections. Silhouette line charts are useful for demonstrating fluctuations in data. Figure 19.7 shows blood loss after a woman's aorta was pierced during laparoscopic surgery.

Tip

It is important that the data not be distorted in the process of creating the graph.

For example, changing the baseline from 0 to 100 pounds changes the angles of the lines in Figures 19.8 and 19.9. This type of manipulation of the data will likely draw an objection that it is misleading.

Line graphs may be used to show change over time. When two values are used on the same graph, the lines should be sufficiently different to provide contrast. Use of one solid line and one broken line or two different colors are standard methods for differentiat-

continued on page 419

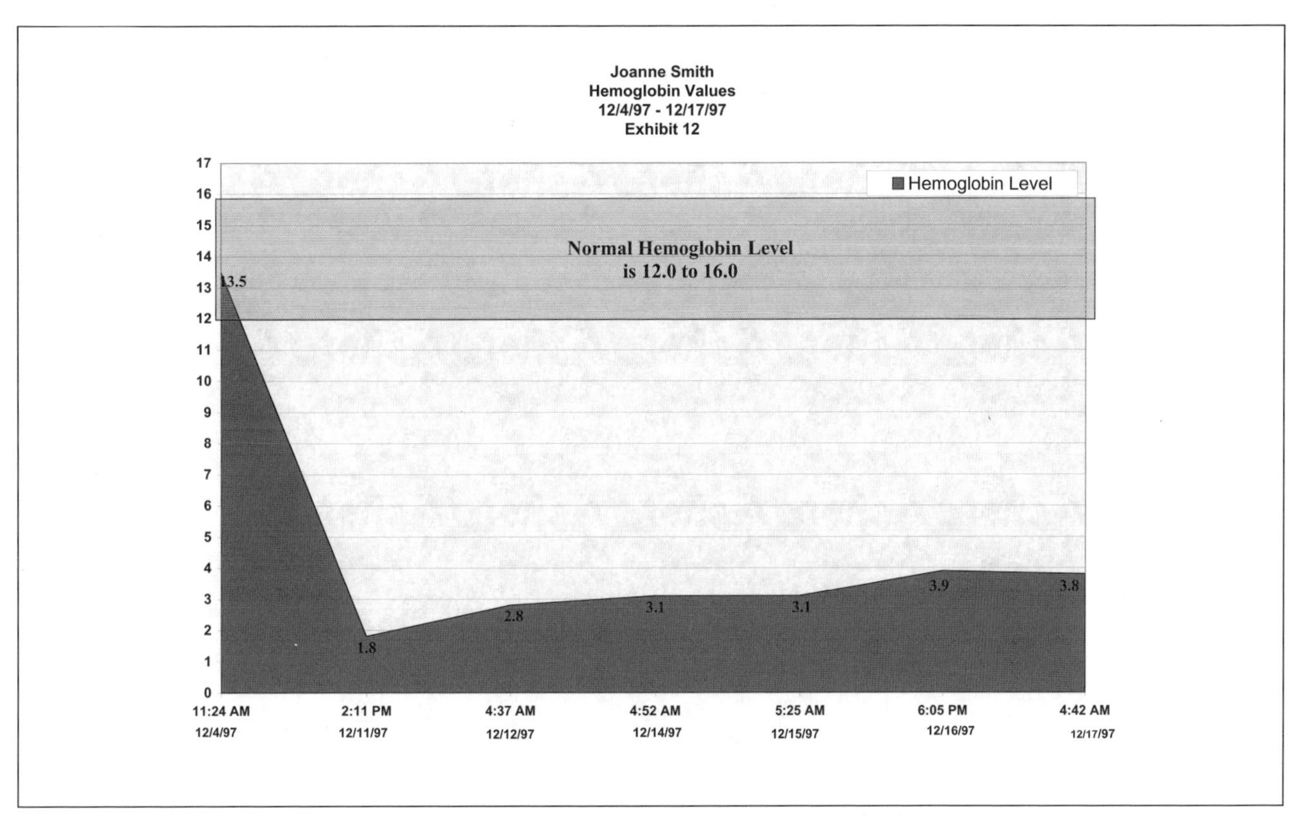

Figure 19.7 *Silhouette chart created in Microsoft Excel showing blood loss after a surgical injury, courtesy of Med League Support Services, Inc., Flemington, NJ*

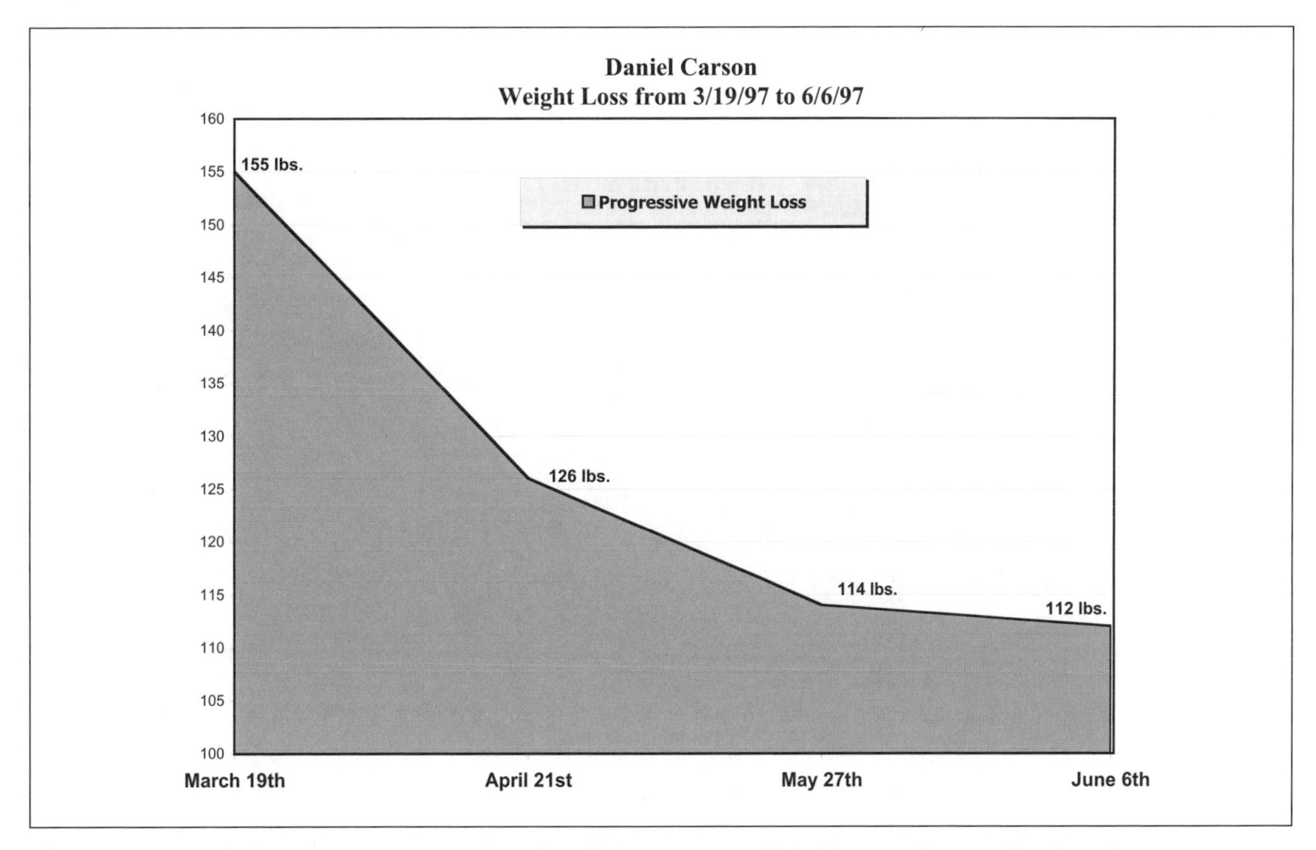

Figure 19.8 *Weight loss using 100 pounds as baseline, courtesy of Med League Support Services, Inc.*

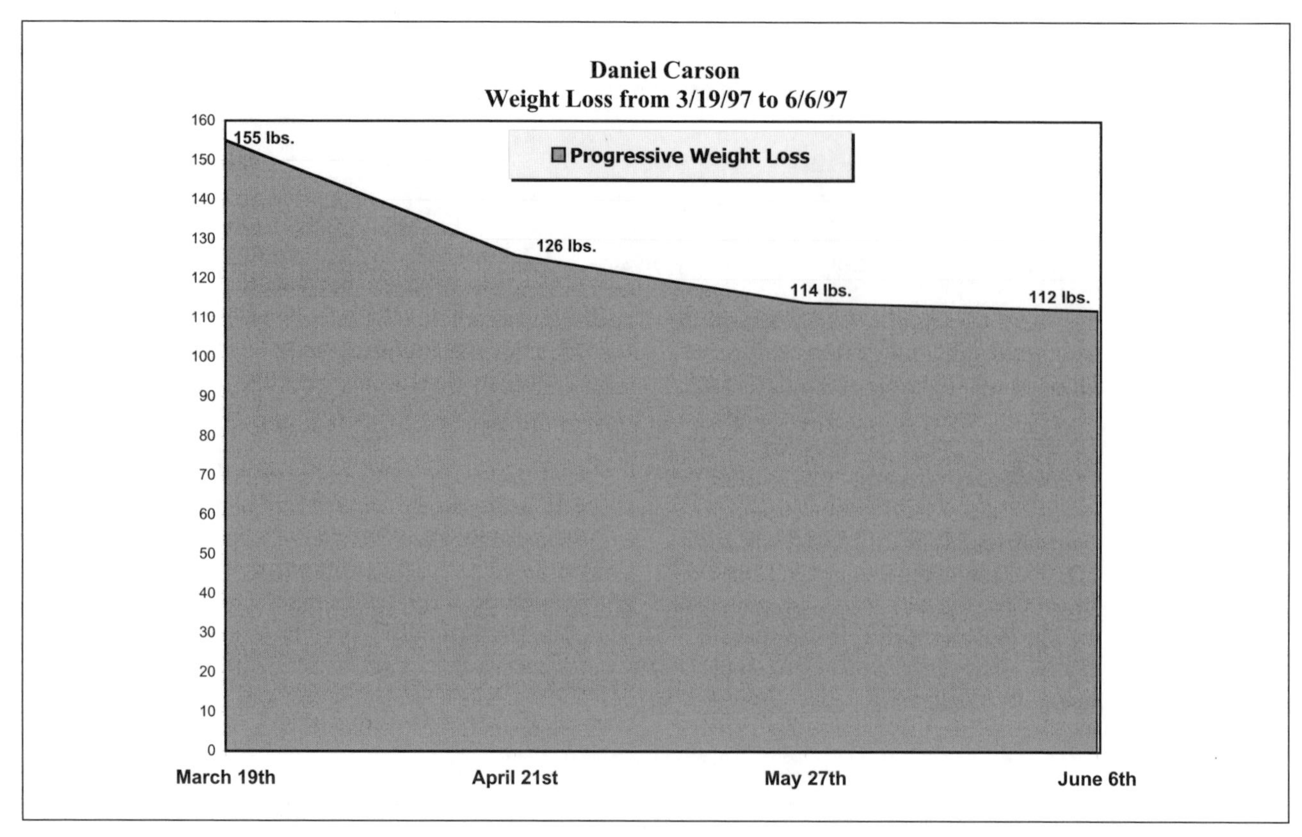

Figure 19.9 Weight loss using 0 pounds as a baseline, courtesy of Med League Support Services, Inc

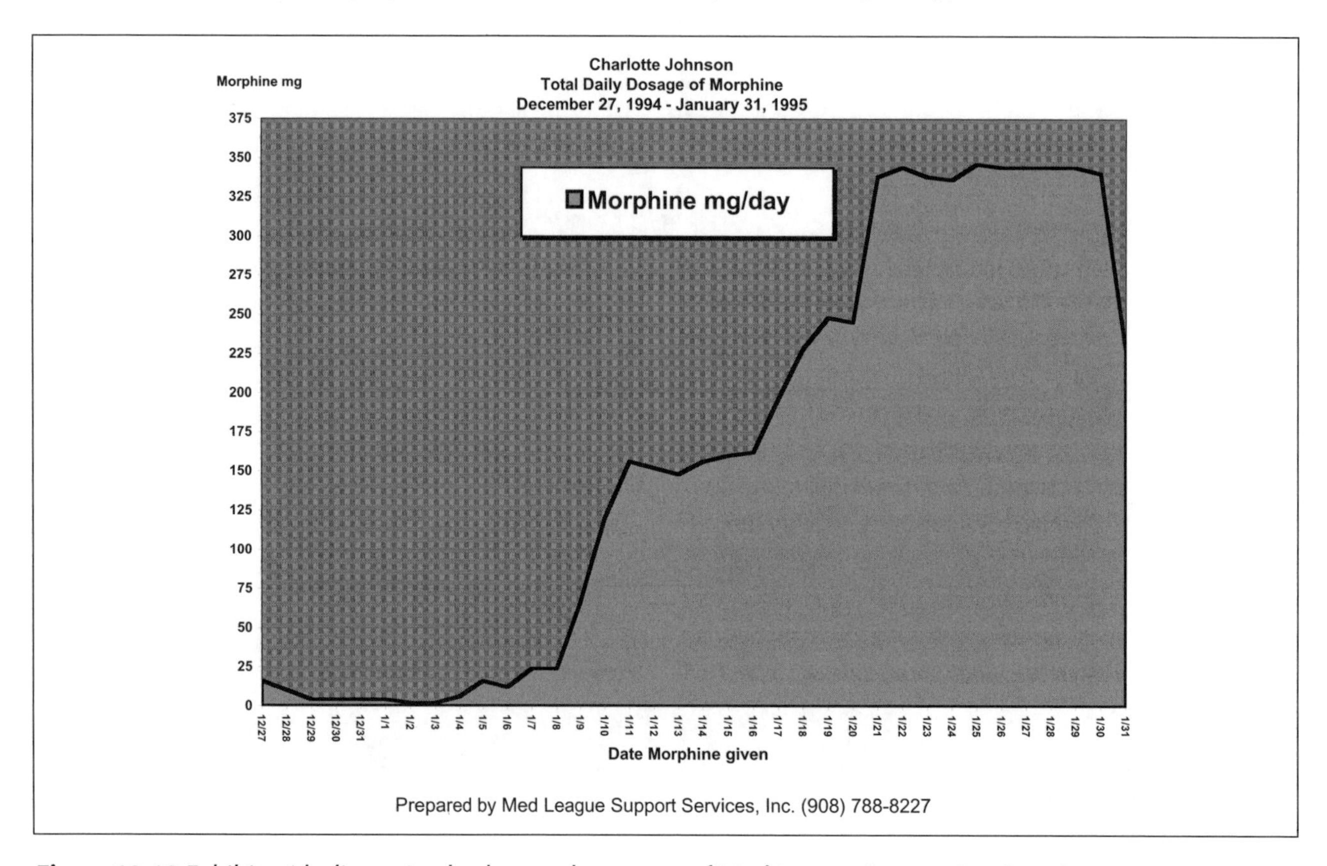

Figure 19.10 Exhibit with distracting background, courtesy of Med League Support Services, Inc

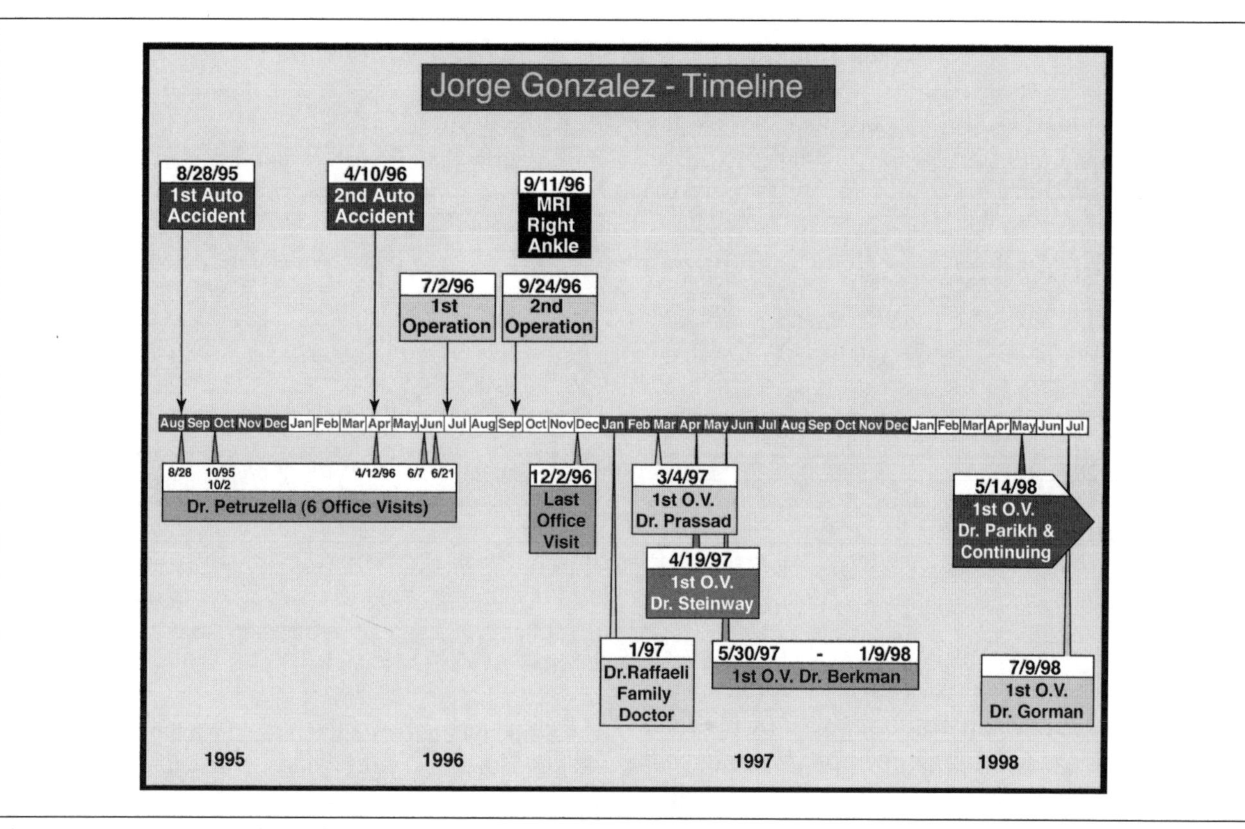

Figure 19.11 *Horizontal timeline, courtesy of the Evidence Store*

ing the lines.[11] Avoid using more than two lines on a line chart. The additional lines increase the difficulty of deciphering the data.

Clear, detailed labeling should eliminate ambiguity. The title should be in a large font with a brief name. Units of measurement should be standardized. For example, if data are presented showing the amount of pain medication the patient needed each day, a standard twenty-four-hour period should be used rather than varying the time frame. If labels are used and unless the type of data is obvious, the name of the vertical (Y) axis should be at the top of the axis and the name of the horizontal (X) axis should be centered below the axis. A key can be included in the white space within the chart.

The focus of the graphic presentation must be on the data. The background should not be distracting. Avoid using designs that look like they are vibrating or moving in the background, as shown in Figure 19.10.

3. Timelines

Timelines are invaluable whenever the jury will be expected to understand a sequence of events. Timelines are often used as part of the damages presentation, documenting, as in other cases, the course of treatment of the patient. This should include the lengths of hospitalizations, duration of critical care, surgeries, and follow-up therapies. The purpose of the timeline might be to illustrate multiple consequences of an injury. Noted trial lawyer Jerry Spence preaches the importance of telling a story to the jury. A timeline suggests by its very nature that there was a sequence of events and problems as a result of an injury.

Tip

Timelines help put the entire aftermath into perspective. They give the jury a better understanding of the time span in which the events took place and assist in analyzing the relationship of events in time.

It is critical to check and double-check all the information that goes on any timeline, especially one that plots medical treatment. A legal nurse consultant should be employed to sort thoroughly all the records

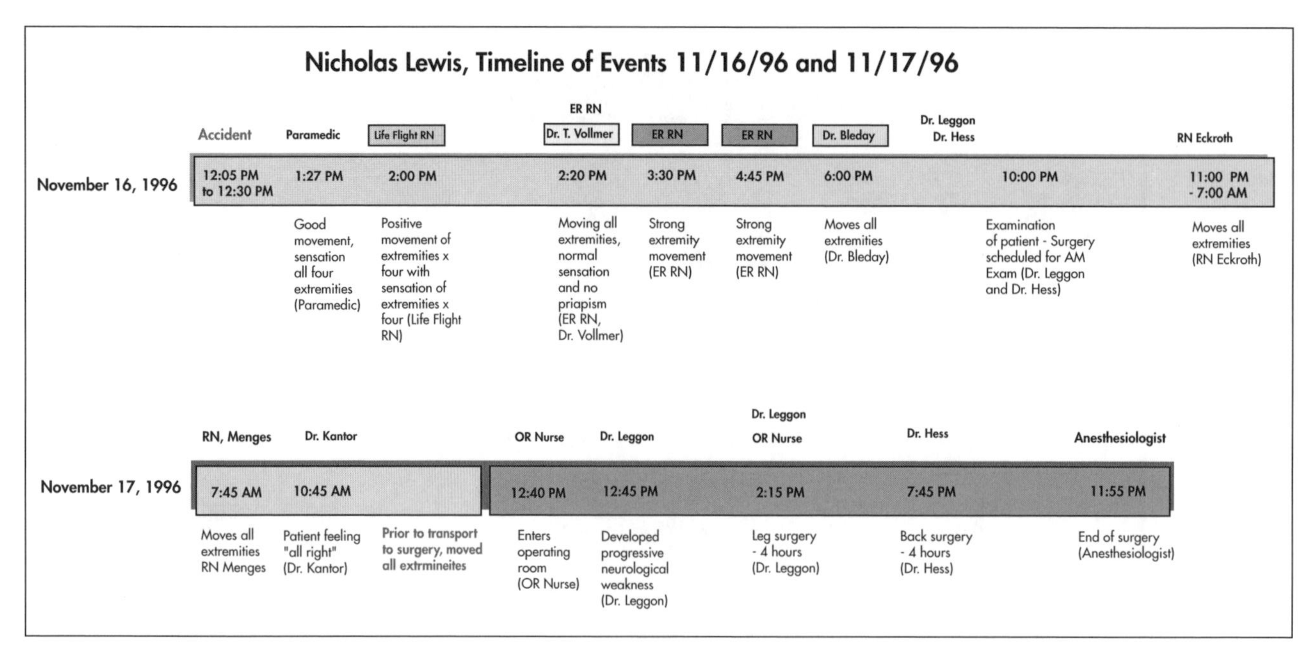

***Figure 19.12** Horizontal timeline, courtesy of Med League Support Services, Inc.*

into categories and dates of care for this purpose. Such a consultant should be used in all major cases to assist with the extraction and organization of the medical records, especially when there are handwritten progress notes that may contain abbreviations and language not familiar to a nonmedical person such as an attorney or paralegal. Very often it is possible to confuse insurance payment dates on doctors' bills for dates of treatment which can cause enough errors in an exhibit to warrant its exclusion from use.

A number of timeline formats can be created. Such exhibits can be prepared as either linear timelines (see Figure 19.11) or calendar chronologies. A common method of displaying this type of information is to use a horizontal line with boxes containing key data above and below the line. In a case involving a delay in performing surgery on a man who became paralyzed, the timeline could have been presented in a horizontal, vertical, or graphical manner. (See Figures 19.12–9.14.)

Simple timelines can be created in a sequential manner. If the timeline focuses on the events that occurred over minutes or hours, clock symbols with the appropriate time can be included on the timeline. The event that occurred at each timeframe can be placed next to or under each clock symbol. An effective way to depict changes in appearance and scarring over time is to build a graphic with photographs of the plaintiff. The photographs may be scanned and placed along a horizontal line labeled with the date of each photograph. At a glance, the juror can see the changes in the plaintiff's appearance. Another application of this concept is to place photographs of a pressure sore along a horizontal plane, showing the changes in the stage of the sore over time.

Tip

A major benefit of preparing timelines for cases is that the process forces the attorney to organize the information coherently in advance of trial.

It is not necessary to put every detail on a timeline. This exhibit is merely a tool to help organize the case for the jury and serve as an anchor for key points of theory and information. A timeline gives the trial attorney something to point to during presentation of the case. It is important, as with other exhibits, to tell the jury what the attorney wants them to see in the timeline. Once they are told, they too will see what the attorney sees.

The attorney with prepared timelines is better prepared for trial or settlement conferences. Displaying such exhibits during settlement conferences can be an effective strategy. Not only does it help the defendant see the merits of the plaintiff's case, it shows counsel's preparedness and commitment. It also demonstrates

Nicholas Lewis Timeline

November 16, 1996

12:05 PM to 12:30 PM	Accident
1:27 PM	Good movement, sensation all four extremities (Paramedic)
2:00 PM	Positive movement of extremities x four with sensation of extremities x four (Life Flight RN)
2:20 PM	Moving all extremities, normal sensation (ER RN, Dr. Villes)
3:30 PM	Strong extremity movement (ER RN)
4:45 PM	Strong extremity movement (ER RN)
6:00 PM	Moves all extremities (Dr. Block)
10:00 PM	Examination of patient - surgery scheduled for AM exam (Dr. Lorton, Dr. Hantas)
11:00 PM - 7:00 AM	Moves all extremities (RN Stanley)

November 17, 1996

7:45 AM	Moves all extremities (LPN Miller)
10:45 AM	Patient feeling "all right" (Dr. Cohen)
	Prior to transport to surgery, moving all extremities (LPN Miller)
12:40 PM	Enters operating room (OR Nurse)
12:45 PM	Developed progressive neurological weakness (Dr. Lorton)
2:15 PM	Leg surgery - 4 hours (Dr. Lorton)

Figure 19.13 *Vertical timeline, courtesy of Med League Support Services, Inc.*

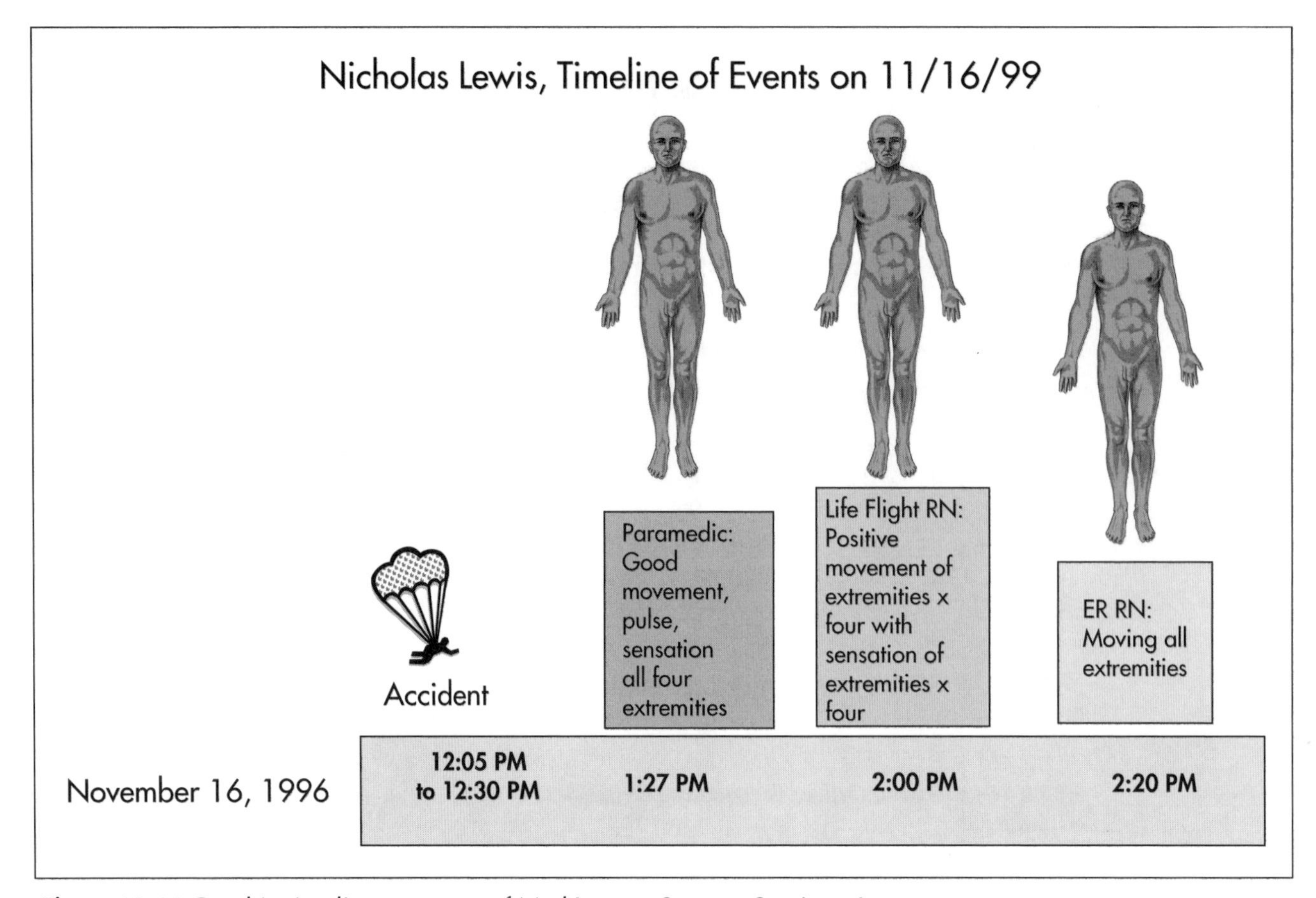

Figure 19.14 *Graphic timeline, courtesy of Med League Support Services, Inc.*

that the attorney is prepared to fund demonstrative evidence and suggests that other exhibits may be in preparation. This is a win-win situation for the attorney. Even if the case settles before trial, early preparation of demonstrative evidence can be viewed as an investment rather than an expense. It may help increase the other side's settlement offer.

Suspense can be created in the courtroom by keeping all portions of the time line covered except the portion being discussed by the witness. Each section is revealed to discuss the events associated with the pain and suffering experienced by the plaintiff. The timeline can be developed using a magnetic board or Velcro exhibits with the units of time printed on the board so that labels identifying individual events can be affixed as the testimony occurs. Timelines can also be displayed using projectors.[1]

G. Anatomical models

The jurors' rudimentary knowledge of human anatomy is quickly and effectively enhanced by models and charts. Just as with the preparation of x-rays exhibits, any meeting with medical witnesses should include a review of a model or chart that can be used at trial. Medical witnesses, particularly specialists, can be a valuable source for such material. Practitioners sometimes have functional anatomical models in the office that can be brought to court. It is important, however, for the attorney to see these models ahead of time. Often the models in the doctor's possession are small and may not be suitable for courtroom use because of their lack of detail. The most accurate anatomical models are cast from natural specimens and are better for trial use. They are also less likely to draw objections. Some models, such as those of the eye, ear, and heart come in larger sizes for use as teaching tools in classrooms. For trial, try to get the largest accurate model available for each part of the anatomy. Sources for anatomical models are easily found on the Internet. Catalogues of anatomical models geared to first-aid squads, or medical and nursing schools are also rich sources. Order them early and ask about the return policy in case the model does not completely suit the case. Ask about rental for expensive models that may be used only once. Some businesses and manufacturers may rent models that are used for display, trade shows, or for other promotional purposes. They may also have some models in stock that are slightly shopworn but would be completely suitable for trial at a reduced price.

Manufacturers who cater to orthopaedic surgeons provide models useful in teaching surgery. Special models can be created on demand using the patient's x-rays. For example, an osteoporotic (soft) bone or a fracture can be replicated in material that has the look and feel of bone. The substance can be drilled in the courtroom with standard orthopaedic instruments. Hardware can be attached to illustrate fixation of fractures or correction of vertebral fractures. Other body parts may be made into models using a process called stereolithography. A plastic-based model is created using two-dimensional data. For example, a skull containing a hemorrhage can be created from the patient's diagnostic studies.

Tip

One advantage of models is that they give the jury a three-dimensional sense of the body part. Models can also be compared with radiology films of the injury to show the nature and extent of the injury. Models require a witness to identify and describe them. A model admitted into evidence and left on counsel's table can be a powerful reminder of important testimony as the trial progresses.

H. Medical illustrations

Anatomical charts and illustrations may be a less expensive alternative to cumbersome models. Illustrations may also have the advantage of captions and labels that teach without the need for testimony.

1. Sources of illustrations

One source of anatomical charts is the doctor who will testify. The doctor may have examples in the office or as part of any lecture package. Counsel should ask the doctor for any textbooks that might illustrate the condition or injury. Especially when it comes to unique surgical procedures, the expert may have the most extensive library from which to select potential exhibits. The illustrations can be copied, with permission, from these books and made into demonstrative evidence. For copyrighted materials, counsel should obtain written permission to reproduce illustrations for the courtroom. Some authors and publishers will require a fee for onetime use; others may only require that the exhibit cite the source text and the publisher.

Many companies sell laminated and foldout anatomical posters that may be suitable for trial use. Generally, however, they are made for the classroom and are too detailed. They may contain too many images or too much text for effective use. Medical books or illustrations intended for consumers may give clearer descriptions, especially those directed at children and young adults. Some books on the market make anatomy simple or show how the body works. These simple illustrations may be adaptable for trial use, assuming that permission is obtained from the publisher.

Many books on human anatomy have been published for a wide variety of readers. Some contain color photographs of cadavers and are generally too graphic for the courtroom. Books such as *Grant's Atlas of Anatomy* and the *Atlas of Human Anatomy* by Frank H. Netter are good sources for material. The Netter atlas, published by IKON Learning Systems, Teterboro, NJ, is probably the most widely recognized collection of anatomical illustrations. Originally published as the Ciba Collection, Dr. Netter's lifework has been placed in one volume, carefully organized by body region, with a complete index for easy reference. While also copyrighted, the Netter material is now available through a network of licensed vendors who are authorized to make enlargements from electronic files. Attorneys can refer to the plates in the atlas and order trial exhibits that can be customized for each case. While not allowed to change the art itself, Netter agents can add or delete any or all of the captions as they appear on the page, making the exhibits more jury-friendly and case-specific. Titles can be changed to better address the topic of the exhibit, and the background can even be changed to black to prevent annotations. Look for Netter agents at www.netterart.com.

2. Custom illustrations

Colorizations of CT scans or MRI films can highlight various anatomical structures so that they can be easily identified. Color adds a focal point to conditions such as hematomas, tumors, and clots. Herniated discs can be colorized to identify the disc components and to locate the spinal cord and surrounding anatomy. Ligaments in the knee can be colorized to isolate the relevant structures, or tears in a meniscus can be colored to correspond with the diagnosis and subsequent surgical treatment. A photograph of the surgical scar placed next to the x-ray adds to the effect.

Consider making custom, case-specific illustrations to show surgical procedures (see Figure 19.15) or unique injuries, such as the eye perforation seen in Figure 19.16 or the scrotal injury depicted in Figure 19.17. These should be based on the diagnostic films and can help the jury understand the nature of the injury or condition. An effective way to personalize the illustration is to superimpose the anatomical images over a photograph of the patient's actual face or body.

Surgical storyboards help the medical witness to explain the procedures used to treat a particular problem or injury. It is important to select a medical illustrator with proper training and experience in medical-legal work to interpret the medical reports. Medical illustrators work closely with the doctor in creating exhibits that accurately recreate the surgery performed. When working with an illustrator for the first time, ask to see samples of prior work. Determine whether a juror would be able to understand the anatomy and the procedure being shown. Is the exhibit well organized,

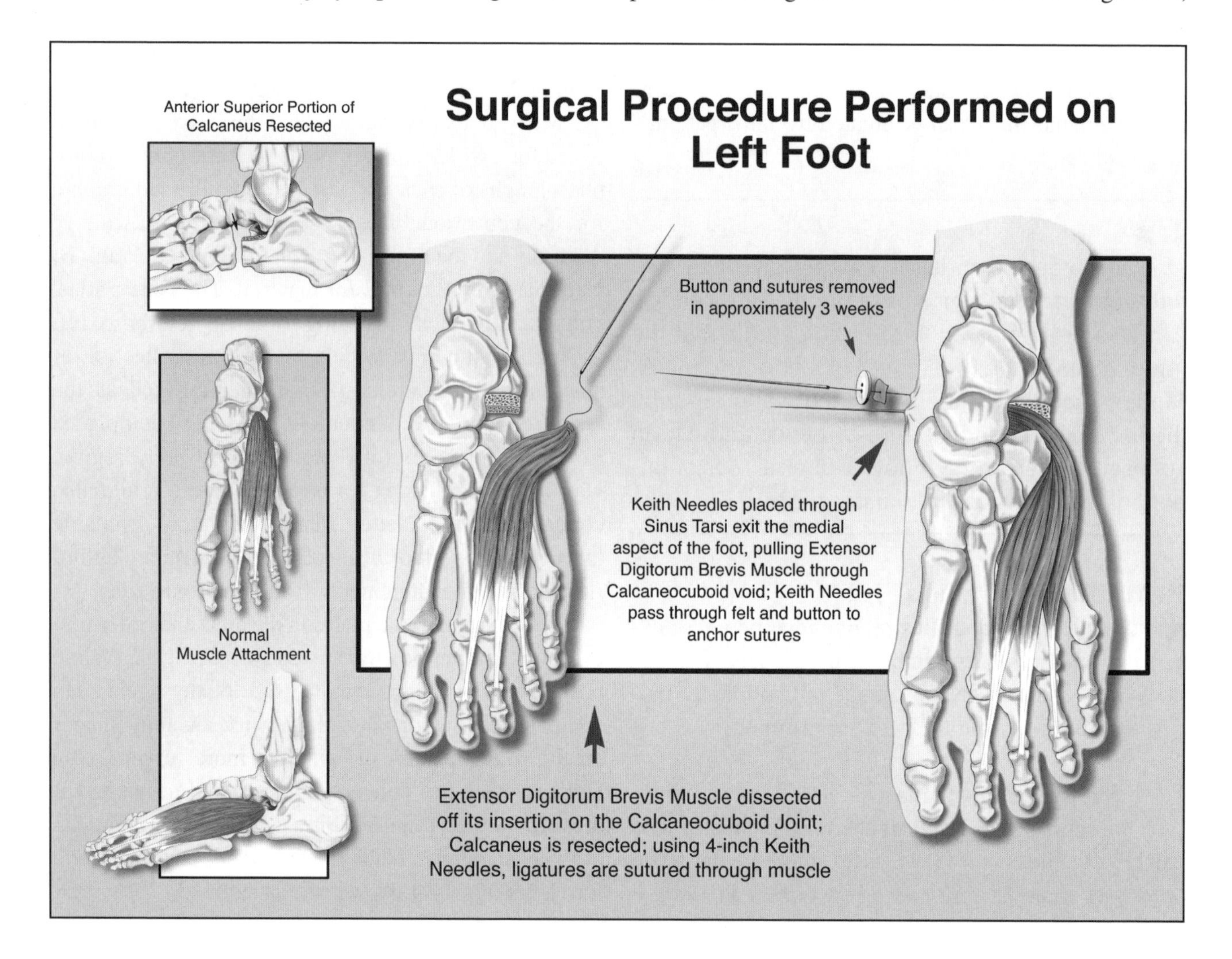

***Figure 19.15** Surgical story board of foot surgery, courtesy of Georgia A. Herbst, Body of Evidence LLC, Edison, NJ; prepared for Gerald Stockman, Esq., Lawrenceville, NJ.*

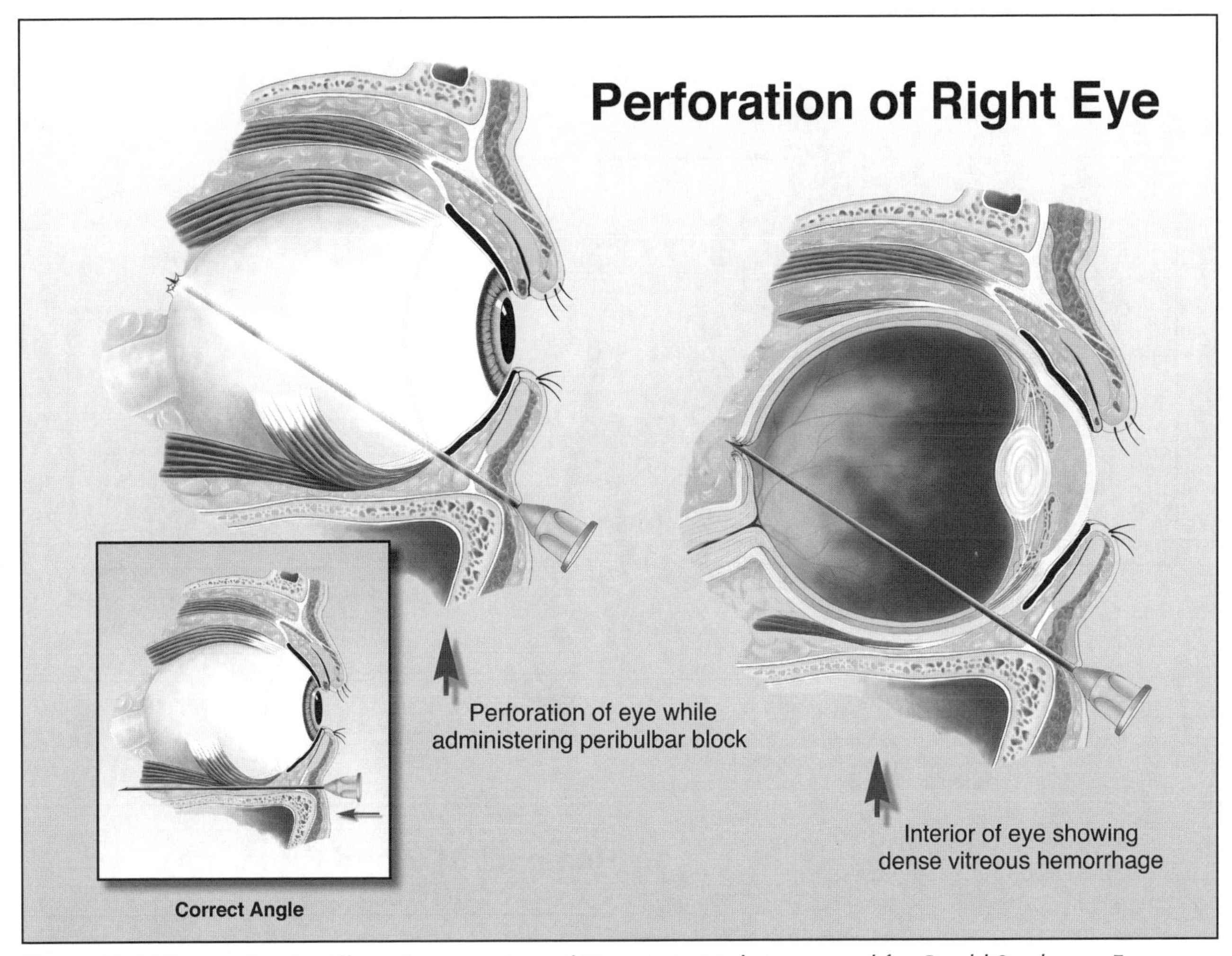

Figure 19.16 *Eye perforation illustration, courtesy of Georgia A. Herbst, prepared for Gerald Stockman, Esq., Lawrenceville, NJ*

are the captions legible, and is the art done in such a way as to allow the attorney to explain to someone else the procedure described?

Tip

It is critical to give the medical illustrator sufficient time to prepare the exhibits. Achieving an effective image may require many drafts.

Medical illustrators will need the operative reports, pertinent films, and reports to create an effective case-specific medical exhibit. Whenever possible, good quality copies of these items should be provided, along with the name and phone number of the expert. Experts should be notified that a particular medical illustrator will be working on the case. Tell the illustrator and the expert to cooperate with each other.

If possible, submit a sketch, no matter how rough or crude, of the projected image of the final product. Even this small effort can save time and money in delivering a finished product to everyone's satisfaction and within budget. Files can be e-mailed for review or placed on an extranet (a secure part of a website) if all parties have the proper access. This can save time. However, try not to rely on the modern conveniences of fax and e-mail to shorten the lead time; the production time required to create such exhibits is not affected by these modern delivery mechanisms.

Use of a large (60–72 point) font increases readability of labels for anatomical parts. The exhibits should include orientation drawings so that a jury can identify the location of the closeup. Presentation of the normal anatomy next to an image of the injury permits the jury to compare the two. To avoid confusing the trier of fact, the normal image should be in the same

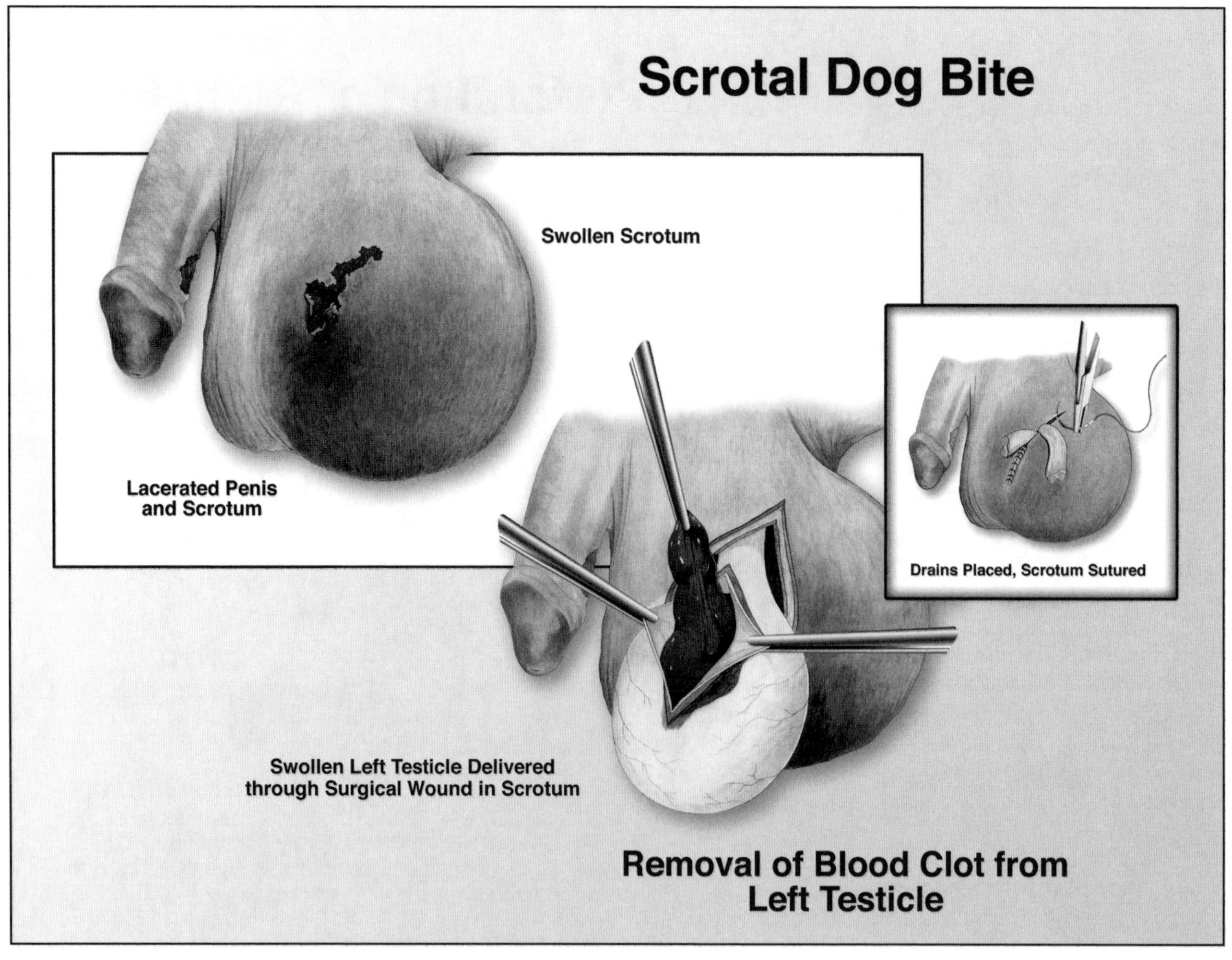

Figure 19.17 *Scrotal injury, courtesy of Georgia A. Herbst, prepared for the Law Office of Rosenfelt & D'Amato, Clifton, NJ*

anatomical position as the image of the client's injury.[14] The images should be kept simple. Medical illustrations should be carefully checked by the expert witness to ensure that the illustrations are accurate.

Since most medical-legal illustrators now work in computer format, 8.5 × 11 inch printouts can be requested for preliminary use, settlement brochures, and expert approval. The attorney need only order the final enlargements as trial approaches.

I. Medical equipment

Among the most powerful of all demonstrative evidence, medical equipment conveys the realities of health care. Many jurors have some familiarity with medical equipment from their own experiences or from popular television shows based on the events of hospitals. However, this knowledge is incomplete. Small pieces of medical equipment may be supplied by the treating physician, expert witness, or manufacturer of a product. The catalogues of many manufacturers are available on the Internet. Whenever possible, the equipment should be seen and touched by the judge and jury. Replicas of orthopaedic appliances (pins, plates, rods) inserted after a fracture should be brought to the courtroom for the jury to see and touch. Consider the effect of handling a capped syringe, a scalpel, or a vest restraint. Medical equipment helps to convey the totality of the patient's experiences.

Tip

While it is impractical or impossible to bring into the courtroom large or expensive pieces of equipment, such as ventilators, CT scanners, hospital beds, or operating room tables, it is possible to show them to a jury through photographs or videotape.

Textbooks, articles, medical supply catalogs, and product brochures are all sources of photographs of medical equipment. Examples of images of medical equipment that can profoundly affect jurors include intracranial pressure bolts, tracheostomies, halo traction, rotating beds, ventilators, suction equipment, external fixators, splints used for fractures, and dermatomes used for skin grafting.

J. Pain medications

The pain and suffering the plaintiff experienced can be illustrated through a variety of formats, as described above. One of the key pieces of information is the amount of pain medication the plaintiff received during a specific timeframe. This can be presented in a number of ways:

- a bar chart showing the number of pain pills taken each day (Figure 19.18),
- a line chart showing the number of injections for pain needed each day (Figure 19.19),
- a graphics image showing syringes needed each day for pain (Figure 19.20), or
- a jar full of jelly beans with each piece of candy representing a pill.

The creation of this type of exhibit requires the ability to analyze the medical record, looking for each place where pain medications would be documented. A legal nurse consultant can be an invaluable resource for analyzing this information.

K. Computer animations

Computer technology can be used to explain the mechanism of injury. This can be combined with footage showing the effects of the injury by stripping away the body's anatomy in layers, detailing the injury to the muscular, vascular, nervous, and skeletal systems. The mechanism of injury of a head injury can be illustrated

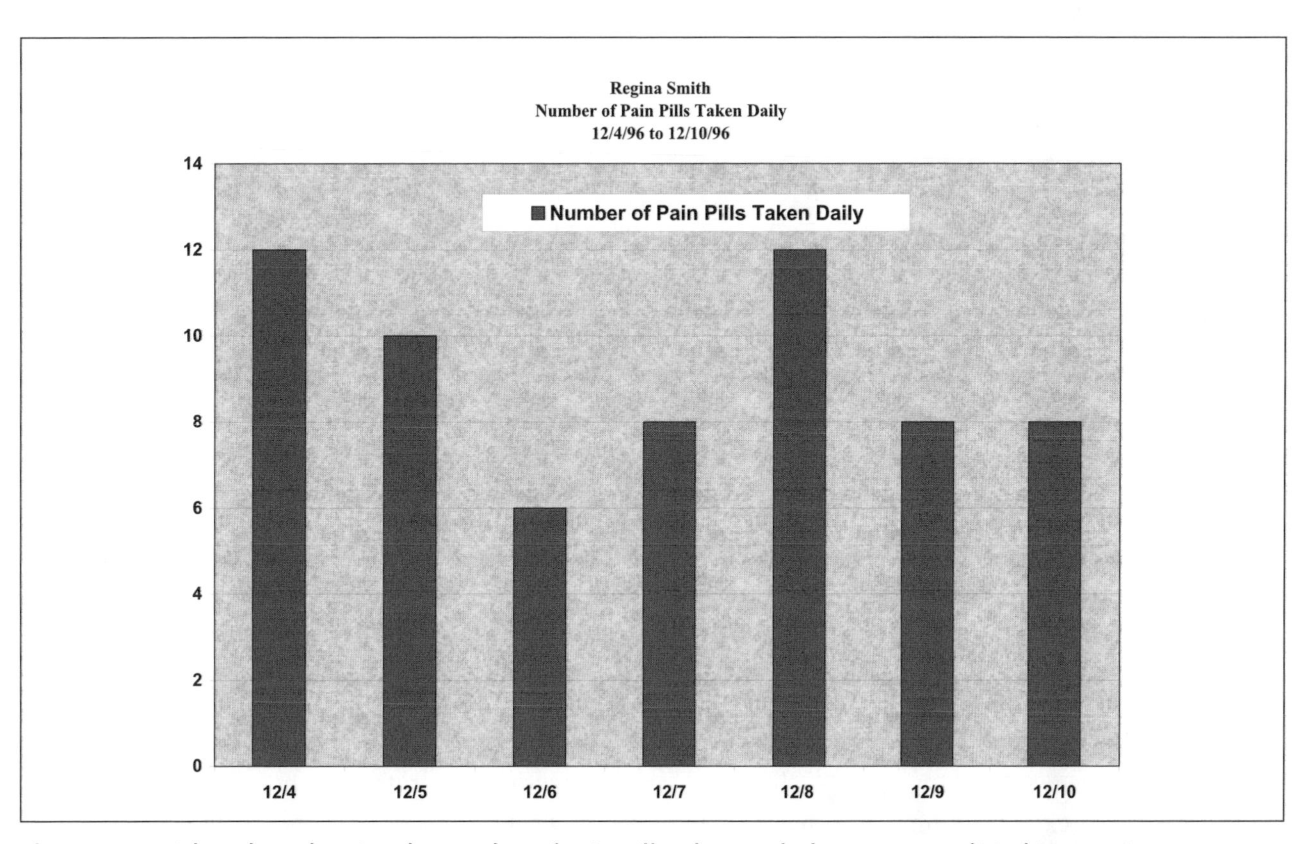

Figure 19.18 A bar chart showing the number of pain pills taken each day, courtesy of Med League Support Services, Inc.

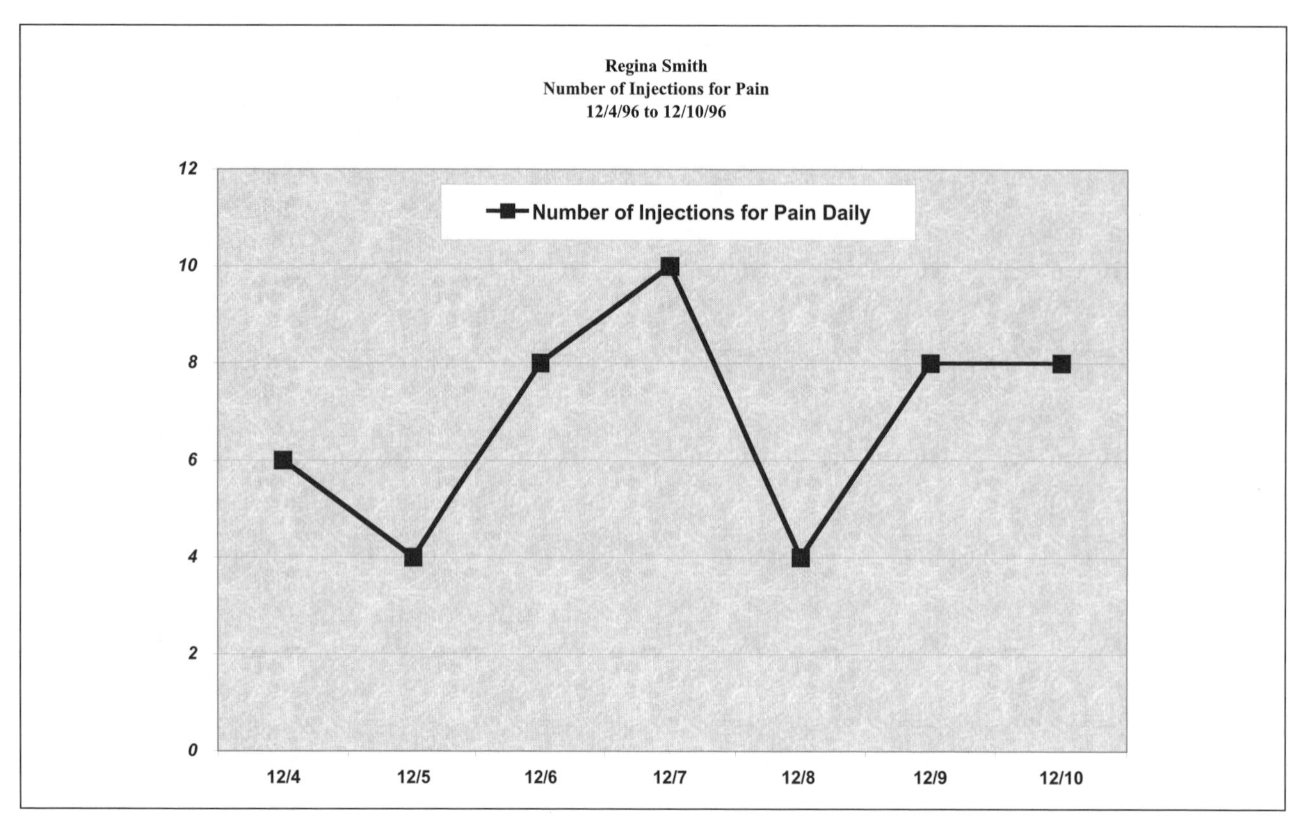

Figure 19.19 *A line chart showing the number of injections for pain needed each day, courtesy of Med League Support Services, Inc.*

by showing how a damaged ceiling tile could have fallen causing injury.

Tip

Trips, slips, and falls of all kinds can also be demonstrated to show, based on the information supplied by the expert, how an injury could have occurred one way and not another. Such visual support can go a long way in refuting adverse theories of liability or proximate cause.

Computer animations that merely illustrate the subject at issue are generally accepted as graphic depictions in the same way as diagrams that are hand-drawn on a blackboard. However, computer animations that are generated solely by the software are subject to more stringent evidentiary requirements. When combined with an audio track, animations can serve as absentee advocates in the settlement process, effectively making the case every time and anywhere the videotape is played. When included in a video settlement package, its impact gives the viewer a taste of how the jury will react to the visuals during trial.

A computer-generated animation or reenactment can provide a very persuasive visual presentation to the jury. Such animations can be very time consuming and expensive to produce. Moreover, because of their expense, care must be taken to ensure a proper foundation will be laid to allow admission at trial.

19.3 Design Principles

With the use of presentation software the ability to create slides, transparencies, enlargements, or presentation slides has never been easier. Adherence to design principles described below will aid in the jury's ability to understand the material presented on computer monitors and thus help the attorney achieve the objectives of the presentation. The ease of understanding an exhibit is improved by adhering to design principles. Tufte defined graphic excellence as "that which gives to the viewer the greatest number of ideas in the shortest time with the least ink in the smallest space."[13] It is essential to convey to the graphics person exactly what

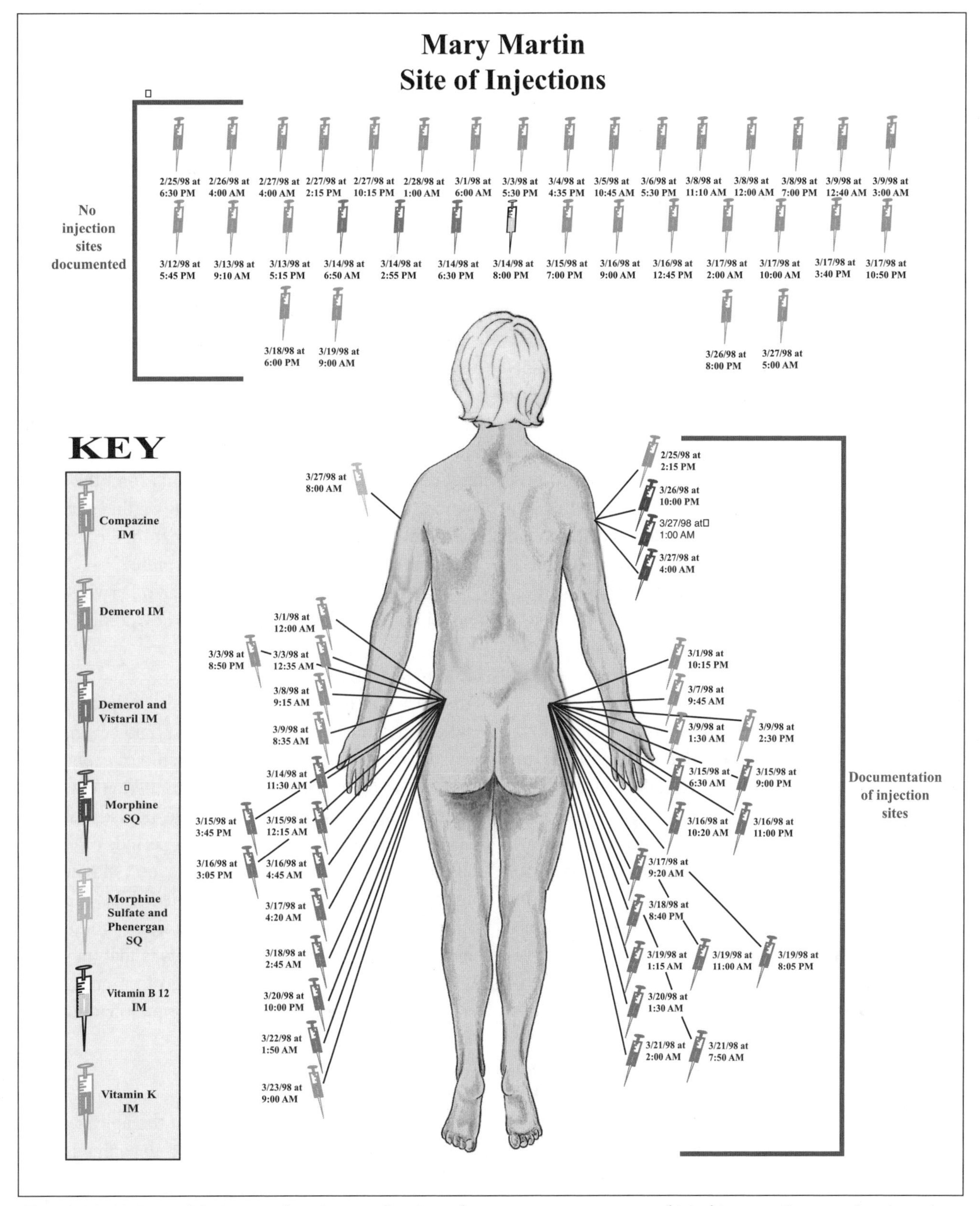

Figure 19.20 *A graphic image showing medications for symptoms, courtesy of Med League Support Services, Inc.*

the attorney wants the jury to understand from any exhibit. The next section includes pointers for exhibit design.

A. Comprehension

Several techniques are useful for increasing the jury's comprehension. Allow the screen to be displayed for at least thirty seconds to enable the jury to read the material. Keep in mind that the material needs to be at the appropriate reading level for the jury. The average reading level of adults is between the eighth and ninth grade level, with one in five adults reading at or below the fifth grade level. Studies have shown that adults read at levels four to five grades below the highest completed grade.[15] A safe assumption is that the average juror has a seventh grade education, and 10% of all jurors may be illiterate, although few will admit this. The attorney can indirectly address this by reading key points from an enlargement of a medical record or read the screen as it is being presented. Comprehension of material will be enhanced by keeping it big, simple, and clear. Note the presence of glare in a courtroom. The glare should be reduced to enhance readability.

B. Color

Color is an important element when designing exhibits. Color should enhance rather than distract from the facts. More so than the ability to read the text, color can convey important messages by creating emotional responses with complementary and contrasting hues.

Using red for intensive care periods, orange for acute hospital stays, yellow for surgeries, and green for physical therapy periods can effectively carry themes throughout a timeline. Yellow (with black lettering) is used to highlight surgery as the most critical time of treatment. Details about multiple surgeries will jump off the chart by using this color combination. The color combination of black on yellow or yellow on black is the one that most stimulates the eye for attention. It is important that counsel understands the psychology of color and uses it as part of the presentation.

Color combinations that are most effective include, in order of readability, are

1. black on yellow
2. black on white, pale blue or grey
3. dark blue or green on white
4. white on dark blue

Warm colors such as red, orange, yellow, and green draw attention to a key point. Cool colors, such as blue, green, or violet are useful for backgrounds. Color can be used to link different types of exhibits. For example, all exhibits that deal with liability may have a red border. Damages exhibits may use blue borders. The consistent use of colors helps to organize the material for both the attorney and the jury.

The attorney should also be aware of the possibility that one or more of the jurors will be color blind. There are several variations of color blindness, which may influence the juror's ability to interpret the information. The attorney's presentation or the witness's testimony must take into account that the color blind juror will need to have the data interpreted.

Adding simple spots of color to an otherwise black and white exhibit draws attention to key points.

C. Time frames

Timelines and graphs should generally be prepared to scale. Each time period represented should be similarly sized to avoid distorting the relationship of events.

Chronologies can be prepared by listing events in sequence no matter how much time passed between each one. In timelines that span long periods of time, it may be better to prepare two exhibits: one showing the big picture and the other a larger scale exhibit focusing only on the time or date of the specific event. One inherent problem with timeline exhibits is that they tend to be larger than most charts. This in turn creates the tendency to crowd too much information onto one page.

D. Fonts and design

Fonts can have a profound effect on the ability of the jurors to read the exhibit. Avoid using all capital letters, condensed, very thin or very fat letters, or flowery scripts as labels on exhibits, as this increases the difficulty reading the label. The use of serif fonts, such as Times New Roman, is preferred over sans serif fonts, such as Ariel, to improve readability. One consistent font should be used throughout the exhibit. The font should not switch from italics to bold to underline without a logical reason. When a series of related slides are presented, the consistency of the format will help enhance the comprehension of the material.

Words should be spelled out rather than be printed using abbreviations that may not be familiar to the jury. In most cases graph or timeline should be laid out in a horizontal (landscape) manner with length greater than the height. Words should be read from left to right rather than from top to bottom.

The exhibits should be balanced, attractive, and have a realistic scale. The maximum number of letters per line on an exhibit should not exceed thirty to thirty-five. The exhibit should be readable from the back row of a jury box or a distance of about 20 feet. An adequate amount of white space will increase readability. White space refers to allowing sufficient borders and space within the exhibit to avoid the crowding of information.

E. Considerations for older jurors

Chances are high that at least one older person will be selected for the jury. Visual deficits of this population influence exhibit design. Age-related visual changes include difficulty focusing, delayed glare recovery, decreased sensitivity to light, loss of depth perception, and constriction of peripheral vision. Older jurors will need more time to change focus if objects are viewed at varying distances. Glare needs to be reduced by pulling curtains to avoid having the jury face the sun or a light source. Many older persons require up to three times more light to see as well as a twenty-five-year-old person, so the room cannot be too dim. Avoid using blues and greens on the same graphic. These colors are the most difficult for older eyes to distinguish given their closeness on the color spectrum. Reds, oranges and yellows are most easily seen. Use lettering or graphics colors that contrast with their background.

Tip

Avoid using ink in the same color as the paper, such as dark green ink on light green background. Avoid using light or bright letters on dark backgrounds. When a highly visible color, such as bright yellow, is placed against a black background the edges of the letter tend to vibrate and appear indistinct.[16]

F. Revisions

Graphics will improve as they are edited. It is essential to allow enough time in the planning process to permit these modifications to occur. The client, if possible, as well as family members should have an opportunity to review such exhibits. T. S. Eliot emphasized the "capital importance of criticism in the work of creation itself. Probably, indeed, the larger part of the labor of an author in composing his work is critical labor; the labor of sifting, combining, constructing, expunging, correcting, testing: this frightful toll is as much critical as creative."[13]

19.4 Overview of Presentation Systems

Counsel can select from a variety of methods of presenting evidence. The four basic approaches are:

- paper system
- optical projector with screen
- electronic projector
- digital system

A. Paper system

The paper system is the most commonly used method of presenting demonstrative evidence. It has the highest comfort level and requires the lowest skill level. A sketch pad on an easel is the simplest form of a paper exhibit. The attorney writes key words or dates on a large pad clamped to the top of an easel. Dark markers on a light background will be most legible. The letters must be large enough to read, written on a straight line, and in legible handwriting.

The traditional method of publishing an exhibit at trial is to circulate it among the jurors after it has been admitted. Not only does this take time but it dampens the jury's psychological reaction to the exhibit. Enlargements of documents or illustrations maintain impact and improve the efficiency of the courtroom exhibits. The practice of enlarging documents is not new, but it is generally done in a terribly unfocused manner. Enlarging a document does not always make it more effective unless the attorney tells the jury what they should understand from the visual evidence.

Tip

If an exhibit's purpose focuses on specific wording, it may be preferable to create "blow-out" or "isolation" exhibits, enlarging only the key words or phrases that the jury needs to understand.

If the original document is handwritten, it is often helpful to have a typeset transcription made of the otherwise illegible script and enlarge that rather than the actual original. Enlarging an otherwise illegible entry does not improve its readability. Transcription can be helpful when the document is written with abbreviations and symbols that would not be known to lay jurors. The transcription can be made using the actual words represented by the symbols, but care must be taken to obtain an accurate reading of the entry from its creator or the witness who will interpret it. Translation of abbreviations or symbols is an important goal of pretrial depositions.

The acceptability of highlighting portions of documents for the jury to focus on depends on the court and the jurisdiction. Some judges do not allow highlighting in yellow or other colors before the exhibit is used. Others prefer that the exhibits be shown without highlighting at all. Instead of highlighting, a transparent overlay containing yellow film material that emphasizes key words or entries achieves the same result. Generally, if counsel will be asking a witness a question that begins with "I would now like to draw your attention to," this is the time to consider some form of highlighted exhibit so the jury can easily follow along. One technique is to offer the original document, and put up the highlighted document to emphasize a key point.

If the intention is to review a document quickly with a witness, and its volume is greater than its content, a flip chart can be easily made. It may consist of a series of enlargements of the pages, bound at the top with only the bottom page mounted for use on an easel. This gives the trial attorney the dynamic tool needed to work both quickly and economically through a document when it is not the primary exhibit but warrants more than mere identification.

An add-on exhibit can be created for use with cross-examining an expert. For example, the attorney may want to challenge the conclusions of a life care planner. The opposing expert's key table is enlarged. One column or part of a column is covered and replaced with the expert's numbers. During cross-examination, the attorney forces the expert to re-examine her own exhibit without keeping her own exhibit before the judge and jury the whole time. The attorney can alter the opposing expert's exhibit in a number of different ways using only the materials prepared by the attorney. As the questioning proceeds, counsel asks the expert to assume the accuracy of substitute figures for each of the items on the life care plan. This method of altering numbers can also be effectively performed with a computer.

Enlargements are typically placed on an easel. A good easel is lightweight, quiet, has an adjustable mechanism to hold exhibits of various sizes, includes a clamp device at the top for a sketch pad, and supports the exhibits in such a way that the jury can see them fully. Exhibits frames are also used with paper enlargements. These are lightweight frames that set up in minutes. Cloth panels are attached to the frames. Velcro is used to hold the enlargement on the frame. The exhibit frame permits the attorney to mount several 30 × 40 inch charts or boards side by side.

1. Advantages

Trial-size exhibits are familiar to trial attorneys and judges. The trial attorney is unlikely to encounter any resistance from the judge regarding the use of the enlarged documents. The use of posters, enlargements of medical illustrations, or key documents does not rely on technology in the courtroom. There is no need to be concerned with electrical outlets or equipment failure. Successful use of this presentation system relies on adequate lighting and properly sized exhibits. A minimum amount of equipment is needed, consisting primarily of an easel and a marker or pointer. A clear no-glare overlay can be added to the front of the exhibit. This allows the use of markers without affecting the original document. If the attorney is concerned that the adversary will also mark on the same exhibit, the exhibit can be designed with two overlays: one for defense's counsel, and one for plaintiff's counsel.

Counsel is able to select the appropriate exhibits and place them on and off the easel without assistance.

Little can go wrong with the use of enlarged documents, with the exception of forgetting to bring them to court, getting them hopelessly out of order if a large number of enlargements are to be used, or selecting documents for enlargement that have inadequate type size. It is relatively easy to create exhibit notebooks for the jury, if permitted in the locale, from paper exhibits. Key documents reproduced in 8.5 × 11 inch size can be placed in indexed binders so the jury can refer to them during deliberations.

2. Disadvantages

The printing and mounting of each exhibit can be costly, running from $50 to $200 or more for each board. The disadvantages of using enlarged pages include the need for advance selection and preparation and their unwieldy size. Also it is difficult to anticipate correctly which pages are going to be crucial at a trial. Companies that enlarge exhibits usually require some lead time. The ability to add another finished mounted exhibit after the beginning of trial may be severely hampered by the availability of the outside vendor. Only a few law firms with high volume trial work have created their own in-house graphics departments, whose staff can provide last-minute support. Most trial attorneys will continue to need to plan exhibits ahead of time to avoid last minute changes.

Tip

A final disadvantage is that when a full page of a record is enlarged and placed on an easel in front of the jury, the jurors may become distracted by reading the entire page instead of the section that is the subject of the testimony of the witness. This can be remedied by using yellow highlighters.

B. Optical (transparency) projector and screen systems

The next step up from enlargements of documents is the use of a transparency shown on projectors. The image may appear on a screen or a light-colored wall. A favorite tool of lecturers, the transparency projector is a versatile tool. With properly created transparencies, the projector shows key medical documents, major points in opening and closing arguments, medical illustrations and so on. The transparency may be covered by a clear plastic overlay. A witness can make marks on the transparency without affecting the original image.

Several strategies make the handling of transparencies easier. Use masking tape to create a window or border on the glass plate of the projector. This prevents light from the bulb from leaking around its edges. This also makes it easier to align the transparency on the plate. Keeping in mind that the projector's plate measures 10 inches × 10 inches, another option is to copy documents at 95% of their size so that the transparencies will fit more exactly on the plate.

If the transparency is going to be placed in a cardboard frame, holes can be punched in the top of the frame. A plastic bar with corresponding prongs can be taped to the glass plate of the transparency projector. This will permit the operator of the machine to line up each transparency in the correct position. The cardboard frame can be punched on the left border so it will fit in a three ring binder. Each transparency can be returned to its place behind a number tab in the binder and easily located if the attorney needs it again.[1]

The projector must be adjusted so that the image is even on the screen. A keystone effect (the top of the image is wider than the bottom) is created when the projector is not properly adjusted for the screen. The keystone effect increases the difficulty of reading the image.

1. Advantages

Transparencies are easily made. Most office copiers or laser printers can be used to create transparencies using film specific to that machine. A box of transparency film is inexpensive. Film with colored borders, which adds visual interest, is also available. It takes more time to plan and properly design a transparency than it does to print it on the copier. The actual production of the transparency takes seconds. Revision is quick and easy. Key portions of the document can be highlighted with yellow or colored transparency film laid on top of the original film.

Tip

Expert witnesses with teaching backgrounds are often comfortable with the use of transparency projectors. They may already have appropriate transparencies prepared to teach some of the medical issues in the case. For example, an orthopaedic surgeon may have transparencies of the hip joint or of the plates and screws that are commonly used to repair a fall related fracture of the leg.

Another advantage of this equipment is that little can go wrong with the operation of the projector. Bulbs in projectors rarely burn out, although it is important to have a spare bulb and know how to change it. Lightweight, quiet, and portable projectors make use of the projector much easier than in the past.

2. Disadvantages

Trial attorneys soon learn that courtrooms come in all sizes and shapes, just like people. Courtroom wall surfaces and ambient light in the room may make it difficult to see the image unless the lights are dimmed. Dark panels on the walls may require the use of a screen, or tall windows may flood the room with too much light. It may be impossible to place the machine in a position so that the jury and judge can see the screen in some courtrooms. The ideal position for the jury is to have the screen parallel to the jury box. If the jury box is at a ninety-degree angle from the judge, this may place the screen in such a way that the judge cannot see the image. The judge has more flexibility than does the jury in terms of changing position but is sometimes reluctant to get off the bench in order to view the image, particularly when the projector is heavily used. A small table for the projector is an important piece of equipment. Do not assume that the courtroom furniture will suit the attorney's needs. One of the authors (PI) once observed a judge become angry because the projector was balanced on the edge of the witness box in order to project an image onto the wall. The placement of equipment needs to be thought out ahead of time, well before the appearance of the projector in the courtroom.

Like enlargements of key documents, transparencies have a maddening habit of getting out of order. The trial attorney may be so focused on the presentation of the case that the need to sort through a pile of transparencies may be too distracting. An assistant such as a legal nurse consultant, paralegal, or associate may be needed to maintain order and select the appropriate transparency at the right time. Good labeling of each transparency is a requirement.

Most medical records are printed in portrait mode (with 8.5 inches running across the top of the document). This layout is ideally suited for the transparency projector. However, it is common for some documents, such as those in a nursing home chart, to have a different format. Nursing home medication administration records and treatment records are commonly created in landscape format. The layout of the projector makes it difficult to show a landscape document without repeatedly sliding it across the glass in order to show portions of the document. The transparency projector does not have the capability of zooming in on an image.

C. Electronic projectors and visual presenters

America is a visually oriented culture. Both at home and at work, Americans spend an increasing amount of time obtaining information from television and computer screens. Movies, network television, cable television, videos, MTV, web TV, computer games, DVDs, and the Internet, among others, provide information visually and audibly. To convey information effectively to potential jurors in the courtroom, trial lawyers need to consider employing electronic technology.

A number of companies sell projectors that can be used to display a wide variety of objects. These projectors allow documents to be placed on the machine and projected onto a screen for the jury to view. The setup is a vertically mounted video camera that can zoom in on any document or object and send the signal to a projector or video monitor. Electronic projectors function as updated versions of overhead projectors but do not require transparencies. The projector can display timelines, charts, medical records, slides, film negatives, excerpts from books, graphs, medical illustrations, and photographs. The projector can focus on small objects, making it easy for the jury to see the object without the distraction of passing it around the jury box. The electronic projector may be combined with a computer, printer, videotape player, or laser disc. X-rays may be viewed with the use of the visual presenter coupled with an artist's rendition of the x-rays to make the images more understandable to the jury. Visual presenters are widely available through legal specialty vendors or audiovisual supply houses.

Tip

Although it is tempting to look at the screen, the attorney should direct her attention to the fact finder. She should not read material from a monitor or projection screen. She should consider whether it would be more effective to display the visual, and then describe it, or to first explain what the jury will see, and then lay the image on the screen.[6]

1. Advantages

The visual presenter is a versatile machine that has a wide variety of uses. It has an unparalleled ability to display small objects or focus in on minute details of a medical record. Its use does not require dimming lights. The output of the camera may be connected to a television monitor or series of monitors that permits the jury, counsel, and judge to see the images simultaneously.

The visual presenter is a good first step for lawyers who have had no experience using any kind of technology. It is a good complement to more sophisticated display techniques such as using the laptop computer, and it is a reliable backup in case a computer crashes. It works best with material that once enlarged sufficiently is clear without much additional highlighting or marking.[6]

The projector may be attached to a VCR so that a record can be made of the presentation, or to show video footage or a computer animation. The projector is often used in conjunction with a light pen which permits drawing on the image. With the touch of a button the highlighting can be erased or the image printed for use by the jury during deliberations. The use of a visual presenter avoids having to hold up enlargements of pictures or other documents or having to place them on easels. It also avoids the expense of having to have documents enlarged for presentation.

2. Disadvantages

Most documents are vertical (portrait) in format, and most video monitors are oriented horizontally (landscape). Also, the image resolution of text in a video monitor is not as good as a transparency projector. The visual presenter is appropriate to use when the volume of its use justifies the expense. Renting projectors may be possible for law firms that have only an occasional need. The attorney planning to use this equipment during a trial should allow plenty of time for setting up the equipment. It may be necessary to have another person available to run the projector. There is a higher risk of equipment failure in this system. Some jurors who do not watch much television may be suspicious of the presentation, characterizing it as a slick presentation that may not be completely accurate.

D. Digital system

With the decreasing cost of computers and graphics software, attorneys now have the means to create effective charts, drawings, graphs, and diagrams with minimal expense. Once generated, these graphics can be enlarged for traditional exhibits or they can be projected from a laptop computer through a video projector. The attorney can use a computer monitor to display deposition transcripts and photographs. Depositions can be saved on the computer in digital or video form and instantly used to cross-examine a witness.

In a digital system, all documents are converted to digital form and stored on a CD-ROM or hard drive of a laptop computer. All applicable medical records would be scanned, saved, and projected on a monitor or series of monitors. Once stored, these documents can be indexed or bar-coded to allow immediate retrieval during the direct or cross-examination. When the image is projected, the attorney can take a witness through a document, medical illustration, x-ray, photograph, or virtually any other evidence in the case very efficiently and with maximum effect. Using a specific screen (Smart Board), the attorney or witness can use a fingertip to underline text or to enlarge sections of documents. Presentation software can be used to show images of medical equipment or key points in a summation.

Software used to create slide shows (PowerPoint, Presentation, and other packages) is an invaluable tool for creating effective slides. Common uses include creating timelines, bulleted or numbered lists of key points, text quotations, and summaries of testimony. Slides may be combined with scanned photographs of the client, medical equipment, or pages from the medical record. Changes can be made onsite, such as deleting slides that the judge rules are not admissible.

Tip

The professionalism of the slide show should be in keeping with the courtroom environment. Although special effects are possible, such as dropping letters one by one from the top of the screen, or having slide transitions that zoom away, the tone should be sedate. Short is powerful for PowerPoint. Remember the famous billboard rule: don't put more on a slide that you could read if it were printed on a billboard and you were driving by at 40 miles per hour in your car.[17]

The split-screen capability of the computer can be used to place documents side by side or to present video testimony with the script running next to it. Presentation software published for the legal market, such as Sanction II, Summation, TrialPro, and TrialDirector, incorporates the ability to store deposition transcripts, scanned documents, and videoclips and to highlight text. These packages are typically expensive, may be designed to be used together, and require a learning curve.

Attorneys using this software often have a person in the courtroom to run the program so the attorney can concentrate on keeping a smooth flow of testimony. This person should be introduced during the opening statement. The attorney will explain the monitors and projector and inform the jury how they will be used during the trial.[6]

1. Advantages

The primary benefits of using computer-generated graphics are their ease of modification and relatively low cost. Key portions of the medical record can be transcribed and placed in boxes next to the actual page. In most cases, the typed text in the boxes will be much easier to read than the original. Hundreds of thousands of potential exhibits can be stored and retrieved in milliseconds. The ability to project specific pages of the medical record and to zoom into key portions eliminates the need to enlarge and mount specific pages or documents. The attorney can switch from one exhibit or page to another with ease.

Video monitors have a much higher resolution than do screens used with transparency projectors, television monitors, or visual presenters. The technology keeps the jury's interest alive by varying the images and making them interesting.[1] This technology has been shown to decrease the length of a trial. This point appeals to busy trial lawyers, jurors, and judges. If a day-in-the-life videotape or a deposition will be shown, adding a video document camera or laptop for a PowerPoint presentation is not as much of a problem as bringing the same equipment in to display just a few documents or charts.

2. Disadvantages

One consideration in using the newer technology in the courtroom is the cost-benefit ratio, taking into consideration the amount of material that will be presented and the cost to rent, transport, set up, and run the equipment needed. In those firms that own their equipment and have an appropriate litigation support staff, this is not as much of a concern. In other firms that do not do as much trial work, the cost of setting up equipment, wiring, monitors, screens, and so forth in those courtrooms that are not so equipped can be out of line with the benefits of their use.

The selection, scanning, and organization of key pieces of medical evidence take time. This is not a presentation style that can be left until the last minute. Planning is necessary for the selection of exhibits, the set up of the equipment, and the redundant backup system that will increase the comfort of the attorney.

Environmental barriers may be encountered, such as an inadequate electrical supply or glare. A technician may be needed to run the equipment, decreasing the attorney's control over the presentation of the material. There are risks of technical problems and equipment failure. Unlike mounted exhibits, once the computer monitor is turned off, the image disappears and cannot be referred to later by the jury.

Tip

The size and layout of the courtroom are important considerations. Smaller courtrooms create problems for placing monitors and screens. The use of monitors and computers in the courtroom may meet resistance from the judge and some jurors.

Some judges also have their own likes and dislikes regarding equipment choice and location.

19.5 Summary

Creative development of trial exhibits to establish or refute claims of pain and suffering is limited only by the attorney's imagination and budget. Consideration of a wide range of options helps the attorney understand the key points that need to be made. Counsel should take great care in deciding what material should be presented electronically and what material would be most effective in more tangible, board-on-easel presentations. Even with these disadvantages, it is becoming clearer that more attorneys are exploring this type of technology. A variety of approaches for presenting demonstrative evidence helps to maintain the jurors' interest. Simplicity in design is essential. Courtrooms are being designed or renovated to permit use of computers and monitors. The days of dragging boxes of records to the courtroom are over.

Endnotes

1. Siemer, D., *Tangible Evidence: How to Use Exhibits at Deposition and Trial*, Third Edition. South Bend, IN: National Institute for Trial Advocacy, 1998.

2. Perry, C., "What Evidence Works." *Trial*, December 1999, 66.

3. Heninger, S., "Persuasive Proof." *Trial*, April 2000, 55.

4. McClellan, F., *Medical Malpractice Law Tactics and Ethics*. Philadelphia: Temple University Press, 1994.

5. Paonita, A., "Litigation Support Goes Digital." *New Jersey Law Journal*, April 22, 2002, 30.

6. Siemer, D., Beshkind, D., Bocchino, A., and Rothschild, F., *Effective Use of Courtroom Technology*. Notre Dame, IN: National Institute for Trial Advocacy, 2002.

7. Iwan, L., and Huber, M., "Mistakes to Avoid in the Defense of Damages." *For the Defense,* March, 2002, 38.

8. Gotlieb, H., editor, Suits and Deals, "$462,500 For Slip and No Fall." *New Jersey Law Journal,* May 13, 2002.

9. Laska, L., editor," Negligent Prolonged Use of Gentamicin." *Doe v. Doe, M.D.*, Salt Lake County (UT) District Court, case no. ______, *Medical Malpractice Verdicts, Settlements and Experts,* January 2002, 27.

10. Laska. L., editor, "Malpositioning of Patient's Arm during Hernia Repair Surgery." *David Edin v. Glenn Halff, M.D.; Kenneth Sutin, M.D.; and Tisch Hospital*, Kings County (NY) Supreme Court, index no. 10731/92, *Medical Malpractice Verdicts, Settlements and Experts,* May 2002, 58.

11. Gallagher, M., "Workers' Comp Carrier Is Sanctioned for Hinting Worker Faked Disability." *New Jersey Law Journal,* March 11, 2002, p. 5.

12. Hely, J., and Weiseman, J., "Trustworthiness." In *A Trial Strategy Manual for the Plaintiff's Injury Case in New Jersey.* New Brunswick, NJ: New Jersey Institute for Continuing Legal Education, 1998.

13. Eliot, T.S., "The Function of Criticism." As quoted in Tufte, E., *The Visual Display of Quantitative Information*. Cheshire, CT: Graphics Press, 1983.

14. Delilah Cohn, personal communication, 1998.

15. Brownson, K., "Education Handouts: Are We Wasting Our Time?" *Journal for Nurses in Staff Development,* July/August, 1998, 176.

16. Braun, J., "Handling Witnesses: Techniques for Working with Older Witnesses." In Krisztal, R., editor, *Nursing Home Litigation: Pretrial Practice and Trials.* Tucson: Lawyers & Judges Publishing Co., 2001.

17. Redmon, M., "Are They Really Listening?" *New Jersey Law Journal*, March 11, 2002.

Additional Reading

Siemer, D., Rothschild, F., Stein, E and Solomon, S., *PowerPoint for Litigators.* Notre Dame, IN: National Institute for Trial Advocacy, 2000.

Small, D. and Aresty, N., "Technology in Trial Practice." *Trial*, September 1999, 60.

Vesper, R. and Orr, R., "Making Time Palpable by Using Per-Diem Arguments." *Trial,* October 2002, 58.

Sources of PowerPoint Templates, Images and Tips

www.crystalgraphics.com
www.threedgraphics.com
http://dgl.microsoft.com
http://bitbetter.com/powertips.htm
http://bitbetter.com/powerlinks.htm

Sites for Improving Presentation Skills

www.presentations.com
www.presentersuniversity.com
www.powerpointers.com
www.wilderpresentations.com

Chapter 20

Ante-Mortem Damages

Tom Vesper, Esq.

Synopsis

20.1 Introduction

The majority of jurisdictions in the United States recognize that a decedent's conscious pain and suffering prior to death is a recoverable element of damages under both survival statutes and the hybrid type of enlarged survival or wrongful death statutes.[1,2] The converse is likewise true: if there was no conscious fear, anxiety, pain or suffering, and death was truly instantaneous, then there could be no recovery for such pain and suffering of the deceased. Short periods of insensibility intervening between a fatally traumatic injury and death have been held to afford no basis for separate jury estimation or award of damages for "conscious pain and suffering.[2] In most jurisdictions the compensable injury is always referred to in terms of conscious pain and suffering. Conjecture or speculation as to whether the decedent was conscious will not suffice.

It is we plaintiffs' trial lawyers who must help the survivors of a wrongful death to recover emotionally as well as financially from the negligently or recklessly caused death of a loved one. Full and fair compensation requires attention to the ante-mortem, noneconomic, human losses suffered by the deceased. This is always a very sensitive and upsetting subject. However, to represent and advise the plaintiff's attorney's clients properly and arrive at a proper evaluation of a wrongful death case, it is a necessary question. How and when to address the issue usually depend on the facts and circumstances of each case and the parties involved.

Tip

Often, for emotional, expedient, economic, uneducated, or misinformed reasons, some lawyers and clients do not immediately and thoroughly investigate whether the decedent in fact suffered any fear, anxiety, distress or physical pain prior to an allegedly instantaneous death.

When any fatality such as an auto crash has occurred, the plaintiff's attorney's clients often receive secondhand information, which is usually not thoroughly examined and analyzed, from supposed professionals at the scene of the fatality. The attorneys and investigators for both sides are often told the decedent died instantly, peacefully or suddenly and in no pain. Second- or third-hand unsupported and unimpeached accounts of instant death often lead to an overlooked and unrecovered quantum of damage, to wit: pre-impact fear and anxiety, as well as suffering upon impact and thereafter until a point in time—which may be seconds or minutes—when the decedent was rendered unconscious or dead.

20.2 Before Death (Ante-Mortem) Distress, Fear, and Anxiety

Conscious awareness of approaching death has been found to be a proper element to consider in evaluating mental suffering. Before death, or ante-mortem, fright or distress is defined as the distress suffered by the decedent upon the realization of peril. *Green v. Hale*, 590 S.W. 2d 231 (Tex. Civ. App. Tyler 1979) (quoting *Jenkins v. Hennigan*, 298 S.W. 905, 911 (Tex. Civ. App. 1957); *Hurst Aviation v. Junell*, 642 S.W. 2d 856 (Tex. App. Fort Worth 1982).

Some jurisdictions recognize the decedent's fear and anxiety of impending doom or fear and anxiety of serious injury prior to impact or a traumatic event as a recoverable damage element.[3]

The parents of a fifteen-year-old driver killed when his pickup truck was struck broadside at an intersection brought a wrongful death and survival action. The court found that a $5,000 damage award for pre-impact fright and suffering was not an abuse of discretion simply because plaintiffs offered no proof of consciousness. There was no evidence decedent had seen the oncoming vehicle prior to collision because no skid marks or other evidence showed evasive action. *Thibodeaux v. St. Landry Parish Police Jury* 561 So. 2d 163; (1990, La.App. 3d Cir); But see *St. Clair v. Denny* 245 Kan. 414, 781 P.2d 1043 (1989) (award for pain and suffering denied, in part, because the court found sixty feet of skid marks on highway at scene of fatal collision to be insufficient evidence of decedent's pre-impact emotional distress).

Thibodeaux, supra, is indicative of a modern trend by trial and appellate courts to recognize that no death is truly instantaneous. Therefore, courts such as the Appellate Division of the Supreme Court in New Jersey have almost taken judicial notice of ante-mortem losses and shifted the burden of going forward with proof of no conscious pain to the defense. *Smith v. Whitaker*, 313 N.J. Super. 165 (App.Div. 1998), 160 N.J. 221 (1999); *Tirrell v. Navistar International, Inc.*, 246 N.J. Super 390, cert. denied 126 N.J. 390 (1991); Fed.R.Evid. 201(b).

Tip

Plaintiffs who successfully prove pre-impact distress as an element of a death or survivorship claim for pain and suffering have recovered significant amounts of damages for even seconds of mental anguish.[3]

The amount of time during which the distress was experienced is not necessarily determinative of the amount of the award. See, e.g., *Hurst Aviation v. Junell*, 642 S.W.2d 856, (Tex. App. Fort Worth 1982). This was a $20,000 award upheld despite the brief duration of the victim's mental suffering in light of the court's finding that the pilot could be inferred to have "suffered the horror of his impending doom" as he lost control of his plane. Even in an action where the duration between the decedent's apprehension and injury was brief, a court found that "a tremendous amount of fear could be inferred." *Green v. Hale*, 590 S.W.2d 231 (Tex.Civ.App. Tyler 1979).

One court has allowed an award of $50,000 for pain and suffering despite the coroner's opinion testimony that the decedent died instantly.

In *Hung Chi Ly v. State ex. Rel. Department of Pub. Safety & Corrections*, 633 So. 2d 197 (La. Ct. App. 1st Cir. 1993), cert. denied, 634 So. 2d 835 (La. 1994), supp. op., 633 So. 2d 1223 (La. 1994), a disabled vehicle was struck by another vehicle and then collided with a wall and burst into flames. The court held that the trial court did not err in awarding $50,000 for the pre-death pain and suffering of one of the occupants in the vehicle despite the opinion of the coroner that the decedent had died instantly and did not burn to death.

Because the coroner could not state with medical probability whether the decedent died as a result of the first or second collision, and there was evidence to support the trial court's conclusion that the decedent survived for the period of time between the first and second impacts.

A New Jersey appellate court summarized the minimal evidence that is sufficient to sustain an award for ante-mortem pain, suffering, and fear:

> The issue of the award for conscious pain and suffering requires little discussion. While it is true that decedent died practically instantaneously after the truck had crushed his chest, there was testimony that he at least raised his head before he died. Defense counsel suggests that this motion was a spasmodic movement after death, and this might be so. Yet, for some finite period the slowly-moving truck dragged decedent under its wheels and the jury was free to infer that decedent had some brief but distinct anticipation of his impending death as well as physical pain and suffering. *Tirrell v. Navistar Int'l, Inc.*, 248 N.J.Super. 390, 591 A. 2d 643 (App. Div. 1991).

The factual considerations for any trial lawyer to consider in proving pre-impact damages will be discussed below. See Section 20.4 below.

Counsel should be aware, however, that some courts are still reluctant to award damages for pre-death distress. See, e.g., *Nye v. Commonwealth, Dept. of Transp.*, 31 Pa. Super. 209, 480 A.2d 318 (1984). Although most courts hold to the contrary, there are some courts that have found that groans or moans of the decedent are insufficient alone to sustain pain and suffering awards. *Ballou v. Henri Studios, Inc.*, 656 F.2d 1147 (5th Cir. Tex. 1981); see also Boston, G., Kline, D., and Brown, J., *Emotional Injuries: Law and Practice,* Chapter 6:27, West Group, (2002). While denying recovery for pre-impact fright, the court allowed that it might award damages for that element if there was proof that the decedent suffered physical harm. Some courts deny recovery based on the traditional concerns of limiting emotional distress damages. See, e.g., *Fogarty v. Campbell 66 Express, Inc.*, 640 F.Supp. 953 (DC Kan. 1986). In addition, courts may not allow damages for pre-impact distress under the particular test adopted in that jurisdiction to separate lawful emotional distress claims from those for which recovery will be denied.[9]

A New York verdict of $1,125,000 followed an accident involving children who were passengers in a flatbed tow truck. The defendant, driving a farm tractor, ran a stop sign, and collided with the tow truck. The two-year-old passenger suffered a displaced fracture of the second cervical vertebrae requiring surgery, fusion, and the application of a halo brace for six months. The plaintiff contended that her neck movement was significantly and permanently limited as a result of her injuries and she would never be able to participate in sports or recreational activities such as tumbling or playing soccer which involve moving her head around. Her sister was also injured in the accident. The jury determined the defendant farmer was 100% responsible for the accident. The plaintiff was awarded $1,125,000, which included $350,000 for past pain, suffering, and loss of enjoyment of life and $775,000 for future pain and suffering. The father brought a separate claim for his emotional distress as a result of witnessing his children being injured and hospitalized. The jury awarded the father $100,000 for past pain, suffering, and loss of enjoyment of life, $50,000 for future pain and suffering, and $100,000 for his emotional distress. The jury determined that at the time his daughters were injured he was in the "zone of peril." *Beeley v. Spencer*, Index No. 8137/98, Erie County, NY.[4]

In recent years, more courts have allowed recovery for the aspect of emotional distress known as pre-impact distress in wrongful death fact situations that would have been previously denied. See, e.g., *Haley v. Pan American World Airways*, 746 F.2d 311 (5th Cir. 1984) (applying Louisiana law); *Shu-Tao Lin v. McDonnell Douglas Corp.*, 565 F.Supp. 105, (S.D. N.Y. 1983) (applying Michigan law).

If the attorney can establish from eyewitnesses, physical evidence, accident reconstruction, or biomechanical experts that prior to an auto crash the decedent probably saw the impending impact, even if such collision sequences lasted only a matter of seconds, such pre-death distress, fear, and anxiety can result in an award of substantial damages.

In a New Jersey Federal District Court wrongful death trial the author's co-counsel recovered a jury verdict of approximately $900,000 for the pre-impact fear of a passenger who saw a 24-feet-long wooden beam, weighing approximately 350 pounds coming toward him for two or three seconds before it hit him, causing instant unconsciousness. This jury verdict was paid in full by the defendant's insurer. *Hackney v. Hickory Hills Transportation, et al.*, District of N.J., Camden vicinage, case number 97cv3779, (July 1998 verdict).

Courts have even found sufficient evidence of consciousness to support an award for pain and suffering where the victim was in a coma. *Rufino v. United States*, 829 F.2d 354 (2d Cir. 1987).

In a medical malpractice action against a VA hospital for injuries to her husband that rendered him comatose, the wife received an award of $75,000 which was upheld as appropriate compensation for her husband's past and present pain and suffering. Although the husband has no cognitive awareness and limited conscious pain and suffering, the court found other evidence persuasive: observations by doctors and family members that the patient turned away from noxious odors such as ammonia, turned to and from sound, responded to painful stimuli such as pin pricks, opened his eyes on his own, displayed a cough reflex and an ability to swallow, squeezed his left hand on command, and displayed some movement in his extremities. *Rufino v. United States,* 829 F.2d 354 (3d Cir. 1987).

Courts have upheld damage awards for periods of pain or suffering of very short duration. *DeLong v. County of Erie*, 89 A.2d 376, 455 N.Y.S. 2d 887 (4th Dept 1982). In one case a court found damages were due regardless of how quickly unconsciousness resulted where the court believed the victim probably suffered tremendous pain and terror in contemplation of his imminent and horrible death due to the nature of the accident. *Farlow v. Roddy*, 478 So. 2d 953 (La. App. 5th Cir. 1985).

In *Dontas v. New York*, 183 A.D. 2d 868, 584 N.Y.S. 2d 134 (2d Dept 1992), the trial court found the fact that the jaw and teeth of a sixteen-year-old boy whose body was retrieved from a swimming pool were clenched so tightly that artificial respiration had to be administered through the nose showed that he was conscious for a brief period. The expert's opinion testimony was that the drowning victim's clenched jaw was motivated and caused by ante-mortem fear.

20.3 Loss of Enjoyment of Life and the Comatose Victim

In many jurisdictions the strict requirements for proving consciousness are loosening. In recent years, recovery has been allowed in cases where the only proof of consciousness was the fact that the victim was breathing and moaning and was able to respond by squeezing a bystander's finger in response to questions. 24 Proof of Facts 3d 337 (Lawyers Coop).

The widow and children of a worker fatally injured when a metal pole he was using connected with an uninsulated power line brought a wrongful death and survival action against the power company. The survivors were awarded $2,000 for conscious pain and suffering because the court accepted as evidence of pain and suffering the fact that the victim was lying at the bottom of a bin, was breathing, had a bloody cut on his head, and was moaning audibly. Additionally, the court considered the fact that decedent squeezed his wife's hand when she asked him to do so. *Pape v. Kansas Power and Light Co.*, 231 Kan. 441, 647 P.2d 320 33 A.L.R.4th 799 (1982). See also *Fudge v. City of Kansas City*, 239 Kan. 369, 720 P.2d 1093 (1986) (upholding $50,000 award for pain and suffering based on testimony of victim's mother-in-law that victim squeezed her finger several times in response to things she told him about his children and family, despite defense expert testimony that victim was so deeply unconscious he could feel no pain).

Some courts, such as New Jersey, recognize that there are hedonic damages or lost enjoyments of life, for which a deceased plaintiff is entitled to recover. That is, if the deceased is rendered or becomes unconscious after a traumatic event, and there is a period of time during which the unconscious plaintiff lived before death, that period of unconscious loss of life is an element of damage for the jury to evaluate. See, e.g., *Eyoma v. Falco*, 247 N.J. Super. 435 (App. Div. 1991); *Moscatello v. U.M.D.N.J.*, 342 N.J. Super. 351 (App. Div. 2001); *Thomas v. Ford Motor Co.*, 70 F.Supp. 2d 521 (D.N.J. 1999).

In *Eyoma v. Falco*, 247 N.J. Super. 435 (App. Div. 1991), the fatally injured plaintiff lapsed into a coma while in a hospital recovery room after surgery. Plaintiff remained in a comatose state for over one year until his death. In the survival action, the jury awarded among other damages $17,500 for the decedent's loss of enjoyment of life during the time he was comatose.

20.4 Facts and Circumstances Proving Ante-Mortem Damages

In any type of wrongful death case, whether arising out of an auto crash, fall, electrocution, drowning, etc., there are certain factual elements that can prove consciousness, pain, suffering, and pre-impact fear. Some of these factors are described below.

A. Eyewitness testimony

Any credible eyewitness at the scene who saw and/or heard the victim attempt to communicate, respond to stimuli, respond to communication, attempt to escape, attempt to cooperate, or make any facial expression, body movement, or physical indication or sound of conscious pain will be a critically important witness. The lay opinion of an eyewitness that the victim was in pain is usually admissible if there is some credible factual basis and support for such lay observation (Fed. R. Evid. 701).

B. Expert witnesses

Accident reconstruction, biomechanical analysis or pathological evaluation of the accident and injuries inflicted on the victim's body may help prove the very brief but very real pre-mortem pain.

C. Pre-impact warnings

If there were any sounds or actions by the deceased that would reasonably evidence a warning of the impending trauma, such facts would help to establish a pre-impact fear, anxiety, and emotional distress on the part of the deceased. For example, if prior to the auto collision the deceased sounded the horn or braked, such facts would help establish that at least for the time it took to perceive, react, and signal or brake the deceased was aware of and in reasonable apprehension and fear of the oncoming catastrophe. Also, if any visual or audible warnings were made to and probably seen, heard or sensed by the deceased, such evidence would help to prove pre-impact fear.

D. Nature of incident

The amount of time between the probable perception of impending harm and the harm itself may establish the opportunity and likelihood of pre-impact fear, anxiety, and distress. One simple method of proving the time between perception and the traumatic impact is to find eyewitnesses who were in the same or similar position as the plaintiff who can explain when they first observed or sensed the eventual trauma and offer their estimates of the elapsed time. Another method is to employ a qualified accident reconstruction expert or forensic pathologist to examine the scene of the event, any photographs, and other relevant facts in order to estimate the probable time it took for the plaintiff to observe and then feel the traumatic event. In the case of an auto crash the elapsed time could be a matter of seconds. In a drowning event the elapsed time between the onset of the trauma and the unconsciousness or death of the plaintiff may be a matter of minutes.

E. Internal injuries or evidence consistent with pain

Internal injuries such as torn blood vessels and crushed internal organs where the plaintiff probably internally bled to death, are the type of sequelae that lend themselves to medical proof of pain and suffering. There may also be internal evidence consistent with conscious pain, such as smoke or soot in the lungs which shows that the deceased breathed in some of the hot, smoke-filled air before perishing in a fire.

Some injuries normally result in instant loss of consciousness: such as decapitation, serious skull or brain injury, or massive injury to a vital organ. These may rule out conscious pain and suffering unless there are eyewitnesses at the scene. Remember, even with a serious skull or brain injury the victim can recover consciousness or lapse in and out of consciousness.

F. Painfully obvious external injuries

Some external injuries to the human body are readily associated with painful consequences. These include deep lacerations into fleshy parts of the body, burns, dismemberment, compound fractures of arms or legs, and severance or mutilation of body parts.

G. Mechanism of injury

Mental anguish, terror or fright prior to unconsciousness can occur by the decedent observing a mutilating injury to herself.

H. Cause and manner of death

The actual split second sequence of the traumatic events upon the decedent's body may reveal the actual pain endured, even if briefly.

I. Express declarations of pain

Any express statements or declarations of pain by the deceased are very probative.

J. Any communication

Any form of verbal or non verbal communication by the decedent is important.

K. Attempts to communicate

Any response or attempt to respond to questions or communications such as speaking, attempting to speak, or attempting to give a signal shows some level of consciousness.

L. Attempts to escape or avoid impact or injury

Evidence of swerving, skid marks, attempted or actual walking, crawling, running away from the point of impact, or an attempt to ease the pain by some change of position can be indicative of both pre-impact distress and post impact pain and suffering.

M. Signs of evacuation

Evacuation is inferred by physical indications of movement from the original site of injury. Evidence the fatally injured victim moved himself from the original place of injury can help prove there was conscious pain during that time period.

N. Cooperation

Cooperation may be shown by making rational responses or following orders or instructions given by others rendering aid, by taking stimulants or nourishment, turning over, lifting arms, or other acts.

O. Response to stimuli

The victim may have cringed or attempted avoidance of painful stimuli. Discomfort experienced just from being touched or lifted may show a conscious level of suffering. Observations of the deceased by police, firefighters, EMTs, or any member of the rescue squad on the scene shortly after the traumatic event are vitally important. Even cringing or avoiding stimuli which are not normally painful, such as being lifted, is an indication of conscious pain. Also the Glasgow Coma Score completed by the rescue squad or the ER personnel can be very useful.

P. Facial expressions

Any facial signs, grimaces, or eye movements associated with pain may be reported by eyewitnesses. Some of these expressions may be the twisting or biting the lips, closing the eyes, wrinkling the forehead, and crying or the appearance of tears in the eyes.

Q. Movement

Twisting, writhing, struggling and other movements suggest pain. Contrast such meaningful movements with involuntary and unconscious twitching.

R. Difficulty breathing

Gasping for breath, grunting, exhaling, and breathing with difficulty can indicate pain.

S. Involuntary expressions of pain

Moaning, groaning, grunting, crying, and so forth may be observed or documented in records of the first responders to the scene.

T. Involuntary physiological changes

Increased heart rate, sweating, pupil dilation, bladder and bowel incontinence, muscular tremors, increased respiration, restriction of coronary arteries, hyper-irritability of the nervous system, and other symptoms of shock may be noted.

20.5 The Usual Defensive Positions or Arguments

The usual defensive reaction and counter-proofs to any claim of pre-impact fear or pre-mortem pain are to try by proof, argument, or innuendo to undermine or discredit any witnesses or opinion testimony. There may be an eyewitness who observed the circumstances and facts leading up to and following the traumatic event, such as the plaintiff's reaction to or attempt to escape from the impending doom and the plaintiff's final agony. If there is such an eyewitness, that witness's ability to observe and recall will be tested by the defense.

For example, if the eyewitness was not standing close to the deceased, an argument may be made that the witness was too far away to hear accurately the deceased's moaning, or in the alternative that there were other sounds which the witness could have mistaken or confused as coming from the deceased. If an expert pathologist for the plaintiff concludes that there was pain from the auto crash injuries, the defense might hire an expert pathologist to opine that there was a strong probability that due to the severity or type of injury that the deceased was rendered unconscious or was in a state of shock immediately after the impact.

A jury found that security bars on a bedroom window contributed to a death in a fire that destroyed twenty-four apartments. One person died. The suit did not seek compensation for lost earnings of this man but included a count for his pain and suffering in the moments before his death. The defense, however, presented expert testimony from a pathologist that the person never woke up when the fire erupted. The jury awarded $540,000.[5]

Some of the more frequently used defense tactics are described below.

A. Instantaneous death

As discussed above, some injuries are usually not consistent with residual pain. See Section 20.4. The primary example is a severe head trauma or decapitation that would usually result in unconsciousness. Another classic injury which most medical experts agree will most likely cause instant death is the hangman's fracture. That is how the separation of the spinal cord between C-1 and C-2 is often described. Several forensic experts have analogized this type injury to this author as "turning the lights of life off by literally pulling the electrical cord out of its socket." The unfortunate victim of a hanging or an impact which severs the spinal cord at that location is presumed to feel nothing. The defense will always look for any type of injury that normally would produce immediate unconsciousness.

B. Finding fault with eyewitness observations

As with any eyewitness account in any type of litigation, the defense will try to discredit any testimony about the deceased's expressions of pain, by suggesting that the eyewitness was either incapable, mistaken, or in some way biased and therefore not an objectively accurate reporter of what was seen or heard.

C. Involuntary or voluntary movements

The defense may try to characterize the facial expressions, communications, attempts to communicate, signs of movement away from the danger, responses to stimuli and any sounds or movement by the deceased as involuntary and not the reaction of someone who was consciously aware of what was happening. One defense expert tried to analogize the grasping and reaching of a dying man trapped under the dual tires of a bus to the involuntary movements of "a chicken that twitches after its head is chopped off."

D. The battle of the experts

Sometimes the defense will hire accident reconstruction, medical, and pathology experts to opine that the time of the accident sequence or the aftermath of the trauma is inconsistent with any pre-impact awareness or knowledge. They will argue that any pre-mortem pain was brief if or nonexistent because death or unconsciousness was instantaneous upon the traumatic event. Usually, these experts are not very effective when confronted with independent eyewitness testimony of pre-impact or post-impact signs of life from the deceased.

E. Shock

To discount the probability of consciousness the defense often attempts through expert or nonexpert (on-the-scene EMTs and nurses) witnesses to imply that the injured plaintiff was in a state of shock and therefore unconscious to any pain. Shock may be primary or neurogenic shock which is the result of the stunning effect of the fatal injuries. Remember that a person may be partly unconscious or stunned but not completely without consciousness of pain.

Tip

A severe hemorrhage, dismemberment, or loss of blood which contributes to the lack of blood returning to the heart can also be a cause of shock. However, any medical treatment which was given to the deceased with the aim of treating and combating shock may be helpful to refute the possibility of an unconscious state of shock.

F. Analgesia: Alcohol, drugs, or other pain relief

Another tactic used to discount pre-impact fear as well as ante-mortem pain and suffering is to show that the deceased was either unconscious prior to impact or was so sedated by alcohol, drugs, or a combination thereof in the body that the traumatic event was just a mere bump or a very slight amount of painful stimuli.

This argument was used in *Donagan v. Altman et al.* Bars on a bedroom window prevented a thirty-eight-year-old man from escaping from a nighttime house fire. The decedent had a blood alcohol level of 0.22 at the time of his death. The defendant contended that the tenant was negligent in going to bed while a candle was still burning. The defense argued that the combination of intoxication and carbon monoxide from the fire itself resulted in the decedent dying without regaining consciousness. The defendant maintained that shortly after discovering the fire the tenant of the apartment had advised an upstairs neighbor that she had attempted in vain to awaken the decedent. The defendant contended that this statement was evidence and should be admitted as an excited utterance hearsay exception, relying on this statement to show an absence of conscious pain and suffering. The plaintiff countered that the decedent's body was found by firefighters completely off the bed, nude except for his watch, and that his hand was in a hole in the wall. The plaintiff maintained that based on this evidence it was clear that the decedent had attempted to escape in panic. The plaintiff's forensic pathologist was of the opinion that the decedent was conscious during a period of time which ranged from one minute to ten minutes until succumbing to smoke inhalation but indicated that such consciousness was towards the lower end of the scale. The plaintiff contended that the panic, pain and suffering experienced during this period was clearly severe. The jury found the defendant landlord and managing agent 85% negligent and the decedent 15% negligent. They then rendered a gross award of $540,000 which was molded accordingly. *Donagan v. Altman et al.*, Docket no. L-00578-00, Camden County, NJ.[6]

If alcohol or drugs are discovered in the autopsy, then the plaintiff's counsel should consult an expert. A pathologist or a forensic toxicologist is skilled at determining whether the BAC (blood alcohol concentration) or amount of sedatives in the deceased were capable of analgesia or blocking out the pain of the traumatic event even though the deceased was conscious at the time. Once again, an eyewitness who saw and heard the sounds or cries of pain from the deceased will usually outweigh any esoteric expert opinion about the anesthetizing effects of alcohol, and drugs. Even an intoxicated person can and will feel excruciating pain.

20.6 The Usual Suspects or Witnesses to the Final Agony

Often in wrongful death cases the police, emergency medical technicians, police accident reconstructionist and medical examiners write reports. Sometimes their reports are cryptic or may imply that the deceased was unconscious at the scene. The plaintiff's attorney should not trust the written reports of EMTs, police, or even the medical examiner. Often police and EMTs arrive at the scene minutes, if not longer, after the initial trauma. At that point the victim may have lapsed into unconsciousness; however, prior to the arrival of the police or EMTs there may have been conscious pain and suffering.

Tip

Even when EMTs and police are on the scene immediately, they may not recognize or record accurately that the movement or sounds made by the deceased evidenced pain and discomfort.

Many times the EMTs do not want to make an already tragic situation more so by informing the family of suffering prior to death. The author knows of many instances where EMT reports were written, or the boxes on a form checked off, in such a misleading way that one could easily interpret the report as stating there was no consciousness whatsoever when in fact the victim was in agonizing pain for minutes.

Medical examiners or coroners, depending on their levels of skill and expertise, often do not consider whether there were any periods of conscious pain and suffering before the ultimate demise of the victim. They are concerned with the cause of, and not the circumstances leading up to, the death. Some medical examiners are intellectually dishonest; that is, they are not intellectually rigorous in their analyses unless they are working for a county prosecutor or district attorney in the prosecution of a criminal defendant. In the criminal case context, the more pain inflicted by the accused, the more serious the crime and punishment. Civil cases seeking compensation become too tedious, burdensome, or politically incorrect for some MEs. Therefore, they deliberately or unconsciously avoid conflicts or confrontation about whether the injuries to the decedent caused any pain or suffering prior to the ultimate death. The author's suggestion is to not trust any medical examiner until and unless an independent forensic pathologist is consulted. The attorney who is not assured of the integrity and ability of the medical examiners should hire his own forensic pathologist. Particularly if there are no eyewitnesses to any pain before death, the attorney should ask the consulting pathologist or medical examiner whether or not the decedent's injuries could have produced any physical suffering and pain prior to causing ultimate unconsciousness.

20.7 Obtaining the Statements of Witnesses

Before employing a forensic pathologist to analyze a wrongful death claim for conscious pain and suffering, consider initially interviewing all the witnesses at the scene. Such witnesses include any tow truck operators or firemen involved in extracting or removing vehicles, the police, and rescue or ambulance crews involved with the removal of the decedent's body. Any and all eyewitnesses at the scene, particularly those present before the arrival of the emergency or rescue squads, should be interviewed.

As with any witness, there are several different methods to obtain witness statements concerning the pre-mortem elements of damage. The witness can be interviewed in person, over the telephone, or even by regular mail or e-mail. The preferred method is to conduct the interview and obtain the witnesses' sworn statements in person. This method, just as any face-to-face interview or deposition, allows the attorney, either alone or with an investigator, an opportunity to evaluate the demeanor and perceptive abilities of the witness. An in-person or telephonic interview allows for a more probing discussion of what exactly was observed, and the surrounding circumstances of the observations.

Tip

It is better practice for the attorney to obtain the witnesses statements using a professional legal investigator. If an investigator is not available, the attorney should try to have a staff member or some other person available for the interview as a corroborating witness

---

A good suggestion is to follow the better practice of some attorneys and have a certified court reporter with a stenographic machine take a sworn or affirmed statement from the witness and then send the witness a copy of that certified transcript. This avoids the ethical and evidentiary dilemma of the trial lawyer becoming a witness in the event the witness later recants or accuses the attorney or interrogator of being unprofessional, overbearing, inaccurate, incomplete, or deceitful in the recording of the statement. It is for this reason that any statement taken from a witness should be tape recorded and then typed and given to the witness to read and sign. Any corrections made by the witness are initialed by the witness. Another method of taking an in-person statement is to have the witness or the investigator handwrite the statement, and at that time have the witness read, correct with initials, and sign the document with the clear written statement to the effect that the witness has read it and swears to the truthfulness and completeness of the statement.

Some insurance companies use tape recorded telephone interviews with its insured clients and witnesses.

These can be and often are very useful. The three main disadvantages of a taped telephone interview are

- the inability of the witness to authenticate or verify the accuracy and completeness of the typed statement,
- the loss of personal and visual contact with the witness to assess any negative demeanor traits or idiosyncrasies, and
- the inability to obtain or use any exhibits with the witness, such as photographs or scale drawings.

The inability of a telephonically interviewed witness to read and amend, correct, or supplement the taped statement can be very important if the statement is not thorough on a particular issue. For example, if the witness says "I think the deceased was in pain," but there is no explanation for that observation, later the witness may recant and change her mind to say "Well, I said I thought that was true then, but I'm not sure anymore." A witness who says over the telephone that he "saw" or "heard" something at a great distance. When confronted in person may reveal he was very much physically incapable of such perceptions. The personal interaction with a witness cannot be overrated. Often a witness will recall important facts when the interviewer shows the witness a photo, drawing, or other piece of evidence. There are many times when the witness will produce her own photographs or the witness will draw a diagram to help the attorney understand what she saw and heard. These important exhibits cannot be obtained or created as effectively by telephone or correspondence.

The actual questioning of any witness can be conducted by any one of many recognized methods. One way is to ask a very general and open-ended question such as "What, if anything, did you observe?" or "What, if any, sounds or actions did the deceased make?" These types of questions call for a narrative from the witness. Another method is to ask a more focused set of questions. For example: "There were skid marks found prior to the point of impact." (Show the witness the police report or photographs.) "Did you see or hear any sounds of braking or warning prior to the collision?" Depending on the personality, attitude, and communication style of the witness, the ability to engage and continue in conversation and discussion on the part of the interrogator, and time allowed for the interview, most witness interviews are a combination of both general and specific questioning.

Tip

The style and mode of the interview are truly irrelevant if the witness is treated professionally, fairly, and accurately. If the witness is told for whom or on behalf of which interested party the statement is being taken, and the witness is treated sensitively and politely and afforded the opportunity to review his statement for completeness and accuracy, then there will rarely be any problems later on with that witness. Conducting a fair and accurate interview will thwart any attempt by the defense or the witness to suggest later to the judge or jury that the witness was in some way tricked, misled, or mistreated.

It is important to remember that in a wrongful death case the witness may also have been traumatized by the event. The witness may not want to recall the gruesome details of the accident or the aftermath. Nevertheless, it is the challenge of the investigator to explain and then as delicately as possible obtain as many details as possible to prove any pre-impact actions as well as post traumatic signs of the deceased's conscious pain and suffering. Whether it is to establish liability or damages the witness's important recollections must be gathered and recorded accurately, in a way that does not unnecessarily traumatize or offend the witness. For example, in most cases it is not necessary to show lay witnesses any autopsy photographs or to try in any way to inflame their passions or dislike for one side or the other. The best course is to treat the witness the same as you would the client or a member of your own family who had recently experienced a horrible event.

Be very careful to avoid witness statements that are pure conclusions or net opinions. Being sensitive to the emotions of the witness to a wrongful death and the resulting agony does not mean that the attorney can gloss over important details for the sake of brevity or to avoid a distasteful and disagreeable subject such as pain. The worst statement that can be obtained from any witness is the unsupported conclusory statement or net opinion. That is a term usually used by courts to refer to an expert whose opinion has no factual basis. It is usually excluded as being non-evidentiary and little more that the expert's personal speculation on a topic. A witness who gives a mere conclusion with no foundation is also not permitted to testify to the unsupported conclusion. For example, a witness cannot state that a driver was speeding without first laying a foundation that the witness did have the experience to judge speed and the opportunity to observe the speeding car. An example of a net opinion is for a witness to state, "I observed that the deceased was in conscious pain and suffering for ten minutes." That statement standing alone proves very little for the proponent or opponent of the statement. There is no factual basis for the witness to give what is in essence a layperson's opinion. It is much more relevant and useful for any litigation or settlement purposes for the witness to describe in detail all the facts which go into the witness's analysis, and reasoning and form the basis of that witness's conclusion. For example, it is much more effective for the witness to describe how she came upon the scene and how she "held the dying woman for approximately the ten to fifteen minutes it took for the police to respond to my call for help" (which can be corroborated by the police and EMT call logs) "and I watched, felt and heard the painful groaning or whispered expressions of pain . . . and I saw the woman's face wince and felt her body twist and contort every time there was an audible scream (or other sound of pain)."

Another point to remember when interviewing any witness to the deceased's pain and suffering is the familiarity or past relationship of the witness with the deceased. That is, any person may be allowed to give a nonexpert or lay opinion if she was familiar with the deceased's pre-impact physical condition and non-painful state of being. This permits the witness to give a trustworthy account of the physical and mental condition of the deceased. This is true even though the witness may not recall any one detail or may find it difficult to express in words exactly the facts and conditions also which led him to the opinion that the deceased was consciously suffering pain. Therefore, the witness may still have experienced through all the senses enough information from the totality of the circumstances to give a lay opinion about any conscious pain and suffering of the deceased. Most courts will allow that nonexpert's opinion to be received by the jury in order to assist the trier of fact on that issue under this circumstance: the witness has a clear recollection that the totality of the circumstances which were observed was sufficient to leave on his memory the indelible impression that the person he knew prior to the trauma was in pain.

A good outline to follow for a witness's statement on the issue of conscious pain and suffering is to talk first about the facts and then get into a discussion of the witness's opinions. Each witness should be questioned as to whether there were any sounds or movements by the decedent which in any way indicated the decedent was conscious and in discomfort or pain. See Section 20.4 above for some of the factors to look for and use when questioning witnesses about pre-mortem damages.

Tip

After all the facts and circumstances are gathered, the witness should be asked her personal opinion about the deceased's conscious awareness of the impending traumatic event and any consciousness and pain of the deceased and the approximate time or duration of that fear, anxiety, and pain.

20.8 Sources of Witnesses

Every written report from every police, fire, and EMT unit that responded to the scene will contain the names of witnesses to the post-impact condition and conduct of the deceased. All the personnel on the scene will not be listed in one police report or one EMT log. This is because there are often several different police, county medical examiner, fire, and rescue units dispatched to the scene of a fatal accident.

Examine all tapes of radio messages from police, fire, EMT, and ambulance personnel. Be aware that some 911 tapes are quickly erased and reused so there should be a rapid effort to identify and secure a copy of the audio tape. Examine all audio tapes, videotapes, or photographs from any news media or shutterbugs. These videos and photographs may have captured the faces in the crowd of bystander witnesses who may have seen either the traumatic event or the immediate aftermath and the conscious conduct of the deceased. Note: the term shutterbug is used by some to describe a professional or amateur photographer who takes photos of accidents and sells them to news media, insurance companies, and attorneys for both sides of civil litigation. Most shutterbugs have a police scanner radio which they use to monitor accidents and emergency events so they can arrive at the scene in order to photograph and sometimes also videotape the accident scene.

Another useful tool for attorneys to locate eyewitnesses is to canvass the area and look for surveillance cameras. That is, to send a professional investigator to the scene of the accident—regardless whether the area is a commercial, residential, or rural neighborhood—and simply knock on the doors of every home, store, or building within a reasonable radius of the accident to determine whether anyone saw or heard anything before or after the incident in question. Also look carefully and inquire to determine whether there is any form of surveillance, such as video cameras, in the area which may have recorded the events leading up to and immediately after the incident.

Interview all witnesses at the scene and all medical personnel who helped extract and deliver the deceased to the hospital. DOA (dead on arrival) on a medical provider's form does not necessarily mean the deceased was dead or unconscious at the scene and en route to the ER.

20.9 Use of a Forensic Pathologist

If there is a gap between the arrival of eyewitnesses and the impact, and it appears the nature of the injuries would not have caused immediate unconsciousness, the attorney should consider consulting a forensic pathologist to determine whether or not there would have been any conscious pain and suffering. Typically in fire, drowning, and falling deaths a forensic pathologist can help assist the attorney in evaluating the extent, type, and quality of ante-mortem fear, anxiety, and pain. For example, in a fire case where the deceased was found dead in his bed, the autopsy finding of the existence of soot in the throat and lungs will help to establish the fact that the deceased probably died choking to death on the hot smoke of the fire rather than being overcome in his sleep from carbon monoxide poisoning and thereby dying a painless death. In cases where internal bleeding is a primary cause of death, a pathologist can usually extrapolate from the autopsy findings, even without eyewitnesses, to give a probable scenario of the final minutes of such a painful death.

A woman was stabbed seventy-five times by a man who was hired as a home health aide for her husband, an Alzheimer's patient, when the man came to the house for a robbery. Her multiple stab wounds resulted in massive loss of blood. The plaintiff's theory of severe conscious pain and suffering was supported by autopsy evidence which reflected she was conscious while twenty-seven of the seventy-five stab wounds were inflicted. There was also evidence of defensive wounds on her arms and hands. The case was filed against the agency that hired the aide who killed the woman, under the negligent hiring theory that the defendant agency had failed to perform an adequate background check. The aide had a prior conviction for burglary and been fired from a nursing home. *Baskin v. The Nurse Connection, Inc.*, tried in Ocean County, New Jersey, resulted in a $46 million jury verdict. The defense was planning to file a motion to set aside the verdict.[7]

The sources, references and leads for finding an honest, competent, and effective expert pathologist are as diverse as the sources for any forensic expert witness. The starting point for most cases is to consult with the medical examiner, coroner, or the assistant who performed the final examination (often at the scene or in the ER), and the pathologist who conducted the autopsy. In addition to the medical examiner and pathologist, if the deceased did survive long enough to receive emergency medical care at a hospital, then the treating doctors and nurses may prove to be a valuable source of expertise to explain whether the deceased was in any conscious pain during the ER or ICU stages. See Chapter 8, "Emergency Care Pain and Suffering," and Chapter 14, "Pain and Suffering in the Intensive Care Unit," for more information.

Good sources for experts are colleges or medical schools that teach pathology. Professors of pathology usually are former medical examiners or have enough traumatic injury experience that they can explain, based on the medical and autopsy records and the factual and opinion testimony of eyewitnesses what in all probability was the nature and extent of the pain experienced by the deceased. Other sources for forensic pathologists are the National Association of Medical Examiners and the American Academy of Forensic Sciences, which has a special section of its membership for pathologists.

One of the plaintiffs' trial bar's oldest and most used resources for forensic experts, including the fields of pathology, accident reconstruction, and biomechanics, is Harry Philo's *Lawyer's Desk Reference*.[8] Now in its ninth edition, this multivolume set is a tort lawyer's primer for finding and proving the standard of care in any type of tort case, as well as finding qualified experts in almost every field of forensic endeavor.

As with any new and unfamiliar expert, the attorney and clients are better served if the attorney obtains some references and checks into the expert's past litigation history. Every state has a trial lawyers association for plaintiffs' lawyers, and the defense bar likewise has its own networks of lawyers. Therefore it is recommended that prior to retaining and consulting with any forensic pathologist the attorney should obtain some commentary or feedback from other members of the trial bar who have either used or opposed the expert in litigation.

There may be eyewitnesses who saw or ear witnesses who heard events of the traumatic incident unfold, or who observed or overheard the person in distress after the incident and who are of the lay opinion that the person was suffering. If so, the plaintiff's attorney should nevertheless employ a forensic pathologist to confirm and medically corroborate the lay testimony. Based on the eye or ear witness accounts and the nature and mechanism of the injuries, it may not be merely medically possible, but rather medically probable, that the deceased suffered pain and physical distress.

Tip

Many times the forensic pathologist can actually describe in very realistic detail the mechanism and cause of the victim's pain as it occurred in the last minutes of life. This, if done sensitively, succinctly, and objectively, can have a tremendous effect in making a jury aware of the victim's very painful and terrifying last moments on Earth.

20.10 Conclusion

In addition to establishing the economic loss to the survivors for the wrongful death of a human being, plaintiffs' trial lawyers must evaluate whether or not the client's spouse, child or relative suffered to any extent. It is the attorney's duty to discover, evaluate and demand full and fair damages for the decedent as if he or she had survived the fatal incident. That is, if the pre-impact fear and the post impact suffering of your client were not fatal, and the plaintiff had survived after the ten minutes or ten months of conscious pain or unconscious loss of enjoying life, such a horrifying experience would be an important element of damages. Because the plaintiff did not recover from the fatal injury or make a miraculous recovery does not lessen the outrageous and hideous manner by which the plaintiff died. Even if the veil of death fell over the deceased in a manner of seconds, or even if the deceased was in an unconscious state for a matter of days, any reasonable person on a jury will award money damages for the value of that final period of time. No one should have to die in pain. No one should lose the last few precious minutes, hours, or days of life in a wrongfully induced coma. The fact that the injured person is deceased and no longer available to explain all the pain and anguish experienced is no reason to abandon or overlook the final agony. The deceased cannot tell the jury in his own words what he did or said before dying. The deceased cannot describe his unfinished business, his last wishes, or how he would have preferred to die. One of the attorney's jobs is, through careful preparation and investigation, to explain what the deceased's last enjoyments of life would have been and with whom. The final suffering may have been a combination of fear, anxiety, terror, and pain. The final moments may have included pain, suffering and agony from the fatal injury. Prior to impact there may have been fear, anxiety, and terror that occur when seeing your life flash before you or witnessing your impending doom. These final experiences of life are something that all attorneys must visualize and analyze with trained accident investigators, reconstruction experts, and medical consultants.

Determining whether the deceased victim suffered should be more than simply a cursory question or two of a few witnesses or a review of secondhand accounts that may or may not be accurate. The attorney must faithfully evaluate the wrongful death case. Witnesses at the scene should be questioned and the fatal injuries analyzed in toto by a professional forensic pathologist or medical expert with traumatic medicine experience. Then, and only then, can the plaintiffs' attorneys faithfully discharge their duty to all clients by helping the survivors obtain compensation for the suffering that occurred to their loved ones during their last conscious moments.

Endnotes

1. Speiser, S., *Recovery for Wrongful Death*, Second Edition., Vol. 2, §14:8. Eagan, MN: Lawyers Co-Op, 1975.

2. Speiser, S. *Recovery for Wrongful Death and Injury*, Third Edition, Vol. 3, §14:8. Deerfield, IL: Clark, Boardman, & Callahan, 1992.

3. Fuchsberg, A., "Damages for Pre-Impact Terror." *Trial Law Quarterly 29* 16(3)1984.

4. Zarin, I., editor, "$1,125,000 Verdict. *Beeley v. Spencer*, index no. 8137/98, *New Jersey Jury Verdict Review and Analysis*, 23 (3), July 2002.

5. Suits and Deals, "$540,000 for Premises Liability." *New Jersey Law Journal*, August 12, 2002, 8.

6. "$540,000 Gross Verdict, *Donagan v. Altman*." *New Jersey Jury Verdict Review and Analysis*, 23 (4), September 2002, 13.

7. Top 20 Personal Injury Awards of the Year, "$40.6 M for Deadly Assault in Nursing (sic) Home." *New Jersey Law Journal*, September 16, 2002, S1.

8. Philo, H., and Philo, H. Jr., *Lawyers Desk Reference*, Ninth Edition. Eagan, MN: West Group, 2001.

9. See Speiser, supra, § 16 for detailed discussion of pre-impact distress damages under the old Impact Rule; Speiser, supra, § 17 for detailed discussion of pre-impact distress damages under the Zone of Danger Test. The zone of danger usually applies to a plaintiff who survives a crash or traumatic event. That is, a plaintiff who is close enough or within the zone of danger which results from a negligent act can, in some jurisdictions, bring a cause of action for emotional distress caused by the wrongdoer.

Additional Reading

Boston, G.W., Kline, D.B., and Brown, J.A., *Emotional Injuries, Law and Practice*. Eagan, MN: West Group, 2002.

Breckler, A., "Pain and Suffering." 23 *Am Jur POF 2d* 1, 1980.

"Case Proves Senior Verdicts Can Be Large; Attorneys Focused on Pain and Suffering of a 70-Year-Old Air Crash Victim." 80 *ABA J* 2:28, 1995.

"Compensation for Pain to Unconscious Victim Upheld by Court." 31 *Trial* 7:110 (1995).

"Conscious Pain and Suffering." 4 *Am Jur POF* 73, 1960.

"Conveying Psychological Pain and Suffering: Juror Empathy is Key." 29 *Trial* 10:16, 1993.

"Damages Awarded for Loss of Enjoyment of Life, Even Though Patient Is Unaware of Such Loss because of a Comatose Condition." 38 *Tr Law Guide* 1:57, 1994.

"Emotional Damages due to Wrongful Death—What Are They Worth?" 13 *Behav Sci & L* 1:43, 1995.

"Explaining Pain: How You Do It, Who Can Help." 30 *TRIAL* 11:92, 1994.

"Hedonic Damages in Personal Injury and Wrongful Death Cases." 60 *Def Couns J* 118, 1993.

"Hedonic Damages . . . How Far Can Economics Go?" 47 *Wash St BJ* 47, 1993.

"How Lawyers Win Those Big 'Pain and Suffering' Awards." 71 *Med Economics* 12:34, 1994.

Khare, M.N., "Proof of Damages for Decedent's Pain and Suffering." 24 *Am Jur POF 3d* 337, 1994.

Koskoff, Y., "The Nature of Pain and Suffering." 13 *TRIAL* 21, July 1977.

Koskoff, Y., "Proving Suffering—A New Challenge." *Trial,* 46, July 1978.

Laycock, D., "The Death of the Irreparable Injury Rule." 103 *Harvard Law Review* 688, 1990.

Lee, J.D., and Lindahl, B.A., *Modern Tort Law, Liability and Litigation*, Second Edition. Eagan, MN: West Group, 2002.

Leebron, D., "Final Moments: Damages for Pain and Suffering Prior to Death." 64 *New York University Law Review,* 1989; reprinted in 39, *Defense Law Journal* 133, 1990.

Martin, E., "Limiting Damages for Pain and Suffering—Arguments Pro and Con." 10 *American Journal of Trial Advocacy* 317 Fall 1986.

McClurg, A., "It's a Wonderful Life: The Case for Hedonic Damages in Wrongful Death Cases." 66 *Notre Dame Law Review* 57 1990.

Minzer, M., Nates, J., Kimball, C., and Axelrod, D., *Damages in Tort Actions*. Conklin, NY: Matthew Bender, 1987.

Note, "Hedonic Damages for Wrongful Death: Are Tortfeasors Getting Away with Murder?" 78 *Georgetown Law Journal* 1687, 1990.

"Perception and Awareness after Brain Damage." 4 *Curr Opin Neurobiol* 2:252, 1994.

"Permitting Recovery for Pre-Impact Emotional Distress." 28 *Boston College Law Review* 881 1987.

Prosser, W., and Keeton, W., *Law of Torts*, Fifth Edition. Belmont, CA: West Wadsworth, 1984.

Spector, R., "Pain and Suffering: Current Concepts." 34 *Med Trial Technique Q* 202, 1987.

Speiser, S., *Recovery for Wrongful Death*, Second Edition. Lawyers Co-Op, 1975, and Supp., 1988.

Stolker, C., "The Unconscious Plaintiff: Consciousness as a Prerequisite for Compensation for Non-Pecuniary Loss." 39 *International and Comparative Law Quarterly* 82, 1990.

Strawinski, J., "Pre-Impact Pain and Suffering." 26 *Georgia Bar Journal* 60(8), 1989.

"The Application of the Hedonic Damages Concept to Wrongful Death and Personal Injury Litigation." 7 *J Forens Econ* 143, 1994.

"The Misapplication of the Hedonic Damages Concept to Wrongful Death and Personal Injury Litigation: A Comment." 6 *J Forens Sci* 273, 1993.

"The Non-Pecuniary Costs of Accidents: Pain-and-Suffering Damages in Tort Law." 108 *Harv Law Review* 8:1787, 1995.

"Using Experts to Prove Personal Injury Damages." 5 *Prac Litig* 5:69, 1994.

Verdict for pain upheld despite unconsciousness, 141 *Chi Daily L Bull* 77:3, 1995.

Vilensky, R., "Recovery for Pre-Impact Terror and Fear of Impending Death Overlooked and Underrated." 63 *New York State Bar Journal* 11(4), 1991.

Wecht, C., "Cause of Death as Determined by an Autopsy." 39 *Am Jur POF2d* 1, 1984.

Additional Readings by Author

"Anxiety, Fear, Pain and Suffering: Overlooked Elements of Wrongful Death Damages." *The Trial Lawyer*, Vol. 24, No. I, Jan/Feb 2001, p. 45–50.

ATLA Deposition Notebook, Second Edition. Eagan, MN: West Group, 2000.

ATLA Trial Notebook, Fourth Edition. Eagan, MN: West Group, 2000.

Deposition Notebook, Third Edition. New Brunswick, NJ: New Jersey Institute for Continuing Legal Education, 2000.

"Direct Examination: A to Z, Vol. 20." *Trial Diplomacy Journal* No. 5, Sep–Oct 1997, p. 291.

"Effective Settlement Techniques and the Settlement Brochure." In *Excellence in Advocacy*. Washington, DC: ATLA Press, 1992, 305–326.

"Final Act and Curtain Call for the Trial Lawyer: Some Thoughts and Theories about Closing Argument in a New Jersey Wrongful Death Case." NJ ICLE Wrongful Death Seminar paper, Oct 24, 1992.

"How to Prepare and Use a Trial Notebook." In *Excellence in Advocacy*. Washington, DC: ATLA Press, 1992, 239–267.

"How to Try a Wrongful Death Case in New Jersey: Plaintiff's Opening Statement." NJ ICLE, Seminar paper, January 1986, April 1989, October 1992.

"Overcoming Stereotypes: Don't Sell Damages Short When the Client's Elderly." 9 *NJ Lawyer* 2065, Oct 16, 2000, p B5–B8.

Trial Notebook, Third Edition. New Brunswick, NJ: New Jersey Institute for Continuing Legal Education, 2000.

"Underestimated Plaintiffs: Proof and Argument of Damages in Cases Involving the Elderly." *The Trial Lawyer*, Vol. 23, No. 6, Nov/Dec 2000, p. 488–494.

Vesper, T., Baker, Schorr, and King, *All About Auto Cases and Accident Investigation*. Professional Education Systems Institute, 2001.

Vesper, T., and Orr, R., "Make Time Palpable by Using Per-Diem Arguments." *Trial*, Oct 2002, p.59–65.

"What to Pack Up in Your Ol' Kit Bag for Discovery and Trial: An Introduction to Notebooks." *The Trial Lawyer*, March-April 1999, Vol.22, No.2, p.142–151.

Chapter 21

A Defense Attorney's Perspective

J. Michael West, Esq. and Thomas C. Broderick, Esq.

Synopsis

21. 1 Introduction

The defense lawyer confronts the plaintiff's claims of physical injury and resultant pain and suffering in every personal injury lawsuit. Whether the case involves a resolved acute injury where the plaintiff is not claiming any permanent damages or is a case with severe injuries and permanency, the defense lawyer must evaluate the extent of the damages. The evaluation may result in demonstrating to the plaintiff's attorney and the plaintiff the limitations of their claim. This effort helps in reaching a reasonable settlement or in convincing a jury that the plaintiff and her attorney greatly exaggerate the pain and suffering experienced and to be experienced by the plaintiff. The jury is therefore guided in arriving at an award for the plaintiff that is appropriate for the plaintiff's condition. Just as the diagnostician considers and rules out any number of disease processes when seeing an ill patient, the defense attorney must always consider, and if appropriate rule out, the possibility that the plaintiff is a malingerer or at least greatly exaggerating the effects of the injury. The gathering of the information regarding the plaintiff and her injury, and the defense lawyer's knowledge of the medicine, is used to create a plan to attack pain and suffering claims either in the negotiation stage or if the case is not resolved by settlement at trial. Over 95% of personal injury lawsuits are resolved prior to trial. The defense lawyer's skills in minimizing damage claims are most important in the pretrial and negotiation phases of litigation.

Tip

When cases do go to a jury verdict, typically 40% to 60% of the damages awarded are for intangible pain and suffering, so the lawyer must be prepared to attack this element of damages at trial.

21.2 Categories of Pain and Suffering Claims

The defense typically faces three general categories of pain and suffering issues: exaggeration of damages, severe and permanent injuries, and malingering.

A. Exaggeration

The most common case is the exaggerating plaintiff. Either during the pretrial and negotiation stage of the case or during the trial the plaintiff and the plaintiff's attorney seek to optimize the recovery for all elements of damages, including pain and suffering. The plaintiff's attorney may have had the client complete an extensive damages questionnaire, detailing not only the plaintiff's medical history, the onset of symptoms related to the occurrence, the resolution and return of those symptoms, but also how the symptoms affected or will affect the daily activities of the plaintiff and her enjoyment of life. Prior to the plaintiff's deposition and testimony at trial, the plaintiff's testimony will likely be rehearsed in order that it has the maximum impact on the listeners and to ensure that no key elements of damages are overlooked. It is clear to the plaintiff and the plaintiff's attorney that there is a correlation between the severity and longevity of the complaints and symptoms and the potential recovery by settlement or verdict. In short, most plaintiffs will exaggerate. Partial exaggeration is more commonly encountered than malingering. Some may refer to this as partial malingering—the conscious exaggeration of symptoms that do exist.[1]

Defense lawyers would argue that most personal injury cases and workers' compensation cases involve some degree of exaggeration of symptoms by the claimant. The reason is straightforward and a basic principle of management and child rearing: you get the behavior you reward. Since the amount of compensation is directly proportional to the severity of the injury and the resultant pain and suffering caused by the injury, claimants have a strong motivation to exaggerate the pain and suffering resulting from their injury. Plaintiffs who exaggerate the pain and suffering experienced may also be exaggerating the physical limitations caused by an injury.

B. Severe and permanent damages

The defense lawyer will also confront cases where damages are severe and permanent and the plaintiff does not exaggerate the pain and suffering element. The plaintiff's lawyer will argue for a significant award, and the defense lawyer must counter those arguments as well as he can, relying on the facts and the common sense of the trier of fact.

C. Malingering

The last category rarely encountered (or is it seldom recognized?) is the malingering plaintiff: a plaintiff who is faking injury or illness for personal gain.[1] This is the most difficult for the defense attorney to refute and may also be difficult for the medical experts and the trier of fact to detect.

This chapter covers the topic of the malingerer, as this plaintiff presents unique problems for the defense lawyer. The material discusses pain and suffering damage issues in the pretrial and trial stage.

21.3 Malingering in Pain and Suffering Claims

Malingered physical and mental disease appears to be nearly as old as recorded history. One early example comes from the Old Testament:

> And David arose, and fled that day for fear of Saul and went to Achish the king of Gath. And the servants of Achish said unto him, "Is this not David the king of the land? Did they not sing one to another of him in dances, saying, Saul hath slain his thousands, and David his ten thousands?" And David laid up these words in his heart, and was sore afraid of Achish the king of Gath. And he changed his behavior before them, and feigned himself mad in their hands, and scrabbled on the doors of the gate, and let his spittle fall down upon his beard. Then said Achish unto his servants, "Lo, ye see the man is mad: Why then have ye brought him to me?"[2]

A. Definitions

Many of the civil and criminal laws of the various state governments and the federal government rest squarely on the concept of intent. Despite the complete lack of medical or scientifically objective testing capable of demonstrating intent, every day, in courtrooms across the country, laypeople are required to determine intent. Although technological advances in lie detection have moved from polygraph to voice analysis, no method has proven sufficiently accurate. Sodium amytal is sometimes useful in recovering genuinely repressed memories, but it is not reliable in ascertaining the truth. One half of the subjects in Redlich's study[3] were able to maintain a lie under the influence of sodium amytal. Similarly, despite decades of studies demonstrating the lack of evidence supporting the proposition that the average person can detect testimonial falsehood at any statistical rate better than pure chance,[4,5] nevertheless, lay jurors are called on by the legal system to detect and to punish falsehood. References to the concepts of intent and falsehood are common within the context of law. The following examples are taken from *Black's Law Dictionary*:

> **fraud**. A false representation of a matter of fact, whether by words or by conduct, by false or misleading allegations, or by concealment of that which should have been disclosed, which deceives and is intended to deceive another so that he shall act upon it to his legal injury.
>
> **falsehood**. A statement or assertion known to be untrue, and intended to deceive. A willful act or declaration contrary to the truth. It is committed either by the willful act of the party, or by dissimulation, or by words. A fabrication.
>
> **perjury**. In criminal law, the willful assertion as to a matter of fact, opinion, belief, or knowledge, made by a witness in a judicial proceeding as part of his evidence, either upon oath or in any form allowed by law to be substituted for an oath, whether such evidence is given in open court, or in an affidavit, or otherwise, such assertion being material to the issue or point of inquiry and intended by such witness to be false.[6]

In the case of a pure fraud, it is not possible to attempt to categorize the typical presentations. The diversity and number of possible fraudulent liability claims are limited only by the plaintiff's imagination. Several true examples include:

- A handwritten document allegedly written in 1993 which was plaintiff's Exhibit "A" was shown to have been written on paper with a watermark that was not in existence until 1994.
- The defendant neurologist in a medical malpractice case relied upon his consultant's report allegedly created in 1997, which a computer analyst proved (from an investigation of the computer's hard drive) to have been fraudulently pieced together on a computer in 1999.
- A ballistics expert proved that the plaintiff's claims of having been shot in the back, in cold blood, by a security guard were scientifically impossible; an investigator uncovered an eyewitness who saw the plaintiff manufacturing false evidence.

Tip

The only sure bet is that attorneys are not likely to find fraud unless they are actively looking for it.

While concepts of intent and falsehood are the norm in the practical application of law, such concepts are the exception to the practical application of medicine. One aberration, however, is the diagnosis of malingering: malingering is a medical diagnosis, not a legal term of art, yet the medical definition of malingering employs the concepts of intent and falsehood. The *Diagnostic and Statistical Manual of Mental Disorders*, Fourth Edition (DSM-IV)[7] defines malingering as follows:

> V65.2 Malingering: The essential feature of Malingering is the intentional production of false or grossly exaggerated physical or psychological symptoms, motivated by external incentives such as . . . obtaining financial compensation . . . . malingering should be strongly suspected if any combination of the following is noted:
>
> - Medicolegal context of presentation (e.g., the person is referred by an attorney to the clinician for examination);
> - Marked discrepancy between the person's claimed stress or disability and the objective findings;
> - Lack of cooperation during the diagnostic evaluation and in complying with the prescribed treatment regimen;
> - The presence of Antisocial Personality Disorder.

Malingering is listed in the *DSM-IV*[7] as a condition not attributable to a mental disorder. It is defined as the intentional production of false or grossly exaggerated physical or psychological symptoms motivated by external incentives, such as financial compensation. Several other terms are useful in the description of malingering phenomena. Pure malingering is the feigning of disease when it does not exist at all in a particular patient. Partial malingering is the conscious exaggeration of existing symptoms or the fraudulent assertion that prior genuine symptoms are still present.

There are a host of medical and psychiatric conditions, other than malingering, which do involve conscious faking (e.g., Munchausen syndrome, factitious disorder, and conversion disorder). There is, however, no medical or psychiatric condition involving conscious faking, other than malingering, where the fraud is motivated by financial gain. There are other medical and psychiatric conditions which involve supposed physical illness or disorders of the body, where the faked conditions do not in fact exist but which are unconscious faking. An example is pseudo-seizures, which can be either intentional or wholly unconscious. All of these unconscious faking entities, by definition, lack intent to deceive but nevertheless result in claimed illnesses which do not in fact exist.

There are cases where the plaintiff will attribute his pain and suffering to an accident that is the subject of litigation, but the continuing nature of this pain behavior is not caused or related to the accident. This is known as false imputation. The plaintiff may have a sincere belief that the two are related. In these cases the plaintiff has chosen to adopt a sick role. The fact that there is a secondary gain motivation—financial compensation—is a factor in the plaintiff's choice to accept the sick role, but there is no intention to deceive. Expert medical testimony can be used in these cases to establish that the causes of the pain behaviors or sick role have ceased to be the accident, and have shifted to the gains associated with the behaviors.[8]

Review of the patient's medical history can assist in determining if the patient has a chronic pain behavior syndrome that has existed for such a period of time, or is of such a degree, that it cannot be related causally, at least entirely, to the injury that is the subject of the litigation. Under this theory, the defense lawyer need not establish intentionality or suggest the plaintiff is exaggerating or faking.

B. Implications of malingering in the legal system

Defense lawyers should always consider referring large exposure cases to psychiatrists, psychologists, or neurologists when there are suspicions of fraud and malingering. Malingering and exaggeration of damages occur in all types of civil and criminal litigation. One must therefore be assiduous in the investigation and evaluation of a case to try to determine whether malingering or fraud is the most likely explanation.

Tip

Legally, malingering constitutes fraud; if it can be proved, the claimant is not entitled to any payment for the alleged condition.

C. Independent medical examinations or retained physician examinations

Depending on the jurisdiction, the independent medical examination may be an option to assist in limiting pain and suffering damages. The risk is that the report of the independent examiner will confirm or enhance the plaintiff's case. Another option is to have the plaintiff examined by a doctor selected by the defendant. In most jurisdictions this is the procedure. The retained medical examiner should be furnished with as many of the relevant medical records as possible before the examination. While some experts can render a valid opinion based on a review of the records, the medical expert's credibility is greatly enhanced if he or she has conducted an examination of the plaintiff.

Psychiatrists should be asked to perform an independent or insurance medical examination (IME) when the lawyer believes that a personal injury does not exist or that a psychiatric explanation for the symptoms is more likely. An IME may also be appropriate when there are both physical and psychiatric damages claimed, or when only psychiatric damages are claimed.

D. Use of psychiatrists

The diagnosis of malingering requires that the expert obtain information from as many sources as possible. In the case of a head injury, for example, the expert needs all medical records, the statements of witnesses to the individual's behavior in multiple settings, and past school and military records, to name a few. A psychiatrist will take an exhaustive history, perform a neurological exam, and usually request neuropsychological testing. The overall goal is to determine if all the data fit together in a meaningful way to establish a clear and recognized medical condition. When data do not fit into a clear picture one suspects that the case is complicated by other factors. These other factors can include secondary gain, pre-existing conditions, and malingering.

The detection of malingered physical and mental illness has become something more than a cottage industry during the past two decades among psychiatrists and psychologists. There has been a great upsurge in the medical literature[9–11] on such topics as the detection of malingered mental illness and malingering of post-traumatic disorders. Dr. Resnick suggests that the reason malingering is so often overlooked or ignored by medical professionals is that medical professionals do not begin their analyses from the perspective of a healthy suspicion. Dr. Resnick writes:

> Above all, malingering must first be suspected. Separate small clues which would lead to a more detailed investigation may otherwise be overlooked. Prior to seeing the defendant, the examiner should be equipped with as much information as possible—e.g., police reports; witness statements; autopsy findings; past psychiatric records; statements of the defendant; observations by witnesses.[9] [pg. 89]

Interesting case studies and statistical analysis lend support for an attorney's healthy initial skepticism and assumption of malingering. For example, Schretlen reports:

> In civil litigation, forensic psychiatrists and psychologists are frequently asked to determine the authenticity of psychiatric symptoms following trauma. The incidence of feigned psychological symptoms after physical injury is unknown. In 48 out of 50 cases studied, post-accident neuroses had cleared up two years after the claim was settled (Miller, 1961). A U.S. General Accounting Office follow-up study on persons considered 100 percent disabled revealed that approximately 40 percent showed no disability whatsoever after one year.[11] [pg. 455]

Tip

It is often said that pain and suffering damages are difficult to disprove and that the malingering plaintiff is the most difficult of all. While it is certainly true that pain and suffering damages are difficult to disprove, malingering can frequently be proven by direct evidence and by logical attack.

E. Comprehensive record review

If the defense attorney has a case in which there is a suspicion of malingering, or if the pain and suffering and other medically related damages in the case could be significant, the attorney should arrange for a comprehensive review of the medical records by an experienced legal nurse consultant. This should be done as early in the case as possible, and hence the need to pursue aggressively the initial discovery to identify and obtain copies of the medical records. There are several legal consulting services that specialize in this type of medical review. A detailed review of all the medical records by the legal nurse consultant will highlight for the attorney the parts of the medical records that are inconsistent with the allegations of claimed pain and suffering and will contain recommendations for further medical review.

F. Testing

Except in cases where costs are prohibitive, an attorney who suspects malingering should always consider the use of psychological testing. There is no standard battery for such an evaluation. The specific tests to be used must be selected on a case-by-case basis depending on the type of symptoms suspected of being malingered, the person's educational level, the degree of cooperation, and the setting for the evaluation.

A review of the current literature suggests that it would be difficult to defend a clinical opinion on malingering or dissimulation without the results of an MMPI (Minnesota Multiphasic Personality Inventory) or MMPI-2. The MMPI is the most widely used and well researched personality assessment device in the world. The revised MMPI-2 contains seven separate validity scales that are sensitive to a variety of response sets, including faking bad, malingering, exaggeration, faking good, and defensiveness. Standard administration of the test is possible with anyone possessing at least an eighth grade reading level and no visual impairment.[12]

A review of existing peer review articles among psychologists[13–17] reveals a surprising level of accuracy and sophistication in the detection of faked symptoms through application of psychological testing. For example, an article by Dr. Schretlen, published in *Clinical Psychology Review*, indicates that "the majority of studies show that psychological tests can accurately detect faking," and that "simulated mental deficiency appears to be the most easily detected condition."[10] (pg. 457) Dr. Schretlen correctly opines that "it is probably indefensible to render expert testimony regarding the likelihood of malingering without psychological test data bearing on this question."[11] (pg. 457) Using a host of controlled experiments and statistically derived results, Dr. Schretlen makes the case that "faked mental deficiency or retardation can be detected in as many as 87 to 98 percent of cases, with very few false positives."[11] (pg. 457)

Intelligence tests can help reveal faking when the apparent disorder involves mental deficiency, psychosis, or neurologic impairment. Personality testing can be used to reveal an even broader range of malingered pathology than intelligence testing, including: psychosomatic disorders, neuroses, psychosis, organic conditions, and dissimulation.[11]

With regard to purely physical faking of such seemingly subjective symptoms as numbness or nerve irritation, neurologists can provide significant clues to malingering. Armed with the objective proofs associated with a negative EMG, neurologists can employ nerve distribution patterns to show that the claimed symptoms are not consistent with actual anatomical dermatomes and use objective testing such as pin prick analysis to further ferret out the malingerer.

Hunt and Older[18] were the first to describe an empirical strategy for the identification of faking on intelligence tests. It is based on the assumption that "the malingerer is not familiar with the complete picture of the disease he is simulating, and hence is unable to duplicate it." They hypothesized that fakers would fail more of the easy items but pass more of the hard items than mentally deficient subjects. Subsequent studies have refined this item analysis strategy, labeled scatter.[19] The scatter analysis has been the most widely researched strategy to identify faking on intelligence tests, and Schretlen reports, "In every study in which this strategy was used it has been shown to accurately detect faking."[11] Schretlen describes eleven studies that used intelligence tests to detect faked mental deficiency. Without exception, these studies employed the technique of scatter analysis to make the differentiation, and every study validated the technique. The two studies[10,19] that reported hit rates found that 87%–98% of subjects faking mental retardation can be identified using specially adapted intelligence tests, with 5%–16% false positives.[10]

Using intelligence tests in conjunction with other neuropsychological measures, two studies differentiated subjects faking brain damage from genuinely brain-damaged adults with 95%–100% accuracy and fewer than 6% false positives.[20,21] Schretlen differentiated subjects instructed to fake insanity from genuinely impaired subjects with 87%–90% accuracy. False positive rates were zero to 1%.[11] (pg. 458)

G. Clinical indicators of malingering

An attorney should be passably knowledgeable of the clinical indicators used by medical experts to detect the malingering of mental deficiencies. One of the more interesting areas involves the modern analysis of what used to be known as Ganser syndrome.[22] Modern studies show that there is no legitimate psychiatric or physical dysfunction that on the one hand enables the patient to understand the question clearly and the proper analytical framework for developing an answer (applying mathematics to calculate the answer to "what is 2 + 2?") yet provide an approximate answer that is correct in every sense except that the answer barely misses the mark ("2 + 2 = 5"). Patients answering questions with a Ganser approximation are now viewed with great suspicion. Resnick states, "A Ganser reaction is a hypothetical pseudo-stupidity which is now known to be almost always due more to conscious malingering than to unconscious processes." p. 21[22]

Tip

An attorney witnessing Ganser-like responses should immediately seek an independent medical examination of the plaintiff.

Malingerers are eager to call attention to their illnesses, in contrast to most true dementias where the norm is to conceal illness. It is more difficult for malingerers successfully to imitate the form than the content of psychotic thinking.[23] Some malingerers give the appearance of profound concentration before they give absurd answers.[24] Malingerers are unlikely to show the subtle signs of true dementia, such as impaired relatedness, blunted affect, concreteness, digressive speech, or peculiar thinking. It is rare for malingerers to show perseveration (continued repetition of a meaningless word or phrase). The presence of perseveration suggests actual organic damage or an extremely well prepared malingerer. Malingerers' symptoms may fit no known diagnostic entity. Symptoms may have been strung together from various psychoses. Malingerers may claim the sudden onset of a delusion. In reality, systematic delusions usually take several weeks to develop.

Malingerers are likely to have contradictions in their accounts of their illnesses. The contradictions may be evident within the story itself or between the malingerer's version and other evidence. When malingerers are caught in contradictions, they may either sulk or laugh with embarrassment, while the truly impaired will show no affect. Malingerers are more likely to answer "I don't know" to questions about psychotic symptoms such as hallucinations and delusions. Malingerers sometimes accuse clinicians of regarding them as faking. Such behavior is extremely rare in genuinely psychotic persons.[25]

There are a number of signs (shown in Figure 21.1) which may help to identify the deceitful claimant. Patients who exhibit these characteristics create a heightened suspicion for malingering.

All malingerers are actors who portray their psychoses as they understand them, often overacting their parts.[26] The malingerer "sees less than the blind, he hears less than the deaf, and he is more lame than the paralyzed. Determined that his insanity shall not lack multiple and obvious signs, he, so to speak, crowds the canvas, piles symptom upon symptom attaining to a but clumsy caricature of his assumed role."[27]

H. Relevant literature

For a case study on the clinical detection of malingered post traumatic stress syndrome, see Resnick.[10] For an extremely comprehensive analysis of testing strategies for detection of feigned mental illness, see Anderson.[13] There are case studies which conclude that non verbal clues greatly enhance the potential for detecting false testimony, and others that dismiss common misconceptions such as "liars fail to look a person in the eye," and other clinical indicators of false testimony.[28,29]

21.4 Defense Attorney's Strategic Use of Suspicions of Malingering Behavior

A. The first rule: Assume malingering

There is a difference between fraud, malingering, and simply subconsciously faking injury. But the difference is one of degree, and all these are subcategories of a larger animal, which in each case causes the jury to doubt the credibility of the plaintiff's testimony. As is

- dramatic description of pain with overuse of superlatives
- poor localization
- previously described treatment was of no help
- bizarre actions of medications
- disparity of healthy appearance with protestations of pain
- veiled history with extraneous information.
- accompanying neurotic syndromes
- history of many operations on other body areas
- claimed injuries do not match the minor nature of the accident
- the claimed injuries do not match the mechanisms of the injury
- the plaintiff's symptoms do not match the diagnostic testing
- the plaintiff is very knowledgeable about symptoms and treatments for the disorder
- the plaintiff may change doctors when the work release is issued and the plaintiff fails to return to work
- the plaintiff has a history of substance abuse.
- the physician has a pattern of overtreating patients
- there is a delay between the accident and the start of treatment
- the patient has a motive to deceive (pending litigation)
- lack of cooperation during evaluations
- presence of antisocial personality disorder
- poor work record or job satisfaction
- has a large number of symptoms
- has incredible recall of events surrounding the accident
- refusal of employment offers
- recreational activities inconsistent with claimed limitations on work activities
- resistance to seeking reasonable treatments and failure to complete treatment
- self-referrals for treatment

Figure 21.1 *Signs to help identify the deceitful claimant*

often repeated, the single most important element of a plaintiff's evidence in support of pain and suffering damages is credibility. A defense attorney should assume at the outset that a plaintiff is malingering, because this assumption will result in a quest to unearth potential eyewitness testimony, tangible evidence, scientific factors, or medical evidence that supports the defense of malingering. The defense attorney who does not affirmatively dig for the evidence is unlikely to stumble fortuitously across it.

Tip

The first rule of pretrial preparation, which applies from the first day of assignment of a lawsuit, is that the defense attorney should *assume* that the plaintiff is malingering until all attempts at proof of malingering have been exhausted.

B. Juror reactions to malingering

Experienced trial lawyers agree that there are several global truths about jury trials which transcend what might appear to be logical analysis. The facts, and the evidence produced at trial, simply may not be as important as the following seemingly tangential concerns.

- Attorneys don't have to be "liked" by a jury in order to win the respect of a jury, but your client had better be likable.
- A party who is caught in one lie may possibly prevail, but a party caught in multiple lies almost surely loses.
- A party caught in multiple lies will lose even if he or she is "likable," (besides, juries rarely choose to like a liar).
- All other things being equal, the jury despises the party who produces redundant evidence (makes the jury sit one minute longer than necessary to a fair resolution of the conflict), drones on (same reason), produces too many witnesses on identical subjects (same reason), or who presents a boring and uninteresting case.
- A jury appreciates being entertained while they perform their function, including being given a juicy issue to resolve, demonstrative evidence

(the dog and pony show), and learning new scientific methods and teachings, so long as these are made interesting, are simple to understand, and are concisely presented.

There is a certain beauty to the defense of a lawsuit in which there exists substantial (even if not clear and convincing) evidence that the plaintiff is malingering. A charge of malingering makes any trial juicier. A charge of malingering is, by definition, an attack on the credibility of the plaintiff. Since the issue of the plaintiff's pain and suffering is almost never an objective pursuit and almost always largely boils down to the jury's acceptance of the plaintiff's overall credibility, a successful attack on the plaintiff's credibility (relating to other, seemingly unrelated issues) will create a magic bullet, critically wounding or destroying the plaintiff's case on the issue of pain and suffering. Magic is used in the sense that the defense attorney has literally little or nothing to offer on the subject of pain and suffering, yet seriously undermines the plaintiff's claim for pain and suffering damages nonetheless.

Tip

Of course, any attorney who overstates his case risks losing his own credibility. The defense attorney should never be afraid to let the jury know of the evidence supporting malingering.

The issue is not whether to present evidence of malingering, but how to present the evidence. If the plaintiff is truly caught red-handed, the attorney may opt to make the case stand or fall on the issue. Short of that risky approach, there is a wide spectrum of choices, including the other extreme: failure to discuss overtly the evidence of fraud or malingering, while counting on the jury to figure it out for themselves. The rule is simple: never overstate the evidence.

Only where the defense oversells to the jury that the plaintiff is a malingerer and follows with no credible evidence or has the entire accusation thrown back in his or her face will a defense attorney need to fear the presentation of evidence of malingering. The jury knows that the plaintiff's attorney may be asking for more money than the case is worth. The jury will not likely be angry with a defense attorney who professionally and tactfully presents evidence supporting the potential of malingering. Even where the evidence of malingering does not rise to the level of a preponderance of evidence, any success in causing the jury to question the plaintiff's credibility will detract from the potential for excessive damages on the issue of pain and suffering.

Efforts to discover and uncover aspects of possible malingering may lead to a clear and convincing defense on the issue of liability or may simply uncover a few isolated and seemingly unrelated falsehoods in the plaintiff's testimony or medical history. The point for our purposes is that catching the plaintiff in a fraud or a lie—any lie—can so taint and destroy the plaintiff's credibility that the jury simply will not listen to the plaintiff's claims of pain and suffering. By successfully impugning the plaintiff's credibility on liability issues, the attorney has in one fell swoop undercut the plaintiff's claim for pain and suffering damages. It cannot be overstated that a successful attack on the plaintiff's credibility (even on issues absolutely unrelated to pain and suffering) often spills over, very negatively affecting the plaintiff's claim for pain and suffering damages.

C. The second rule: Assume your case will go to trial

Although 95% of personal injury lawsuits are resolved prior to trial, it is generally true that the defense attorney cannot predict which case will be the one in twenty that will go to jury.

Nowhere is this rule more important than involves the relationship between proof of malingering vis-á-vis the plaintiff's claim for pain and suffering damages. The hard truth is, despite thorough and diligent trial preparation, a defense attorney will frequently have no direct evidence or tangible proofs sufficient to counter the plaintiff's subjective claims of pain and suffering. Only a collateral attack on the plaintiff's credibility with evidence of falsehoods or malingering may ultimately be available to the defense attorney at trial. Therefore, proper preparation for trial requires an affirmative pursuit of potential falsehood or malingering on the part of the plaintiff.

While it is easy to announce the policy that a lawyer must treat each and every case as if the case will go to trial, it is nevertheless fair to ask whether such a policy would not be impossibly daunting in actual practice. Fortunately, perhaps, the actual practice of law is governed by economic reality. If the correctly assessed value of a given case is nominal, the defense attorney would be misdirected to believe that proper trial preparation should include hiring an investigator, retaining numerous expert witnesses, employing an economist, and paying for a jury consultant. The cost of trial preparation would be triple or quadruple the cost of a quick resolution. While it is always true that each case should be handled as if it were going to trial, proper preparation for trial is very different depending on the economic realities and potential exposure associated with each individual lawsuit.

The legal literature is replete with materials on presentation of damage evidence in order to maximize recovery and in defending against damage evidence in attempts to reduce damages. These works deal with

- economic damages,
- loss of income,
- loss of future income,
- medical expenses,
- medical expenses reasonably expected to be incurred in the future,
- how to present economic testimony,
- how to refute the plaintiff's economist,
- how to reduce economic losses to present cash value, and
- using an annuitist to reduce damage awards.

The materials are limited when it comes to advice on how to refute the plaintiff's claim for pain and suffering damages. In most cases, pain and suffering damages are not subject to direct attack, only to collateral attack and argument. One of the most successful forms of collateral attack on the issue of pain and suffering involves attacking the plaintiff's credibility. Happily, a successful attack on the plaintiff's credibility on any issue in the lawsuit tends to weaken the plaintiff's claims for pain and suffering.

Upon the initial receipt of the plaintiff's pleadings, the defense attorney usually does not have sufficient information to assess the degree of damages claimed. It is often not possible to categorize the damages exposure immediately. This initial period of ignorance creates a dilemma. In a slip and fall lawsuit where the only injury is a broken finger, with no claim of any permanent injury, it would be prohibitively expensive to hire an investigator, obtain a medical records review by a physician, or to hire an economist. The value of the case makes any of these strategies economically undesirable. Yet, in a death case, or other litigation involving potentially substantial damage exposure, the defense attorney would be well advised to hire an experienced investigator on day one and to interview every potential witness at great length. Remember that witnesses will often subconsciously bend over backwards to support the side which first meets, befriends, and interviews them. In addition, written discovery answers from the plaintiff may be many months in arriving, while the investigator might uncover critical evidence within hours of being hired—evidence which might evaporate with the passage of time.

D. Medical professionals and malingering

1. Consultants

A substantial lawsuit financially justifies the immediate retention of a medical expert, but not merely to review the medical records. The attorney's role at trial includes providing an explanation of complicated medical issues, quickly, concisely, and in a manner that is colorful and interesting to the jury, preferably making use of demonstrative aids. Rather than trying to learn the medicine through the dry and mechanistic approach of book learning, set a meeting very early with the retained medical professional, such as a legal nurse consultant. Have the medical professional teach you the medicine. Ask him or her to bring accurate medical diagrams, pictures, and visual aids. Ask for a description of the most authoritative text on the subject, thereby substantially reducing the attorney's research time. A lawyer is unlikely to ever compete with a doctor in the doctor's chosen field of medicine, but a lawyer most certainly can become a master of the tiny realm of medicine which is precisely at issue in the litigation. Not only will such knowledge be critical to any potentially successful cross-examination of the plaintiff's experts, but such knowledge will be surprisingly helpful throughout the discovery process. It can be used to formulate precise topics and questions for use at the plaintiff's deposition regarding her claims of pain and suffering, potential disabilities, and loss of a normal life.

Exploring the issue of malingering and fraud can produce hard, objective evidence in areas other than liability. One of the most interesting areas involves medical issues relating to the brain. One true-life example involved a plaintiff who was negligently hit on the head, and who allegedly developed uncontrollable and permanent seizures. The matter appeared to be a multimillion dollar case. However, a plaintiff who is in fact faking seizures might be well advised never to fake a seizure while connected to an EEG (electroencephalogram). It is medically impossible to fake a seizure while hooked to an EEG, and the doctors can explain the science to the jury with great precision, exposing the plaintiff as a fraud. The plaintiff is unlikely to be aware of the sophisticated advances that have taken place over the past few decades. Today, the regions of the brain and their general functions have been largely mapped. Woe to a malingering plaintiff who claims that a focal density on the brain stem has caused problems with short-term memory loss. This is not medically possible. Woe to the plaintiff's neuropsychologist who is prepared to testify to the plaintiff's loss of cognitive function, where the injury is allegedly to the brain stem. A plaintiff may believe that brain injuries are easy to fake because the brain is so complex. The plaintiff will be unhappily surprised by the science that can be brought to bear against him. This is hard, objective science that can catch the malingering plaintiff red-handed.

The reader may say: "I don't know anything about recent scientific discoveries related to the brain, and the medicine seems extremely complex." And that is the point.

Tip

The attorney's job is to locate a well credentialed expert or consultant and to get tutored by that expert on the medicine that is at issue. A substantial lawsuit justifies the expense associated with this simple approach. By the time of trial, the attorney will be prepared to teach the subject matter to the jury, beginning in voir dire and opening statement.

---

2. Treating physicians

A young attorney must come to understand an important distinction between trial lawyers and physicians. Unlike a forensic psychiatrist or neuropsychologist, most physicians are not trained to identify instances of exaggeration and malingering. In fact, physicians are trained to trust the oral history provided by the patient. If the treating physician doubted the valid complaints of a patient and failed to treat appropriately in the face of these subjective complaints, that might be the basis for a malpractice lawsuit. The physician-patient relationship could not survive a process where the complaints of the patient are subjected to a trial in the examining room. The ethical canons taught to the treating physician since the time of medical school have instilled in the physician an instinctive logical methodology that literally rests on the cornerstone of trust in the patient.

An experienced trial attorney can learn how to remove that cornerstone and topple the entire syllogism on which the treating physician has built his analysis. It is a fact of life, both medical and legal, that there are patients whose medical history contains a fraud or whose symptoms are exaggerations, but a defense attorney should never expect a treating physician to testify that a patient may be a malingerer. An attorney who capably learns the medicine, and who is unfettered by the ethics-driven thought process which requires the physician to trust the patient, is in a better position to analyze the lawsuit than is the plaintiff's treating physician.

Tip

The attorney has access to much more information than the treating physician. The treating physician carries only one trump card, that being knowledge of the medicine. An attorney can take away that trump card by learning the medicine.

There is another reason it is generally not wise to ask the treating physician whether she suspects her own patient to be a malingerer. The treating physician generally is not a qualified expert on the topic! Malingering is an intentional act by definition. The only medical professionals qualified to investigate scientifically the patient's intentions and motivations are psychiatrists, psychologists, neuropsychologists, and perhaps neurologists. A good approach, when an attorney suspects malingering, is to retain one or more of those experts. Armed with the factual and evidentiary matters that are causing the attorney to become suspicious, the forensic psychiatrist can probe the plaintiff with questions. Often there are questions which were never asked by the defense attorney at the plaintiff's deposition. The questioning by the psychiatrist offers a free second deposition. The psychologist can ask more questions, but this time employing standardized questions in the format of the Minnesota Multiphasic Personality Inventory (MMPI) and Derrogatis Symptom Checklist, which can once again lend hard, scientific evidence to the supposedly intangible proof of malingering.

A frequently successful tactic is simply to let the treater off of the hook. Verify with the treater at deposition that the treater is bound by medical ethics to begin her entire analysis on the cornerstone of trust and belief of the patient. Verify that the treater's role is the opposite of a jury, not to question the patient's veracity, but to begin her entire analysis on the basis of trust. Verify that the treater is not a psychiatrist and is not an expert on the diagnosis of malingering. Get the treater to admit that he would defer to the analysis of specialists on the topic. Then be prepared to call just such a specialist at trial, whenever appropriate.

In summary, the defense attorney must begin the analysis of each lawsuit firmly assuming (1) that the plaintiff is a malingerer and (2) that the case will go to trial. However, the attorney must be forgiven in the smaller cases for electing not to employ the tools most likely to expose malingering or to purchase the tools and experts necessary to maximize trial presentation. In short, the routine and standardized discovery practice exemplified by interrogatory, document production, and depositions of the plaintiff and the plaintiff's treating physicians may be the only tools available in low exposure cases. However, even these rudimentary tools can be used to maximum potential, in a manner calculated to limit and reduce the plaintiff's claim for pain and suffering damages.

21.5 Evidentiary Concerns Related to Malingering

In those cases in which the defense attorney has attempted but failed to expose any element of fraud or malingering in the plaintiff's evidence, the materials that follow should assist the defense practitioner to limit the plaintiff's damages. In those cases in which the defense attorney has built a case for fraud or malingering on the part of the plaintiff, the following materials should still be employed by the defense attorney but may become less important to the jury because a successful attack on the plaintiff's credibility on issues unrelated to pain and suffering remains the best defense to the plaintiff's direct claims of pain and suffering. Pain and suffering is all about credibility. If the defense attorney can cause the jury to disbelieve the plaintiff, on any issue, such will carry forward when the plaintiff asks the jury to trust him regarding the pain and suffering which he claims to be experiencing.

Tip

A defense attorney facing a plaintiff's claim for pain and suffering damages will generally want to place a falsehood, uttered by the plaintiff, on *any* topic, before the jury. However, the defense attorney must always give consideration to the possible application of Federal Rule of Evidence 403, and the prohibition against cross-examination upon collateral matters.

For example, in a lawsuit in which the plaintiff allegedly injured his left knee, the plaintiff's interrogatory answers denied any medical treatment for any condition during the five years prior to the accident. At deposition, the plaintiff again denied any medical treatment for any condition during the past five years. The defense investigator uncovered an acquaintance of the plaintiff who revealed that the plaintiff told the witness all about the plaintiff's ongoing medical treatment for severe arthritis in the plaintiff's right knee. These conversations occurred just a few weeks before the plaintiff's deposition. The defense attorney may be excited about catching the plaintiff in a lie but may be unhappily surprised when the judge bars any reference to this evidence at trial. The untruth has apparently nothing to do with the issue at trial relating to the plaintiff's left knee. Therefore any attempted cross-examination might well run afoul of the rule against cross-examination on collateral issues. Further, the plaintiff's untruth seemingly bears little or no relevance as to the plaintiff's alleged injury to his left knee, while the evidence of the untruth is highly prejudicial, possibly requiring exclusion pursuant to Federal Rule of Evidence 403.

The defense attorney who is defending the case on the assumption that the lawsuit will go to trial, and on the further assumption that catching the plaintiff in a lie is important, will understand that early intervention can often resolve the problem. An orthopaedic surgeon, retained by the defense, may determine that the ongoing arthritis in the right knee supports the physician's medical diagnosis that the plaintiff's current left knee complaints are merely arthritic and the result of a disease not a trauma. This simple expedient converts the evidence from being potentially collateral and undoubtedly resolves any Rule 403 potential. The defendant's case gets better with the addition of the orthopaedic opinion, and, perhaps more important, the untruth is placed in front of the jury. The desire to have the opportunity to place a plaintiff's falsehood before the jury is great incentive to become a master of the rules of evidence. For example, analysis of the application of the rule against hearsay testimony and the evidentiary doctrine of recent fabrication would be wise in the above scenario.

Similarly, while most attorneys understand that a pretrial motion in limine can generally be brought to exclude evidence, far fewer attorneys take advantage of the availability of an evidentiary tool known as an affirmative motion in limine. If the attorney is uncertain of the admissibility of evidence at trial and therefore hesitates to mention the evidence in an opening statement, the simple cure is to request a pretrial affirmative ruling, in limine, which is the opposite of the typically employed motion in limine. It is almost always best to obtain the judge's ruling on critical evidentiary issues before trial, as opposed to being unhappily surprised after trial has begun. A second benefit of employing an affirmative motion in limine is that the judge is not caught in the middle of trial attempting to decide a complex issue by the seat of her pants. The point, however, is that machinations to obtain the introduction of the plaintiff's falsehood, on any topic, are worth the effort because, so often, the only possible attack on pain and suffering damages is to successfully attack the plaintiff's credibility generally.

21.6 Pain and Suffering Damages—Pretrial Considerations

A. Law of intangible damages

"The unliquidated and indeterminate nature of damages for pain and suffering brings them within the ambit of general damages and opens the door to their becoming the most substantial item of recovery."[30] The plaintiff has the burden of proof from a strictly legal standpoint on all issues in the case, including damages. The defense lawyer should approach the issues of damages, or more to the point, refuting the plaintiff's damage claims, as if the burden of proof rests with the defendant. In fact, there is probably a higher burden on the defense attorney. The plaintiff can testify as to how much pain she suffers and can tell the jurors how the pain and resultant suffering affects every aspect of her life, from her work to her relationships with her spouse, her children, her friends, and her pets. Since pain can only be described and conveyed by the sufferer, who are the defendants to dispute it? While the plaintiff's attorney must meet foundational requirements to introduce evidence of pain and suffering, most of those are easily and routinely met as the plaintiff is certainly competent to testify as to the pain she experiences and the limitations and suffering that the pain causes. Only in the most extreme cases will a challenge to medical evidence be sustained, usually when there is a dispute as to the adequacy of the evidence to support a charge to the jury that they may consider an award for future pain and suffering. Indeed, the burden is on the defense lawyer, from the beginning of the litigation, to investigate and lay the groundwork for the introduction of evidence during the trial that will either refute the plaintiff's claims, or seriously limit any award. This is especially the case where the defense lawyer will try to convince the trier of fact that the plaintiff is a malingerer.

The plaintiff has a duty to submit to reasonable medical care and treatment intended to improve the plaintiff's condition and reduce or eliminate the consequences of the defendant's negligent act.[31] Pain and suffering damages can be challenged if the plaintiff does not comply with her treater's treatment plan, such as the failure to undertake or complete physical therapy. The plaintiff is not required to undergo extensive surgical procedures that present a risk of enhanced or additional injury.[32]

B. Physician's role

Treating physicians generally are not trained to look for exaggeration of symptoms and complaints. They are trained to be sympathetic to their patient's condition and in general should be expected to trust their patients.

If they doubted the valid complaints of a patient and failed to treat appropriately, that would be malpractice. The physician-patient relationship could not survive a process where the complaints of the patient are subjected to a trial in the examining room. The physician who can assist the defense lawyer in establishing a defense will usually be the retained expert.

The effective use of medical and other expert testimony is vital to the defense ability to refute damages for pain and suffering and in the identification of malingerers. Depending on the individual case, the defense lawyer has two sources of expert medical testimony: the cross-examination of the plaintiff's medical witnesses, and the testimony of the defendant's retained experts.

The defense lawyer generally will cross-examine treaters called by the plaintiff. There may be occasions when the defense lawyer will call a treater in the defense case. The plaintiff may not call treaters who are of the opinion that the plaintiff has recovered from her injuries. In those cases where the plaintiff has been treated by a series of doctors and not cooperated with the recommended treatments, the defense lawyer should consider calling those physicians to establish that pattern, which is consistent with the malingering plaintiff. Where the plaintiff sees multiple physicians in order to obtain multiple prescriptions, that testimony will establish one of the secondary gains that support the plaintiff's pain behavior.

The defense lawyer uses the retained expert to refute or reduce pain and suffering damages. Depending on the type of injuries alleged, the experts retained might include a neuropsychologist, orthopaedist, and psychiatrist.

The neuropsychologist is typically used in alleged brain injury cases. The neuropsychologist oversees the administration of a group of tests used to assess short and long-term memory loss, intellectual capacity, and other areas of cognition. The evaluation of a patient by a neuropsychologist may provide objective data to establish that a claimant is malingering or exaggerating deficits.

The orthopaedic surgeon, either a treater or a retained expert, can evaluate the claimant's injury and symptoms, administer tests, and provide testimony as to whether the symptoms and complaints are consistent with the objective findings.[33] There are a number of other clinical examination tests that can aid in determining if pain is anatomically caused, psychogenic, or feigned.[34]

Psychiatric testimony can point out discrepancies between the signs and symptoms of accepted depressive conditions or posttraumatic stress disorder and the signs and symptoms related or exhibited by a claimant. To the extent the claimant's symptoms are inconsistent with what is normally found, that can be evidence of malingering or exaggeration.

Tip

The most determined and skillful malingerers will have done their homework and may be able to deceive the psychiatrist.

C. Investigation and discovery

The defense damages case is won or lost in the discovery stage. It is here that the defense can discover and assemble the evidence that will either help to reduce the award or expose the plaintiff's case as fraudulent. This investigation must go beyond the routine filing of interrogatories and rote deposition practice. The defense lawyer, with the aid of paralegals, legal nurse consultants, investigators, and the medical expert, works to unearth evidence inconsistent with the claimant's pain case. The following are areas of investigation which may assist in defending against the plaintiff's pain case and support the defendant's case. Particular attention should be directed to any information which can call into question the credibility of the plaintiff or witnesses who will be called to testify at trial for the plaintiff. Since the pain and suffering element of damages is overwhelmingly subjective, the more issues the jury has with the credibility of the plaintiff's case, the less likely the jury will be to believe any aspect of the plaintiff's case, on both liability and damages.

Tip

A successful challenge to the pain and suffering element of the case may assist in obtaining a defense verdict on liability or a reduced damage award.

1. Biomechanics of the accident

Consider a biomechanical expert when the forces associated with the alleged occurrence do not seem capable of causing the alleged injury. An understanding of the accident mechanics is essential to determining if there is a correlation between the accident and the plaintiff's claimed injury. This is especially true in those cases where the injuries do not result in any objectively verifiable diagnosis. In the classic soft tissue injury case, reviewing the police report, witness statements, photographs of the vehicles involved in an automobile accident, the ambulance records and paramedic records are all essential steps in preparing a defense. The depositions of all individuals who observed or interviewed the claimant in the hours after the accident are also important. Accident reconstruction experts may be necessary in order to establish that the accident mechanics could not have produced the necessary forces to result in the claimed injury. For more information see Klepatsky.[35]

2. Medical records

The medical records provide information that will either support the plaintiff's claims of injury and resultant pain or provide the evidentiary basis to prove exaggeration or fabrication. Nurses' notes and physical therapy records typically are more detailed than other parts of the medical records and should be examined closely. The nursing admission assessments will contain a detailed history of the plaintiff's condition, often in the plaintiff's own words as provided to the nurse. Patients often tell their healthcare providers information that they may not reveal to their attorneys. Information about prior injuries or surgeries may be located in the nursing admission assessment. The nurse's daily notes also will usually contain information not only as to the observations of the plaintiff by the nurse but also the plaintiff's statements to the nurse. The defense should obtain medical records as far back as possible. Keep in mind that the fact the plaintiff never injured the part of the body at issue or never complained of similar pain is not detrimental to the case. The medical records may contain information as to other diseases, physical or mental, which may be the cause of the current pain complaints. Prior medical records may also detail drug seeking behaviors, as evidenced by frequent visits to the emergency department or to a variety of providers in order to obtain narcotics for pain. The drug seeking plaintiff tends to visit several physicians at the same time and does not tell each physician that others are also ordering drugs for him. Drug seeking patients may claim that they lost their prescriptions. Pharmacy records should be obtained to determine if the plaintiff was obtaining prescriptions from several providers and to look for a pattern of frequent refills of narcotics. Keep in mind that the plaintiff with severe pain may not be drug seeking but may legitimately need frequent refills of pain relievers. See Iyer[36] for more information on analysis of medical records of suspected malingerers.

Physical therapy records are particularly useful. Physical therapy is usually started after the plaintiff has recovered from the acute phase of the injury. The initial assessment of the plaintiff's condition at the start of therapy is detailed, as are the notes, including statements of the plaintiff to the therapist about the plaintiff's condition. The therapist will note whether or not the patient is compliant and whether the objectives of therapy have been achieved, including the reduction or elimination of pain symptoms. The therapist may also enter comments about the amount of effort the plaintiff is exerting during treatment. Occasionally comments will indicate doubt about the validity of the plaintiff's injuries, such as "When she does not realize she is being observed, she moves with ease." Look for statements indicating that the plaintiff was injured by performing activities that are inconsistent with the claimed limitations. For example, the physical therapy records may state that the plaintiff was injured while water skiing over the weekend. This would be particularly pertinent when the plaintiff requires a walker to come for therapy!

Look for noncompliance in the medical records. Determine if the plaintiff kept appointment with the physician and physical therapist or was a no show (NS) or did not keep appointment (DNKA). If the treater has prescribed a course of medication, or physical therapy for the plaintiff or given the plaintiff instructions on lifestyle changes, the records may also include information on whether the plaintiff has complied with the recommended therapies and treatment. The failure of the plaintiff to comply will be a factor that can assist in reducing the plaintiff's recovery for pain and suffering damages. It may be indicative of the lack of serious pain, or the jurors may interpret the noncompliance as an element that will cause them to limit the award.

Tip

Entries that the plaintiff is ready to return to work are useful, particularly when they describe the level of the patient's function and reduction or elimination of pain symptoms. Note when the patient achieves maximal medical improvement, and if this designation stimulates seeking care from a new round of physicians.

Prior medical records will establish whether the plaintiff has suffered in the past from symptoms similar to what the plaintiff claims in the present lawsuit. The plaintiff's attorney may argue that the defendant is still responsible for an aggravation of a previous injury or condition, which may be the case. However, the plaintiff may have denied any previous pain or limitations in her deposition or to an examining doctor, and those admissions, coupled with the medical history prior to the accident, will affect the plaintiff's credibility and the jury's willingness to award significant damages.

3. Employment records

Employment records may contain examinations by company physicians, which may indicate similar complaints of pain prior to the accident or absence of complaints of pain following the accident. These records may also reveal that the plaintiff was involved in other work accidents before or after the one being litigated. In some cases, the other accidents caused most of all of the injury now being disputed in the current litigation.

If the plaintiff's work activities are inconsistent with his claimed limitations due to pain, introduction of this evidence will damage the credibility of the pain and suffering claims. The attorney should obtain the complete employment records, including the personnel file that contains performance evaluations, disciplinary reports, and reports concerning disability claims. Ask for all personnel records including workers' compensation claims filed by the plaintiff. If the claimant is a union member, there may be a separate file that can be obtained from the union that will include information on job assignments.

4. Interrogatories

The defense attorney should aggressively obtain complete disclosure from the plaintiff through interrogatories of all prior and subsequent treatment, residences, spouses, employers, prior and subsequent injuries, schools attended, and the names of anyone who may have information concerning the plaintiff's alleged pain and suffering element of damages. This would include everyone who knows the plaintiff and has had an opportunity to observe the plaintiff go about his daily activities.

5. Depositions

Only after the medical, employment, educational and other public records have been reviewed should the defense lawyer commence the deposition of the plaintiff. The portion of the deposition that focuses on pain and suffering elements of damages must be as thorough and as well prepared as the parts of the deposition covering liability and other damage elements. The questions the attorney will ask at a deposition are similar to questions that would be included in a thorough medical history.

Tip

The defense attorney must get the plaintiff to commit to as many specifics of the pain as possible. The more specific the questions and answers, the more inconsistencies will be discovered in the plaintiff's pain case. Malingerers and partial exaggerators will testify as to symptomatology unrelated to their injuries.

Consider videotaping all key witnesses at their depositions. These depositions can then be shown to focus groups or mock jurors to gauge the potential reaction to the damages testimony and assist the defense attorney in developing strategies to refute the pain and suffering damages case.

Questions from the checklist shown in Figure 21.2 can be used for the deposition examination of the plaintiff and can also be adapted for the depositions of other damages witnesses, including family members and physicians.

6. Witnesses

The plaintiff's attorney will call witnesses to establish the plaintiff's right to an award for pain and suffering damages. Many attorneys believe that it is more effective to establish the plaintiff's justification for pain and suffering damages through the testimony of family members, coworkers, neighbors, and medical providers. Note this comment by David Ball, a psychologist: "Do not use your client as a main source of testimony about his harms or you will turn him into a whiner. Jurors do not give much money to whiners. It is better to have your client talk about how he deals with and tries to overcome the problems everyone else has described."[37] The plaintiff can adopt a more reasonable position on the witness stand and not appear to be overreaching or whining. It is a serious mistake for a defense lawyer not to be prepared for this approach. Ideally the defense lawyer will have deposed all the damages witnesses and have committed them to their testimony before the trial.

The plaintiff's attorney will submit her case for pain and suffering damages through the testimony of the plaintiff, family members, coworkers, friends, treaters, and medical experts. Deposition testimony of all potential witnesses is essential to set limits on what the individuals can testify to at trial (at least without the risk of impeachment and attacks on credibility). The deposition testimony of these pain and suffering witnesses is also essential to set the stage for settlement negotiations. Admissions elicited from the plaintiff in her deposition and the favorable testimony from the other witnesses may assist in achieving a reasonable resolution of the matter.

Depositions of family members, coworkers, and neighbors must be as detailed on the pain and suffering element of damages as the deposition of the plaintiff. The plaintiff's attorney will put in his pain and suffering damages case through the testimony of these witnesses. Consider taking depositions of the following individuals: family members, coworkers, friends, former girlfriend, boyfriends, spouses and ex in-laws.

a. Family members. Family members are in the best position to observe and report on the claimant's pain status. The depositions should be detailed and the testimony should be as specific as possible as to what they observed, including limitations on activities, complaints of pain by the claimant, and mood changes. Family members sometimes take offense at a relative's attempts to feign injury or symptoms for financial gain and are willing to testify against them.

b. Coworkers. Coworkers should be asked to describe what they observed about the work activities of the plaintiff. They may have pertinent observations about the limitations or lack thereof of the injured worker. Additional responsibilities may be given to the coworkers as a result of the feigned limitations of the claimant, setting the scene for resentment. Coworkers who believe that the plaintiff may be malingering or exaggerating limitations may be outraged by this behavior, because it conflicts with their ethical beliefs or loyalty to the company.

c. Neighbors. Neighbors can report on activities taken outside and around the home. They may observe the claimant doing yard work and other household tasks, contradicting the plaintiff's claims.

d. Former girlfriends, boyfriend, spouses, and in-laws. Just as an ex-spouse turns in the philanderer to the IRS, ex-spouses, girlfriends, and boyfriends should not be overlooked as a potential source of information to reduce the plaintiff's damage claims. In many in-

- What is the location of the pain?
- When did the pain start?
- When did the pain stop?
- What affects the pain?
- What makes the pain worse?
- What affords relief?
- What aggravates the pain?
- What treatment was given?
- What time of day is the pain at its worst?
- In what position is the pain at its worst?
- What is the response to each treatment?
- What is the character of the pain?
- What does your pain feel like?
- Is the pain:
  - sharp
  - cutting
  - hot
  - burning
  - tingling
  - throbbing
  - nauseating?[37]
- How constant or continuous is the pain?
- How do you rate your pain on a scale of . . . ?
- What medicine do you take for your pain?
- When do you take your pain medication?
- Does the pain medication relieve your pain and how much relief?
- When was the last time you took pain medication and what did you take? Why?
- Were there episodes of pain predating the accident and when did they resolve?
- Were there previous injuries to the same part of the body?
- Were there previous serious injuries?
- Did you tell medical treaters about your pain?
- What did you tell nurses about your pain?
- What did you tell your spouse, or family members about your pain?
- Have you told your co-workers about your pain?
- Does pain affect your sleep?
- Does pain affect your appetite?
- Have you lost weight?
- Have you gained weight?
- How has the pain affected your marriage or relations with family members?
- What kind of pain threshold do you have?
- Have you experienced pain like this before?
- Is this the worst pain you ever experienced?
- What have you changed because of the pain? How?
- Do you exercise?
- What types of exercises do you do?
- When was your last vacation?
- Where did you go and with whom did you travel?
- What did you do on your vacation?
- What housework do you do?
- Do you keep a diary?
- Did you keep a diary before the accident?
- Were you asked to keep a pain diary? By whom?
- Do you keep a journal on your home or work computer?
- Do you have a computer at home and do you use it for e-mail?
- Did you e-mail you doctor about your condition?
- Did you send e-mails to your family members or
- friends about your condition?
- Did you follow all your physician's instructions?
- Did you follow all of your physical therapist's instructions?
- What was your response to the physical therapy?
- Was any of the physical therapy painful?
- Did you receive instruction sheets from your physician, nurse, or physical therapist?
- What did you tell your doctor about your pain?
- When was your last visit to your doctor?
- What did you tell the doctor, nurse, or physical therapist about your pain at your last visit?

Figure 21.2 *Deposition questions on pain and suffering elements of damages*

stances they will have gone on vacations with their ex-spouses and they may have photographs or videotapes of the plaintiff engaging in activities inconsistent with limitations the plaintiff is now claiming. This person may enthusiastically turn in the former relation.

7. Other lawsuits, workers' compensation claims, and nonlitigated claims

Multiple claims are another indicator of possible malingering or partial malingering. The discovery records obtained in other lawsuits often lead to medical treatment that the plaintiff has not disclosed in this case.

8. Criminal record

A past criminal record is an indicator that raises the suspicion level for malingering or exaggeration. In certain cases, prior convictions may be admissible to call into question the credibility of the plaintiff.

9. Surveillance

Surveillance tapes, if done in public and not an invasion of the plaintiff's privacy expectations (within the home), can be an effective response to day-in-the-life films. The defense should use only reputable surveillance firms that understand the privacy laws and limitations. The defense should use the tapes only when the tapes clearly show that either the plaintiff's testimony or the plaintiff's day-in-the-life production misrepresents the plaintiff's limitations and activities. For more information on surveillance tapes, see Chapter 19, "Trial Exhibits, Preparation and Use."

10. Vacation travel—hobbies

Vacation travel by the plaintiff is often inconsistent with the claimed pain, suffering, and limitations on physical activities. Hobbies, such as gardening, wood working, golf, fishing, and other activities that require concentration and dexterity can be used to raise questions about claimed pain and suffering.

11. Credit cards

Credit card records provide information not only about medical treatment, but about possible vacation travel, household projects, and recreational activities.

12. Income tax returns

The plaintiff's income tax returns are usually obtained to verify lost income claims. However, the records may also contain information on the occupations of the claimant and spouse for a joint return. The plaintiff's statements as to his occupation may be inconsistent with limitations claimed in the litigation and may lead to other avenues for obtaining information that can be used to attack the plaintiff's credibility.

13. Notice to produce other documents

The notice to produce documents should include a request for

- all photographs of the plaintiff,
- videotapes of the plaintiff (including vacations),
- pain diaries,
- journals,
- letters to family, friends, employers, and physicians concerning the condition of the plaintiff and copies of all e-mail records,
- a complete copy of the plaintiff's computer hard drive,
- copies of phone records,
- day-in-the-life videos (including all video recorded, not just the edited version),
- income tax returns,
- credit card receipts, and
- copies of cancelled checks and bank account records.

Any documents that will help the defense lawyer investigate the activities of the plaintiff both before and after the accident should be obtained to the extent allowed in the jurisdiction.

Much of the information that can be obtained through income tax records, credit card records, and employment records may not be directly related to the issue of pain and suffering but may lead to the discovery of material that directly affects the claim for pain and suffering damages.

D. Experts

1. Medical

Prior to taking the deposition of the plaintiff's treating physicians and medical experts, the defense lawyer should determine what records have been provided to the doctors for review. The medical experts, especially treaters, are often unaware of other medical treatment received by their patients.

The treating physicians and the other medical experts should be thoroughly examined on the extent to which the patient's complaints are correlated to specific objective test results. The physicians should be asked for their opinions as to what extent the plaintiff's overall ability to function has been compromised, if at all. Most doctors (with the exception of medical providers who continually treat and overtreat, meaning that they derive a significant portion of their income from multiple return visits) will volunteer that their treatment has been concluded with at least some degree of improvement. Surgeons will generally testify that the surgical procedures were successful and accomplished the desired result from a technical and objective perspective.

2. Life expectancy experts

Damages for future pain and suffering may be awarded based on the plaintiff's life expectancy as introduced into evidence by the plaintiff. The plaintiff may have chronic conditions that will result in a reduced life expectancy. The standard life expectancy tables do not take into account an individual plaintiff, since they represent the average life expectancy for very large groups. A sixty-year-old woman with brittle diabetes, chronic obstructive pulmonary disease, chronic congestive heart failure, and morbid obesity, will have, according to the life expectancy tables, the same life expectancy as a sixty-year-old woman with no chronic or acute diseases, who eats correctly and exercises every day.

Tip

While one can certainly hope that jurors, exercising their good common sense, will take the plaintiff's poor physical condition and chronic diseases into account when determining an award for future damages, it is far more effective to call an expert to testify on life expectancy of individuals with medical conditions that reduce the individual's life expectancy.

---

3. Biomechanical expert testimony

In many cases, particularly automobile collision cases, the defense will claim that the forces of the impact could not have caused the plaintiff's alleged injuries. Biomechanical engineers can provide a scientific basis to introduce testimony questioning the existence of the injuries and the credibility of the plaintiff.

E. Settlement negotiations

Most cases are settled. The plaintiff does less well on medical malpractice cases that go to trial. From 1994 to 2000, the plaintiff's probability of recovery through a verdict was 34%.[38] In those cases where there are severe injuries and the risk of large damage awards, early mediation or other types of alternative dispute resolution should be considered.

F. Using mediators to address unreasonable expectations for pain and suffering damage awards

In those cases where there is little dispute on the liability issues, the plaintiff, or the plaintiff and her attorney, may have unreasonable expectations about the value of the case. Assuming that the defense has been aggressively preparing its damages case, an experienced mediator, agreeable to both sides, can assist in resolving the claim. In some cases this may be the best way to control the risk of the subjective nature of the award for pain and suffering and other intangible damages.

G. Mock trials and mock jurors

The defense lawyer can test approaches to both the liability elements of a case and the damages elements of a case before a mock jury. The lawyer can then discuss the arguments with the jurors and decide which arguments will be most effective in addressing pain and suffering elements and which arguments should be avoided. The lawyer can do this on an informal basis with associates, coworkers, family members and friends. A trial consulting company can handle the arrangements which can include selecting mock jurors representative of the venire the attorney will encounter in court and then videotaping the mock jurors' deliberations as they discuss the lawyer's approach to the damage issues and their reaction to the lawyer and her arguments.

21.7 Damages for Pain and Suffering

The plaintiff experiences the damages, and it is usually the plaintiff's testimony and testimony about observations of the plaintiff by others that the plaintiff uses to prove this element of damages. (In wrongful death cases there can be a presumption, depending on the circumstances of the case, that the plaintiff experienced pain and suffering during a period of consciousness before death. See Chapter 20, "Ante-Mortem Damages," for more information.) Prior to the commencement of the trial, the defense lawyer will have built the case for the direct (where possible) and collateral attacks on the pain and suffering elements of the case.

A. Pretrial checklist

1. *Daubert* and similar issues

The defense lawyer should anticipate *Daubert* or *Frye* type challenges to the testimony of her experts, especially when the expert testimony is of the type not usually seen by the plaintiff or the trial judge.

The defendant should expect these challenges for biomechanical experts, life expectancy experts, and some types of medical testimony when the subject of the medical testimony will involve psychological or other testing methods designed to identify malingerers or greatly exaggerated injury claims.[39]

2. Defense theory on damages

The defense attorney will have a unifying theory of his case on the liability issues. The defense attorney should also develop a theory or theories on the damages issues in the case. This theory may not be a part of the opening statement, but it will certainly be a part of the examination of all the witnesses whose testimony will bear on the damages aspects of the case, the jury instructions, and the closing arguments.

3. Identification of damages issues

Each damage issue should be identified with a well conceived plan on how it will be addressed at trial. Pain and suffering issues can be difficult to address due to their subjective nature. If the testimony of the plaintiff's witnesses does not support a claim for the award of future pain and suffering damages, the defense attorney should be prepared to address that aspect. If there are caps or limitations on noneconomic damages, which include pain and suffering, the appropriate jury instructions or motions for reduction of damages should be prepared in advance.

4. Economic damages experts, annuitists, and life expectancy experts

Strictly speaking, the economist experts or the annuitists will not testify on pain and suffering damage issues. However, their testimony is important as they will address life expectancies and present cash value, and these factors will influence the jury's award for each element of damages, including the award for the intangible damages for pain and suffering.

B. Jury selection

1. Deselecting jurors sympathetic to plaintiff's damages arguments

The defense lawyer will not be able to have all the jurors fit the ideal juror profile. While the ideal profile can be a guide, a realistic goal is to deselect jurors who are particularly averse to the defense case. There are possible jurors that experience has shown may be more sympathetic to plaintiff's damages arguments and should be deselected if possible.

Tip

The facts of each case should be considered and if possible the plaintiff's testimony, claimed medical condition, and appearance should be tested with associates, friends, and family members to gauge their reaction to the plaintiff's pain and suffering claims. A simple and effective method of doing this is to videotape the deposition of the plaintiff. The videotape can then be shown to others, including professionally organized mock juries or focus groups, to aid in the preparation of the defense case and damage arguments.

People who may be good plaintiff's damages jurors include

- teachers,
- jurors or family members of jurors with serious injuries or chronic pain issues,
- chronic pain sufferers,

- migraine headache sufferers, and
- baby boomers.

In those cases where there could be a significant damage award, including damages for pain and suffering, the defense team should consider using a jury consultant. The jury consultant can assist in building a profile of a juror who would be the least sympathetic to the plaintiff's damages arguments. Again, depending on the potential damage award, the jury consultant can participate in court with the jury selection process.

2. Attorney credibility and jury selection

The attorney's credibility with the jurors is essential to a successful damages argument. If permitted in the jurisdiction, the defense lawyer should use the jury selection process to establish a connection with the jurors. If the lawyer does not sense that an individual juror is a person the lawyer can relate to and connect with, the feeling may be mutual and will make it more difficult for the attorney to argue his case successfully with that juror.

3. Desensitizing the jurors in severe injury cases

In cases where there are severe injuries and the plaintiff intends to display those injuries graphically to the jury by means of photographs or a day-in-the-life video, it may be advisable to request that the prospective jurors have an opportunity to view the potentially inflammatory materials before voir dire. After the prospective jurors see the day-in-the-life video or the other emotionally charged material, there may be jurors who will deselect themselves on the basis that they could not be fair to the parties in deciding the case.

Tip

The more the jurors see the material, the less emotionally charged the material will become, and the jurors will be better equipped to deliberate in a more objective fashion (as the emotional aspect of viewing material of this type will never be completely eliminated).

Require the plaintiff to be in court for jury selection. In cases where the plaintiff has either deforming or severe injuries resulting in a substantial handicap, the plaintiff's attorney may not have the plaintiff appear in the courtroom until after the jury has been empanelled. The plaintiff will then appear at some later time in the plaintiff's case, with great emotional impact. In order to minimize this potential, and again to ensure that the jurors selected have an opportunity to pass on the damages issues with a reasonable degree of objectivity, the defense lawyer should present a motion to the court requiring the plaintiff to be in court for jury selection. If it is not possible to do this for the entire jury selection process, each panel of prospective jurors should have the opportunity to see the plaintiff in the courtroom before the jury selection process.

C. Opening statements

In most cases, the defense attorney may choose to avoid discussing damages at all in the opening statement. This is particularly true when the attorney has a strong liability case. In this circumstance, it is probably best to focus the jury strongly on the liability issues and how the evidence in the case will clearly demonstrate that the plaintiff is not entitled to any recovery.

In cases where the defendant will charge that the plaintiff is a malingerer, the defendant will have the burden of proving that proposition and should address the factual basis for the claim in the opening statement—providing that the attorney is confident that the case is strong and the evidence will be admitted.

In cases where the defendant is essentially trying the case on damages, or the damages may be so significant that a large part of the defense case will include the presentation of evidence on damages, the damage and pain and suffering issues must be addressed in the opening statement.

As with all opening statements, the attorney should not tell the jurors about any testimony or other evidence if there is a doubt concerning admissibility. In those instances the attorney should request the court to rule on admissibility before opening statements. The failure to produce evidence discussed in the opening statement will be extremely damaging to the defendant's case, and the defense lawyer's credibility and will not be overlooked by the plaintiff's attorney in her closing argument.

D. Evidence

The defense's response to the plaintiff's pain and suffering damages case will consist of the cross-examination of the plaintiff's damages witnesses and the testimony of those witnesses called by the defense in their case. Typically, the defense attorney will call his own medical witnesses. In addition, the defense may call other acquaintances of the plaintiff who will testify they have not observed the limitations claimed by the plaintiff or that the plaintiff had not complained of pain.

E. Closing arguments

There are very few, if any, cases where the defense counsel should not argue damages. Occasionally a commentator will urge that arguing damage is an implicit admission of liability. Most jurors will understand once it is explained to them that an attorney should address the key issues of the other side's case. In fact, jurors expect the lawyer to address key issues, and a credible, well organized, and persuasive argument on damages supported by the evidence will enhance the defendant attorney's credibility with the jurors on the liability issues as well as the damage issues. The jurors cannot be left to speculate what an appropriate award for pain and suffering will be. Remember, we have taken the perspective that defendants have the burden of proof to establish a reasonable damage award, not only on the easily quantifiable elements—medical bills and wage loss—but also on the subjective elements of pain, suffering, and loss of a normal life.

Tip

Most experienced defense lawyers will argue damages and strongly believe that not to do so verges on malpractice.[40]

---

1. Arguing damages

The argument on damages for pain and suffering must be tailored to the evidence. In cases where the objectively demonstrable physical organic injury is severe and limiting, defense counsel may be confined to suggesting to the jury a reasonable dollar amount for the damage elements. The amount suggested must be credible and supported by references to the relevant evidence and the good common sense of the jurors. In serious injury cases, the subject must be approached with compassion and sensitivity to the injured plaintiff and the family.

Tip

Rest assured that the jurors will expect the defense to give them guidance. They have already heard what the plaintiff's attorney has suggested (if permitted to do so in the jurisdiction) is a reasonable and fair dollar amount for the pain and suffering the plaintiff experienced and will expect the defense lawyer to respond.

In those cases where questions have been raised concerning the extent of the plaintiff's injuries and recovery, the argument should be detailed with references to the evidence adduced at trial, including the significant portions of the testimony of the medical experts, medical records, the testimony of independent witnesses, and the plaintiff's own testimony. The more of the plaintiff's testimony that can be woven into the defense attorney's closing argument and the testimony of the plaintiff's treating physicians and retained expert medical witnesses, the more inroads can be made into the plaintiff's damage arguments. The basis of the defense attorney's closing argument will have been created long before the start of the trial during discovery, particularly the depositions of the plaintiff, medical treaters, and witnesses, and from the reports of the defense medical experts.

2. Guiding the jury on plaintiff's request for subjective pain and suffering awards and intangible damages

This part of the closing argument is the most difficult and requires the most preparation. It is difficult because it is intangible and subjective. The challenge for the defense lawyer is to take the intangible and make it concrete. This is done by analogies and comparison. The plaintiff's complaints of pain are related to the everyday challenges the common person faces. The plaintiff's complaints of back pain are neutralized by comparison to the occasional and sometimes chronic back pain many of us experience, caused not by trauma, but by life—aging, childbirth, gardening, or sports. Even if these conditions in the plaintiff were arguably caused by an act of the defendant, the rest of us who experience these conditions as a result of nature's gifts deal with them and go on with our lives. The lawyer should consult the many excellent collections of closing arguments and study the arguments of defense attorneys who have successfully challenged the pain and suffering parts of plaintiffs' cases.

3. Arguments about the malingering plaintiff

When the defense lawyer sums up her case on damages and the assertion is that the plaintiff is a malingerer, the defense lawyer is arguing that the plaintiff is a liar, a cheat, and a fraud. The defense lawyer is putting her credibility on the line, and the evidence that has been introduced into the case must clearly support this argument. There is no subtlety in this argument. The case should be made objectively, with detailed references to the proofs. The attorney should point out the inconsistencies between the plaintiff's self-imposed limitations and his actual activities. Perhaps the treater, while unwilling to admit that the patient is a malingerer, concedes that there is little if any objective correlation between the complaints and the medical and psychological testing. If the defense attorney is fortunate enough to have a smoking gun surveillance video, a portion of it should be played during the defense closing argument.

Tip

All the defense lawyer's arguments should be directed to the common sense of the jurors and be supported by the evidence.

F. Jury instructions and closing arguments

The jury instructions given on the pain and suffering element of damages will vary according to jurisdiction. Typically, the jury will be instructed that they must "fix the amount of money which will reasonably and fairly compensate the plaintiff for any of the following elements of damages proved by the evidence to have resulted from the negligence of the defendant, taking into consideration the nature, extent and duration of the injury."[41] The specific elements of damage that can have an effect on an award for pain and suffering may include

- the aggravation of any pre-existing ailment or condition,[42]
- the disfigurement resulting from the injury,
- the pain and suffering experienced and reasonably certain to be experienced in the future as a result of the injuries,[43] and
- the emotional distress experienced (and reasonably certain to be experienced in the future).[44]

While only one of these instructions specifically describes pain and suffering as an element of damages, other elements on which the jury is instructed could add or detract from a pain and suffering award. The fact that there is an aggravation of a pre-existing injury, while usually legally compensable, may raise an issue in the juror's minds as to the causal relationship between the accident and continued complaints of pain.

Tip

If the plaintiff has not met her burden of introducing evidence that there will be future pain and suffering, the defendant should tender instructions omitting any reference to future pain and suffering damages.

One of the most powerful ways to reduce pain and suffering awards is in the general instructions which give the jurors the general principles that guide their deliberations:

- "Your verdict must not be based on speculation, prejudice or sympathy."
- "You may use common sense gained from your experiences in life in evaluating what you see and hear during trial."
- "You are the only judges of the credibility of the witnesses . . . In evaluating the credibility of a witness you may consider that witness' ability and opportunity to observe, memory, manner, interest, bias, qualifications, experience, and any previous inconsistent statement or act by the witness concerning an issue important to the case."[45]

The attorney should weave these general instructions into her argument on damages, just as she would on the liability issues in her closing. The lawyer should note the emphasis in the instructions that the damages should be reasonable and fair and give the jurors a reasonable and fair figure for the pain and suffering element, along with the evidentiary and common sense explanation for the lawyer's suggestion.

In the appropriate case where the plaintiff has not followed medical instructions, not completed medical treatment, or has been non-compliant with physical therapy, and where the defense experts have testified that reasonable non-invasive therapies were available, an instruction similar to the following should be given: "Whether any of these elements of damage have been proven is up for you to decide. In fixing the amount of money which will reasonably and fairly compensate the plaintiff, you are to consider that an injured person must exercise ordinary care to obtain medical treatment. Damages proximately caused by a failure to exercise such care cannot be recovered."[46]

21.8 Conclusion

The pain and suffering element of damages cannot be overlooked in the litigation of a personal injury lawsuit. Since damages for this element are subjective and impossible to quantify, the defense is at great risk of a significant damage award on this element alone if it is overlooked until shortly before trial. The lawyer's pretrial checklist should include a workup of this element, just as liability issues and economic issues are addressed. An early comprehensive review of the medical records by an experienced legal nurse consultant is an excellent starting point, along with review of the many other records available to the defense that may suggest areas of further investigation and alert the defense attorney to a possible malingering or substantial exaggeration of pain and suffering damage claims. The credibility of the plaintiff and the defense lawyer will be evaluated, and the defense lawyer must have presented credible evidence to raise a doubt in the jurors' minds as to the extent of the pain and suffering experienced. Even though subjective, the defense lawyer can use a combination of the expert's testimony, the testimony of the witnesses, including the plaintiff, and the good common sense of the jurors to defeat fraudulent claims and guide the jurors to reaching verdicts that provide appropriate, not excessive, awards for claimants who are entitled to recovery.

Endnotes

1. Friedland, S.I, "Law, Science and Malingering." *30 Ariz. St. L.J.* 337,1998.

2. 1 Samuel 21: 12, 13 and 14; *King James Bible*, Moody Bible Institute, 1978.

3. Redlich, R.C., Rovitz, L.J., and Dession, G.H., "Narcoanalysis and the Truth." *American Journal of Psychiatry*, 107: 586–593, 1951.

4. Maier, N.R., and Thurber, J.A., "Accuracy of Judgments of Deception When an Interview Is Watched, Heard, and Read." *Personnel Psychology*, 21:23–30, 1968.

5. Ekman, P., and O'Sullivan, M., "Who Can Catch a Liar." *American Psychologist*, 46: 913–920, 1991.

6. *Black's Law Dictionary*, Fifth Edition. St. Paul, MN: West Publishing Company, 1993.

7. American Psychiatric Association, *Diagnostic and Statistical Manual of Mental Disorders*, Fourth Edition. Washington, DC: American Psychiatric Association, 1994, p. 309.

8. Ferrari, R., Kwan, O. and Friel, J., "Illness Behavior and Adoption of the Sick Role in Whiplash Claimants." *BC Medical Journal*, 44 (5) June 2000.

9. Resnick, P., "The Detection of Malingered Mental Illness." In Resnick, P., *Clinical Assessment of Malingering and Deception*. Cleveland: Walter Library Pub., 1988.

10. Resnick, P., "Malingering of Post-Traumatic Disorders." In Resnick, P., *Clinical Assessment of Malingering and Deception*. Cleveland: Walter Library Pub., 1988.

11. Schretlen, D., "The Use of Psychological Tests to Identify Malingered Symptoms of Mental Disorder." *Clinical Psychology Review*, Vol. 8, pp. 451–476, 1988.

12. Graham, J.R., *MMPI-2: Assessing Personality and Psychopathology.* New York: Oxford University Press, 1990.

13. Anderson, E.W., Trethowan, W.H., and Kenna, J.C., "An Experimental Investigation of Simulation and Pseudo-

dementia." *Acta Psychiatrica et Neurologica Scandinavica*, Vol 34, Supplement 132 (whole issue), 1986.

14. Goodwin, D.W., and Rosenthal, R., "Clinical Significance of Hallucinations in Psychiatric Disorders: A Study of 116 Hallucinatory Patients." *Archives of General Psychiatry* 24:76–80, 1971.

15. Resnick, P., "Malingered psychosis." In *Clinical Assessment of Malingering and Deception.* New York: Guilford Press, 1988.

16. Wettstein, R., "Malingering and Deception: An Update." *Behavioral Sciences and the Law,* Vol. 8 No. 1 (whole issue), 1990.

17. Ziskin, J., and Faust, D., *Coping with Psychiatric and Psychological Testimony*, Fourth Edition, Vol. I, II and III. Marina Del Ray, CA: Law and Psychology Press, 1988.

18. Hunt, W.A. and Older, H.J., "Detection of Malingering through Psychometric Tests." *Naval Medical Bulletin*, 41:1318–1323, 1943.

19. Goldstein, H., "A Malingering Key for Mental Tests." *Psychological Bulletin*, 42:215–255, 1945.

20. Heaton, R.K., Smith, H.H., Lehman, R.A., and Vogt, A.T., "Prospects for Faking Believable Deficits on Neuropsychological Testing." *Journal of Consulting and Clinical Psychology*, 46: 892–900, 1978.

21. Goebel, R.A., "Detection of Faking on the Halstead-Reitan Neuropsychological Test Battery." *Journal of Clinical Psychology*, 39: 731–741, 1983.

22. Cavanaugh, J., editor, *Behavioral Sciences and The Law, Malingering and Deception.* New York: Van Nostrand Reinhold Publishing Company, 1983.

23. Sherman, M., Trief, P. and Sprafkin, Q.R., "Impression Management in the Psychiatric Interview: Quality, Style and Individual Differences." *Journal of Consulting and Clinical Psychology*, 43: 867–871, 1975.

24. MacDonald, J., "The Simulation of Mental Disease." *Psychiatry and the Criminal.* Springfield, IL: C. Thomas Company, 1976.

25. Davidson, H.A., *Forensic Psychiatry*, Second Edition. New York: The Ronald Press, 1965.

26. Ossipov, V.P., "Malingering: The Simulation of Psychosis." *Bulletin of the Menninger Clinic*, 8: 31–42, 1944.

27. Jones, A.B., and Llewellyn, *Malingering*. London: Helnmann, 1917.

28. Ekman, P., and O'Sullivan, M., "Who Can Catch a Liar." *American Psychologist*, 46: 913–920, 1991.

29. Maier, N.R., and Thurber, J.A., "Accuracy of Judgments of Deception When an Interview Is Watched, Heard, and Read." *Personnel Psychology*, 21:23–30, 1968.

30. Bender, M., Minzer, M., Nates, J.H., Kimball, C.D., Axelrod, D.T., Goldstein, R.P., and Conason, R.L., *Damages in Tort Actions.* New York, 1985.

31. See Illinois Pattern Jury Instructions, Civil, 33.01 and comments.

32. *Hall v. Dumitru*, 250 Ill.App.3d 759, 620 N.E.2d 669, 189 Ill. Dec. 700, 1993.

33. Miller, T.R., *Evaluating Orthopedic Disability, A Commonsense Approach,* Second Edition. Oradell, NJ: Medical Economics Books, 1987.

34. Frost, "Diagnosing Musculoskeletal Disability of Psychogenic Origin in Orthopedic Practice." 82 *Clinical Orthopedics and Related Research,* 108-22, 1972.

35. Klepatsky, A., "Common Mechanisms of Injury in Personal Injury Cases." In Iyer, P., editor, *Principles and Practices of Legal Nurse Consulting,* Second Edition. Boca Raton: CRC Press, 2003.

36. Iyer, P., "The Malingering Plaintiff." *Journal of Legal Nurse Consulting*, January 2000.

37. Ball, D., *David Ball on Damages: A Plaintiff Attorney's Guide for Personal Iinjury and Wrongful Death Cases.* Notre Dame, IN: National Institute for Trial Advocacy, 2001.

38. Shannon, J., and Boxold, D., *Medical Malpractice: Verdicts, Settlements and Statistical Analysis.* Horsham, PA: LRP Publications, 2002.

39. Baute, P., "Expert Witnessing and *Daubert*: Is Your Expert Witness Prepared for a *Daubert/Kumho* Challenge?" *The Forensic Examiner,* http://www.acfe.com/02.23.02/forensic_examiner-articles.php?PHPSESSID=481673ea85844ce243f4b4cc4d3eb356.

40. Montgomery, C., "Keeping Damages Fair and Reasonable." In Warsaw, J., editor, *Masters of Trial Practice.* New York: John Wiley & Sons, 1988.

41. Illinois Pattern Jury Instructions, Civil 30.00.

42. Illinois Pattern Jury Instructions, Civil 30.03.

43. Illinois Pattern Jury Instructions, Civil 30.05.

44. Illinois Pattern Jury Instructions, Civil 30.05.01.

45. Illinois Pattern Jury Instructions, Civil, 1.01.

46. Illinois Pattern Jury Instructions, Civil 33.01.

Additional Reading

Kagehiro, D., and Minick, R., "How Juries Determine Damages Awards." *For the Defense,* July 2002, 19.

Speckart, G., and McLennon, L., "Excessive Damages Awards and Tactics for Containment, Part I." *For the Defense*, October 2002, 20.

Speckart, G., and McLennon, L., "Excessive Damages Awards and Tactics for Containment, Part II." *For the Defense*, November 2002, 17.

Chapter 22

A Plaintiffs' Attorney's Perspective

Thomas Duffy, Esq.

Synopsis

22.1 Introduction

This material is intended for the plaintiff's attorney who is preparing a case for trial. It primarily focuses on the presentation of evidence before a jury. The ideas and techniques can also be persuasive to judges, defense counsel and insurance company claims adjusters. However, because they are continuously exposed to personal injury claims, they often become hardened to such claims and fail to appreciate the nuances of how an injury has affected the client.

Many professional evaluations of a personal injury claim are based upon the hard and fast rule of some multiplier of the specials (i.e., the client's past and future medical bills and lost wages). A common multiplier is three. Thus, if the client has specials totaling $10,000, then the claims adjuster may conclude that the full value of the case is about $30,000. While this may work for the self-limiting soft tissue injury case, it is an imprecise tool for evaluating cases where the client's pain and suffering are not reflected in the amount of his medical bills and lost wages. Furthermore, the traditional collateral source rule is being significantly restricted or eliminated in many jurisdictions, and an injured party's recovery is often limited to his pain and suffering.

22.2 What Is Pain and Suffering?

A quick look at any dictionary will reveal a rather standard definition for both pain and suffering. These definitions are irrelevant to the trial attorney. Instead, a trial attorney must consider the type of damages that will be recoverable under the laws of the jurisdiction where the case is being tried, and most importantly, what the jury instructions will be at trial. All jurisdictions provide for a recovery of damages beyond just pain and suffering. They are usually referred to as noneconomic damages.

Tip

From the outset, the trial lawyer's preparation of the case must be guided by the likely jury instructions for recoverable noneconomic damages.

Generally, recoverable elements of a plaintiff's noneconomic damages will include all of his past, present, and future

- physical pain,
- mental anguish,
- discomfort,
- inconvenience,
- distress,
- embarrassment and humiliation,
- disfigurement, and
- loss and decrease in the ability to enjoy life's pleasures to the same extent as before the accident.

These elements of damages must be kept in mind while preparing the case. It is the job of the trial attorney to identify and effectively present these damages to the jury. That job begins with the initial interview of the prospective client and does not end until the closing argument to the jury.

22.3 Initial Interview

Besides addressing issues of liability, the initial interview must be used to determine immediately what the perspective client's noneconomic losses may be, and whether they can be effectively presented to a jury. The medium is often the message, and in jury trials, the primary medium is the plaintiff herself. Thus, the attorney's first impression of the client is extremely important. If her initial reaction to the client is negative, then expect that the jury's reaction will also be negative. While representing a client over the extended period of time that it takes for a case to come to trial, lawyers often develop a form of denial. The considerable investment of time and money into the case will begin to cloud the lawyer's initial impression that the client has exaggerated his injuries. The lawyer is then unable to evaluate the case objectively. Unlike the lawyer, the jurors will be in the client's presence for a relatively short period of time, and their impressions of the client will usually be molded quickly.

Tip

The jurors' impressions are much more likely to be consistent with the attorney's impression of the client during the initial interview than on the first day of trial.

If the plaintiff's attorney does not personally like the client but finds him to be realistic regarding his complaints, then a jury is almost certain to feel similarly. Thus, during the initial interview, the trial attorney should make an assessment as to whether the complaints of the individual make sense and whether these complaints will mean anything to a jury. The middle-aged, overweight seamstress with a back injury who claims that her life will never be the same because she is unable to make her yearly ski trip to Aspen may truly believe this is catastrophic. However, if the client does not have a true, sincere, and concrete loss, then that perspective client's claim must be evaluated for what it is. No amount of persuasion or spin can convince the present day juror that substantial compensation is due for a relatively minor setback in a plaintiff's life.

Certainly, the client who has suffered an amputation, paralysis, loss of vision, and cognitive losses has sustained genuine pain and suffering. It is the job of the trial attorney to present concrete and insightful evidence of the consequences of the injury sustained by the plaintiff. The terms pain and suffering, in the abstract, do not mean much to jurors. It is only through seeing and hearing real examples of the plaintiff's loss of life's pleasures that a jury can begin to grasp the effect that an injury has had on him and his family. The trial attorney must become personally familiar with his client. In order for the attorney to convey a complete and compelling picture of client's injury to a jury, a sense of trust and openness must be established so that the client is willing to divulge to the attorney even the most personal consequences of the injury.

22.4 Initial Review

Counsel must obtain any and all records that are available for his client. An assumption must be made in the serious injury case that the defendants will subpoena all the plaintiff's records. In addition to obtaining medical records from before and after the injury, plaintiff's employment and school records must be obtained. These records can reveal hidden gems of information that can be explored during both direct and cross-examination. For example, a high school record that shows that the plaintiff had perfect attendance can be used effectively to cross-examine a defense vocational expert who is trying to convince a jury that the plaintiff's inability to return to work is actually due to a lack of motivation on his part. Likewise, school records may show that the plaintiff had varsity letters in three sports. Although the plaintiff can testify about his athletic ability prior to his injury himself, his credibility can be supported with the school records.

Additionally, all records should be obtained so that any possibly negative information can be defused. The plaintiff's involvement in a prior lawsuit will probably be the subject of discovery. Any negative aspects in that prior lawsuit should be addressed candidly. It is of the utmost importance that the client's very strong case not be destroyed by losing credibility on irrelevant and collateral matters.

22.5 Early Documentation

Early photographic documentation of the plaintiff's injury is crucial to the presentation of a case before a jury. Besides helping to establish liability, photographs of serious damage to a motor vehicle or collapse of a building must be obtained in order to corroborate the seriousness of the plaintiff's injuries. Likewise, the early stages of the plaintiff's injury must be documented.

Tip

It is much better to have a photograph and decide not to use it at trial because it may be too graphic, than not have such a photograph when the jury is very receptive to the case and would welcome the additional information.

In serious personal injury cases, the attorney cannot rely on a friend or family member to photograph the plaintiff's injuries. It is relatively inexpensive to have the plaintiff photographed by a professional photographer. Furthermore, black and white photographs taken by a professional photographer are often more effective than color photographs since they give the jury the impression that these photographs were taken for serious professional reasons.

If the plaintiff is hospitalized for an extended period of time, photographs of the plaintiff in the hospital with intravenous therapy or traction are appropriate. If the plaintiff is undergoing extensive painful physical therapy, it is also important to document this therapy. It is extremely effective to videotape early therapy, such as the plaintiff attempting to walk with a prosthesis or regain use of a paralyzed limb. Evidentiary objections may arise at trial concerning the validity of the videotape, but abbreviated forms of these videotapes can usually be introduced through the testimony of a therapist or the plaintiff herself.

Scenes of serious accidents are often photographed by freelance photographers who then offer to sell the photographs to news agencies, attorneys, insurance companies or others who may be involved in litigation after the accident. An effort should be made to see if any photographs of the accident were taken. A photograph of plaintiff being put into a helicopter and removed from the accident scene can be very effective in helping the plaintiff explain the fear and pain that she felt following the accident.

In order to give perspective to the client's injuries, the attorney should obtain photographs and videotape that show the client before the accident. For example, clients with serious back injuries will often gain significant weight because they are unable to exercise as much as they did before the injury, and this can be shown through a comparison of before and after photographs. Similarly, a videotape showing the client playing catch with his son before the accident can be a striking contrast to the person in the wheelchair that the jury will see in the courtroom.

22.6 Following the Client's Progress

The attorney must become intimately familiar with the plaintiff. It is imperative that the attorney visit the home of a client with serious injuries. It is only there that he can appreciate such facts as client's wheelchair not being able to fit into the first floor bathroom of his home and that he has to crawl up the stairs to use the second floor bathroom.

In the comfort of their home, family members are more apt to reveal personal information concerning the consequences of the plaintiff's injuries, such as the fact that the plaintiff's teenage children can no longer have visitors come to the home since their father is now forced to use a hospital bed in the living room. The attorney should also speak to the plaintiff, her spouse and sometime their children, separately. Concerned about embarrassing or depressing their spouse or parent, they will often privately disclose additional ways in which the plaintiff's injury has affected their family that they would be uncomfortable discussing together.

Regular contact must be maintained between the attorney and client. The attorney should tell the client to contact him after each substantial hospitalization. This serves several purposes. It fosters the necessary rapport between counsel and his client. It also allows plaintiff's counsel to have a firsthand report which should then be memorialized. Changes in the client's condition are often omitted from the medical records. An extremely painful or unusual treatment, such as numerous injections, may not be adequately disclosed by reading the medical records. Furthermore, by the time the case comes to trial, the client may forget the nature and extent of the pain he experienced from his treatment. Counsel can use his memoranda of conversations with plaintiff to refresh his client's recollection.

Plaintiff's main treating doctors and therapist should be interviewed in person by counsel. It is important for them to understand that the attorney cares for the well being of the client. One or several of these individuals will be required to be witnesses at trial. It is best to establish an early rapport with the treating doctor so that the doctor's presentation at trial, most likely in the form of a videotaped deposition, will not be flat and impersonal.

22.7 Responding to Written Discovery

Responses to all written discovery should be prepared with the idea that it may ultimately be read to a jury. Except for cases involving a fatality, cognitive deficits, or a minor, discovery should be answered in the first person. Furthermore, unlike answers to interrogatories relating to liability issues, answers to interrogatories relating to issues of pain and suffering should usually be detailed and specific. This is particularly true for questions in discovery concerning the effect of the injury on the plaintiff. These answers must be candid and factual, and they can also be used to express the nature of the plaintiff's injuries.

If these discovery answers are reviewed by defendant's experts, then plaintiff's counsel can use the discovery answers on cross-examination. For example, the following answer could be given to an interrogatory requesting information about various doctors seen by the plaintiff:

> I saw Dr. Jones, and I believe he gave me nine injections in my spine and three injections in my neck. Each of these injections was with a needle that I believe was about four inches long. I had to sit on the table and bend over when he made the injections in my spine. During one of the injections, my bladder let go and I made a mess on the examining table. I was extremely embarrassed by this.

It would be very helpful if counsel has the opportunity to read this interrogatory answer to the jury during the cross-examination of defendant's experts. Thus, counsel must take the time to answer the interrogatories with the foresight that they may be used as both a sword and shield at trial.

22.8 Preparation for Deposition

Prior to the deposition of the plaintiff, counsel must be fully aware of the contents of the file. A cursory review of the medical records, pleadings, and discovery that has been exchanged is insufficient. All the plaintiff's medical records should be read and summarized prior to preparing him for his deposition.

Tip

Any inconsistencies in the medical records should be discussed with the client so that he can be prepared to explain or possibly challenge them at the deposition.

The deposition preparation session should take place at least one week prior to the deposition. This gives the attorney and the client ample time to deal with any problem that may arise. The initial preparation session is often scheduled for the morning of or the day before the deposition. The one or two hours immediately before the deposition is insufficient time to prepare the client. Furthermore, if the session scheduled the day before the deposition is delayed because the client developed a transportation or child care problem, then there will also be inadequate time for preparation.

Adequate time should be set aside during the preparation session for explaining the reason for the deposition and the techniques that defense counsel is expected to use. Counsel should carefully instruct the client that all questions must be candid and truthful, but that the deposition is not the client's day in court. The deposition is not the client's opportunity to tell the complete story of the case. Instead, the deposition is a procedure used by the defendant's attorney to obtain information that she can use to defend the case. Although the client should fully respond to the questions asked at the deposition, an answer should be narrowly confined to the question, and unnecessary elaboration should be avoided. The client must understand that at a later time, a different form of preparation will take place for trial. At the trial, the client's own counsel will ask open ended and non-leading questions, and the client will be expected to provide more detailed and expansive answers.

Clients often have more of a tendency to understate the severity of their injuries than they do to exaggerate them. The client should be told to be candid about the ways in which the injury affects his life. For example, if asked "How are you doing today?" during a regular conversation with an acquaintance, the client might be expected to shrug off the question by saying "fine" even though he actually has pain that his medication is unable to alleviate completely. If that same question were asked at the deposition, the client must understand that he cannot play stoic and understate his condition. Instead, he needs to respond candidly and fully to the question asked.

At the end of the first deposition preparation session, counsel should give both the plaintiff and her spouse written homework. They should be asked to prepare a comprehensive list of everything that has changed in their lives as a result of the plaintiff's injury, and it should be completed before the deposition. This list is different from a daily diary that attorneys sometimes request their clients to prepare. This author does not advocate keeping a daily diary of events. A diary is usually discoverable, will probably be requested by the defendant, and can often be used against the client unless he is a very prolific writer. For example, if a client goes from making daily entries in his dairy for three months, to an entry every second or third day for several months, and then to an entry once every other week for the remaining period before trial, a skillful defense attorney will often argue that the diary shows that plaintiff's problems diminished over time.

Tip

Plaintiffs also tend to understate their condition in the diary with notations of "good" or "not bad today". This is somewhat ironic considering that clients are often making these notations while confined to a wheelchair or bed.

On the other hand, the clients' homework that details all the changes in their lives caused by the accident should be protected from disclosure by the attorney-client privilege. It is being prepared for and directly communicated to counsel. During the final preparation session on the morning of the deposition, counsel should review the list. It is sometimes advisable to review the list with the client and her spouse together and separately. Without the other one present, the client and the spouse will often elaborate on many more changes that have occurred in the plaintiff's life.

Some of the basic instructions that should always be given to the client before a deposition include:

- Listen carefully to the questions asked at the deposition, and to let the questioner know if you did not hear or understand any question.

- Just answer the question—nothing more or less. The answer can be as short as "yes" or "no," or it can be lengthy so long as it is responsive. Through his testimony, the client should not provide information that was not requested. For example, if asked, "On what date did you see Dr. Smith?" a proper response could be, "I don't recall." An improper response would be, "I don't recall, but I could probably tell you if I reviewed my diary." The client was not asked how he could refresh his recollection, and his answer has needlessly disclosed the existence of a diary that the defendant may not have previously sought to inspect.

- If the question relates to a document, the client should read the entire document in order to confirm that the document is authentic and to know the context of any portion of the document referenced by the questioner.

- There are three ways that a question can be answered. First, "I don't know." If the client does not know the answer, he must not guess or speculate about the answer. Second, "I don't recall." This obviously means that the client knew the answer at one time but not now. The client should understand that just because he does not recall a fact at the deposition does not mean that he will be precluded from testifying about the fact at trial. Prior to trial, he is permitted to have his recollection of the answer refreshed by an epiphany, reviewing documents, and speaking to other people.

- Third and most often, the client knows the answer. An answer is known either exactly or approximately. While it is appropriate for the client to approximate an answer, it is important for the client to state on the record that his answer is an approximation. If the client is asked, "How often do you feel pain in your back?" then the client should testify, "About once or twice a week." Thus, if the client testifies at trial that he was experiencing pain in his back three times a week, he cannot be effectively impeached with his prior deposition testimony since "three" is consistent with "about once or twice."

- The client should also be told that he should request a break during the deposition if he feels that he needs one for any reason.

If the client is adequately prepared, his attorney's principal role at the deposition should be limited to preserving proper objections to the questions. Except to correct or clarify earlier testimony, the attorney should not ask her own client any questions during the deposition. Generally, any testimony elicited from the attorney's own client does not have any evidentiary value other than to deny or explain a prior inconsistent statement.

The deposition can actually add to the settlement value of the client's case if the defense attorney is left with the impression that the client was credible, was able to handle the deposition on his own, and will be able to testify effectively at trial.

Tip

The attorney whose client is unprepared may attempt to obstruct the deposition by making speeches that suggest answers to the client, requesting an inordinate number of breaks in order to confer with the client, or instruct the client not to answer difficult but proper questions. This conduct usually leaves the defense attorney with the impression that the client is not completely candid, needs the protection of his attorney, and will be unable to withstand vigorous cross-examination at trial where such obstructions will not be tolerated by the judge. Ultimately, it needlessly decreases the settlement value of the case.

22.9 Final Preparation for Trial

A. Demonstrative evidence

Demonstrative evidence is essential to the trial attorney's task of conveying a real and complete picture of the plaintiff's pain and suffering to the jury. Prior to trial, counsel needs to select the photographs that best depict the plaintiff's injuries. It is preferable to show scars, burns, and other disfigurement through photographs taken by a professional photographer. Juries do not react favorably to clients being asked to disrobe on the witness stand. It is often more effective for the client or treating doctor to show an injury through a photograph rather than have the plaintiff pull up her shirt.

Treatment calendars can be effective evidence. They summarize the client's hospitalizations or other treatment. For example, treatment calendars can show the daily agony suffered by the plaintiff by detailing the amount of morphine, blood transfusions, or debridement sessions that plaintiff required. Treatment calendars also provide the jury with a stronger impression of the length of the plaintiff's treatment. It is more effective for the jury to see details about the three months that the plaintiff was hospitalized than to merely hear testimony about it.

Medical illustrations of the plaintiff's injury should also be prepared. They can be obtained from medical textbooks or professional graphic artists. Similarly, if the client has an orthopaedic injury that is shown on x-rays, enlargement negatives of the x-rays must be made. The enlarged negative x-rays are relatively inexpensive and are particularly effective if the client has any type of permanently installed hardware in her body. There is no requirement that every exhibit prepared for trial be used at trial. Therefore, it is always better to err on the side of preparing too many exhibits than too few.

A day-in-the-life film shows the daily activities of the client, and it must be considered for any client who requires extensive care. Fortunately, most jurors do not know and are unable to appreciate fully the pain and suffering of a seriously injured person. The film helps bring the reality of that plaintiff's hardships to life. The film does not have to be limited to one day or encompass an entire day. The content is far more important than the length of the film. If the plaintiff has genuine difficulty washing her face or combing her hair in order to get ready to leave the house in the morning, there is nothing wrong with showing a jury the difficulty that she has in performing those simple tasks that most of us take for granted. If the plaintiff is a tetraplegic, the film will show the pain and suffering he must go though each morning in order to just get out of bed. Beyond the helplessness of being unable to get out of bed without the assistance of a nurse, there can be excruciating muscle spasms. The jurors will obtain a much deeper insight of the plaintiff's hardship from seeing this than hearing about it.

It is generally believed that the attorney should not be present during the filming of the day-in-the-life video. The attorney's presence could suggest to the jury that the film was choreographed. In order to place the film in perspective, the jury should also be shown photographs and videotape of the client from before the accident. This will provide the jury with a better appreciation for the normal and active lifestyle that was lost. A few significant photographs should be enlarged to poster size. Some attorneys prefer to show photographs through a slide presentation and placing a title slide before each slide, such as "Johnny's sixth birthday" or "Johnny in the nursing home." It is a matter of preference.[1] See Chapter 18, "Trial Exhibits: Legal and Strategic Considerations," and Chapter 19, "Trial Exhibits: Preparation and Use," for more information.

B. Selection of witnesses

The plaintiff will obviously testify about the changes in her life. It is helpful to use another witness, such as a brother or sister, to testify about the plaintiff's condition prior to the injury. They can testify about family vacations that plaintiff went on prior to the accident. A high school friend can talk about what it was like for the plaintiff to play on a team that won the state championship. An employer can talk about how the plaintiff always appeared for work and loved his job. This testimony will provide the jury with concrete examples of the losses suffered by the plaintiff due to her injury. Preparation of these witnesses should not involve any detailed discussion of the liability issues in the case since they may be subject to cross-examination about what they were told by counsel.

Tip

If possible, both the plaintiff and her spouse must testify at trial. Only one or two other witnesses are necessary to show the changes that have occurred in the plaintiff's life.

C. Preparing witnesses for trial

In preparing the plaintiff for trial as opposed to a deposition, the plaintiff should be advised that she is now going to be principally concerned with answering questions from her own counsel rather than the opposition's counsel. The preparation sessions should occur at the plaintiff's home. This will give counsel access to a great deal of information concerning the plaintiff that would not be available in an office interview. For example, the plaintiff may have a picture of herself that will trigger discussions of the plaintiff's love for skiing. She may have a trophy from a bowling tournament that will disclose that she belonged to a bowling league for fifteen years prior to the accident, and her inability to bowl and maintain her friendships with other league members has left a significant void in her life.

Tip

Most people on juries cannot easily grasp abstract concepts, and they may become callous after seeing the plaintiff in the courtroom.

Therefore, statements by the plaintiff like "my life has become a living hell" or "nothing is the same" do not make much of an impression on a juror. By the conclusion of the trial, the jury needs to have a strong appreciation for the hardships that the plaintiff has and will continue to encounter for the rest of her life. Jurors must come to understand that although this is the plaintiff's day in court, the hardships rained upon the plaintiff and her family from the injury will continue well beyond that day.

In order meaningfully to convey to the jury the physical and emotional effect of the injury, plaintiffs must be prepared to testify about several specific examples of how their life has been changed by their injury. If possible, examples should include the effect on watershed events as well as daily life. The plaintiff's inability to attend his son's graduation from college or daughter's wedding would be very poignant examples of the personal effect of the injury. If a plaintiff is homebound, he needs to be prepared to explain to the jury that he now faces being alone for seven or eight hours each day after his children leave for school and his wife leaves for work. He needs to be able to explain how the mailman appearing at noon is the highlight of his day. If his wife left the setting for the air-conditioning too high, he is unable to turn it off himself because he cannot reach the switch. He can explain how he sits shivering, waiting for someone to come home and turn down the air-conditioning. These are the types of examples that must be used in order for the jury to understand fully the effect that a serious injury has on an individual and his family.

By the time the preparation for trial begins, counsel should be adequately familiar with the plaintiff's personal life so that he is comfortable discussing these incidents. The plaintiff should be told that he is going to be asked about these incidents and that he should explain them in conversational tones. A preparation session concerning the pain and suffering issues should not take the form of a question and answer session. This causes the spontaneity and the impact of the evidence at trial to be lessened.

An attorney whose husband was injured in a motor vehicle accident described how her own husband reacted to being disabled.

> I have lugged bags of groceries out to the car while my husband walked beside me embarrassed and empty-handed. I have felt his frustration as I struggled in the ice and mud to change our van's flat tire while he stood by with clenched fists. I have shoveled snow and looked up to see Bill watching me from our window as I heaved shovels of snow. He didn't need to tell me how he felt. His pain showed in his face.[2]

Some years later, the attorney applied this experience to her own cases. She was representing Glenn, a man who was injured in a trip and fall. The trial started the week after the city had received back-to-back record snowfalls of almost 22 inches each. The attorney asked Glenn's wife who had shoveled that snow. She said that she had with her husband watching her work through their picture window. Then the attorney asked the plaintiff how it made him feel when he watched her do his job. He was shocked at the question; I hadn't told him it was coming. "Like less than a man, like less than a man," he murmured. The judge granted a recess so the crusty plaintiff and several jurors could compose themselves. The jury returned a substantial verdict in favor of Glenn.[2] Consider how the testimony elicited in this example would have been different if Glenn had been forewarned of the question he would be asked.

22.10 Opening Statement

The trial attorney's opening statement should not beat about the bush. The jury should be directly told who the client is, why she is in court and what she wants. The opening statement should be factual and not just argument. The opening statement should not usually exceed twenty minutes. The plaintiff's attorney's demeanor and tone during the opening statement will normally be more reserved than during the closing argument. Moreover, if permitted to do so, it is often advisable to use exhibits in the opening statement. A photograph of the severely damaged automobile can lend credibility to the claim that the plaintiff was seriously injured even before there has been any testimony.

The client is not just a name but a person who grew up in the neighborhood, went to high school where he met and fell in love with his wife, had three children, became a member of the local union, and worked his way up to being shop steward.

He was able to support his family financially, coached his son's little league baseball team, and looked forward to his annual family trip to the national parks where he would fish, swim and hike with his wife and children. He is in court because the defendant took much of that away from him due to its negligence or defective product, and this is the only means by which he and his family can obtain the compensation to which they are entitled. The jury should not only be told that plaintiff's serious injury has changed his life, but the attorney needs to explain how it was changed. Due to his serious injury, plaintiff is no longer able to work and support his family, coach his son's baseball team, and take those annual trips to the national parks.

The following is an excerpt of an opening statement for a plaintiff who lost the vision in his left eye due to medical malpractice. His right eye was already impaired.

> Paul lost the vision in his left eye because the doctor delayed in treating the infection in his eye. Paul can sometimes see hand motions. He can sometimes see a little light at the top of his eye. But he is pretty much blind in that left eye. And you will hear him explain the consequences of that. He will tell you he gets this sharp pain occasionally in his left eye. He will explain to you that he really can't drive anymore, that he has to rely on his right eye, which is his bad eye. In order to get to work he has to drive to the Wawa, which is a couple of blocks from his house, and wait for his brother-in-law to arrive there and get in his car and drive him to work. He will explain to you how at work where he used to be a forklift driver he can't drive a forklift anymore, and they put him in a special section where he repairs the broken beer cases, a job that's really a job for somebody that is just starting out.
>
> He will explain to you and Karen will explain to you how this has changed their complete lives, how if he wants to get a haircut and go back to his old barber in South Philly what he has to do is have his wife drive him there and wait, and how if he wants to go to see his family or go Christmas shopping or if he's at a wedding and he has to go to the bathroom and the hallway is dark, his wife has to escort him to the bathroom.
>
> Paul and Karen will explain to you how their lives have been changed by this. He will also explain to you how he had to turn down a job promotion that he was working for and that he had tried to get his whole life because he can't see in the warehouse. He will tell you that the owner of the place is a fellow that's ninety-six years old and how he's afraid that when that owner dies or moves on to retirement eventually that the new people will say we don't need a guy driving a forklift or being around forklifts who has vision in only one eye.

The ultimate intent is to provide the jury with concrete examples of how plaintiff's injury has changed his life so that the jury can appropriately compensate the plaintiff for his losses.

22.11 Presentation of Evidence

The presentation of pain and suffering evidence to a jury is an intricate balancing act. On the one hand, the trial attorney must not trivialize the case by permitting the plaintiff to exaggerate his complaints and inconveniences. On the other hand, the trial attorney needs to present testimony and exhibits that will convey to the jury the full extent of the plaintiff's losses. For example, rather than trying to sell the jury on the exaggerated notion that she has constant pain in her broken arm which severely limits its use, the plaintiff's testimony may be more effective if she tells the jury that her arm has healed and only occasionally bothers her during certain changes in the weather. This candid testimony can then be corroborated by presenting to the jury the x-rays of the arm that show not only the fracture but also the surgical screws that remain in her arm.

Tip

In determining how to present the case to the jury, the trial attorney must be personally familiar with *every* item of testimonial and demonstrative evidence in the case; both the good and bad. The trial attorney must then marshal that portion of the evidence that will demonstrate the true extent of the plaintiff's pain and suffering, as well as defuse the defendant's attempt to trivialize or mitigate the injury.

Testimonial evidence will usually come from the plaintiff, the best friend, spouse, other relatives and friends, plaintiff's boss and coworkers, expert and treating physicians, nurses, and psychiatrist. It is unnecessary, and can be counterproductive, to call each of these types of witnesses. The plaintiff and his spouse are the principal medium for showing the effects of the injury, and the attorney must carefully select one to three other witnesses who can effectively corroborate that testimony through a different perspective. Demonstrative evidence will normally include a selection of the photographs, charts, medical records, diagnostic films, and videos obtained or developed prior to trial.

Among the most important trial decisions of the trial attorney is when to call the plaintiff as a witness, and whether the plaintiff should be present in the courtroom prior to her testimony. There are no hard and fast rules on this. The jury normally wants to hear from the plaintiff more than any other witness, and it is sometimes possible to build the jury's anticipation by delaying the plaintiff's testimony. This is particularly true when the plaintiff's testimony is not critical to establishing liability, either because liability is conceded or the plaintiff's injury has left her with no recollection of the accident. When the plaintiff is wheelchair bound and still undergoing extensive rehabilitation, significant thought should be given as to whether the plaintiff should be in the court at any time other than for her testimony and the closing arguments. There can be a very dramatic effect from the jury seeing the plaintiff for the first time as she is wheeled to the area of the witness stand. The plaintiff's testimony may be less compelling if the jury has been watching the plaintiff in the courtroom for a few days before she testifies and, in a strange way, have become more accustomed to her physical condition.

When testifying during direct examination, fact witnesses should generally focus their attention on the questioner, both when listening and answering questions. The witnesses should not look at the jury. If allowed by the court, the attorney may want to consider positioning herself near the jurors when conducting direct examination. The direct examination should be conversational and unrehearsed. If the examination is rehearsed, the jury will likely know this and find the testimony less credible. This does not mean that the witness should be unprepared for the questions asked. To the contrary, the witness should be fully familiar with the areas of examination. However, the witness should not be given a script, nor should the attorney read from one. The questions and answers must be spontaneous.

There should also be spontaneity in the direct examination of experts. However, while the examination of fact witnesses should resemble a conversation between two people in which the jury gets to listen, the examination of an expert should resemble a lesson. The expert should direct her attention to the jury and explain with common parlance her opinions and the reason for them. The expert is the teacher, and the jurors are the students. If the expert uses a word or phrase that is overly technical, the attorney must ask the expert to explain the meaning of the word or phrase.

When possible, exhibits should be used during the direct examination of witnesses. Direct examination of witnesses can be fairly dry. Exhibits can make it more interesting to the jury. For example, instead of merely asking the life care expert to testify regarding the number of past and future injections the plaintiff will need to endure, the expert should be provided with a chart or illustration that shows the injections. The expert should explain to the jury the purpose of the exhibit and refer to it while testifying regarding its subject matter. Thus, instead of merely testifying that "Mr. Smith had twenty-two injections of Demerol and Vistaril IM between March 14, 1998, and March 21, 1998," the expert could refer to an exhibit that illustrates the date, time, type, and location on the body of each injection and testify, "I have prepared this document for the purpose of showing the injections that Mr. Smith had during his treatment at General Hospital. The information on the document is based on Mr. Smith's medical records. As you can see, between March 14, 1998, and March 21, 1998, Mr. Smith had twenty-two injections of Demerol and Vistaril IM in the upper right and left buttock areas."

Similarly, instead of having a fact witness testify about the severity of the damage to the vehicle caused by the accident, the witness should identify a photograph of the damaged vehicle. A family member can be used to narrate a day-in-the-life video. For example, the wife of a wheelchair bound plaintiff can explain,

> What the film is showing now is the powder room on the first floor of our house, which is the only bathroom Jim can use because he cannot climb the stairs to go to the larger bathroom in the bedroom. Jim has a lot of trouble using this powder room since he obviously cannot fit into it with his wheel-

> chair, and somebody always has to help him get from his wheelchair to the toilet.

For a catastrophically injured plaintiff, it is advisable to have someone other than the plaintiff himself detail the way in which his injuries have adversely affected his life. The jury would recognize the indignity of the plaintiff having to describe his own incontinence. The jury could even hold this against the attorney. Instead, the plaintiff should be asked to detail the things that he enjoyed doing before the accident and what he misses doing the most since the accident. A family member or close friend should be used to detail the things that the plaintiff is unable to do since the accident and the physical and emotional pain that he has endured since then.

Testimony concerning pain and suffering should address the plaintiff's past, present, and future. The past should cover the period before the accident. If the plaintiff had a similar injury prior to the accident in question, the plaintiff's attorney must squarely address the issue before defense counsel raises it on cross-examination. If he does not do so, the jury will likely think that he is hiding something and attach more significance to the fact than it may deserve. The plaintiff should explain the circumstances of the prior injury and whether it had fully resolved prior to the accident in question or whether the prior injury was exacerbated by it. If his injury was exacerbated by the accident, the plaintiff should testify about ways in which the exacerbation has adversely affected his life. He should give examples of things that he is unable to do now that he could previously do even with the prior injury. A truck driver may have been able to continue to drive a truck with a bulging disk, but he is now unable to because the accident caused the same disk to herniate. The exacerbation may have caused the plaintiff to begin to use pain medication or increase the dosage or strength of previously prescribed pain medication.

The plaintiff's present condition must also be candidly addressed. If some or all of the plaintiff's injuries have resolved prior to trial, then the plaintiff must say so. Plaintiffs sometimes lose credibility by claiming that all the injuries that they suffered in the accident remain unresolved. The plaintiff may have a real and legitimate scarring injury that the jury devalues because they do not believe his testimony that he still has constant pain in the area of the scarring several years after the accident. The plaintiff must be cautioned not to overreach.

The plaintiff's future pain and suffering can be established through fact and expert testimony. Fact witnesses can testify about the lack of improvement in the plaintiff's condition and that his inability to do specific tasks has not improved since the accident. With this information, the jury can reasonably infer that plaintiff's condition will persist into the future. Counsel should also call a medical expert to testify regarding the plaintiff's prognosis. The physician should testify regarding the probability that the plaintiff's current pain and physical limitations will continue. A vocational expert should be called to testify regarding the effect that the plaintiff's injury will have on her ability to work in the future. The vocational expert should consider the plaintiff's current and expected future condition.

It is important to use specific examples of the limitations placed upon the plaintiff by his injuries. It is not effective merely to have the plaintiff testify that "I can no longer do my job." Instead, the plaintiff or a co-worker needs to explain the specific tasks involved with the plaintiff's job and why he is unable to do them. For example, if the plaintiff is no longer able to work in a warehouse because the accident impaired his hearing, the jury needs to understand clearly that his impaired hearing poses a risk to him in a loud environment where there is moving equipment such as fork-lifts. It also needs to be conveyed to the jury that the plaintiff has worked as a warehouseman most of his adult life and has attained a level of seniority and accompanying self-worth. A demotion or firing will not only have an economic effect upon the plaintiff and his family but also an emotional effect. Sometimes the plaintiff is able to retain his job only because of the goodwill he has with his employer. In such cases, the plaintiff or his wife should explain the emotional injury that results from thinking of oneself as a charity case, or living with the fear of losing his job if the ownership in the company ever changed.

The plaintiff also needs to be prepared for cross-examination. Trial counsel should anticipate every area of questioning and review those areas with the plaintiff before he testifies. The plaintiff should never be surprised by an area of questioning during cross-examination. As with direct examination, a script should not be used. The plaintiff should be instructed to answer the questions directly and not attempt to avoid providing an answer. It is painfully obvious to the jury and everyone else in the courtroom when a witness is being nonresponsive to a question, and it can hurt the credibility of the witness. The plaintiff should also be instructed about her demeanor. She should not be argumentative, angry, loud, discourteous, or overly emotional. Jurors, like most bystanders to a conversation, do not want to listen to an argument. The jury will likely credit the plaintiff if she resists defense counsel's attempt to provoke her.

The evidence presented at trial must be credible, spontaneous, and as interesting as possible. This can be accomplished through well prepared witnesses and the use of demonstrative aids. In the end, the evidence presented at trial should allow the jury to have a clear insight into the physical and emotional effects the injury has had, is having, and will likely have on the life of the plaintiff and her family.

22.12 The Closing Argument

By the time the trial attorney is prepared to make her closing argument, the jury should already know and appreciate the severity of the plaintiff's injury as well as its physical and emotional effect upon the plaintiff and his family. The closing argument should reinforce the jury's understanding and forcefully explain that their principal function is to determine an adequate award for the plaintiff's pain and suffering.

Damages are usually argued near the end of the attorney's closing. When the attorney begins to discuss damages, the issue of money should be addressed up front. The jury should be told that while it is natural for people to be uneasy about discussing money, they need to understand that our legal system is one in which wrongly injured people are compensated by money. We are no longer in the primitive era of "an eye for an eye and a tooth for a tooth." Instead, the plaintiffs are entitled to be fairly and adequately compensated for the rest of their lives. Do not beg. It is a legal right.

Tip

The closing argument should explain each of the elements of pain and suffering that the plaintiffs are entitled to receive under the law, including past, present, and future physical pain, mental anguish, discomfort, inconvenience, distress, embarrassment, humiliation, disfigurement, and loss of life's pleasures.

The jury should be told that the reason they are there is to determine the value of these elements of damages. A computer can be use to tabulate the plaintiff's economic damages, including medical bills and lost wages. However, a computer cannot feel physical or emotional pain, and only the jury can determine a fair and adequate compensation.

These elements of noneconomic damages should be shown on an enlarged chart along with the special or economic damages. Selected exhibits of plaintiff's injury may also be used. For example, in a disfigurement case, the attorney may want to show an enlarged photograph of the client's scar or burn. However, if the photograph is very graphic and has already been seen by the jury, the attorney may gain more favor with the jury by merely reminding the jury of the photograph and explaining that you will not expose them to it again.

As in the opening statement and direct examination of the witnesses, the attorney's closing argument must set forth concrete examples of how the injury has changed the life of the plaintiff and his family. Furthermore, the closing is uniquely suited for explaining to the jury how the injury has harmed the very dignity of the person. The plaintiff's own self image is fractured. He is no longer able to view himself as a good financial provider for his family. She is no longer able to speak to someone in a social setting without thinking that they are looking at her disfigurement. He is no longer able to go to a restaurant or shop for a birthday gift without asking his wife to drive him, and it makes him feel like a burden to his wife. She thought that she married a partner in life, and now she feels like a caretaker and hates herself for sometimes wishing she never married him. These are the personal burdens of the clients that can be used very effectively in the closing, and which can only be learned through a close relationship with them.

The trial lawyer must also impress on the jury that this is the plaintiff's only day in court. This is particularly important in a case involving a permanent injury. The jury should be told that if the plaintiff's award later turns out to be inadequate, he cannot return to court and ask for more compensation. Instead, the jury needs to determine an amount of compensation for pain and suffering that will last the plaintiff for the rest of his life.

The following is an excerpt of the closing argument for the same plaintiff who lost the vision in his left eye due to medical malpractice, and his right eye was already impaired.

> Now, the other portion of the case, which I would submit is as important or more important, is the question of damages. And the way that I was brought up, I was always uneasy as a young lawyer trying cases asking people about money and suggesting to people about money. And then I came to understand that our system of law is a system where people are compensated by money. That is a simple fact. We are no longer in an era or a primitive time where it's an eye for an eye and a tooth for a tooth, where we would take somebody from the hospital and give them bad vision in their right eye and say, okay, now we're equal.
>
> We don't do that. You folks are here because we have to come up with a number that will fairly and adequately compensate Paul and Karen for the rest of their lives.
>
> And I told you Paul said one thing to me and here's what he said: But, you know, when this is all said and done and I get up on Thursday morning, I'm still going to be blind. So you have to realize that whatever award you make has to last Paul and Karen for the rest of their lives and has to compensate them for the rest of their lives. I made up a chart. And the judge is going to instruct you about damages. And these are some of the items of damages that under our law in the Commonwealth of Pennsylvania people are entitled to recover. And I would suggest to you that the Smiths are entitled to recover certain items.
>
> Now we do everything by computers. And a computer can come in and do these calculations and a computer can figure out what Mr. Jones [the economist expert] figured out, including how many hours did you work, what was your job, what were the fringe benefits, and come up with a number.
>
> I would submit to you that the other numbers that are on this chart that deal with pain and suffering are why you are here. A computer cannot feel pain, or past pain and suffering. You have to award Paul for those three eye procedures. You have to award Paul for all the times he's got that stabbing pain in his eye. I haven't heard any doctor come in and tell you that doesn't happen.
>
> You have to award Paul for future pain and suffering, the stabbing in the eye, the headache that it causes a couple of times a week he said for two or three hours. You have to award Paul for disfigurement. What's the disfigurement? Well, you see his eye, you saw him testify, how his left eye is. A computer doesn't know what disfigurement is. I will bet that everybody in this courtroom that when they went to the ladies or the men's room turned and looked in the mirror to see how they look, is their tie straight, is their hair combed before they came back into the room here.
>
> And every time Paul looks in the mirror, to the extent that he can see himself, he has to see that he's got this problem with his eye. He has to know when he talks to people that they're looking at his eye and wondering what's going on with it. That's disfigurement.
>
> You have to consider past and future loss of life's pleasures. You have to award Paul for that. You heard the testimony. A computer doesn't know what it's like to want to play a game of cards with the guys down the block. A computer doesn't know what it's like to have someone say, "Pop Pop, do you want to catch a ball?" We used this as an example. Imagine you need to go for a haircut or to go visit your relatives, and to realize that you are a prisoner. You have to ask your wife "will you drive me down for the haircut, will you wait outside for the haircut, and when I'm done will you take me home?" Or consider that this time of year you want to do some Christmas shopping. You can't go to the mall. You can't go out and take a walk around the neighborhood. You can't even buy a gift for someone because you have to ask your wife to take you.
>
> A computer doesn't know what it's like to be a man and you go to a wedding or you go to a first communion or a bar mitzvah, and when you have to go to the bathroom you have to say, "Will you take

me, Karen?" A computer doesn't know what it's like to get up at 4:00 and 5:00 o'clock in the morning to sneak to work before the traffic comes on the street, because you don't want to drive and you can't drive. The computer doesn't know what it's like with all those things—you people know what that's like.

These things are all gone for Paul. Paul is forced to be a prisoner, and he has to depend on Karen. And you're going to be asked to make an award for Karen. You heard her explain how her life has changed. And I made a decision yesterday. I did not make that woman cry, and I cut off the testimony without going into every detail again. I wanted to leave them with dignity.

Now, every one of those items they have to be compensated for, for the rest of Paul's life. And the judge will instruct you how long that life is expected to be. And you have to think about that on a day-to-day basis. If you lost a foot you would probably be better off than if you lost your eye. They talk about your sight being your most precious gift.

Paul and Karen came to me three years ago. They asked me, "Mr. Duffy, can you take our case? We think that the doctor made a mistake. Our family needs help." And I agreed to represent them. And I have tried as best I can to represent them. And I have done everything I can to do the best job for them. They are no longer in my hands. They are now in your hands. And I would ask you to do the best you can for them too.

The jury came back with an award of $5 million for Paul and $1 million for his wife.

Again, the ultimate intent of the closing argument is to have the jury view the clients as real people, possible friends or neighbors. Make the jury believe that a large award for the clients is not only the right thing to do, but that the law entitles the clients to such an award. This is done by sharing with the jury a clear insight into the life the clients had before the injury, how that life has changed in many large and subtle ways due to the injury, and how they are entitled to be compensated under the law.

Endnotes

1. Lawrence, R., "What Good Will Money Do?" *Trial*, September 2002, 28.

2. Wivell, M., "Lessons from Life—'How does that make you feel'." *Trial*, July 2000, accessed online at www.rkmc.com/news.articles.read1.cfm.

Additional Reading

Ball, D., *David Ball on Damages: A Plaintiff Attorney's Guide for Personal Iinjury and Wrongful Death Cases.* Notre Dame, IN: National Institute for Trial Advocacy, 2001.

Papadakis, M., *Civil Trial Practice: Winning Techniques of Successful Trial Attorneys*. Tucson: Lawyers & Judges Publishing Co., 2000.

Polchinski, P., *Elements of Trial Practice*. Tucson: Lawyers & Judges Publishing Co., 2000.

About the Editor

Patricia Iyer, MSN, RN, LNCC, edited this book and wrote two chapters: "Organization and Analysis of Medical Records" and "The Expert Fact Witness." She coauthored the chapters: "Suffering: A Multidimensional Concept," "Trial Exhibits: Strategic and Legal Considerations," and "Trial Exhibits: Preparation and Use." Ms. Iyer's experience as an author and editor began in 1980. She has written numerous articles, coauthored or edited nine textbooks written for nurses and attorneys, and edited four case studies published by the American Association of Legal Nurse Consultants. Before this project, her most recent editorial involvement was serving as the chief editor of *Principles and Practices of Legal Nurse Consulting*, Second Edition (2003), the core curriculum of legal nurse consulting. Ms. Iyer is a frequent lecturer to attorneys, paralegals, nurses, and legal nurse consultants. She has appeared several times on Law Journal TV and on American Airlines' inflight entertainment radio programming as part of a program on the nursing shortage. After entering the field of legal nurse consulting as a medical surgical expert witness in 1987, in 1989, she established Med League Support Services, Inc., an independent legal nurse consulting firm located in Flemington, New Jersey. Nurse Iyer has served on the national board of the American Association of Legal Nurse Consulting in the role of secretary, director at large, president elect, president, and past president, with her term as past president being completed in April 2004.

Certified by the American Association of Legal Nurse Consulting, Ms. Iyer began her nursing career by earning a diploma in nursing from Muhlenberg Hospital School of Nursing in Plainfield, New Jersey. She earned her bachelors of science in nursing and a masters of science in nursing from the University of Pennsylvania in Philadelphia.

About the Authors

Stephen Appelbaum, CEP, EPIC, is co-author of the chapters "Trial Exhibits: Legal and Strategic Considerations" and "Trial Exhibits: Preparation and Use." He is a graduate of Rochester Institute of Technology with a degree in photographic illustration. He began his legal career doing fire photography for insurance companies and expanded to all forms of forensic work including liability claims assignments and work for plaintiffs' attorneys as well. In 1988, he started the Evidence Store, which is a walk-in retail store in Union, New Jersey, for trial attorneys. When he moved into his new facility in 1998, he added a full-sized courtroom for the purpose of conducting mock trials and for teaching demonstrative evidence techniques. The Evidence Store provides all forms of legal photography, video, and litigation graphics. Mr. Appelbaum has lectured nationally to photography organizations, local and state bar associations, numerous Inns of Court as well as having been featured on national and local radio and television programs. He is a former editor of the *Journal of Evidence Photography* and is a member of the Board of Directors of the Evidence Photographers International Council. He is also a member of the American Society of Trial Consultants and the Professional Photographers of America.

Carol Anne Bales, RN, MSN, AOCN, CCRP, authored the chapter, "Cancer Pain and Suffering." In her current role as the Director of Clinical Research for the Seton Healthcare Network in Austin, Texas, she collaborates with oncology staff members to provide investigational treatment options for patients. She is currently actively involved in clinical research studies of pharmaceutical treatments of non-small cell lung cancer and early stage breast cancer patients. She provides consultation to principal investigators and hospital nursing staff regarding FDA and DHHS clinical research regulations and good clinical practice. She has served as a study coordinator for more than forty clinical research studies in the past ten years. Carol serves as an active member of two institutional review boards and is the current chair of the Seton HealthCare Network's Clinical Research Steering Committee. She received her undergraduate education at Georgetown University School of Nursing and her master's degree in community health nursing from the University of Texas at Austin School of Nursing. She received the honor of "Outstanding MSN Student" for attaining the highest GPA in her class during her MSN program. Prior to this, she provided direct patient care on an inpatient oncology unit, delivering nursing care for chemotherapy and supportive care needs of acutely ill oncology patients.

Carol is an active member of the Oncology Nursing Society and holds certifications in Advanced Oncology Nursing and as a SoCRA certified Clinical Research Professional. She is an active member of the Association of Clinical Research Professionals, Texas Nurses Association, the Society of Clinical Research Associates, and the American Cancer Society. Carol also is an American Red Cross Nurse and is a certified member of her local ARC Disaster Team. Carol has co-authored two chapters addressing chemotherapy treatment and interdisciplinary review in the *ONS Guide to Cancer Clinical Trials Nursing, 2000.*

Thomas C. Broderick, Esq., co-author of the chapter "The Defense Attorney's Perspective" about limiting damage awards for pain and suffering, is currently an assistant vice-president in the Claim Legal/Staff Attorney Department for the St. Paul Fire and Marine Insurance Company. Mr. Broderick is a 1976 graduate of the University of Notre Dame Law School. Since 1977, he has concentrated his practice in the defense of personal injury lawsuits in Chicago, Illinois. Mr. Broderick has tried cases involving medical malpractice, products liability and construction matters. In his present position, he is responsible for twelve Staff Attorney offices in ten states handling insurance defense matters.

I. Larry Cohen, MD, FCCP, FCCM, authored the chapter "Pain and Suffering in the Intensive Care Unit." He is currently a tenured associate professor of anesthesiology, medicine and surgery at SUNY Buffalo and Associate Director of Critical Care at Roswell Park Cancer Institute. His medical practice is limited to critical care, and over the past seventeen years he has accumulated a wide range of experience with medical and surgical patients in both ICU (intensive care unit) and ILCU (intermediate level of care unit) settings. Before his current position he served in various leadership roles: Co-Director SICU (surgical intensive care unit), Director of ILCU, Director of Critical Care Research, and director of a home infusion program.

Larry holds certifications in internal medicine and critical care medicine and is a fellow of the American College of Chest Physicians and the College of Critical Care Medicine. He reviews articles for a number of journals and has participated on several national medical leadership committees. He is the author of nearly 100 papers or chapters and has given more than 100 lectures in local, and national, and international settings. His most recent award was "Outstanding Teacher Award 2001–2002" for the Department of Anesthesiology at SUNY (Buffalo).

Yvonne D'Arcy, MS, CRNP, CNS, wrote the chapter "Pain Assessment." Currently Ms. D'Arcy is the Nurse Practitioner for Pain Management and the Pain and Palliative Care Outcomes Manager at Suburban Hospital, Bethesda, MD. Before moving to Suburban Hospital Ms. D'Arcy was the coordinator of the Johns Hopkins Oncology Pain Service at the Sidney Kimmel Comprehensive Cancer Center, Baltimore, Maryland. She has also worked for Mayo Clinic Jacksonville, Florida, where she was the coordinator of the acute pain service and the supervisor of the Chronic Pain Clinic.

In 1995 Ms. D'Arcy graduated from Winona State University, Winona, Minnesota, with a master of science degree on a clinical nurse specialist track. In 1999, she received a certification as a nurse practitioner from the University of Florida, Jacksonville campus. Currently Ms. D'Arcy holds professional memberships in the American Pain Society, the American Society of Pain Management Nurses, and the Oncology Nursing Society. She has served on the Board of Directors for the American Society of Pain Management Nurses and is currently the Chairperson of their Clinical Practice Committee. Ms. D'Arcy writes and presents frequently on various pain management topics and issues both nationally and internationally. Additionally, she has consulted with attorneys as an expert witness.

Michael D'Lugo, Esq., coauthored the chapter "Pain and Suffering in Pediatric Neurology." He is an associate for the Orlando office of Wicker, Smith, O'Hara, McCoy, Graham & Ford, P.A. Mr. D'Lugo became a member of the Florida Bar in 1994. In 1995, he became employed by Wicker, Smith, O'Hara, McCoy, Graham & Ford, P.A,. and has been employed with them ever since. The majority of the work he performs relates to the defense of healthcare professionals. Mr. D'Lugo's practice is concentrated in two specific areas: appellate practice and administrative law. As an appellate attorney, Mr. D'Lugo has handled dozens of appeals, including final appeals, interlocutory appeals, and petitions for extraordinary writs. As an administrative law practitioner, he represents healthcare providers whose licenses to practice are under investigation by the state of Florida's Department of Health. In addition to Florida state courts, Mr. D'Lugo is admitted to practice in the Middle District of Florida, the Eleventh Circuit Court of Appeals, and the Supreme Court of the United States. His undergraduate degree in modern European history is from Columbia University, and he received his juris doctor from Boston University School of Law in 1994. He lectures on administrative law issues involving healthcare providers, preservation of appellate remedies, and evidentiary issues.

Thomas Duffy, Esq. Author of "A Plaintiffs' Attorney's Perspective," Mr. Duffy is a successful plaintiffs' attorney with Duffy and Keenan in Philadelphia. He practices in the area of medical malpractice, professional malpractice litigation, catastrophic injury, aviation law, motor vehicles, and injuries. Mr. Duffy is a graduate of Temple University. He is a member of the Philadelphia Disciplinary Board Hearing Committee, the New Jersey State and American Bar Associations, New Jersey, Pennsylvania, and Philadelphia Trial Lawyers Associations, and the Association of Trial Lawyers of America. Tom is a licensed commercial pilot and a member of the Temple University Academy of Trial Advocacy. He is admitted to practice law in Pennsylvania and New Jersey.

Richard Ford, Esq., coauthored "Pain and Suffering in Pediatric Neurology." He is the Resident Managing Partner for the Orlando office of Wicker, Smith, O'Hara, McCoy, Graham & Ford, P.A. Mr. Ford became a member of the Florida Bar in 1979 and received his initial training at the State Attorney's office, working for Janet Reno as a murder prosecutor. In 1983 he became employed by Wicker, Smith, and, except for a six-month hiatus, has been with them since. In 1983, he began representing physicians and was asked to open the Orlando office in 1988. The majority of the work he performs relates to the defense of healthcare professionals. He has experience in over 100 civil jury trials, which include not only medical malpractice cases but also products liability, legal malpractice, construction litigation, general negligence, and automobile liability. Mr. Ford is also a board certified civil trial lawyer, certified with the National Board of Trial Advocacy and a board certified civil trial specialist. He is a member of the Federal Bar for the Southern (trial), Middle and Northern Districts of Florida and the United States Court of Appeals for the Eleventh Circuit. His undergraduate degree in political science is from the University of Florida and he attended Boston University School of Law and received his juris doctor in 1979. He continues to lecture on legal issues in healthcare, nursing home litigation, medical malpractice, and cross-examination.

Suzanne Frederick, MSN, RN, wrote the chapter "Pain and Suffering in the Elderly Population." She is a practicing RN in the nursing home and hospital setting. She received a bachelor of science in nursing from the University of Mary-Hardin Baylor in Belton, Texas and a master of science in nursing from the University of Texas in Arlington. She is certified in gerontological nursing. She has over nineteen years of experience in bedside nursing including ICU, ER, med-surg, nursing home, nursing education, and administration. She is actively employed by a nursing home and hospital. Suzanne has consulted with both plaintiffs' and defense attorneys and has testified in deposition and trial in nursing home and hospital cases. She lives and works in Waco, Texas.

Guy Fried, MD, coauthor of "Spinal Cord Injury," has been an attending physician and Outpatient Medical Director at Magee Rehabilitation Hospital in Philadelphia since 1989. Since 1996, he has also served as an assistant clinical professor of rehabilitation medicine at Thomas Jefferson University. Dr. Fried is board certified in physical medicine and rehabilitation with further board certifications in pain management, spinal cord injury, and electrodiagnostic medicine. He is also an item writer for the spinal cord injury sub-specialization board of the American Board of Physical Medicine and Rehabilitation. In addition, he holds membership in many professional organizations.

Dr. Fried earned a B.A. in psychology with additional studies in chemistry, biology, and economics from Hofstra University in New York in 1981. He attained his medical degree from Yale Medical School in 1985. Dr. Fried did internship and residency at Thomas Jefferson University Hospital in Philadelphia, serving as Chief Resident in 1989. He has twice received the Thomas Jefferson Rehab Residency "Attending of the Year" award for teaching. In 2002, he was selected by *Philadelphia Magazine* as a "Top Doc" in rehabilitation medicine. Dr. Fried also has vast teaching experience with physician colleagues, medical residents, and students as well as allied health professionals. He has given numerous professional presentations throughout the country. Dr. Fried has published a variety of articles on such topics as clinical evaluation, spinal cord injury, spasticity management, and the use of botulinum toxin.

He maintains an interest in the legal aspects of medicine and has served as a consultant and expert within both the medical and the legal communities.

Karen Mandzak Fried, MSN, RN, CRRN, CCM, Rehabilitation Consultant, coauthored the chapter "Spinal Cord Injury." Karen has over twenty years' experience as a consultant and expert in rehabilitation nursing. She has served in various capacities in clinical care, education, administration, quality outcomes, case management, and life care planning in a variety of positions such as a clinical nurse specialist, faculty member, nurse administrator, Coordinator of Quality Outcomes, and legal nurse consultant.

Karen received her B.S.N from Thomas Jefferson University College of Health Professions in 1979. In 1983, she received her M.S.N from the University of Pennsylvania on a full VA health professional scholarship. She has served as a faculty member at Lankenau Hospital School of Nursing and the College of Health Professions at Thomas Jefferson University. She was also honored as the first recipient of the "McGraw Achievement Award for Outstanding Nursing Practice" from the Philadelphia chapter of ARN. Ms. Mandzak Fried has presented at numerous regional, national, and international professional meetings as well as lectured for nursing, allied health and legal audiences. She is also the author and co-author of many publications in nursing and medical publications such as the *Rehabilitation Core Curriculum*, *Trauma Quarterly*, *Critical Care Clinics*, and a rehabilitation nursing textbook. Her background and expertise have been used within both the medical and legal communities.

Reneé Holleran, PhD, RN, CEN, CCRN, CFRN, authored "Pain and Suffering in Emergency Care." Reneé is the Chief Flight Nurse and Emergency Clinical Nurse Specialist at University Hospital in Cincinnati, Ohio. She has been practicing in transport nursing for seventeen years and in emergency nursing for over twenty-five years. As an advanced practice nurse, she performs direct patient care, and writes and lectures throughout the world. Reneé is the editor of *Air and Surface Patient Transport: Principles and Practice* published by Mosby. She is also the co-editor of the *Air Medical Journal*. She has been involved in providing legal expertise since 1984 for emergency nursing and transport. She is a member of the Emergency Nurses Association, American Association of Critical Nurses, and Air and Surface Transport Nurses Association. Reneé is a practicing nurse representative for the Commission for Collegeant Nursing Education.

Diane Hudson-Barr, PhD, RN, coauthored the chapter "Pain and Suffering of Children." She is the Clinical Nurse Specialist in Neonatology at Brenner Children's Hospital at Wake Forest University Baptist Medical Center in Winston-Salem, North Carolina and an adjunct assistant professor at the School of Nursing at the University of North Carolina at Chapel Hill. She received her B.S.N and Ph.D. from the University of North Carolina at Chapel Hill and her M.S.N from the University of Pennsylvania. She is a member of National Association of Neonatal Nurses, Academy of Neonatal Nurses, Sigma Theta Tau and the Society of Pediatric Nurses. Her areas of clinical interest are pain management in neonates and developmental care.

Kelly A. Jaszarowski, MSN, RN, CNS, ANP, CWOCN, wrote two chapters, "Ostomy and Incontinence" and "Wounds and Burns." She received her master's of science in nursing from Indiana University. She completed her undergraduate studies at the University of Illinois, Springfield. Ms. Jaszarowski is also a graduate of the Abbott Northwestern Enterostomal Therapy Nursing Education Program. Ms. Jaszarowski has been a wound, ostomy, and continence nurse specialist since 1990. She has been a recipient of the Excellence in Clinical Practice award presented by the Delta Omicron Chapter of Sigma Theta Tau recognizing her expertise in the specialty. Additionally, she has been a two-time recipient of the Most Educational Enterostomal Therapy Nursing award presented by her peers.

Ms. Jaszarowski has been very active in the Wound, Ostomy, and Continence Nursing Society (WOCN). She has served nationally as treasurer and secretary as well as a director. Ms. Jaszarowski has been active on the regional level where she has served on a variety of committees as both a member and a committee chairperson. Her clinical practice expertise encompasses a variety of healthcare settings.

Sally Lambert, PhD, RN, the coauthor of "Pain and Suffering of Children," is a clinical nurse specialist in pediatrics at Rainbow Babies and Children's Hospital, University Hospitals Health System in Cleveland, Ohio, and an assistant clinical professor at Frances Payne Bolton School of Nursing, Case Western Reserve University. She graduated from the Ohio State University with a B.S.N and M.S. in pediatric nursing and a Ph.D. from Case Western Reserve University. She is a member of the International Association for the Study of Pain, Society of Pediatric Nursing and, Sigma Theta Tau. She specializes in pediatric pain management with expertise in hypnosis.

Nancy E. Mooney, MA, RN, ONC, author of "Pain and Suffering in Orthopaedics," is currently the Pain Management Coordinator at Lenox Hill Hospital in New York City. In this role, she is responsible for educating and coaching staff on pain management standards. She is a graduate of Kings County Hospital School of Nursing, with a B.S. in nursing from the University of North Carolina at Chapel Hill, and a Masters in nursing education from New York University. A past president of the National Association of Orthopaedic Nurses (1996–97), Ms. Mooney has worked in the clinical specialty of orthopaedics in many roles—staff nurse, educator, nurse manager, and director of nursing. She has been certified in the specialty of orthopaedic nursing since 1988 and has published on a variety of topics in both pain management and orthopaedics. She is a member of several professional organizations, including the American Society for Pain Management Nurses and Sigma Theta Tau International.

Dorene A. O'Hara, MD, MSE, wrote the chapter "Pain Management." She received her medical degree from Harvard Medical School and completed a pharmacology research fellowship at Northwestern and a pain fellowship at UMDNJ, New Jersey Medical School. She specializes in anesthesia. Dr. O'Hara has been a director of pain clinics at University of Pennsylvania, Robert Wood Johnson Medical School, and Metropolitan Hospital Center, NY, NY, and has served as a medical-legal expert for more than ten years. Dr. O'Hara is the author of *Heal the Pain, Comfort the Spirit,* University of Pennsylvania Press (2002), and of numerous publications and lecture on the subject of pain management. She has fifteen years' teaching clinical anesthesia and pain management in university programs.

John Parisi, Esq., coauthored two chapters, "Trial Exhibits: Legal and Strategic Considerations" and "Trial Exhibits: Preparation and Use." He began as an associate with Shamberg, Johnson & Bergman, Chartered, in Overland Park, Kansas in 1989, becoming a partner with the firm in 1994. He practices in the area of general tort law, medical malpractice, products liability, false claim, or *qui tam* matters, nursing home abuse cases, and environmental law. Prior to obtaining his law degree and joining Shamberg, Johnson & Bergman in 1989, John was a professional archaeologist for ten years. He conducted numerous archaeological excavations of historic Euroamerican and prehistoric Indian sites, primarily in Missouri and Kansas. He has also participated in an archaeological survey for prehistoric sites in the Republic of Egypt in the western Sahara desert. As a lawyer, he has utilized skills developed as an archaeologist, particularly in the area of environmental law, where his knowledge of geology, geomorphology, and hydrology has proved to be valuable in toxic tort cases.

Michael A. Pollack, MD, coauthored "Pain and Suffering in Pediatric Neurology." He is a graduate of the Albert Einstein College of Medicine in New York and is certified in neurology (with special competence in child neurology) by the American Board of Psychiatry and Neurology. He is also certified in pediatrics and clinical neurophysiology. More recently, he completed the Executive M.B.A. program at the Crummer Graduate School of Business, Rollins College, Winter Park, Florida. Dr. Pollack has practiced pediatric neurology for more than twenty-five years and is currently Chief of the Neurology Division, Nemours Children's Clinic, Orlando, Florida.

Lisa Stepp, PhD, MS, RN, APN, AOCN, CRNH, wrote the chapter "A Psychologist's View of Pain and Suffering." She attended Baylor University, completing her bachelor of science in nursing. She received her master of science from Texas Woman's University and graduated from Columbus University with a Ph.D. in psychology. Dr. Stepp practiced as an oncology nurse from 1988 to 1996. She currently holds a license as an advanced practice nurse in oncology for the state of Texas, as well as an advanced certification in oncology from the Oncology Nursing Society. Her extensive experience in hospice and palliative care led her to serve as the Hospice Special Interest Group chairperson for the Oncology Nursing Society for two years. Dr. Stepp is also a fellow in the American Academy of Pain Management and continues to volunteer for the American Cancer Society and Leukemia/Lymphoma Society of America. Throughout her career, Dr. Stepp has been involved in the care of individuals experiencing different types of pain, suffering, and loss. She has instructed care givers and clinicians on the holistic care required by pain and hospice patients. As a sought-after speaker, both nationally and internationally, Lisa has spoken to numerous groups on a wide variety of topics ranging from end-of-life issues to pain management and legal-ethical issues in the medical community. She currently works as a medical science liaison in industry.

Randall Thomas, PhD, CRC, NCC, author of "Life Care Planning and Chronic Pain," is president of the National Center for Life Care Planning. Dr. Thomas is active in the area of rehabilitation and life care planning. He is a licensed psychologist, a certified rehabilitation counselor, and a national certified counselor. During his career, he has provided psychological and vocational services to patients with catastrophic injuries. In addition, he has provided testimony in over 500 cases and has been qualified as an expert in state and federal courts in the fields of psychology, loss of earnings capacity, and life care planning. He provides consultation and education to life care planners and attorneys regarding evaluation of reliability and credibility of life care plans. He is active in several national associations and has presented educational programs and seminars at national and state conferences. He has spoken on subjects such as life care planning, chronic pain, case management, ethics, and technology. Dr. Thomas served as chair of the forensic section of the International Association of Rehabilitation Professionals. He serves on the editorial board of the *Journal of Life Care Planning* and the editorial board of the *Journal of American Board of Vocational Experts*. He serves as an instructor for the life care planning program sponsored by Intelicus and the University of Florida.

Leta Truett, PhD, RN, coauthored the chapter "Suffering: A Multidimensional Concept." In her current role as an oncology nurse educator, she provides continuing education for oncology nurses and other healthcare providers in a wide range of topics dealing with pain, suffering, anemia, fatigue, complementary therapies, and other side effect management involved in cancer therapy. Prior to this, she worked as an advanced practice nurse in the critical care area for thirteen years and the pain and symptom management service for four years at MD Anderson Cancer Center.

In 1999, Dr. Truett completed her Ph.D. in nursing. Her dissertation was in the area of suffering in the cancer patient population. Her research was focused on describing suffering from the patient's perspective with the goal of increasing the understanding of this complex phenomenon and to assist healthcare professionals to assess and intervene more knowledgeably in this area. As a pilot to the dissertation, Dr. Truett completed a qualitative study that identified themes of suffering used to develop an instrument to describe suffering in a larger patient population.

Tom Vesper, Esq., prepared the chapter "Ante-Mortem Damages." He is a certified civil trial attorney admitted to the bar of New Jersey in 1973. He received his undergraduate education at Villanova University and legal education at Rutgers University where he was a writer and member of the Rutgers-Camden Law Review. He served with the United States Marine Corps Reserve from 1969–1991. He was certified as a UCMJ 27(b) trial counsel and defense counsel by the Secretary of the Navy. The past president of the New Jersey chapter of the Association of Trial Lawyers of America, Tom is a diplomate and sustaining member of the Association of Trial Lawyers of America. He is a fellow of the International Academy of Trial Lawyers and was selected by his peers to be included as one of "The Best Lawyers in America" and a founding member of Trial Lawyers for Public Justice.

A senior partner in the Atlantic City law firm of Westmoreland, Vesper and Schwartz, Tom concentrates on personal injury and wrongful death cases. His litigation specialties and experience include products liability, commercial trucking and bus crashes, negligence, professional negligence, and consumer fraud cases. Certified as a civil trial advocate by the National Board of Trial Advocacy (1980) and New Jersey Supreme Court (1981), Tom is a frequent quest lecturer for ATLA, state trial lawyers associations, bar associations and law schools. A faculty member and past trustee of the National College of Advocacy, he has published articles and lectured on wrongful death, products liability, truck and bus accident reconstructions, discovery, case evaluation, settlement and trial techniques. Tom has lectured and written on the ATLA *Trial Notebook,* Fourth Edition, and ATLA *Deposition Notebook*, Second Edition.

J. Michael West, Esq., co-authored "The Defense Attorney's Perspective." Mr. West is currently Senior Staff Attorney with the Chicago firm of Broderick, Steiger and Maisel. Soon after graduating from the University of Illinois College of Law in 1983, Mr. West took employment as a first assistant state's attorney. Mr. West prosecuted *People v. Doss*, a criminal fraud and perjury case which received national media attention, including a televised presentation by the CBS weekly news commentary, *60 Minutes*. In 1986, Mr. West was appointed Senior Trial Counsel with the Illinois Attorney General's Office under Neil Hartigan, again prosecuting numerous notable fraud and perjury trials. Since 1989, Mr. West has focused exclusively upon the prosecution and defense of civil litigation. He has taken sixty jury trials to verdict, which include not only medical malpractice trials but also products liability, construction litigation, and catastrophic injury trials, with a favorable verdict ratio of 92%. Mr. West received a second state licensure from the Supreme Court of California in 1989. Mr. West is admitted to practice in the United States District Courts for the Northern, Central, and Southern Districts of Illinois, Southern District of California, and the United States Court of Appeals for the Seventh and Ninth Circuits.

Degrees and Certifications

ANP. Advanced nurse practitioner.
AOCN. Advanced oncology certified nurse.
CCM. Certified case manager.
CCRN. Certified critical care nurse.
CCRP. Certified clinical research professional.
CEN. Certified emergency nurse.
CEP. Certified evidence photographer.
CFRN. Certified flight registered nurse.
CNS. Clinical nurse specialist.
CRC. Certified rehabilitation counselor.
CRRN. Certified rehabilitation registered nurse.
CRNH. Certified regsitered nurse hospice.
CRNP. Certified registered nurse practitioner.
CWOCN. Certified wound ostomy continence nurse.
EPIC. Evidence Photographers International Council.
FCCM. Fellow critical care medicine.
FCCP. Fellow of the College of Chest Physicians.
LNCC. Legal nurse consultant certified.
MA. Master of arts.
MS. Master of science.
MSE. Master of science in engineering.
MSN. Master of science in nursing.
NCC. National certified counselor.
ONC. Orthopaedic nurse certified.
Ph.D. Doctor of philosophy.

Index

A

B

C

D

E

F

G

H

I

J

K

L

M

P

Q

R

S